RECEIVED

FEB 1 1963

PRINCIPLES OF ENGINEERING ECONOMY

EUGENE L. GRANT

PROFESSOR OF ECONOMICS OF ENGINEERING

STANFORD UNIVERSITY

W. GRANT IRESON

PROFESSOR OF INDUSTRIAL ENGINEERING

STANFORD UNIVERSITY

FOURTH EDITION

THE RONALD PRESS COMPANY ⸢ NEW YORK

7

Library of Congress Catalog Card Number: 60–6143
PRINTED IN THE UNITED STATES OF AMERICA

Preface

This is a book about a particular type of decision making. It explains the principles and techniques needed for making decisions about the acquisition and retirement of capital goods by industry and government. Normally, such decisions should be made on grounds of long-run economy. Because engineers make many such decisions and make recommendations for many others, the body of principles and techniques relating to them has been called "engineering economy."

The same concepts and methods that are helpful in guiding decisions about investments in capital goods are useful in certain kinds of decisions between alternative types of financing (for example, ownership versus leasing) and in many personal decisions. Applications to these other areas of decision making are also discussed in this book.

The book can be used in two ways. First, it can serve as a college textbook. The material covered is appropriate not only for engineering students but also for students of economics, accounting, finance, and management. Second, it can serve as a working manual for engineers, management personnel, government officials, and others whose duties require them to make decisions about investments in capital goods.

The underlying philosophy regarding comparisons of alternatives is the same as in previous editions. As before, continued emphasis throughout the book is placed on the following two important points:

1. It is prospective *differences* between alternatives that are relevant in their comparison.

2. The fundamental question regarding a proposed investment in capital goods is whether the investment is likely to be recovered plus a return commensurate with the risk and with the return obtainable from other opportunities for the investment of limited funds. The purpose of calculations that involve the time value of money should be to answer this question.

Although its underlying philosophy remains the same, the book has been almost completely rewritten for this Fourth Edition. As in the nearly complete rewritings for the second and third editions, the changes have been aimed in part at the introduction of new material and in part at improved presentation of fundamental principles. Some changes that will be of interest to users of the previous editions are as follows:

1. An increased emphasis on the concept of cash flow helps to clarify such matters as the income tax aspects of decision making, comparisons of alternative financing methods, replacement economy, and increment costs and sunk costs. Moreover, an emphasis on the expression of the differences between alternatives in terms of cash flow makes possible a clearer exposition of an important topic— the calculation of unknown rates of return by correct compound interest methods. (In recent literature, such correct methods are referred to by various names, including "discounted cash flow method" and "investors' method.")

2. Greater stress is placed on the concept of capital rationing and on the use of prospective rate of return as a guide to decision making.

3. Greater stress is placed on methods of analysis that are based on the mathematics of compound interest. Certain approximate methods previously covered in the main body of the text are now discussed in appendixes.

4. Diagrams and mnemonic symbols have been introduced to clarify certain aspects of compound interest.

5. A number of useful new interest tables have been added. These include tables to convert a uniform gradient to an equivalent uniform annual series and to a present worth. They also include present worth tables based on effective interest rates and assuming continuous compounding and the uniform flow of funds throughout stated time periods.

6. One of the appendixes deals with economy studies that assume continuous compounding and the uniform flow of funds. The end-of-year convention is still used throughout the main body of the book.

7. The importance of income tax considerations is stressed early in this edition. As an experiment in their classes, the authors introduced calculations of prospective disbursements for income taxes concurrently with the study of annual costs, present worths, and rates of return. They concluded that better results are obtained if the first examples and problems in the course are based on stipulated

minimum attractive rates of return *before* income taxes and if calculations of the effects of decisions on income taxes are introduced later. However, it seemed desirable in this edition to introduce after-tax studies a little earlier than in the Third Edition—prior to the topics of replacement economy and the comparison of alternative methods of financing.

8. Additional stress is laid on the extent to which after-tax rates of return are influenced by different methods of writing off cost for tax purposes. Depreciation methods authorized under recent tax laws in the United States are explained.

9. Reasons for avoiding certain unsound criteria for evaluating investment proposals are stressed. Particular emphasis is laid on reasons why the primary criteria for investment decisions should not be payoff periods (discussed in Chapter 19) or so-called rates of return by original book or average book methods (discussed in Chapter 10).

10. In the discussion of economy studies for public works, a fuller exposition has been given of the relationship between the benefit-cost ratio as a criterion for investment decisions and the more conventional criteria based on annual costs or prospective rates of return on investment.

11. In order to clarify the presentation of certain topics, several phrases and concepts employed by writers on operations research have been introduced. An extremely useful concept is that of sensitivity. Some useful phrases are suboptimization, system viewpoint, and mathematical model.

In order to make room for the foregoing, certain more specialized topics covered in the Third Edition have been omitted.

The arrangement of the chapters recognizes the fact that some introductory courses in engineering economy are too short to permit a full coverage of the subject. Most of the material in Chapters 1 to 16 is fundamental and should be included in any presentation of basic principles. The subject matter of Chapters 17 to 19 is appropriate for an elementary course if time permits but might also be deferred till an advanced course. Appendixes A to D cover topics that might be omitted in elementary college courses but should be included in advanced courses and in any presentation to persons in industry.

The authors wish to thank Professors Robert Oakford and David Heebink, both of Stanford University, for the programming of the calculation of new tables, and Paul T. Norton, Jr., of St. Petersburg, Florida, for many helpful comments on our manuscript.

We are grateful also to our colleagues on the Stanford industrial
engineering faculty for suggesting a number of our new problems
and examples.

EUGENE L. GRANT

W. GRANT IRESON

Palo Alto, California
    January, 1960

Contents

PART I

Planning Economy Studies for Decision Making

PART II

Interest—The Time Element in Economy

PART III

Techniques for Economy Studies

APPENDIXES

PART I
PLANNING ECONOMY STUDIES FOR DECISION MAKING

1

"Hunch" Decisions Are Dangerous

The question "Will it pay?" is always present in engineering decisions. It may be broken down into several subsidiary questions.

The late General John J. Carty, as chief engineer of the New York Telephone Company, had three such questions that he applied to every engineering proposal that came before him for review:

1. Why do this at all?
2. Why do it now?
3. Why do it this way?

Why do this at all? Will a proposed new enterprise be profitable? Shall an existing enterprise be expanded? Shall existing operating procedures be modified?

Why do it now? Are market conditions favorable to a present development? Shall we build now with excess capacity in advance of demand, or with only sufficient capacity to satisfy the demand immediately in prospect? Are interest rates and business conditions favorable to a present development?

Why do it this way? This choice between alternative ways of doing the same thing is common to all types of engineering activity.

This book deals with certain principles underlying any rational answers to questions of this type. The central problem discussed in the book is how we may judge whether any proposed course of action will prove to be economical in the long run, as compared to other possible alternatives. Such judgment should not be based on an unsupported "hunch"; it requires an economy study. An economy study may be defined as a comparison between alternatives in which the differences between the alternatives are expressed so far as practicable in money terms. Where technical considerations are somehow involved, such a comparison may be called an engineering economy study.

3

Economy in Everyday Life. Although this book deals primarily with engineering economy studies, the principles and techniques herein presented are general in their nature and are applicable to many everyday personal problems. These techniques of analysis are just as useful in many personal decisions as they are in engineering situations. In fact, many examples used in this book deal with economy studies for individuals or families even though the majority deal with studies for business or government. Many decisions between personal alternatives can be made more sensibly if the differences between the alternatives are expressed as far as practicable in terms of prospective money receipts and disbursements and if these money figures are analyzed along the lines developed in this book.

For instance, in a choice between home ownership and renting, it is obvious that many aspects of the matter should be estimated in terms of money as a guide to intelligent decision making. Nevertheless, matters of personal taste that cannot be expressed in money terms often carry much weight in personal decisions. Thus the pride of home ownership may be of great importance to one family and a matter of complete indifference to another.

Economy in Business Enterprise. The problems of economy in business enterprise are considerably less subjective than problems of personal economy. A competitive business enterprise cannot survive unless it makes a profit. It follows that sensible decisions between alternatives must consider the effects of the alternatives on the prospective profits of the enterprise. Alternatives should be judged so far as practicable in terms of prospective receipts and disbursements; they are made commensurable by being expressed in money units.

An Example of a "Hunch" Decision. Many business decisions are made on the basis of guesswork, with very little attempt to consider the various possible alternatives and to judge the differences between them that are measurable in money terms.

For instance, a schoolteacher invested her small savings in a down payment on a rental property. She made this investment without consideration of the relationship between the price of the property, on the one hand, and the prospective receipts from rentals and the disbursements for operation, maintenance, and debt interest and repayment, on the other hand. As a matter of fact, the particular property was greatly overpriced in relation to its prospective earnings and expenses. She finally sold the property several years later at a substantial loss. If she had substituted for her guess that all rental properties were profitable, specific estimates of receipts and disbursements for this particular property, and if she had given consideration to alternative possible investments, she would doubtless have reached the correct conclusion that this rental property was an unwise investment.

The practice of making business decisions on the basis of a "hunch" that a proposal will or will not pay is not confined to persons without business experience. Such a method of solving problems by "going into a trance and coming out with the answer," as one engineer described it, is a method that sometimes appeals to executives responsible for decisions as making minimum demands on their time and effort. The limitations of decisions made in this way are obvious.

Comparing Engineering Alternatives. These limitations are most likely to be apparent when the decisions to be made deal with matters of technology. The businessman who is not technically trained must rely on the engineer's advice as to the probable differences between engineering alternatives. The engineer, on the other hand, needs to translate these differences into money terms in order to make them clear to the businessman. In fact, he must translate them into money terms in order to make commensurable the many different kinds of physical differences that are so frequently involved in a choice between alternative plans.

A "Hunch" Decision in an Industrial Situation. An industrial concern owned its own steam plant, which had been operated for many years to furnish steam for heating, for operation of steam-driven pumps, steam-driven air compressors, and for generation of the electricity needed in the plant for lighting and for the operation of small motors. An increase in the concern's volume of business finally increased the demands for compressed air and for electric energy above the capacity of the existing plant.

Without any engineering survey of the situation, the general manager of the plant contracted to purchase from the local electric light and power company the excess of his needs for electric energy above the amount that could be generated in his existing plant. To meet the increased needs for compressed air, he bought a large electrically driven air compressor.

His decision proved to be an expensive one. The air compressor purchased was a single large unit; it turned out that it was operated most of the time at a very small fraction of its capacity and at a correspondingly very low efficiency. The amount of energy purchased from the power company was insufficient to bring the unit rate into the lower blocks of the company's rate schedule. Occasional breakdowns of one or another of the old steam engines in the company's power plant made the peak load of power purchased very high in proportion to the average purchased; the rate structure was such that this poor "load factor" was reflected in a high rate for the purchased power. No reduction in labor cost for operation of boilers, engines, compressors, and pumps, or in the costs for fuel and maintenance of the old and inefficient prime movers, was possible under the plan adopted by the manager.

An Economy Study To Correct a "Hunch" Decision. Finally an engineer was called in to survey the situation and to make recommendations. He recognized that there were a number of alternatives that had not been considered by the general manager; several of them appeared likely to be more economical than the plan that had been adopted. Thus, it would be possible to increase steam capacity by the addition of new boilers; generating capacity might be increased by the purchase of a steam turbine and generator that because of its greater efficiency would produce more kilowatt-hours of electric energy from the same amount of steam now being used to operate the steam engines; a diesel engine and generator might be purchased for the production of electric energy; the engines might be shut down and all of the electric energy requirements be purchased from the power company, permitting all the steam generated to be used for operation of steam-driven compressors and pumps, and for heating; the compressors and pumps might be electrified, and all electric energy requirements then purchased, with boilers operated for steam heat only in those months in which heating is necessary.

The engineer examined the factory's past requirements for the services that had been provided by the steam plant—heat, pumping, compressed air, and electric energy—and, after consideration of the trend of growth of production and of some changes in production methods that seemed to be in prospect, made a forecast of the needs for these services for several years to come. With this forecast as a basis, he then made preliminary designs for meeting the expected needs by each of the possible alternatives that he had recognized. For each alternative, he then made approximate estimates of the immediate investment required, and of the annual expenditures necessary in the future. With these estimates, he was able to make a preliminary comparison of the long-run economy of the several alternative plans (including as one plan a continuance of the existing scheme), and to select those that seemed to justify detailed study.

Of all of the alternatives given preliminary study, two appeared to be much more economical than any of the others. One was the plan to modernize the power plant by the purchase of one or more steam turbines; the other was the plan for the electrification of the compressors and pumps and the purchase of all power. Each of these plans was given detailed study with complete designs, and with careful estimates of investment costs and operation and maintenance costs.

As is characteristic of all economy studies to determine general policy, each of these designs involved numerous subsidiary alternatives, and each selection between subsidiary alternatives called for a subsidiary economy study. For example, in the first alternative what type and size of turbines should be selected? How many should there be? What boiler pressures should be used? Should the power generation be combined with other steam requirements by selecting turbines that exhaust at pressures that permit the use of their exhaust steam for other purposes? In the second alternative, several different possible power rates were offered by the power company. "Primary" power could be taken at 23,000 volts, requiring the customer to install his own transformers for stepping down the voltage, and, of course, to take the transformer losses involved; a variation of this was an "off-peak" rate with severe restrictions on the maximum power that could be used in certain specified hours of certain months. Two other different rates were available under which the company supplied power at the voltages at which it was to be used. The electrification of compressors and pumps involved several possible alternative designs.

Translating an Engineering Economy Study into a Business Decision. The engineer's estimate showed the alternative involving the steam turbine to require a considerably higher immediate investment than was required by the plan to purchase power; on the other hand, once the investment was made, the turbine plan involved lower prospective annual disbursements. Since the choice between these alternatives would have no influence one way or the other on the factory's revenues, the problem was merely one of comparing future expenditures. The real question was whether the additional investment in the steam turbine plan was justified by the prospective saving in operating costs. Or—stated a little differently—the question was whether it seemed likely that the extra investment would be recovered, plus a return that was attractive in the light of the risk and in the light of the cost of money and of other opportunities for the investment of available funds. In order to answer this question, the expenditures involved in each plan were reduced to equivalent uniform annual cost; this calculation (explained in Chapter 6 of this book) involved assumptions regarding the economic lives of the machines and other equipment required for each plan, and involved the use of an interest rate equal to the rate of return considered necessary to justify an investment of this type.

These financial calculations indicated a slightly lower annual cost for the plan to purchase all power. Before making a final decision between the two plans, however, it was necessary to consider those differences between them that had not been reduced to money terms, the so-called intangibles, irreducible data, or judgment factors.

Certain of these were favorable to the purchase of power. For instance, it was expected that this plan would be somewhat more flexible in time of business depression; in the past, with power generated in the factory's own plant, it had been necessary to keep the power plant operating with a full labor force even when the factory was operating at only a small fraction of its full capacity. There was also a desire on the part of the management to conserve its financial resources by keeping the investment to a minimum, particularly because the recent expansion of the company's business had resulted in the need for increased working capital to finance increased inventories and accounts receivable. On the other hand, a factor unfavorable to the purchase of power was the creation of certain personnel problems; an engine-room force would no longer be needed and a boiler-room force would not be required during the summer months. However, a survey of personnel requirements elsewhere in the plant indicated the probability that these men could be transferred to other jobs. The plan for the purchase of power was, therefore, the one finally selected.

The Place of the Engineer in Industrial Economy Studies. This situation was so complex and involved so many different alternatives—each with different implications about cost—that the general manager's solution, by his method of unsupported "hunch," obviously had little chance to hit on the best answer. Even a "hunch" by an engineer experienced in the design of industrial power plants would not have been reliable. The many circumstances with regard to the existing equipment and the special characteristics of the services required made this a unique situation; it was the engineer's responsibility to make his designs and estimates accordingly. Situations are seldom alike, and each engineering economy study should be made to fit its own special circumstances.

Even though an engineer's "hunch" was not a good way to solve this problem, it is obvious that engineering training and familiarity with industrial power plant practices were necessary for the best solution. Detailed alternatives could not have been set up for comparison, and designs and estimates could not have been made without specialized knowledge. This was an *engineering* economy study, because only an engineer was qualified to make it. That is, only an engineer could deal with the technical considerations involved.

The financial calculations that necessarily followed the engineer's designs and estimates were in no sense an exclusive engineering function. Such calculations might have been made by a business administrator. However, they are such a necessary part of the numerous choices between technical alternatives that are required in every engineering design that the engineer who is not qualified to make them is poorly equipped for his job. A deficiency in this matter is particularly serious in one who has administrative responsibility for technical matters.

It should be noted at this point that these financial calculations in economy studies are based on quite as definite a body of principles as are the engineer's purely technical calculations. Parts II and III of this book are an attempt to present this body of principles.

Recognizing All of the Alternatives. Not only engineering training and experience, but also some imagination may be required to find the most economical method of solving a given problem. It is obvious that one way in which an economy study can reach a wrong conclusion is by the omission of an alternative that is better than those that have been considered. Many examples of this kind might be cited.

For instance, an irrigation district in one of the western states was experiencing great difficulty with the maintenance of many wooden flumes in its 60 miles or so of main canal. The leaks in these flumes due to the decay of lumber contained in them were so bad that it seemed probable that the project could not continue to operate unless it undertook a substantial program of reconstruction. A consulting engineer who was called in to report on the reconstruction program told the district commissioners that it would be necessary for them to spend $1,200,000 to replace all of the old wooden flumes with new wooden flumes. This represented $60 an acre for the 20,000 acres in the district.

When the district's commissioners attempted to sell the district's bonds for this amount, the bond house that they approached sent its engineer to investigate the situation. This engineer made the suggestion that the costs of reconstruction might be reduced and a more permanent ditch might be obtained by substituting earth fills for many of the low flumes that were decayed, rather than installing new flumes. This plan was later carried out under his direction and cost the district about $400,000, or $20 an acre compared with the $60 an acre previously planned. Here was an example where an engineer's failure to consider all the alternatives nearly proved very expensive for his clients.

Many examples of this kind from industrial plants, public utilities, and public works could be cited to emphasize the point that failure to recognize all of the alternatives may lead to the wrong conclusion. Similarly, the unwillingness to consider the alternative of modifying original plans when unforeseen conditions are encountered may result in the unnecessary expenditure of large sums of money. Thus, in constructing drainage ditches where rock is encountered, there may be the possibility of avoiding it through investigation by borings and consequent altered location of the ditch. A similar situation arises when rock can be avoided in highway location by the change of a grade from perhaps 2% to 4%. which would have a negligible effect on the operating cost of the highway as part of a transportation system.

Decisions Are Made at All Levels. Business decisions involving substantial sums are not the exclusive responsibility of the board of directors of the firm or top management. Decisions that have far-reaching results are usually made at all levels of an engineering project. Engineers preparing detailed designs for analysis and estimation must make decisions about the designs and specifications to be incorporated that have important effects on the final cost of the project. There are usually several ways that a particular item can be designed, and the engineer must decide which way to do the job; yet this is but one stage in a series of decisions that will be made before a proposed design evolves for top management's consideration. The engineer who is aware of the alternatives available and who takes a little time to consider the differences in the costs and results of the alternatives contributes more to the final project than the engineer who simply follows former designs and practices.

Suboptimization in Engineering Designs. Engineering projects frequently involve a number of different systems integrated into a single complex structure or operation. The size and complexity of the whole operation may be such that it is practically impossible to determine reliably the most economical over-all combination of the separate components. Deciding to use the most economical alternative for one component may automatically preclude using the most economical alternative for another component, or vice versa. When a large number of components must be considered simultaneously, the problem may become so complex that it cannot be solved within a reasonable time or at a reasonable cost. In such cases engineers have, for many years, divided the whole project into several smaller problems and made an engineering economy study to determine the most economical alternative for each problem separately. When the several problems are considered as a whole, it is not necessarily true that the optimal design has been chosen.

The rather descriptive term "suboptimization" has been used in operations research literature in recent years to describe this approach to problem solution. Engineering economy principles are applicable to the suboptimization practices and help to keep the engineer's attention focused on the relevant factors of the problems.

Imperfect Alternatives Are Sometimes the Most Economical. The satisfaction of the engineer's sense of perfection is not a necessary prerequisite for the most economical alternative. Sometimes it happens that a careful study will show that an alternative that at first was summarily rejected affords the most economical solution of a given problem.

An illustration of this is the case of a geographically diversified group of public utility companies that had occasion to buy a great many poles. Poles come in a number of classes, AA, A, B, C, D, E, F, and G, depending upon the top diameter and the butt diameter. The past practice of these companies in pole selection was based on their experience of what had proved to be satisfactory rather than on any considerations of theoretical design, and usually involved purchasing no poles below class B.

Someone suggested analyzing pole requirements on the basis of such factors as the expected storm loads in different areas and the importance of each line to the entire system. This analysis showed that many of the lighter grades of poles that had not been purchased in the past were satisfactory for certain conditions. Thus a pole of type D in Alabama might prove to be the equal in carrying capacity with respect to its probable load of a pole of type A in Minnesota. As a result of this fact finding about storm loads in various areas and about the importance of different classes of lines, standards were set up to control their purchase for the varying requirements.

Savings were effected because cheaper poles were used in many cases. Additional savings resulted because the distribution of pole requirements among all of the classes made it possible to use a "wood's run" of poles, so that lumber companies were able to set a considerably lower price on poles A and B than they were able to set when they had difficulty in selling their other classes.

A second illustration of the lack of economy of a policy that seemed perfect from the technician's viewpoint is the case of a company that was making weekly tests and adjustments of certain automatic equipment as part of its program of plant maintenance. One engineer suggested that the troubles that required these adjustments had very little effect on the operation of the equipment. To demonstrate this, he sealed up a portion of the equipment so that it could not be tested and adjusted for a period of a year. The operation of the sealed equipment was not materially affected. As a result, a greatly modified program of testing and adjustment was adopted, saving the company many thousands of dollars every year.

Another illustration is the case of a state highway commission that made a general requirement that all highway survey parties should check their highway curves on closing by an amount that would not exceed a certain maximum figure. Survey parties were expected to secure this maximum allowable closure or rerun the curve until they did secure it, regardless of the surrounding conditions. The closure required was a reasonable one in level country where no difficulties were encountered, but its requirement on surveys for mountain roads where the line had to be cut through brush proved to be very uneconomical. Many curves had to be rerun half a dozen times or so before this closure was secured. After it was secured, it did not make any practical difference in improving the location of the highway.

Words Vs. Monetary Figures as a Basis for Decision Making. The methods of analysis and comparison as explained in this book are in considerable contrast with a type of analysis often encountered in the business world. Engineering economy studies stress the importance of clearly identifying the alternative ways of solving a particular problem and the reduction of these alternatives to numerical data that can be compared on a monetary basis.

The alternative method of analysis involves itemizing in terms of words the differences between the alternatives. This itemization of the differences in terms of words often is a good way to begin an engineering economy study. If, however, the differences thus expressed are not reduced to monetary terms as far as possible, the analysis by words is likely to lead to erroneous conclusions. One weakness of the latter method lies in the fact that frequently the advantages and disadvantages of a particular alternative are listed in such a way that the same advantage or disadvantage may be enumerated more than once under different terminology. It is also true that when a series of advantages are listed there is a tendency to weight all of them equally even though their monetary effects may be very different or may even be nonexistent. There is no easy way by which these advantages or disadvantages can be evaluated reliably without reducing them to money differences. A hazard of this technique is that the decision will be unduly influenced by pure weight of words.

As an example, let us consider a proposal that incandescent lamps in an industrial plant be replaced by fluorescent fixtures. An engineer who made this proposal enumerated the advantages and disadvantages as follows:

Advantages:

1. More light for the same amount of power
2. Smaller number of fixtures
3. Less frequent lamp replacement
4. Lower maintenance costs
5. Better light
6. Less heat to be dissipated
7. Improvement of lighting without having to install new, larger conductors
8. Improved working conditions
9. Less eye fatigue for employees
10. Better quality product
11. Better employee morale

Disadvantages:

1. Higher investment in fixtures
2. Higher unit lamp cost
3. Labor cost of installation
4. Interruption of work during installation
5. "Flicker" may occur and be very annoying

A casual examination of this list of advantages and disadvantages will reveal that several of them overlap and that they are not mutually exclusive. With no other information available, the executive would be in a poor position to make a decision. The advantages and disadvantages are important to the decision chiefly as they affect the concern's cash flow. Any advantages or disadvantages that cannot be evaluated in monetary terms can only be used as judgment factors or imponderables, and would not be commensurable with the others. The engineering economy method requires that an attempt be made to evaluate the advantages and disadvantages in monetary units that will make them commensurable. It would try to distinguish clearly between those advantages and disadvantages that can be reduced to money terms and those not so reducible. When these monetary differences are expressed as cash flow (disbursements and receipts over the years), there is a reliable basis for decision making.

Summary. The more important ideas contained in this chapter may be restated briefly in somewhat different language as follows:

Preconceived notions as to what it is economical to do under a given set of circumstances are likely to be a poor guide to business policy. It is particularly true, where matters of technology are involved, that what is needed are not intuitive judgments, but rather careful detailed estimates of prospective receipts and disbursements for specific alternatives. Often some engineering imagination is required in order to include all of the promising alternatives.

Many engineering economy studies finally reduce to the question "Does it seem likely that a proposed investment will ultimately be recovered, plus a return that seems attractive considering prospective returns obtainable in investments of like risk?" If decisions regarding proposed investments are made without any attempt to define clearly the possible alternatives in any situation, and to reduce those alternatives to a basis that makes them commensurable, it seems certain that many unwise investments will be made, and many wise ones will fail to be made. The only units that make commensurable alternatives that are physically different are money units; therefore, the attempt to answer the question "Will a proposed investment pay?" involves reducing engineering estimates to money terms. This must be followed by financial calculations that involve the use of an interest rate or the determination of a prospective rate of return. Finally, the choice between alternatives must also give weight to those prospective differences between them that it has been impracticable to reduce to money terms.

Problems

1–1. Describe an example of a "hunch" decision in a situation familiar to you, and explain briefly how you would proceed to analyze a similar problem.

1–2. The owner of a party fishing boat has lost a number of days of operation because the engine of his boat has broken down several times, necessitating a day of overhaul each time. He is afraid that a continuation will earn him a reputation for unreliable operation and that soon he will be unable to book parties for his boat. What alternatives are open to him? Enumerate the probable effects of each alternative on his cash receipts and disbursements.

1–3. A manufacturing concern's volume of business has grown to the point where there is no longer room for efficient operation in the single factory building owned by the company. What alternative methods of caring for this increased volume of business might be considered?

1–4. What are the alternative methods that your college might consider for the provision of janitorial service to the college buildings?

1–5. What are the alternative ways through which you might provide housing for yourself while in college? List the items of cash disbursements and receipts that might be affected by each of the alternatives.

1–6. An industrial concern is moving from its old plant building to a new, larger one, 10 miles away. It has about 200 machines about the size and weight of a number 2 milling machine to be moved. List the factors that might be considered in selecting the alternative methods that might be used in making the move.

1–7. What are the possible alternative ways of transporting limestone from the quarry face to the crusher, a distance of 400 ft. now? As more limestone is removed this distance will become greater. About 150 tons of stone are moved each day.

1–8. What are the possible alternatives in the provision of electric power for a ranch that is 5 miles from a public utility power line?

2

Decisions Are Between Alternatives

The conduct of all personal, government, and business activity requires a successive series of decisions—decisions between possible alternatives with reference to the future. These decisions are of all degrees of importance, varying from trivial matters to matters of major policy. Some of them are made by intuitive judgments or "hunches" without any conscious attempt to express the alternatives to be compared in commensurable terms, or perhaps even to see clearly what the alternatives really are. Others, however, involve choices between definite alternatives that have been made commensurable by reducing them to terms of money and time. There is much evidence that many of these latter decisions, based on conscious economy studies involving estimates of expected costs (and possible revenues) are incorrectly made because of the failure of the estimator to reason clearly about the *differences* between alternatives that involve common elements.

What Is the "Cost" of an Automobile Trip? To illustrate the type of error that may occur if alternatives are not clearly defined, let us consider a familiar and relatively simple situation. Suppose it is desired to estimate the cost of a 600-mile automobile trip.

Bill Jones, who had agreed to "share the cost" of such a trip to be taken in the car of his friend Tom Smith, may calculate only the expected out-of-pocket expense for gasoline. If Smith's car makes 15 miles to the gallon and gasoline costs 33 cents per gallon, this is 2.2 cents per mile. Jones therefore concluded that the trip will cost $13.20.

Tom Smith, on the other hand, may estimate all of the costs associated with the ownership and operation of his automobile over its expected life in his service, in order to find an average cost per mile. His car had a first cost of $3,000; he expects to drive it 10,000 miles per year for 4 years; at the end of this time he hopes to realize $1,000 from its sale. His estimates of total cost might be as follows:

1.	Gasoline (40,000 miles at 2.2¢ per mile)	$ 880
2.	Oil and grease	260
3.	Tires	150
4.	Repairs and maintenance	570
5.	Insurance	500
6.	Storage (48 months at $10 per month)	480
7.	License fees and property taxes	200
8.	Total depreciation in 4 years ($3,000 − $1,000)	2,000
9.	Interest on investment in car	360
	(This is based on average interest at 4% per annum; the method of calculation is explained in Appendix A.)	
		$5,400

Divided among 40,000 miles of travel, this is an average cost of 13.5 cents per mile. At this rate a 600-mile trip appears to cost $81.

The Concept of Cost Must Be Related to Specific Alternatives if It Is To Be a Reliable Guide to Decisions. The second of these two figures for the cost of a given service is 614% of the first one. At first glance it would appear that one or the other of the two figures must be wide of its mark. However, a more critical consideration will disclose that the simple question "What is its cost?" with reference to a particular service does not define any mark for the estimator to shoot at.

To use a cost figure as a basis for a decision, it is necessary to have clearly in mind the alternatives between which it is desired to decide. Otherwise, certain costs which, after a clear definition of alternatives, would be recognized as common to both, may be given weight in influencing the choice. It is dangerous to base conclusions on average costs without regard to the specific alternatives that it is intended to compare. The fact that widely differing cost figures may be required for different decisions about a given service may be illustrated by examining some of the different pairs of alternatives that might arise relative to the service of a given automobile.

A Situation in Which It Is Necessary To Estimate Total Cost of Ownership and Operation. If Tom Smith did not own an automobile, and wanted to decide whether or not to purchase one, he might set up the following alternatives for comparison:

Alternative A. Buy a $3,000 car and operate it approximately 10,000 miles per year for the next 4 years.

Alternative B. Do not buy a car. Use some other means of transportation, such as railway, streetcar, bus, taxicab, his friends' automobiles, and his own legs for part of the contemplated mileage and do without the rest.

If these are the alternatives, all of the items included in his estimate of $5,400 for 4 years' service are disbursements[1] that will take place if Alternative A is selected, and that will not take place if Alternative B is selected. Thus, the unit cost of 9 cents per mile is relevant to Smith's decision whether or not to own a car. The total cost (which in this case is more important than the average cost per unit of service) of $5,400 should be compared with the costs associated with Alternative B. The higher cost of A, if any, should then be judged in the light of differences that are not reducible to money terms, and in the light of Smith's prospective ability to pay this higher cost.

A Situation in Which It Is Necessary To Estimate the Increment Cost of an Added Service. If Smith has already purchased an automobile and intends to continue to own and operate it, but is undecided about the annual mileage he will drive, the kinds of alternatives to be compared are quite different. In order to determine the effect on cost of driving extra miles, he might set up two alternatives differing only in the annual mileage. He would then make his decision on the basis of the increment cost, the extra cost incurred for the extra mileage, compared with the extra service. His two alternatives might be:

Alternative A. Continue to own the car, driving it 12,500 miles per year for 4 years before disposing of it.

Alternative B. Continue to own the car, driving it 10,000 miles per year for 4 years before disposing of it.

In comparing these alternatives, it is necessary to consider the various elements of total cost of ownership that have already been listed, item by item, and estimate the effect on each of a total increase of 10,000 miles in the mileage driven over the life of the car.

Item 1 (gasoline) and item 2 (oil and grease) may be expected to increase at least in proportion to the increase in mileage. It is likely that the increase would be somewhat more than in direct proportion, because of the tendency of the rate of consumption of fuel and lubricants to increase after a car has been driven a good many miles. Perhaps if the car had averaged 15 miles per gallon in its first 40,000 miles, it might average only 14.3 miles per gallon in the following

---

[1] That is, they are all disbursements with the possible exception of interest which might in some cases be a disbursement and in others an income given up—an opportunity foregone. The reasons for including interest in such a study regardless of whether or not it is an actual disbursement are explained in Chapter 9.

10,000 miles. In general, item 3 (tires) may be expected to increase in proportion to driving mileage; the actual effect of any proposed increase in mileage will depend on whether it requires the purchase of additional tires during the extended period of service. Item 4 (repairs and maintenance) will doubtless tend to increase somewhat more than in direct proportion to mileage.

On the other hand, item 5 (insurance), item 6 (storage), and item 7 (license fees and property taxes) will be unchanged by an increase in mileage driven in any given time. Because the secondhand price of automobiles seems to depend almost entirely on age and not on miles driven, it is probable that the estimated realizable value after 4 years will be affected very little, if at all, by an increase of 25% in total mileage. If this is the case, neither item 8 (total depreciation) nor item 9 (interest) will be changed by the contemplated increase in mileage.

Smith might make his estimate of the extra costs associated with increasing his total expected mileage from 40,000 to 50,000 somewhat as follows:

1. Gasoline (10,000 miles at 2.3¢ per mile) $230
2. Oil and grease 60
3. Tires 50
4. Repairs and maintenance 250

$590

If this estimate is correct, so that an increase of 10,000 miles would increase total costs by $590, then the average cost for each increased mile of travel is 5.9 cents. This unit increment cost might then be applied to the mileage of any proposed trip, in order to get an idea of how the proposed trip will affect automobile costs in the long run. If this is done for a proposed 600-mile trip, the conclusion will be that this trip ultimately will be responsible for $35.40 of extra expense.[2]

It will be noted that although this estimated unit increment cost of 5.9 cents per mile is much less than the estimated 13.5 cents per mile for ownership and operation over the life of the automobile, it is more than two and a half times the 2.2 cents per mile estimate that

[2] Incidentally, it may be noted that the question of what, in equity, Bill Jones ought to pay when he rides in Tom Smith's car "sharing the cost" of a trip is a question of social conduct that cannot be answered by an economy study. All an economy study can do is to disclose the expected differences between alternatives. Thus, if Tom is making the trip in any event, an economy study might indicate that the least he could afford to accept from Bill without loss would be nothing at all; this is the difference between the alternatives: (A) make the trip, taking Bill along, and (B) make the trip, leaving Bill behind. On the other hand, if he is making the trip entirely for Bill's convenience, his estimates would appear to indicate that the least he could afford to take for a 600-mile trip is $35.40; here the alternatives are: (A) make the trip with Bill, and (B) do not make the trip at all.

Bill Jones made for the out-of-pocket expense of a short trip. The difference between the 5.9 cent and the 13.5 cent figures lies in those costs that are "fixed" by the decision to buy and to continue to own and operate the car, and that are, therefore, independent of its miles of operation. On the other hand, the difference between the 2.2 cent and the 5.9 cent figures is the difference between short-run and long-run viewpoints. It may well be true that the only out-of-pocket expenses of a 600-mile trip will be for the gasoline; nevertheless, the long-run effect of increasing the number of miles of operation of an automobile will be to increase the expenditures for lubricants, tires, and repairs.

A Situation in Which It Is Necessary To Estimate the Costs of Continuing a Machine in Service. If Smith purchases an automobile, and then has misgivings as to whether or not he can afford to continue to own and operate it, the alternatives that present themselves to him are still different, and different cost figures from any we have yet discussed will be required as a basis for his decision. Suppose he sets up the following alternatives for comparison:

Alternative A. Continue to own the car, driving it 10,000 miles per year for 4 years.

Alternative B. Immediately dispose of the car for the best price obtainable, thereafter using other means of transportation.

In considering the difference between these two alternatives, it is necessary to recognize that the $3,000 purchase price of the car has already been spent, no matter which alternative is chosen. The important question here is not the past outlay for the car, but rather the "best price obtainable" for it if Alternative B is selected.

If Smith's decision had been made, say, in 1947, when it was possible to sell certain makes of new cars in a so-called used car market at several hundred dollars more than the purchase price, this best price obtainable might have been $3,500. If so, Smith's question would obviously have been whether or not he could afford to continue to own an automobile that he could sell for $3,500. On the other hand, if his decision is to be made under the more normal conditions where the resale price of a new automobile is substantially below its purchase price, even though the car may have been driven only a few miles, the best price obtainable might possibly be $2,300. Under these circumstances, Smith's question is whether or not he can afford to continue to own an automobile that he could sell for $2,300. The $700 difference between the $3,000 purchase price and the $2,300 resale price is gone whether he keeps the car or disposes of it at once.

The principles underlying financial calculations to determine whether or not to continue to own a given asset enter into a wide variety of engineering economy studies. These principles are developed at some length in Chapters 14 and 16. At this point it is sufficient to note that there is a substantial difference in principle between a decision whether or not to acquire an asset and a decision whether or not to continue to own and operate that asset once it is acquired. To guide the latter type of decision intelligently, attention must be focused on the net realizable value of the machine (that is, on the prospective net receipts from its sale if it should be disposed of). Once an asset has been purchased, its purchase price has been paid regardless of whether it is continued in service or disposed of at once. This past investment may be thought of as a "sunk cost" that, generally speaking, has no relevance in decisions for the future.

Comparing Alternatives in Business Situations. These examples from the familiar situation of automobile ownership have illustrated the necessity for recognizing definite alternatives to be compared before using cost as a basis for decisions. No doubt the different kinds of relevant "costs" that should be considered in automobile ownership and operation are recognized in their qualitative aspects by many automobile owners. However, even in these relatively simple situations that have been discussed, it will be noted that in order to express differences quantitatively we were obliged to make assumptions which, in order to be definite, were somewhat arbitrary. For instance, in order to estimate increment costs per mile of operation, we found it necessary to assume two definite total mileages, and to assume that the 4-year period of ownership would be unchanged by a change in the total miles of operation.

In industry, the circumstances in which comparisons are made are likely to be more involved. The machines and structures that are the subjects of engineering economy studies are generally parts of a complex plant, and this complexity may create difficulties in differentiating the effects of alternatives. As has been stated, industrialists are often misled as to the costs that are relevant to particular decisions by failure to define alternatives clearly. In industrial situations, even more than in the automobile cost illustration, it is necessary to make definite assumptions in order to have a basis for decisions.

Considering Alternatives in Pairs. In the majority of the examples of engineering economy studies in this book, only two alternatives have been set up for comparison. This simplification of practical situations has been made in order to emphasize the principles involved in making these comparisons. The reader is hereby warned that in engineering practice there may be many alternatives; in fact, the important part of the engineer's job sometimes is to hunt for other alternatives than those which have been considered. However, the principles that apply in comparing two alternatives will apply to any number. Even though there are many alternatives to be considered, it is often most convenient to consider them in pairs, making successive eliminations of the less economical ones.

Irreducible Data in Comparing Alternatives. In the case of the alternatives involving Tom Smith's decision whether or not to purchase a car, we noted briefly that there would be certain advantages and certain hazards incident to the ownership of an automobile that could not be reduced to money terms, but, nevertheless, would have considerable influence on Smith's choice.

This is characteristic of many economy studies. Although the reduction of units that would otherwise be incommensurable (for example, tons of coal, pounds of structural steel, barrels of cement, gallons of oil, kilowatt-hours of electric energy, hours of skilled machinists' labor, hours of common labor) to terms of money and time is essential to all business decisions are not made entirely on "hunch," some differences between alternatives will generally remain that cannot be reduced to money terms. In an economy study it is as much a part of the estimator's duty to note these irreducibles as it is to predict the money receipts and disbursements at various dates. The final decision must give weight to the irreducible differences, as well as to the money differences.

Differences Between Alternatives Are in the Future. If it is recognized that only those matters that are different as between two alternatives are relevant to their comparison, it should be obvious that everything that has happened in the past is irrelevant, except as it may help in the prediction of the future. Whatever has already happened is past and gone, regardless of which of two future alternatives is selected. This implies, among other things, that apportionments against future times of expenditures already past should not be included in economy studies. It also implies that economy studies are based on forecasts, and that their conclusions are dependent on predictions of future events, predictions that are either conscious forecasts or implied ones.

The Limitations of Accounting as a Basis for Estimates in Economy Studies. Generally speaking, the accounts of an enterprise constitute the source of information that has the greatest potential value in making estimates for economy studies. Neverthe-less, the uncritical use of accounting figures is responsible for many errors in such estimates. There are a number of important differ-ences between the point of view of accounting and that which should be taken in an economy study.

Accounting involves a recording of past receipts and expenditures. It deals only with what happened regarding policies actually fol-lowed and is not concerned with alternatives that might have been followed; it is concerned more with average costs than with differ-ences in cost. It involves apportionment of past costs against future periods of time, and apportionment of joint costs between various services or products. It does not involve consideration of the time value of money.

Engineering economy, on the other hand, always involves alter-natives; it deals with prospective differences between future alter-natives. It is concerned with differences between costs rather than apportionments of costs. It does involve consideration of the time value of money.

The statement is sometimes made that economy studies are merely a matter of accurate cost accounting. Such a statement in-volves a failure to comprehend these fundamental differences in point of view. In Part III of this book, there are given a number of instances in which this confusion of viewpoint has resulted in incor-rect conclusions on matters of economy.

The principle emphasized in this chapter is that it is always *differences* that are significant in economy studies, and that the concept of cost, in order to be a useful guide to business decisions, must be related to specific alternatives to be compared. The di-versity of alternatives that must be compared in business situations is such that no routine systematic procedure can be expected to give directly the "cost" figures that are needed for all comparisons.

An Analogy Between Engineering Mechanics and Engineering Economy. Once the alternatives in an economy study have been clearly defined and the differences between the alternatives have been expressed, in so far as practicable, in terms of prospective re-ceipts and disbursements, the analyst is in a position to make the necessary financial calculations to compare his alternatives. Up to this point, what he has done has been somewhat comparable to the setting up of a "free-body diagram" for the solution of a problem in statics as part of the design of a structure.

In the design of an engineering structure, it is necessary to fore-cast the service that the structure is to perform and the loads to which it will be subjected. This forecast must be translated into

terms of forces, just as forecasts in an economy study must be translated into terms of money. These forecast forces are the "known"
elements of the problem in mechanics thus created, and it becomes
necessary to solve for certain unknowns—for instance, the stresses
in the members of a truss. To solve for these unknowns, it is necessary to consider the structure or some portion of it as a "free body"
in equilibrium, and to observe what is known and what is to be
found out about the forces acting on it. A "free-body diagram"
serves to separate the relevant from the irrelevant elements of the
problem.

When a free-body diagram has been constructed for a problem
that is statically determinate, the solution of the problem is a
matter of making calculations based on certain simple and definite
principles. Experience indicates that students learning this branch
of engineering mechanics find much more difficulty in separating the
relevant and irrelevant elements of a problem by the construction
of a free-body diagram than in solving the problem once the free-
body diagram is correctly drawn.

The same relationship between the difficulty of defining a problem and the difficulty of solving it exists in engineering economy.
Because of difficulties such as those already pointed out in this chapter, it is easy to introduce irrelevant receipts or disbursements in
setting up the money time series that are to be compared. Once
these series have been set up, their comparison is a matter of relatively simple arithmetic.

It is helpful in analyzing engineering economy problems to use a
special diagram to show the receipts and disbursements in relation
to time. After the cash flow is represented by this diagram, the solution is a matter of making the proper calculations, just as in using
the free-body diagram in structural analysis. Figure 2–1 illustrates
a helpful way to diagram the cash flow of a problem from two different viewpoints. In this illustration one diagram represents the cash
flow for the lender and the other represents the cash flow for the
borrower. The horizontal distance represents time, with upward
arrows indicating receipts and downward arrows representing disbursements. This diagram shows what happens when one person
borrows $10,000 from another person and repays it by paying an
annual interest of 6% and a final payment of $10,000 plus the inter-
est due at the end of the last year.

The diagram of the cash flow is analogous to the free-body diagram of analytical mechanics in that by the introduction of the time
value of money, the receipts are made equivalent to the disbursements. ("Equivalence" will be introduced in Chapter 3.) The in-

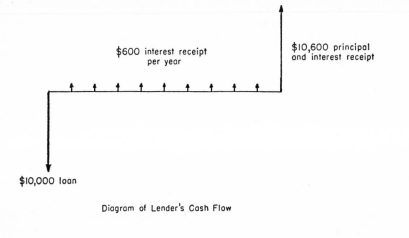

$600 interest receipt
per year

$10,600 principal
and interest receipt

$10,000 loan

Diagram of Lender's Cash Flow

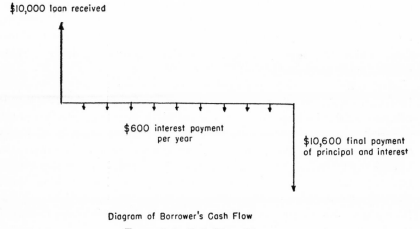

$10,000 loan received

$600 interest payment
per year

$10,600 final payment
of principal and interest

Diagram of Borrower's Cash Flow

FIGURE 2–1. Cash Flow Diagrams

terest rate of 6% makes the series of payments equivalent to the original $10,000 borrowed. When any two of the three factors (interest rate, series of receipts, and series of disbursements) are known, the third factor can be computed, and the cash flow diagram is of direct assistance in setting up the equations for the solution.

Financial Calculations Involving the Time Value of Money. Just as it is necessary to understand the principles of statics in order to design structures, so it is necessary to understand the principles of compound interest in order to make engineering economy studies in which time is an element. Figure 2–1 demonstrates the fact that interest calculations are necessary to obtain a correct comparison of the receipts and disbursements which are made at different dates.

Although the principles underlying calculations that involve the time value of money are just as definite and exact as the principles of theoretical mechanics, it is necessary to know certain conventional approximations that are sometimes used by engineers and businessmen. Also, it is important to understand the circumstances in which these approximations are likely to be satisfactory and those in which they may be misleading.

The fundamental questions that these interest calculations are designed to answer is whether a proposed investment will be recovered with a sufficiently attractive return. The next seven chapters of this book (Part II) are devoted to the study of the principles underlying calculations involving time value of money.

Drawing Conclusions from Economy Studies. The objective of the economy study is a choice between alternatives. In so far as the differences between alternatives have been expressed in money terms, the alternatives may be compared by financial calculations such as are described in Part II. But these financial calculations do not settle the problem of choice.

There are generally some differences that it has not been practicable to convert into definite money receipts or disbursements because of the lack of any basis for specific estimates, even though the estimator may feel confident that they will ultimately influence receipts or disbursements in a particular direction.

For instance, consider the problem of selection of pumping equipment for a deep well. The three common types available are the deep-well reciprocating pump, the deep-well centrifugal or turbine pump, and the air lift. Each of these will be most advantageous under certain conditions.

In making a comparison for a given installation, it is possible to estimate with reasonable accuracy the first cost of each type, including suitable prime mover equipment and housing. It may also be possible to estimate operating expenses for power and attendance.

But it may be difficult to express quantitatively the items of reliability and maintenance cost. For instance, if the water to be pumped contains sand or gritty material in appreciable amounts, the air-lift pump is likely to give the best service, as it has no working parts and is not greatly affected by such materials in the water.

The leathers and valves in reciprocating pumps require frequent renewals under such conditions. The impellers and bearings of turbine pumps are worn by the gritty material, and replacements or repairs are needed at intervals. Thus, the sand content of the water to be pumped might be a determining judgment factor in favor of the air-lift pump in some cases, in spite of the difficulty of expressing the resulting advantage of improved service and reduced maintenance costs in definite dollars-and-cents terms.

For another illustration, consider the case of a single-track railroad that is trying to determine the advisability of installing automatic block signals. Studies on other railroads may indicate approximately what may be expected in the saving of road time of freight trains, and it may be possible to translate this fairly well into a predictable dollars-and-cents saving. Train stops will be reduced in a predictable amount, and an analysis of the cost of a train stop may reduce this saving to dollars and cents. The same business may be handled in the same time with fewer cars and engines, and this may result in a saving in capital charges. The capacity of the line will be increased, and this factor might be translated into increased probable future earnings after the traffic has increased above present capacity.

But there are many factors favorable to an automatic signal system that may not be translated into money values with any pretense of accuracy, and that are, nevertheless, important intangible judgment factors in influencing the final decision. These will include such matters as increased safety, increased capacity of the train dispatcher to manage effectively due to cutting down the number of train orders, reduction in damage to contents of freight cars due to reduced number of train stops, and better public relations with shippers on account of increased speed of delivery.

Judgment factors or irreducible data such as these necessarily enter into many engineering economy studies. As previously stated, every prospective difference between two alternatives is relevant to the choice between them, whether or not the difference has been reduced to money terms. Various types of irreducibles are illustrated in Part III, which gives many examples of different types of economy studies.

Whose Viewpoint? The point of view of this book is that enterprises are run to be profitable to their owners,[3] and that comparisons of long-run economy must be made from this viewpoint. In

---

[3] But note the distinction in modern corporate enterprise between ownership and management. Business decisions in large corporations are made by the managers, not by the owners. For an elaboration of this distinction, see A. A. Berle and G. C. Means, *The Modern Corporation and Private Property* (New York: The Macmillan Co., 1932).

the case of economy studies for public works, such as are discussed in Chapter 18, this *owner* viewpoint involves all of the people of a particular political subdivision.

Of course the best choice from the viewpoint of the owners of a particular enterprise is not necessarily the best choice from the viewpoint of everyone else. To use an extreme illustration, the adoption by one producer of machinery that reduces his costs may be decidedly a detriment to his competitors. This difference in interests extends even to public works; for instance, channel improvement to effect flood relief in one community may tend to increase flood magnitudes downstream.

If we wish to view matters from the broad viewpoint of the general welfare, and to determine the effect thereon of particular decisions made from the standpoint of the owners of business enterprises, the problem is obviously more complicated. The viewpoint should be the same; that is, all prospective differences between alternatives are relevant to their comparison. The practical difficulty is to trace the different long-run effects on all of the various groups within the general public.

To do this is a problem for the economic theorist and the economic statistician. In general, except in the case of economy studies for federal public works, it is beyond the scope of this book.

Income Taxes in Economy Studies. In comparing alternatives for private industry and for individuals, an important difference in cash flow often is the difference in cash flow for income taxes. Like all prospective receipts and disbursements influenced by a choice between alternatives, expected outlays for income taxes require consideration in engineering economy studies. Ideally, it would be desirable to explain the techniques of engineering economy in a way that would introduce all of the elements of the study at the outset. Experience has shown, however, that the introduction of too many ideas and concepts at one time is not as good as a step-by-step presentation, which ultimately results in better understanding of the whole subject matter.

The place of income tax matters in this book may be brought out by another analogy from the field of engineering mechanics. In order to understand the behavior of elastic bodies, it is first necessary to study the behavior of rigid bodies. This is widely recognized as the best approach to the development of the principles of mechanics, even though there is no such thing as a perfectly rigid body. Moreover, many actual design problems involving the principles of mechanics can be solved well enough for practical purposes on the assumption that the bodies involved are rigid.

Similarly, in the field of engineering economy, it is advantageous to start with simple examples of the effects of income taxes that omit the specialized and complex aspects of tax law. In Chapters 6 to 14, alternatives are compared *before* income taxes, using a minimum attractive rate of return before taxes. Income taxes are considered only in specifying the ratio between the minimum attractive rates of return before and after income taxes. Often this type of treatment of income taxes gives the same results that would be obtained by a more critical treatment of the matter. Nevertheless, there are many cases in which sound conclusions from economy studies cannot be obtained unless income taxes are treated in a more sophisticated manner. Such cases are discussed in Chapter 15 and thereafter.

To carry the mechanics analogy a little further, it may be noted that it is possible for writers on mechanics to present the general principles of elasticity in a simple way, so that these principles may be used effectively in solving the ordinary problems confronting the structural designer and the designer of machines. Nevertheless, there are certain problems in elasticity that are extremely complicated and are only understood by a limited number of specialists who have devoted a lifetime of study to this particular field. A similar situation exists with respect to income tax matters in economy studies. The general relationship between income taxes and economy studies is simple enough, and is presented in Chapter 15 in a way that will be helpful to the analyst dealing with ordinary problems. However, some income tax matters are so complicated and technical that they are understood only by specialists in the field of income taxation. Chapter 15 attempts to indicate the general circumstances in which it is desirable to have the advice of specialists.

Conclusions of Part I. An economy study is not an instrument of precision; it is necessarily based on estimates that are subject to error and may sometimes be based on assumptions that are not valid. Nevertheless, the chance of getting the right answer in comparing technological alternatives is much greater with detailed estimates of money receipts and disbursements than if decisions are made on the basis of someone's intuition or prejudice. In this connection it should be emphasized that it is prospective *differences* that are significant in every comparison. An economy study starts from now; all events that have already happened, have happened regardless of which alternative is selected and are thus irrelevant. Similarly, future events that are expected to happen, regardless of which alternative is selected, are also irrelevant.

The dollar (or other money unit) is the standard of value that makes commensurable, differences that would otherwise be incommensurable. However, dollar comparisons do not do this until the interest factor has been introduced—until the time value of money has been considered. We now turn, therefore, to the consideration of calculations that involve the time value of money.

Problems

2–1. You have traveled from your home to the city of Z on a 150-day limit round-trip bus ticket for which you paid $57. The one-way bus fare from your home to Z is $33.50; if you do not use the return half of your ticket, the bus company will redeem it at the difference between the round-trip price and the one-way fare.

(a) Assume it is necessary for you to stay in Z until after the return date limit. What is the lowest price at which you could afford to sell the return half of your ticket to a friend rather than turn it in for credit to the bus company?

(b) If you plan to return home by bus before the return date, what is the lowest price at which you could afford to sell the return half of your ticket?

2–2. What differences can you see in the reasoning that ought to influence the decisions of Brown and Green in the situations described as follows?

Brown wishes to raise $3,000 immediately to make a down payment on the purchase of a home. He has only two possible sources of funds. (1) He may sell 60 shares of XYZ & Co. stock that is currently paying annual dividends of $3 a share. He bought this stock a few years ago for $70 a share; its present market price is $50 a share. Or (2) he may borrow $3,000 at 6% interest from his life insurance company with his life insurance policy as security.

Green also wishes to raise $3,000 immediately to make a down payment on the purchase of a home. He also has only two possible sources of funds. (1) He may sell 60 shares of XYZ & Co. stock that is currently paying annual dividends of $3 a share. He bought his stock for $35 a share a year or so before Brown made his purchase; its present market price is $50 a share. Or (2) he may borrow $3,000 at 6% interest from his life insurance company with his life insurance policy as security.

2–3. A family uses 110 kilowatt-hours of electricity per month, purchased under the following rate:

Service charge per month	$0.40
First 35 kw-hr per month	0.035 per kw-hr
Next 65 kw-hr per month	0.024 per kw-hr
Next 100 kw-hr per month	0.016 per kw-hr
All excess kw-hr per month	0.010 per kw-hr

The monthly bill is $3.35, or a little over 3 cents per kw-hr.

(a) The purchase of an electric range is considered. It is believed that this may use 100 kw-hr per month. For the purpose of judging the economy of this range as compared with some other method of cooking, what should be considered as the "cost" of this 100 kw-hr?

(b) It is proposed to economize by using lamps of lower wattage. It is believed that this will save 20 kw-hr per month. For the purpose of deciding whether or not to make this change, what should be considered as the "cost" of this 20 kw-hr?

2–4. A small machine shop with 30 HP of connected load purchases electricity under the following monthly rate:

First ....   50 kw-hr per HP of connected load at **2.8** cents per kw-hr
Next ....   50 kw-hr per HP of connected load at **1.8** cents per kw-hr
Next ....   150 kw-hr per HP of connected load at **1.0** cents per kw-hr
All over .....   250 kw-hr per HP of connected load at **0.75** cents per kw-hr

The shop uses 2,800 kw-hr per month. The monthly bill is $65.40. This is determined by figuring the first block of 50(30) = 1,500 kw-hr at 2.8 cents plus the remaining 1,300 kw-hr (which is less than the 1,500 kw-hr that might be included in the second block) at 1.8 cents. The average cost per kw-hr is 2.34 cents, that is, $65.40 divided by 2,800.

(a) Suppose the proprietor of the shop has the chance to secure additional business that will require him to operate his existing equipment more hours per day. This will use an extra 1,200 kw-hr per month. In order to get this business, he must make his bid as low as possible. What is the lowest figure that he might reasonably consider to be the "cost" of this additional energy? What is this per kw-hr?

(b) He contemplates installing certain new machines that will reduce the labor time required on certain operations. These will increase the connected load by 10 HP, but, as they will operate only on certain special jobs, will add only 100 kw-hr per month. In a study to determine the economy of installing these new machines, what should be considered as the "cost" of this energy? What is this per kw-hr?

2–5. A graduate student has been forced by a housing shortage to take a room several miles from his campus. He can ride the city bus to and from the campus, ride a bicycle, or buy a car for his transportation. If he decides to buy a car, he will plan to dispose of it at the end of the school year. What items should he consider in the "cost" of owning and operating the car when trying to reach a decision on the advisability of buying it?

If, after he bought the car, a sudden change in his financial circumstances made it advisable for him to consider disposing of it immediately, what differences would there be between his analysis now and the original analysis before he purchased the car?

2–6. You are considering the immediate purchase of a color television set for your home. You expect that within 2 years the cost of such a set will be substantially reduced due to economies realized through quantity production, and that the quality of performance of a set purchased 2 years hence will be better than that of a set purchased at once. Explain how this expectation should influence your views of the "cost" of having the services of a color television set during the next 2 years.

2–7. A small airplane for sport flying has a first cost of $6,000. The estimated disbursements in connection with its ownership and operation during the first year of its life (400 flying hours) are $1,600. Its resale value at the end of the first year is $4,000. The estimated disbursements in connection with its ownership and operation during the second year of its life (again flying 400 hours) are $1,800. Its resale value at the end of the second year is $3,200.

(a) Neglecting interest, what would be the net cost to the owner if he sold the plane at the end of 2 years? What is this per hour?

(b) Assume he has used the plane for one year. Neglecting interest, what will be the net cost to him to extend the service through the second year rather than dispose of the plane at the end of the first year? What is this per hour of flying time?

2–8. The owner of a small resort hotel is considering the construction of a swimming pool for the use of its guests. The pool will cost $7,000, and the owner believes that the pool will attract additional guests as well as justify higher rates. He has facilities for 30 guests and has had 70% occupancy at $9 a day during the last three seasons. The season is 14 weeks. The cost to operate the pool (including a lifeguard) for a season is estimated to be $1,100.

(a) What increase in occupancy would be necessary to break even (recover capital at zero interest rate) in 10 years if the rates are unchanged? Assume that operating costs other than those connected with the pool will be unaffected by a moderate change in the per cent of occupancy.

(b) If occupancy will decrease to 65% without the pool and remain at 70% with the pool (no change in rate), should the owner build the pool? Make the same assumptions as in (a).

Part II

INTEREST—THE TIME ELEMENT
IN ECONOMY

3

Equivalence

Most problems in economy involve determining what is economical in the long run, that is, over a considerable period of time. In such problems it is necessary to recognize the time value of money; because of the existence of interest, a dollar now is worth more than the prospect of a dollar next year or at some later date.

Definition of Interest. Interest may be defined as money paid for the use of borrowed money. Or, broadly speaking, interest may be thought of as the return obtainable by the productive investment of capital. While the point of view required in dealing with problems in engineering economy is the one implied in the latter broader definition, it is, nevertheless, desirable to start the discussion of interest by considering only situations in which money is actually borrowed. The broader viewpoint is developed in Chapter 6 and thereafter.

Interest Rate. The rate of interest is the ratio between the interest chargeable or payable at the end of a period of time, usually a year or less, and the money owed at the beginning of that period. Thus if $6 of interest is payable annually on a debt of $100, the interest rate is $6/$100 = 0.06 per annum. This is customarily described as an interest rate of 6%, the "per annum" being understood unless some other period of time is definitely stated.

Even though interest is frequently payable oftener than once a year, the interest rate per annum is usually what is meant when an interest rate is stated. Thus rates of 0.005 payable monthly, 0.015 payable quarterly, or 0.03 payable semiannually are all described as 6%. The difference between the payment of interest annually and its payment more frequently is discussed briefly in the next chapter under the heading "Nominal and Effective Interest Rates"; however, this difference is not of great importance in dealing with problems in engineering economy.

Plans for Repayment of Borrowed Money. Consider the plans shown in Table 3–1 by which a loan of $10,000 might be repaid in 10 years with interest at 6% payable annually. In the tables showing these plans, the date of the loan is designated as 0 years and time

TABLE 3–1

Four Plans for Repayment of $10,000 in 10 Years with Interest at 6%

	End of Year	Interest Due (6% of money owed at start of year)	Total Money Owed Before Year-End Payment	Year-End Payment	Money Owed After Year-End Payment
Plan I	0				$10,000
	1	$600	$10,600	$ 600	10,000
	2	600	10,600	600	10,000
	3	600	10,600	600	10,000
	4	600	10,600	600	10,000
	5	600	10,600	600	10,000
	6	600	10,600	600	10,000
	7	600	10,600	600	10,000
	8	600	10,600	600	10,000
	9	600	10,600	600	10,000
	10	600	10,600	10,600	0
Plan II	0				$10,000
	1	$600	$10,600	$1,600	9,000
	2	540	9,540	1,540	8,000
	3	480	8,480	1,480	7,000
	4	420	7,420	1,420	6,000
	5	360	6,360	1,360	5,000
	6	300	5,300	1,300	4,000
	7	240	4,240	1,240	3,000
	8	180	3,180	1,180	2,000
	9	120	2,120	1,120	1,000
	10	60	1,060	1,060	0
Plan III	0				$10,000.00
	1	$600.00	$10,600.00	$1,358.68	9,241.32
	2	554.48	9,795.80	1,358.68	8,437.12
	3	506.23	8,943.35	1,358.68	7,584.67
	4	455.08	8,039.75	1,358.68	6,681.07
	5	400.86	7,081.93	1,358.68	5,723.25
	6	343.40	6,066.65	1,358.68	4,707.98
	7	282.48	4,990.45	1,358.68	3,631.77
	8	217.91	3,849.68	1,358.68	2,491.00
	9	149.46	2,640.46	1,358.68	1,281.78
	10	76.90	1,358.68	1,358.68	0.00
Plan IV	0				$10,000.00
	1	$ 600.00	$10,600.00	$ 0.00	10,600.00
	2	636.00	11,236.00	0.00	11,236.00
	3	674.16	11,910.16	0.00	11,910.16
	4	714.61	12,624.77	0.00	12,624.77
	5	757.49	13,382.26	0.00	13,382.26
	6	802.94	14,185.20	0.00	14,185.20
	7	851.11	15,036.31	0.00	15,036.31
	8	902.18	15,938.49	0.00	15,938.49
	9	956.31	16,894.80	0.00	16,894.80
	10	1,013.69	17,908.49	17,908.49	0.00

is measured in years from that date. The $10,000 is called the *principal* of the loan.

Characteristics of Repayment Plans. The student of engineering economy should carefully examine these four plans because they are representative of various schemes in common use for the repayment of money borrowed for a term of years. Plan I involves no partial payment of principal; only interest is paid each year, and the principal is paid in a lump sum at the end of the period. The cash flow diagram, introduced in Chapter 2, to represent the borrower's receipts and payments for Plan I is shown in Figure 3–1a.

Plans II and III involve systematic reduction of the principal of the debt by uniform repayment of principal with diminishing interest in Plan II and by a scheme that makes the sum of the interest payments and the principal payment uniform in Plan III. The cash flow diagram for Plan II is shown in Figure 3–1b. The cash flow diagram for Plan III is shown in Figure 3–1c.

Plan IV, on the other hand, involves no payment of either principal or interest until the single payment of both at the end of the tenth year. Its diagram is shown in Figure 3–1d.

The advantages and disadvantages of the various plans from the standpoint of different classes of borrowers will be discussed in a later chapter. The point for immediate consideration is their relation to compound interest and to the time value of money.

Compound Interest. In Plan IV, interest is *compounded;* that is, the interest each year is based on the total amount owed at the end of the previous year, a total amount that included the original principal plus the accumulated interest that had not been paid when due. The formulas and tables explained in the next chapter are all based upon the compounding of interest.

The distinction is made, both in the literature of the mathematics of investment and in the law, between *compound interest* and *simple interest.* If in Plan IV a lump-sum payment of principal and interest had been called for at simple rather than compound interest, the only interest payable would have been that charged on the original principal of $10,000. The total payment required under simple interest would thus have been $16,000 instead of the $17,908 that is required under compound interest.

Where money is borrowed for a period of years, the usual business practice is for interest to be due—and nearly always actually paid—annually or oftener. This practice, in effect, involves compound interest, whether considered from the viewpoint of the lender or the borrower. Where interest is paid each year, the lender receives a

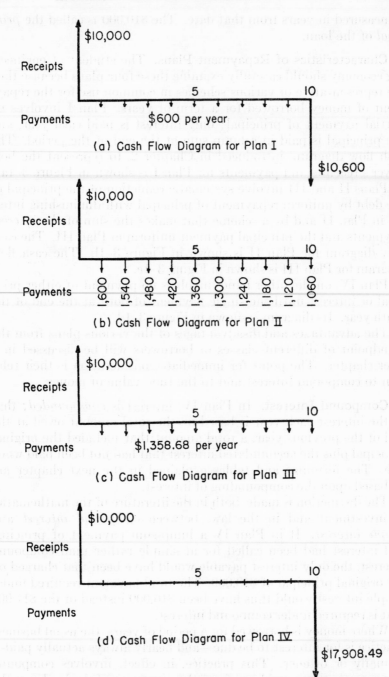

$10,000

Receipts

5   10

Payments $600 per year

(a) Cash Flow Diagram for Plan I

$10,600

$10,000

Receipts

5   10

Payments   1,600 1,540 1,480 1,420 1,360 1,300 1,240 1,180 1,120 1,060

(b) Cash Flow Diagram for Plan II

$10,000

Receipts

5   10

Payments $1,358.68 per year

(c) Cash Flow Diagram for Plan III

$10,000

Receipts

5   10

Payments

(d) Cash Flow Diagram for Plan IV

$17,908.49

FIGURE 3-1. Cash Flow Diagrams for Plans for Repayment of $10,000 in 10 years

payment that he can presumably reinvest at interest if he so desires. For instance in Plan I, which calls for a total payment of $16,000, if the lender reinvested his $600 interest received each year at 6%, he would have $17,908 at the end of the tenth year. Similarly, the borrower, in paying his interest annually, is foregoing the opportunity for a profitable investment of his interest payment that he might have made had the interest payment been deferred.

Thus compound interest is the general practice of the business world, and Plans I, II, and III involve what is, in effect, compound interest, because interest is paid annually in each plan. It will be shown in the following chapters how compound interest formulas may be used in dealing with these various types of repayment situations. Problems in engineering economy generally require consideration of compound interest; simple interest (chiefly of importance in connection with loans for periods of a year or less) will not be discussed further in these pages. Wherever the term "interest" is used, compound interest (i.e., interest due annually or oftener) is implied.

Equivalence. The concept that payments that differ in total magnitude but that are made at different dates may be equivalent to one another is an important one in engineering economy. In developing this concept, we may place side by side for comparison, the $10,000 borrowed and the four series of money payments that we have seen would repay it with interest at 6%. (Payments are shown to four significant figures only.)

TABLE 3–2

FIVE EQUIVALENT SERIES OF PAYMENTS

Year	Investment	I	II	III	IV
0	$10,000				
1		$600	$1,600	$1,359	
2		600	1,540	1,359	
3		600	1,480	1,359	
4		600	1,420	1,359	
5		600	1,360	1,359	
6		600	1,300	1,359	
7		600	1,240	1,359	
8		600	1,180	1,359	
9		600	1,120	1,359	
10		$10,600	1,060	1,359	$17,910

If interest is at 6%, these five sets of payments are equivalent to one another. They are equivalent from the standpoint of a prospective lender (investor) with $10,000, because with that sum he can get any one of the four future series of payments (or more precisely, someone's promise to make the payments) in exchange for the present $10,000. Similarly, from the standpoint of the prospective borrower who needs $10,000 (perhaps to invest productively in his business), the four future series are equivalent to each other and to $10,000 now; because, by agreeing to pay any one of these future series, he may secure the needed present sum.

Obviously, we might think of any number of series of payments that would serve to just repay $10,000 with interest at 6%. All of these would be equivalent to $10,000 now, and to each other.

The meaning of equivalence may be explained by using an analogy from algebra: If a number of things are equal to one thing, then they are equal to each other. Given an interest rate, we may say that any payment or series of payments that will repay a present sum of money with interest at that rate is equivalent to that present sum. Therefore, *all future payments or series of payments that would repay the present sum with interest at the stated rate are equivalent to each other.*

Present [1] Worth. From the foregoing we found that a loan of $10,000 can be repaid with interest in four different ways, involving different amounts of money and at different times over a period of 10 years. To the lender (investor) the loan (investment) is the amount necessary to secure the promise of the future payment or series of payments, with interest at the given rate. The investment necessary to secure the promise of the future payment or payments is the present worth of the future payments. To the borrower, the present worth may be thought of as the present sum that may be secured in exchange for the promise to make specified future payments or series of payments. To both the lender and the borrower the repayment series of payments is equivalent to the present worth. Also, since the four different series of payments are equivalent to the same present worth, the series of payments are equivalent to each other.

Significance of Equivalence in Engineering Economy Studies. The five columns in Table 3–2 show equivalent series of payments; however, the total payments called for are quite different, totaling $10,000, $16,000, $13,300, $13,590, and $17,910, respectively. The longer the repayment period the greater this apparent difference. Thus, if the repayment period were 20 years, the corresponding total payments for similar equivalent series would be $10,000, $22,000, $16,300, $17,436, and $32,070.

[1] Of course the "present" may be moved in the imagination of the computer to any convenient date. Thus we may speak in 1960 of the present worth in 1968 of a payment made in 1975.

Engineering economy studies usually involve making a choice of several alternative plans for accomplishing some objective of providing a given service. If a given service could be provided by five alternative methods requiring payments as shown in the five columns of Table 3–2, all of the alternative plans would be equally economical with interest at 6%; that is, they could each be financed by a present sum of $10,000. This fact would not be evident from a comparison of the total payments called for in the various plans; it would be clear only if the different money series were converted either to equivalent single payments (e.g., present worth) or to equivalent uniform series.

Engineering economy studies usually require some conversion as a basis for intelligent decision. A comparison of total payments involved in alternative plans, without the use of interest factors to convert the two series to make them comparable, is nearly always misleading.

Equivalence Depends on the Interest Rate. It was shown that the five payment series in the columns of Table 3–2 were equivalent because each series would repay an original loan of $10,000 with interest at 6%. These series payments would not be equivalent if the stated interest rate had been anything other than 6%. If the rate is less than 6%, the series of payments in the four plans will repay a greater amount than the present worth of $10,000; if the rate is greater than 6%, they will all repay a lesser amount. Table 3–3 shows the present worths of the four series of payments at various interest rates.

TABLE 3–3

PRESENT WORTHS AT VARIOUS INTEREST RATES OF PAYMENT SERIES SHOWN IN
TABLE 3–2

Interest Rate	Plan I	Plan II	Plan III	Plan IV
0%	$16,000	$13,300	$13,590	$17,910
2%	13,590	12,030	12,210	14,690
4%	11,620	10,940	11,020	12,100
6%	10,000	10,000	10,000	10,000
8%	8,660	9,180	9,120	8,300
10%	7,540	8,460	8,350	6,900

A present sum is always equivalent at some interest rate to a larger future sum of payments. In many engineering economy problems the answer desired is the interest rate that will make two series equivalent to each other; this is often described as the rate of return obtainable on an extra investment. This viewpoint is developed in Chapter 8.

Summary. The main points of this chapter may be stated as follows:

One definition of interest is money paid for the use of borrowed money. The rate of interest may be defined as the ratio between the interest chargeable or payable at the end of a stipulated period of time and the money owed at the beginning of that period. The general practice of the business world is for interest to be chargeable or payable annually or oftener.

Any future payment or series of payments that will exactly repay a present sum with interest at a given rate is *equivalent* to that present sum; all such future payments or series of payments that will repay the given present sum are equivalent to one another. The present sum is the *present worth* of any future payment or series of payments that will exactly repay it with interest at a given rate.

Equivalence calculations are necessary for a fair comparison of different money time series; they are thus usually required in engineering economy studies. Economy studies, however, generally imply a broader definition of interest as the return obtainable by the productive investment of capital.

Problems

3–1. Prepare a table similar to Table 3–1, showing four plans for the repayment of $2,000 in 5 years with interest at 10%. The uniform annual payment in the plan corresponding to Plan III is $527.60.

3–2. Prepare a table similar to Table 3–1, showing four plans for the repayment of $5,000 in 6 years with interest at 4%. The uniform annual payment in the plan corresponding to Plan III is $953.80.

3–3. Prepare a table similar to Plan III of Table 3–1, showing the interest due each year and the money owed after each year-end payment when a debt of $1,000 is repaid in 9 years with interest at 8%. The uniform annual payment is $160.08.

3–4. Prepare a table similar to Plans II and III of Table 3–1, showing the annual repayment (principal and interest) for the repayment of a loan of $2,000 in 5 years with interest at 7%. The annual payment for Plan III is $487.78.

3–5. Prepare a table similar to Plan III of Table 3–1, showing the interest due and the money owed after each year-end payment when a debt of $1,000 is repaid in 6 years, with interest at 8%. The uniform annual payment is $216.32.

4

Interest Formulas

Symbols. These symbols are used in the following explanation of interest formulas:

i represents an interest rate per interest period.

n represents a number of interest periods.

P represents a present sum of money.

S represents a sum of money at the end of n periods from the present date that is equivalent to P with interest i.

R represents the end-of-period payment or receipt in a uniform series continuing for the coming n periods, the entire series equivalent to P at interest rate i.

Although a one-year interest period is used in most of the illustrations in this book, the formulas presented apply to interest periods of any length.

Formulas. The fundamental interest formulas that express the relationship between P, S, and R in terms of i and n are as follows:

Given P, to find S. $S = P(1+i)^n$ (1)

Given S, to find P. $P = S\left[\dfrac{1}{(1+i)^n}\right]$ (2)

Given S, to find R. $R = S\left[\dfrac{i}{(1+i)^n - 1}\right]$ (3)

Given P, to find R. $R = P\left[\dfrac{i(1+i)^n}{(1+i)^n - 1}\right]$ (4)

Or $R = P\left[\dfrac{i}{(1+i)^n - 1} + i\right]$ (4)

Given R, to find S. $S = R\left[\dfrac{(1+i)^n - 1}{i}\right]$ (5)

Given R, to find P. $P = R\left[\dfrac{(1+i)^n - 1}{i(1+i)^n}\right]$ (6)

Or $P = R\left[\dfrac{1}{\dfrac{i}{(1+i)^n - 1} + i}\right]$ (6)

The following explanation of the formulas assumes the interest period as one year; the explanation can be made general by substituting "period" for "year."

Development of Formulas for Single Payments. If P is invested at interest rate i, the interest for the first year is iP and the total amount at the end of the first year is $P + iP = P(1 + i)$.

The second year the interest on this is $iP(1 + i)$, and the amount at the end of this year is $P(1 + i) + iP(1 + i) = P(1 + i)^2$. Similarly, at the end of the third year the amount is $P(1 + i)^3$; at the end of n years it is $P(1 + i)^n$.

This is the formula for the compound amount, S, obtainable in n years from a principal, P,

$$S = P(1 + i)^n \tag{1}$$

If we express P in terms of S, i, and n,

$$P = S\left[\frac{1}{(1 + i)^n}\right] \tag{2}$$

P may then be thought of as the principal that will give a required amount S in n years; in other words, P is the present worth of a payment of S, n years hence.

The expression $(1 + i)^n$ is called the *single payment compound amount factor*. Its reciprocal $1/(1 + i)^n$ is called the *single payment present worth factor*.

Development of Formulas for Uniform Annual Series of End-of-Year Payments. If R is invested at the end of each year for n years, the total amount at the end of n years will obviously be the sum of the compound amounts of the individual investments. The money invested at the end of the first year will earn interest for $(n - 1)$ years; its amount will thus be $R(1 + i)^{n-1}$. The second year's payment will amount to $R(1 + i)^{n-2}$; the third year's to $R(1 + i)^{n-3}$; and so on until the last payment, made at the end of n years, which has earned no interest. The total amount S is $R[1 + (1 + i) + (1 + i)^2 + (1 + i)^3 \ldots + (1 + i)^{n-1}]$.

This expression for S in terms of R may be simplified to its customary form by the following algebraic manipulations:

$$S = R[1 + (1 + i) + (1 + i)^2 \ldots + (1 + i)^{n-2} + (1 + i)^{n-1}]$$

Multiplying both sides of the equation by $(1 + i)$,

$$(1 + i)S = R[(1 + i) + (1 + i)^2 + (1 + i)^3 \ldots + (1 + i)^{n-1} + (1 + i)^n]$$

Subtracting the original equation from this second equation

$$iS = R[(1 + i)^n - 1]$$

Then

$$R = S\left[\frac{i}{(1+i)^n - 1}\right] \tag{3}$$

A fund established to produce a desired amount at the end of a given period of time by means of a series of payments throughout the period is called a *sinking fund*. The expression

$$\frac{i}{(1+i)^n - 1}$$

is called the *sinking fund deposit factor*.

To find the uniform end-of-year payment, R, which can be secured for n years from a present investment, P (as in Plan III of Table 3–1), substitute in equation (3) the value given for S in equation (1):

$$R = S\left[\frac{i}{(1+i)^n - 1}\right] = P(1+i)^n\left[\frac{i}{(1+i)^n - 1}\right]$$

$$= P\left[\frac{i(1+i)^n}{(1+i)^n - 1}\right] \tag{4}$$

This may also be expressed as

$$R = P\left[\frac{i}{(1+i)^n - 1} + i\right] \tag{4}$$

This expression

$$\frac{i(1+i)^n}{(1+i)^n - 1}$$

is called the *capital recovery factor*. As shown by its identity with

$$\left[\frac{i}{(1+i)^n - 1} + i\right]$$

it is always equal to the sinking fund factor plus the interest rate. When multiplied by a present debt (which, from the point of view of the lender, is a present investment), it gives the uniform end-of-year payment necessary to repay the debt (the lender's investment) in n years with interest rate i. This factor, or an approximation to it, is used in the solution of many problems in engineering economy.

Formulas (3) and (4) may be reversed to show S and P in terms of R as follows:

$$S = R\left[\frac{(1+i)^n - 1}{i}\right] \tag{5}$$

$$P = R\left[\frac{(1+i)^n - 1}{i(1+i)^n}\right] \tag{6}$$

The expression

$$\left[\frac{(1+i)^n - 1}{i} \right]$$

is called the *uniform series compound amount factor*. This is usually abbreviated to *series compound amount factor*.

The expression

$$\left[\frac{(1+i)^n - 1}{i\,(1+i)^n} \right]$$

is called the *uniform series present worth factor*. Similarly, this is usually abbreviated to *series present worth factor*.

Mnemonic Symbols. Throughout the later chapters of this book many equations will be written using mnemonic symbols rather than the formulas as given in the previous paragraphs. These symbols are:

pwf′ represents single payment present worth factor.
pwf represents uniform series present worth factor.
caf′ represents single payment compound amount factor.
caf represents uniform series compound amount factor.
sff represents sinking fund factor.
crf represents capital recovery factor.

Using these symbols, equation (5) becomes

$$S = R\,(\text{caf}-i\%-n)$$

which is read, "the compound amount of a series of uniform end-of-period payments R equals R times the uniform series compound amount factor at interest rate i for n periods." By using this form of notation, the equations of any problem can be written and checked, and then the numerical values from the interest tables can be substituted for the required factors. This is analogous to writing equations in engineering mechanics from the free-body diagram, using letters to represent forces and stresses, and then substituting the known values in place of the letters. The equations can be checked for accuracy of principle without becoming involved in the numerical data. The symbols help stress the functions to be performed by the factors.

Interest Tables. The solution of problems in equivalence is greatly facilitated by the use of interest tables. Tables E–1 to E–19 in Appendix E give values of the single payment compound amount factor, single payment present worth factor, the sinking fund deposit factor, the capital recovery factor, the uniform series compound amount factor, and the uniform series present worth factor for each value of n from 1 to 35, and for values of n that are multiples of 5 from 40 to 100. Each interest rate has a separate table; the interest rates given are 1%, $1\frac{1}{4}$%, $1\frac{1}{2}$%, $1\frac{3}{4}$%, 2%, $2\frac{1}{2}$%, 3%, $3\frac{1}{2}$%, 4%, $4\frac{1}{2}$%, 5%, $5\frac{1}{2}$%, 6%, 7%, 8%, 10%, 12%, 15%, and 20%. In addition, Tables E–20 to E–22 give the capital recovery factors, single payment present worth factors, and series present worth factors for interest rates from 25% to 50%.

If the payment given (P, S, or R) is unity (in any units desired, dollars, pounds, pesos, francs, etc.), the factor from the interest tables gives directly the payment to be found. Thus, the respective columns in each table might have been headed:

Compound amount of 1
Present worth of 1
Uniform series that amounts to 1
Uniform series that 1 will purchase
Compound amount of 1 per period
Present worth of 1 per period

Interest tables in books on the mathematics of investment commonly use these headings or some variations of them.

Relationship Between Interest Factors. In using the interest tables, it is desirable that the student be familiar with the simple relationships that exist between the different factors for a given value of i and n. The illustrations given all apply to $i = 0.06$ and $n = 5$. The factors used may be found in Table E–13, Appendix E.

Single payment compound amount factor and single payment present worth factor are reciprocals. Thus

$$\frac{1}{(\text{caf}'-6\%-5)} = (\text{pwf}'-6\%-5) = \frac{1}{1.338} = 0.7473$$

Sinking fund factor and uniform series compound amount factor are reciprocals. Thus

$$\frac{1}{(\text{sff}-6\%-5)} = (\text{caf}-6\%-5) = \frac{1}{0.17740} = 5.637$$

Capital recovery factor and series present worth factor are reciprocals. Thus

$$\frac{1}{(\text{crf}-6\%-5)} = (\text{pwf}-6\%-5) = \frac{1}{0.23470} = 4.212$$

Series compound amount factor equals 1.000 plus sum of first $(n-1)$ terms in column of single payment compound amount factors. Thus

$$(\text{caf–6\%–5}) = 1.000 + (\text{caf'–6\%–1}) + (\text{caf'–6\%–2}) + (\text{caf'–6\%–3})$$
$$+ (\text{caf'–6\%–4})$$

$$= 1.000 + 1.060 + 1.124 + 1.191 + 1.262 = 5.637$$

Series present worth factor equals sum of first n terms of single payment present worth factors. Thus

$$(\text{pwf–6\%–5}) = (\text{pwf'–6\%–1}) + (\text{pwf'–6\%–2}) + (\text{pwf'–6\%–3})$$
$$+ (\text{pwf'–6\%–4}) + (\text{pwf'–6\%–5})$$

$$4.212 = 0.9434 + 0.8900 + 0.8396 + 0.7921 + 0.7473$$

Capital recovery factor equals sinking fund factor plus interest rate. Thus

$$(\text{crf–6\%–5}) = (\text{sff –6\%–5}) + i$$
$$0.23740 = 0.17740 + 0.06$$

Nominal and Effective Interest Rates. Many loan transactions stipulate that interest is computed and charged more often than once a year. For example, interest on deposits in savings banks may be computed and added to the deposit balance four times a year; this is referred to as interest "compounded quarterly." Interest on corporate bond issues usually is payable every 6 months. Building and loan associations, automobile finance companies, and other organizations making personal loans often require that interest be computed monthly.

Consider a loan transaction in which interest is charged at 1% per month. Sometimes such a transaction is described as having an interest rate of 12% per annum. More precisely, this rate should be described as a *nominal* 12% per annum compounded monthly.

It is desirable to recognize that there is a real difference between 1% per month compounded monthly and 12% per annum compounded annually. Assume that $1,000 is borrowed with interest at 1% per month. Using Table E–1, the amount owed at the end of 12 months may be calculated as follows:

$$S = \$1,000 (1.01)^{12}$$
$$= \$1,000 (\text{caf'–1\%–12})$$
$$= \$1,000 (1.127) = \$1,127$$

If the same $1,000 had been borrowed at 12% per annum compounded annually, the amount owed at the end of the year would have been only $1,120, $7 less than $1,127. The monthly compounding at 1% has the same effect on the year-end compound amount as the charging of a rate of 12.7% compounded annually. In the language of financial mathematics, the *effective* interest rate is 12.7%. (If Table E–1 contained one more significant figure in the column of compound amount factors, we would compute the effective interest rate more accurately as 12.68%.)

The phrases *nominal interest rate* and *effective interest rate* may be defined more precisely as follows:

Let interest be compounded m times a year at an interest rate $\dfrac{r}{m}$ per compounding period.

The nominal interest rate per annum $= m\left(\dfrac{r}{m}\right) = r.$

The effective interest rate per annum $= \left(1+\dfrac{r}{m}\right)^m - 1.$

Nominal rates of interest for different numbers of annual compoundings are not comparable with one another until they have been converted into the corresponding effective rate. The more frequent the number of compoundings at a given nominal rate, the greater the difference between the effective and nominal rates. (For example, a nominal rate of 12% compounded semiannually yields an effective rate of 12.36% in contrast to the 12.68% for a nominal 12% compounded monthly.) The higher the nominal rate for a given m, the greater both the absolute and the relative difference between effective and nominal rates. (For example, a nominal rate of 24% compounded monthly yields an effective rate of 26.8%, 2.8% more than the nominal rate. In contrast, the effective rate is only 0.68% above the nominal rate with interest at a nominal 12% compounded monthly.)

In engineering economy studies it usually is preferable to deal with effective interest rates rather than nominal rates.

Continuous Compounding of Interest. The mathematical symbol e (the base of natural or "Napierian" logarithms) may be defined as the limit approached by the quantity $\left(1+\dfrac{1}{k}\right)^k$ as k increases indefinitely. It is shown in textbooks on calculus that $e = 2.71828+$. The common logarithm of e is 0.43429.

If a sum P is invested for n years with a nominal interest rate r and with m compounding periods a year, the compound amount S may be expressed as follows:

$$S = P\left(1+\frac{r}{m}\right)^{mn}$$

If we designate $\frac{m}{r}$ by the symbol k, $m = rk$, and

$$S = P\left(1 + \frac{1}{k}\right)^{rkn} = P\left[\left(1 + \frac{1}{k}\right)^k\right]^{rn}$$

As the number of compounding periods per year, m, increases without limit, so also must k. It follows that the bracketed quantity in the foregoing formula approaches the limit e. Therefore, the limiting value of S is $S = Pe^{rn}$.

With continuous compounding, the single payment compound amount factor (caf') is e^{rn}. The single payment present worth factor (pwf') is, of course, e^{-rn}, the reciprocal of caf'.

Although continuous compounding formulas assume that interest is computed and added to principal at every moment throughout the year, the results obtained using continuous compounding are very close to the results obtained using monthly compounding with a nominal rate r.

Application of Continuous Compounding in Engineering Economy. Although continuous compounding is not used in actual loan transactions, the topic is of importance in connection with certain problems of decision making. Two types of application are important.

In some economy studies it may be desired to recognize that certain receipts or disbursements will be spread throughout a year rather than concentrated at a particular date. Continuous compounding is well adapted to the assumption of a continuous flow of funds at a uniform rate throughout a stated period of time. Formulas and tables that may be used for this purpose are explained in Appendix B.

In the development of certain mathematical models intended as aids to decision making, the mathematical treatment is facilitated by the use of continuous compounding rather than periodic compounding.

Interest Tables for Uniform Gradient. Engineering economy problems frequently involve disbursements or receipts that increase or decrease each year by varying amounts. For example, the maintenance expense for a piece of mechanical equipment may tend to increase somewhat each year. If the increase or decrease is the same every year the yearly increase or decrease is known as a *uniform gradient*. Even when it is reasonable to believe that the annual expenses or receipts will increase or decrease somewhat irregularly, a uniform gradient may be the best and most convenient way to estimate the changing condition.

Since the amount of money is different each year, the uniform series interest factors previously discussed cannot be used and each year's disbursement or receipt must be handled by means of the single payment factors. This time-consuming computation can be avoided by deriving simple formulas for the equivalent cost of a gradient and for the present worth of a gradient for n years.

Figure 4–1 gives the cash flow diagram for a uniform gradient. Using end-of-year payments, the payment the second year is greater

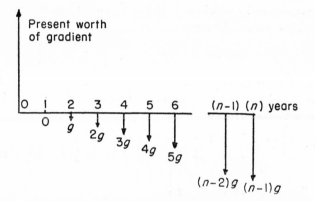

Present worth
of gradient

FIGURE 4–1. Cash Flow Diagram for a Gradient

than the first year by g, the third is g greater than the second year, and so on. Thus, the payments by years are as follows:

End of Year	Payment
1	0
2	g
3	$2g$
4	$3g$
. . . .	
$(n-1)$	$(n-2)g$
n	$(n-1)g$

These payments may be thought of as a set of payments that will accumulate to an amount S at the end of the nth year, and that amount can be converted to a uniform series of payments by multiplying S by the sinking fund factor. For convenience, it can be assumed that a series of annual payments of g is started at the end of the second year, another series of g is started at the end of the third year, and so on. Each of these series terminate at the same time, the end of the nth year. The series compound amount factor can be applied to each series of g per year to determine its compound amount on this terminal date:

Sum of compound amounts

$$= g\left[\frac{(1+i)^{n-1}-1}{i}+\frac{(1+i)^{n-2}-1}{i}\cdots+\frac{(1+i)^2-1}{i}+\frac{(1+i)-1}{i}\right]$$

$$= \frac{g}{i}\left[(1+i)^{n-1}+(1+i)^{n-2}\cdots+(1+i)^2+(1+i)-(n-1)\right]$$

$$= \frac{g}{i}\left[(1+i)^{n-1}+(1+i)^{n-2}\cdots+(1+i)^2+(1+i)+1\right]-\frac{ng}{i}$$

The expression in brackets is the compound amount of a sinking fund of 1 for n years. Hence

$$\text{Sum of compound amounts} = \frac{g}{i}\left[\frac{(1+i)^n-1}{i}\right]-\frac{ng}{i}$$

The equivalent uniform annual figure for n years may be found by multiplying this sum of the compound amounts by the sinking fund factor for n years. Hence

$$R = \frac{g}{i}\left[\frac{(1+i)^n-1}{i}\right]\left[\frac{i}{(1+i)^n-1}\right]-\frac{ng}{i}\left[\frac{i}{(1+i)^n-1}\right]$$

$$= \frac{g}{i}-\frac{ng}{i}\left[\frac{i}{(1+i)^n-1}\right]$$

This is a general expression applicable to any value of n. Values for the equivalent uniform annual cost of a uniform gradient of unity for interest rates of 1%, 2%, 3%, 4%, 5%, 6%, 7%, 8%, 10%, 12%, 15%, 20%, 25%, 30%, 35%, 40%, 45%, and 50%, and for n from 2 to 100 years are given in Table E–23, Appendix E. The use of these gradient factors will be illustrated in Chapter 5.

The factor to convert a gradient series to a present worth may be obtained by multiplying the factor to convert a gradient series to an equivalent uniform annual series by the series present worth factor for n years at interest i. The values of the gradient present worth factors have been computed for various interest rates from 3% to 20% and are given in Table E–24 for values of n from 1 to 35 years.

The mnemonic symbols used for the factors for use in dealing with gradients are:

gf = factor to convert a gradient series to an equivalent annual series
gpwf = factor to convert a gradient series to a present worth.

The relation between these two factors can be shown thus:

$$(\text{gpwf-}i\%\text{-}n) = (\text{gf-}i\%\text{-}n)\ (\text{pwf-}i\%\text{-}n)$$

Finding Unknown Interest Rates. Frequently, the sum to be invested (or loaned) is known, and the prospective future series of money receipts (or plan of repayment) is known, and it is desired to find the interest rate that will be earned on the investment.

When a single payment and a single receipt are involved, when n is known and i is wanted, the problem is quite simple. Formula (1) becomes

$$i = \sqrt[n]{\frac{S}{P}} - 1 \qquad\qquad (7)$$

This may be solved by logarithms.

When a single payment and a uniform series are involved, the problem becomes more complicated to solve directly. When nonuniform payments or receipts are involved, the only reasonable method of solution is by interpolation. The use of the interest tables in Appendix E makes the solution of unknown interest problems relatively simple by the interpolation method. Approximate methods using interpolation are recommended for engineering economy studies and are illustrated and explained in Chapters 5 and 8.

Interest Formulas and Tables in Relation to Engineering Economy. "Will it pay?" (which is the central question of engineering economy) usually means "Will an investment pay?" An investment will not pay unless it can ultimately be repaid with interest. Thus interest enters into most problems in engineering economy.

But the engineer's decision as to whether a proposed investment will pay must be based on estimates rather than on a certain knowledge of the future. Even the most careful estimates are likely to go wrong; frequently, also, engineers' decisions regarding economy must be based on preliminary estimates made in advance of design that necessarily have a considerable danger of large errors.

For this reason great precision is not usually required in interest calculations made for economy studies. For instance, where cost estimates are subject to errors of 5% or 10%, there is no justification for carrying out interest calculations to seven significant figures, as is sometimes done. Interest tables giving three significant figures are adequate for purposes of most economy studies; in many cases slide-rule calculations are entirely satisfactory. Similarly, the difference between paying interest once a year and paying it more often (i.e., the difference between compounding annually and compounding semiannually, quarterly, or monthly—a difference of considerable importance to the financier) is usually neglected in economy studies; the interest rate used in economy studies will frequently be considerably higher than the cost of borrowed money for a number of reasons that are explained in Chapter 9.

Problems

4–1. Develop a formula for the *beginning-of-period* payment, T, into a sinking fund to amount to S at the end of n periods with interest at i per cent per period.

4–2. How could you determine a desired *uniform series compound amount factor*, if you had only

    (a) a table of *single payment compound amount factors?*
    (b) a table of *sinking fund deposit factors?*
    (c) a table of *capital recovery factors?*
    (d) a table of *uniform series present worth factors?*

Illustrate your solution using the 8% table, Table E–15, to obtain the factor for 12 years.

4–3. How would you determine a desired *capital recovery factor*, if you had only

    (a) a table of *single payment compound amount factors?*
    (b) a table of *single payment present worth factors?*
    (c) a table of *sinking fund factors?*
    (d) a table of *uniform series compound amount factors?*
    (e) a table of *uniform series present worth factors?*

Illustrate from the 5% table, Table E–11, showing how you would obtain the desired factor for 10 years.

4–4. What effective interest rate per annum corresponds to a nominal rate of 18% compounded semiannually? Compounded quarterly? Compounded monthly?

4–5. What effective interest rate per annum corresponds to a nominal rate of 12% compounded semiannually? Compounded quarterly?

4–6. The interest rate charged on a small loan is 1½% per month. What nominal and effective rates per annum correspond to this?

5

Solving Interest Problems

This chapter illustrates the use of interest tables and formulas in the solution of practical problems related to economy. Each illustrative example is numbered for convenient reference.

Many of the illustrative examples are stated in several different ways. It is desirable that the student of engineering economy recognize the variety of questions that may be answered by the same equivalence calculation.

In solving any interest problem, it is necessary to note which of the various elements of such problems (i, n, P, S, and R) are known and which are wanted. This is the first step in any solution and follows immediately after the problem statement in each illustrative example.

Unless otherwise stated, it is to be assumed in the following examples that interest is payable (or compounded) annually.

Examples Illustrating the Use of the Interest Factors Relative to Time. The concept of equivalence was introduced in Chapter 3, and Table 3–1 gave four plans for the repayment of a loan with interest. All these plans were equivalent to each other. Examples 5–1 through 5–7 illustrate the use of the interest factors to compute equivalence in terms of both single payments and series of payments over different periods of time. An initial amount of $1,000 is assumed on January 1, 1961, and is converted to equivalent amounts at different times, and finally, the original $1,000 is obtained by converting a series to a single amount as of January 1, 1961. These examples show that "now" or zero time can be assumed at any date, and an equivalent amount or a series of amounts can be obtained for dates either preceding or following the assumed zero time. The cash flow diagrams for Examples 5–1 through 5–7 are shown in Figure 5–1.

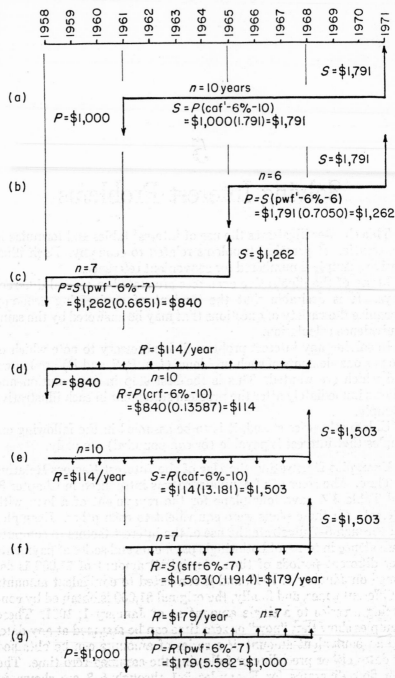

FIGURE 5–1. Use of Interest Factors To Compute Equivalent Amounts and Equivalent Series

EXAMPLE 5–1

If $1,000 is invested at 6% compound interest on January 1, 1961, how much will be accumulated by January 1, 1971? (Figure 5–1a.)

Solution:

$$i = 0.06; n = 10; P = \$1,000; S = ?$$
$$S = P(\text{caf}'\text{-}6\%\text{-}10)$$
$$= \$1,000(1.791) = \$1,791$$

EXAMPLE 5–2

How much would you have to invest at 6% interest on January 1, 1965, in order to accumulate $1,791 on January 1, 1971? (Figure 5–1b.)

Solution:

$$i = 0.06; n = 6; S = \$1,791; P = ?$$

In this case zero time is assumed to be January 1, 1965.

$$P = S(\text{pwf}'\text{-}6\%\text{-}6) = \$1,791(0.7050)$$
$$= \$1,264$$

EXAMPLE 5–3

What is the present worth on January 1, 1958, of $1,264 on January 1, 1965, if the interest is at 6%? (Figure 5–1c.)

Solution:

$$i = 0.06; n = 7; S = \$1,264; P = ?$$
$$P = S(\text{pwf}'\text{-}6\%\text{-}7)$$
$$= \$1,264(0.6651) = \$841$$

EXAMPLE 5–4

If $841 is invested at 6% on January 1, 1958, what equal, year-end withdrawal can be made each year for 10 years, leaving nothing in the fund after the tenth withdrawal? (Figure 5–1d.)

Solution:

$$i = 0.06; n = 10; P = \$841; R = ?$$

Now zero time is January 1, 1958.

$$R = P(\text{crf}\text{-}6\%\text{-}10)$$
$$= \$841(0.13587) = \$114.27$$

EXAMPLE 5–5

How much will be accumulated in a fund, earning 6% interest, at the end of 10 years if $114.27 is deposited at the end of each year for 10 years, beginning in 1958? (Figure 5–1e.)

Solution:

$$i = 0.06; n = 10; R = \$114.27; S = ?$$
$$S = R(\text{caf}\text{-}6\%\text{-}10)$$
$$= \$114.27(13.181) = \$1,506$$

EXAMPLE 5-6

How much must be deposited at 6% each year for 7 years beginning on January 1, 1962, in order to accumulate $1,506 on the date of the last deposit, January 1, 1968? (Figure 5–1f.)

Solution:

$$i = 0.06; n = 7; S = \$1,506; R = ?$$

$$R = S(\text{sff--}6\%\text{--}7)$$

$$= \$1,506(0.11914) = \$179.42$$

EXAMPLE 5-7

How much would you need to deposit at 6% on January 1, 1961, in order to draw out $179.42 at the end of each year for 7 years, leaving nothing in the fund? (Figure 5–1g.)

Solution:

$$i = 0.06; n = 7; R = \$179.42; P = ?$$

$$P = R(\text{pwf--}6\%\text{--}7)$$

$$= \$179.42(5.582) = \$1,001$$

Note that zero time is January 1, 1961, the date on which this series of examples was started. The difference between the original $1,000 and the final $1,001 was due to the fact that five-digit interest tables introduced some very slight errors in the computations. If the interest factors had been carried out to more places, the final answer would have agreed exactly with the original amount.

Comments on Examples 5–1 Through 5–7. These examples illustrate several important points. First, in each simple problem four of the five elements i, n, P, S, and R are present and three of the four elements must be known. In these examples i, n, and one other element were always known. In solving the problem, the known elements are first identified and the unknown or desired element is specified. Then the unknown element is equated to the proper interest factor times the known monetary amount. (If i or n is unknown, then the value of the interest factor must be determined by solving the equation, and the unknown is found by referring to the interest tables and by interpolating, if necessary, between two factors found there. This will be illustrated later in this chapter.)

Next, these examples demonstrate that, with a given interest rate, equivalent single amounts or series of amounts can be found at many different relative times. Thus, all of the following are equivalent to $1,000 now, assuming that "now" is January 1, 1961:

$1,791 10 years hence
$1,264 4 years hence

$841 3 years previously
$114.27 a year (year-end payments) for 10 years beginning 3 years ago
$1,506 7 years hence
$179.42 a year for the next 7 years

Since these amounts or series of amounts are all equivalent to $1,000 now, they must be equivalent to each other. The difference in the timing of the payments or receipts is the significant element in these computations, and it is very important to determine precisely the n for each problem. Dates have been used for these examples, but the n was determined in the solution of each example. Normally it is more convenient to select the starting point in time, calling it date zero or year zero, and to determine the number of years from that selected time. Thus, in Example 5–2, the desired quantity was that necessary investment in 1965 to obtain $1,791 in 1971, and 1965 became a convenient starting point for the example. Year zero is 1965 and 1971 is 6.

Another point that is emphasized in Examples 5–4 through 5–7 is that conventional interest tables and formulas are based upon uniform payments made at the *end* of each period (not at the beginning of the period). The only time this convention may become confusing occurs when one is converting from the compound amount, S, to uniform periodic payments or vice versa. The confusion arises from the fact that the date of the compound amount is the same date as the last of the uniform series of payments or receipts. Practice in using the interest tables will soon eliminate this source of possible confusion.

Examples Involving Conversion of Single Payments at One Date to Equivalent Single Payments at Another Date. Examples of this type involve i, n, P, and S, and any one of these four elements may be unknown. Examples 5–1, 5–2, and 5–3 were of this type, with either P or S unknown. The following examples illustrate other aspects of such problems.

EXAMPLE 5–8

If $2,000 is invested now, $1,500 2 years hence, and $1,000 4 years hence, all at 4%, what will the total amount be 10 years hence?

or

What is the compound amount of $2,000 for 10 years plus $1,500 for 8 years plus $1,000 for 6 years with interest at 4%?

or

What must be the prospective saving 10 years hence in order to justify spending $2,000 now, $1,500 in 2 years, and $1,000 in 4 years, if money is worth 4%?

Solution: It is evident from the cash flow diagram (Figure 5–2a) that this requires three separate calculations: in the first the "present" is now; in the second it is 2 years hence; in the third it is 4 years hence:

$$i = 0.04; \begin{pmatrix} n_1 = 10; P_1 = \$2,000 \\ n_2 = 8; P_2 = \$1,500 \\ n_3 = 6; P_3 = \$1,000 \end{pmatrix}; S = S_1 + S_2 + S_3 = ?$$

$$S_1 = P_1(\text{caf'}-4\%-10) = \$2,000(1.480) = \$2,960$$
$$S_2 = P_2(\text{caf'}-4\%-8) = 1,500(1.369) = 2,053$$
$$S_3 = P_3(\text{caf'}-4\%-6) = 1,000(1.265) = \underline{1,265}$$
$$S = \qquad\qquad\qquad\qquad\qquad\qquad\quad \$6,278$$

EXAMPLE 5–9

What is the compound amount of \$3,500 for 18 years with interest at 4.25%?
Solution:

$$i = 0.0425; n = 18; P = \$3,500; S = ?$$
$$S = P(\text{caf'}-4.25\%-18), \text{ where } (\text{caf'}-4.25\%-18) = (1 + 0.0425)^{18}$$

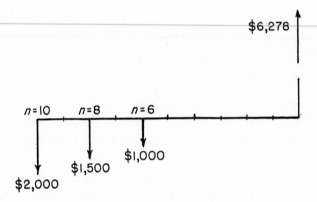

(a) Cash Flow Diagram for Example 5-8

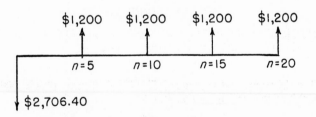

(b) Cash Flow Diagram for Example 5-12

FIGURE 5-2. Cash Flow Diagrams for Examples 5–8 and 5–12

As the tables do not give compound amount factors for 4.25%, the problem must be solved by logarithms:

$$\text{Log } 1.0425 = 0.018076 \qquad \begin{array}{ll} 18 \text{ Log } 1.0425 = 0.32537 \\ \text{Log } 3,500 \quad = 3.54407 \\ \hline \text{Log } S \quad\quad = 3.86944 \\ S \quad\quad\quad = \$7,404 \end{array}$$

An approximate solution may be obtained by linear interpolation between the compound amount factors for 4% and 4½% as follows:

$$(1.04)^{18} = 2.026; \; (1.045)^{18} = 2.208$$

Approximate value of

$$(1.0425)^{18} = 2.026 + \frac{25}{50} (2.208 - 2.026) = 2.117$$

$$\text{Approximate } S = \$3,500(2.117) = \$7,410$$

This particular approximation involves an error of less than one-tenth of 1%. The per cent of error involved in such interpolations increases with an increase in n, and is greater with higher interest rates.

EXAMPLE 5–10

What is the compound amount of $400 for 8 years with interest at 6% compounded semiannually?

Solution: Here the rate per interest period is $6\% \div 2 = 3\%$; the number of periods is $8(2) = 16$:

$$i = 0.03; \; n = 16; P = \$400; S = ?$$

$$S = P(\text{caf}'\text{–}3\%\text{–}16)$$

$$= \$400(1.605) = \$642$$

EXAMPLE 5–11

What is the compound amount of $1,000 for 64 years with interest at 4%?

Solution:

$$i = 0.04; \; n = 64; P = \$1,000; S = ?$$

By noting that the compound amount factor for 64 years, which is not given in our tables, is the product of the respective factors for 60 years and 4 years, this can be solved without recourse to logarithms:

$$S = P(\text{caf}'\text{–}4\%\text{–}60)(\text{caf}'\text{–}4\%\text{–}4)$$

$$= \$1,000(10.520)(1.170) = \$12,308$$

EXAMPLE 5–12

How much invested now at 5% would be just sufficient to provide $1,200 5 years hence, $1,200 10 years hence, $1,200 15 years hence, and $1,200 20 years hence?

or

What is the present worth of $1,200 at the end of each 5 years for the next 20 years if interest is at 5%?

or

What present loan at 5% would be completely paid back by payments of $1,200 at the end of 5, 10, 15, and 20 years?

or

What payment now is acceptable in place of prospective payments of $1,200 at the end of 5, 10, 15, and 20 years, if interest is at 5%?

or

How much is it justifiable to spend now in order to save prospective expenditures of $1,200 at the end of 5, 10, 15, and 20 years if money is worth 5%?

Solution: This cash flow series is shown in Figure 5–2b.

$$i = 0.05; \quad \begin{cases} n_1 = 5; \ S_1 = \$1{,}200 \\ n_2 = 10; \ S_2 = 1{,}200 \\ n_3 = 15; \ S_3 = 1{,}200 \\ n_4 = 20; \ S_4 = 1{,}200 \end{cases} \ ; P = P_1 + P_2 + P_3 + P_4 = \ ?$$

$$P_1 = S_1(\text{pwf}'\text{–}5\%\text{–}5) \ = \$1{,}200(0.7835) = \$ \ \ 940.20$$

$$P_2 = S_2(\text{pwf}'\text{–}5\%\text{–}10) = \ 1{,}200(0.6139) = \ \ \ \ 736.70$$

$$P_3 = S_3(\text{pwf}'\text{–}5\%\text{–}15) = \ 1{,}200(0.4810) = \ \ \ \ 577.20$$

$$P_4 = S_4(\text{pwf}'\text{–}5\%\text{–}20) = \ 1{,}200(0.3769) = \ \ \ \ 452.30$$

$$P = \$2{,}706.40$$

EXAMPLE 5–13

In how many years will an investment of $1,000 now, increase to $2,000 with interest at 3%?

or

How long will it take for money to double itself with interest at 3%?

or

Within how many years must a prospective expenditure of $2,000 be required in order to justify spending $1,000 now to prevent it, if money is worth 3%?

Solution:

$$i = 0.03; \ P = \$1{,}000; \ S = \$2{,}000; \ n = \ ?$$

$$(\text{caf}'\text{–}3\%\text{–}n) = \frac{S}{P} = \frac{\$2{,}000}{\$1{,}000} = 2.000$$

The value of n can be determined by examining the compound amount factors, single payment, in the 3% table, and interpolating between the next higher and next lower values:

$$n = 23, \ (\text{caf}'\text{–}3\%\text{–}23) = 1.974$$

$$n = 24, \ (\text{caf}'\text{–}3\%\text{–}24) = 2.033$$

Therefore

$$n = \text{approximately } 23\tfrac{1}{2} \text{ years}$$

EXAMPLE 5–14

A savings certificate costing $80 now will pay $100 in 5 years. What is the interest rate?

or

At what interest rate will $80 accumulate to $100 in 5 years?

or

Spending $80 now to avoid spending $100 5 years hence is, in effect, securing what interest rate?

Solution:

$$n = 5; P = \$80; S = \$100; i = ?$$

$$(\text{caf}'\text{-}i\text{-}5) = \frac{S}{P} = \frac{\$100}{\$80} = 1.250$$

By interpolation between the next higher and the next lower single payment compound amount factor for 5 years in the interest tables, the approximate interest rate can be determined:

$$i = 0.045, (\text{caf}'\text{-}4.5\%\text{-}5) = 1.246$$

$$i = 0.050, (\text{caf}'\text{-}5\%\text{-}5) = 1.276$$

$$i = 0.045 + 0.005 \left(\frac{1.250 - 1.246}{1.276 - 1.246} \right)$$

$$= 0.0457 \text{ or } 4.57\%$$

A more exact solution may be obtained by using logarithms to solve for the value of i in formula (1), of Chapter 4.

$$i = \sqrt[n]{\frac{S}{P}} - 1 = \sqrt[5]{\frac{100}{80}} - 1 = \sqrt[5]{1.25} - 1$$

$$\text{Log } \sqrt[5]{1.25} = \frac{\text{Log } 1.25}{5} = \frac{0.096910}{5} = 0.019382$$

$$\sqrt[5]{1.25} = 1.04564$$

$$i = 1.04564 - 1.0 = 0.04564 \text{ or } 4.564\%$$

Examples Involving Conversions to or from Uniform Series of Payments.

The general technique for solving a problem involving a uniform series is similar to the technique used in the previous examples. The four elements of such problems are either i, n, R, and P or i, n, R, and S. Note whether it is P or S that enters into the given problem; note which three elements are known and their values. If the unknown, the value of which is desired, is R, P, or S, and the given values of i and n are values for which factors are available in the tables, use the interest tables. Otherwise, solve by interpolation. If i or n is the unknown, an exact solution is seldom possible, and interpolation is employed to obtain an approximate solution. For engineering economy purposes, the errors introduced by straight-line interpolation are usually acceptable, and the solutions obtained thereby are adequate for the decision-making function.

EXAMPLE 5–15

How much must be invested at the end of each year for 30 years in a sinking fund which is to amount to $200,000 at the end of 30 years, if interest is at 4%?

or

What annual investment must be made at 4% to replace a $200,000 structure 30 years hence?

or

What uniform annual expenditure for 30 years is justifiable in order to avoid having to spend $200,000 30 years hence, if money is worth 4%?

Solution:

$$i = 0.04; \ n = 30; \ S = \$200,000; \ R = \ ?$$
$$R = S(\text{sff–}4\%\text{–}30)$$
$$= \$200,000(0.01783) = \$3,566$$

EXAMPLE 5–16

How much would be accumulated in the sinking fund of Example 5–15 at the end of 18 years?

or

If $3,566 is invested at the end of each year for 18 years with interest at 4%, how much will have accumulated at the end of that time?

or

What must be the prospective saving 18 years hence in order to justify spending $3,566 a year for 18 years, if money is worth 4%?

Solution:

$$i = 0.04; \ n = 18; \ R = \$3,566; \ S = \ ?$$
$$S = R(\text{caf–}4\%\text{–}18)$$
$$= \$3,566(25.645) = \$91,450$$

EXAMPLE 5–17 [1]

What annual year-end payment for 10 years is necessary to repay a present loan of $10,000 if interest is at 6%?

or

With interest at 6%, what uniform annual end-of-year payment for 10 years is equivalent to $10,000 now?

or

What 10-year annuity can be purchased for $10,000 if interest is at 6%?

or

If $10,000 is deposited now with interest at 6%, what uniform amount R could be withdrawn at the end of each year for 10 years and have nothing left at the end of the 10th year?

or

What is the annual cost of capital recovery of $10,000 in 10 years with interest at 6%?

or

---

[1] The type of calculation called for in this illustrative example is the most common one used in dealing with the time value of money in economy studies. The reader should examine carefully the different ways in which questions requiring this calculation are phrased.

What is the annual payment for 10 years the present worth of which is $10,000 if interest is at 6%?

or

What annual saving for 10 years must be anticipated to justify an additional present expenditure of $10,000 if money is worth 6%?

Solution:

$$i = 0.06; n = 10; P = \$10,000; R = ?$$
$$R = P(\text{crf-6\%-10})$$
$$= \$10,000(0.13587) = \$1,358.70$$

(The reader will recognize this as the annual repayment used—without explanation of where the figure came from—in Plan III of Table 3–1 in Chapter 3.)

EXAMPLE 5–18

In the loan described in Example 5–17, how much would be owed after the fourth payment had been made?

or

What is the present worth of $1,358.70 a year for 6 years with interest at 6%?

or

What present investment must be made at 6% to secure $1,358.70 a year for 6 years?

or

What present investment is justified in order to make a prospective saving of $1,358.70 a year for 6 years if money is worth 6%?

Solution:

$$i = 0.06; n = 6; R = \$1,358.70; P = ?$$
$$P = R(\text{pwf-6\%-6})$$
$$= \$1,358.70(4.917) = \$6,681$$

(The answer to this problem as phrased in the first of the four statements of the question may also be calculated more exactly and more laboriously by the method of Table 3–1. The answer obtained by a calculation from the interest table should not be expressed to more than the four significant figures given in the table. Thus the $6,681 calculated above corresponds to the figure of $6,681.07 given in Table 3–1.)

EXAMPLE 5–19

A present investment of $50,000 is expected to yield receipts of $7,000 a year for 15 years. What is the approximate rate of return that will be obtained on this investment?

Solution:

$$n = 15; P = \$50,000; R = \$7,000; i = ?$$
$$R = P(\text{crf-}i\text{-15})$$
$$(\text{crf-}i\text{-15}) = \frac{R}{P} = \frac{\$7,000}{\$50,000} = 0.1400$$

This can be solved approximately by interpolation in the interest tables for capital recovery factors:

$$\text{For } i = 10\%, (\text{crf--}10\%\text{--}15) = 0.13147$$
$$i = 12\%, (\text{crf--}12\%\text{--}15) = 0.14682$$

By interpolation,

$$i = 0.10 + \left[\frac{0.1400 - 0.13147}{0.14682 - 0.13147}\right] 0.02$$

$$= 0.111 \text{ or } 11.1\%$$

EXAMPLE 5–20

On the day a baby boy was born, his father decided to establish a fund for his college education by depositing a certain amount in a fund on each of his birthdays from the first through the 18th, so that the son can withdraw $2,000 on his 18th, 19th, 20th, and 21st birthdays. If the fund earns 4% per year, how much must the annual deposit be?

Solution: This example will be used to show how the same problem can be solved several different ways. The answers will be the same in all cases except for the slight errors that result from using the five-digit interest tables. Figure 5–3

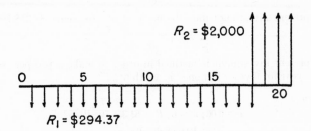

FIGURE 5–3. Cash Flow Diagram for Example 5–20

shows the cash flow diagram for this example. Note that the last deposit is made on the date of the first withdrawal.

$$i = 0.04; n_1 = 18; R_1 = ?$$
$$n_2 = 4; R_2 = \$2,000$$

Method 1: Find the present worth of four single withdrawals at zero date. Multiply that sum by the capital recovery factor for $n = 18$ to obtain the annual deposit, R_1.

$$R_1 = \$2,000[(\text{pwf'--}4\%\text{--}21) + (\text{pwf'--}4\%\text{--}20) + (\text{pwf'--}4\%\text{--}19)$$
$$+ (\text{pwf'--}4\%\text{--}18)](\text{crf--}4\%\text{--}18)$$

$$= 2,000(0.4388 + 0.4564 + 0.4746 + 0.4936)(0.07899) = \$294.38$$

Method 2: Find the present worth at year 18 of the four withdrawals. Find the annual deposit for 18 years to accumulate that sum.

$$R_1 = [\$2,000 + \$2,000(\text{pwf--}4\%\text{--}3)](\text{sff--}4\%\text{--}18)$$

$$= [2,000 + 2,000(2.775)]0.03899 = \$294.37$$

Method 3: Find the compound amount of the uniform series of $2,000 for four years at date 21, and then convert to the present worth at date zero. Multiply by the capital recovery factor.

$$R_1 = \$2,000(\text{caf–4\%–4})(\text{pwf'–4\%–21})(\text{crf–4\%–18})$$
$$= 2,000(4.246)(0.4388)(0.07899) = \$294.37$$

EXAMPLE 5–21

How much can you afford to spend each year for 15 years to avoid spending $1,000 now, $1,500 5 years hence, and $2,000 10 years hence, if money is worth 8%?

or

What is the equivalent annual cost for 15 years of spending $1,000 now, $1,500 5 years hence and $2,000 10 years hence if interest is at 8%?

Solution: In problems of this type it is necessary to find either the present worth or the compound amount first, and then convert to equivalent annual cost, R.

$$i = 8\%; \begin{cases} n_1 = 0; P_1 = \$1,000; \\ n_2 = 5; P_2 = 1,500; \\ n_3 = 10; P_3 = 2,000; \\ n_4 = 15; \end{cases} R = ?$$

Method 1:

$$R = [\$1,000(\text{pwf'–8\%–0}) + \$1,500(\text{pwf'–8\%–5}) + \$2,000(\text{pwf'–8\%–10})](\text{crf–8\%–15})$$
$$= [1,000(1.000) + 1,500(0.6806) + 2,000(0.4632)](0.11683) = \$344.33$$

Method 2:

$$R = [\$1,000(\text{caf'–8\%–15}) + \$1,500(\text{caf'–8\%–10}) + \$2,000(\text{caf'–8\%–5})](\text{sff–8\%–15})$$
$$= [1,000(3.172) + 1,500(2.159) + 2,000(1.469)](0.03683) = \$345.51$$

EXAMPLE 5–22

What is the present worth of $3,000 now, $4,000 5 years hence, and $200 a year for 10 years, if interest is at 10%?

or

What amount can you afford to spend now to avoid spending $3,000 now, $4,000 5 years from now, and $200 a year for 10 years, if money is worth 10%?

Solution:

$$i = 10\%; \begin{cases} n_1 = 0; P_1 = \$3,000; \\ n_2 = 5; P_2 = 4,000; \\ n_3 = 10; R = 200; \end{cases} P = ?$$

$$P = \$3,000(\text{pwf'–10\%–0}) + \$4,000(\text{pwf'–10\%–5}) + \$200(\text{pwf–10\%–10})$$
$$= 3,000(1.000) + 4,000(0.6209) + 200(6.144) = \$6,712$$

Another method would be to find the compound amount at the end of 10 years for the three amounts and then to multiply by the single payment present worth factor for 10 years.

EXAMPLE 5-23

Expenditure now of $1,500 more for a diesel engine than for a comparable gasoline engine will produce an annual fuel saving of $260. How long must this saving continue in order to justify the extra investment now, if money is worth 10%?

Solution:

$$i = 0.10; P = \$1,500; R = \$260; n = \ ?$$

$$\$1,500(\text{crf}-10\%-n) = \$260$$

$$(\text{crf}-10\%-n) = \frac{\$260}{\$1,500} = 0.17333$$

By interpolation,

$$n = 9, \quad (\text{crf}-10\%-9) \ = 0.17364$$

$$n = 10, (\text{crf}-10\%-10) = 0.16275$$

$$n = 9 + 1 \left[\frac{0.17364 - 0.17333}{0.17364 - 0.16275} \right] = 9 + 0.28 = 9.28 \text{ years}$$

Example of the Use of Gradient Factors. The solution of problems involving uniform gradients is similar to the solution of any other compound interest problems. The known elements of the gradient problem are i, n, and g. The unknown element may be either P or R, depending upon whether a present worth or the equivalent annual cost of the gradient is desired. The appropriate factor, from Table E-23 or Table E-24, for the given i and n is multiplied by the gradient, g.

EXAMPLE 5-24

A piece of heavy construction equipment will cost $6,000 new and will have an expected life of 6 years, with no salvage value at the end of its life. The disbursements for taxes, insurance, maintenance, fuels, and lubricants are estimated to be $1,500 the first year, $1,700 the second, $1,900 the third, and continue to increase by $200 each year thereafter.

What is the equivalent annual cost of this piece of equipment if the rate of interest is 12%?

Solution: This example introduces the typical engineering economy problem in that it consists of several different types of disbursements. All must be reduced to the equivalent annual cost and added together.

$$i = 0.12; n = 6; P = \$6,000; R_1 = \ ?$$

$$R_2 = \$1,500$$

$$g = \$200; R_3 = \ ?$$

$$R \ = R_1 + R_2 + R_3$$

$$R_1 = \$6,000(\text{crf}-12\%-6) = \$6,000(0.24323) = \$1,459$$

$$R_2 = \$1,500$$

(The problem stated that the annual maintenance would be $1,500 plus a gradient of $200 per year. The $1,500 requires no conversion because it is in the form of a uniform annual expense.)

$$R_3 = g(\text{gf–}12\%\text{–}6) = \$200(2.17) = \$434$$
$$R = \$1,459 + \$1,500 + \$434 = \$3,393$$

EXAMPLE 5–25

What is the present worth of 6 years of service of the piece of equipment described in Example 5–24 if the interest rate is 12%?

Solution: The initial price of the equipment is already in the form of a present worth, but the annual maintenance expenses must be reduced to a present worth.

$$i = 12\%; n = 6; R = \$1,500; P_1 = \$6,000$$
$$P_2 = \quad ?$$
$$g = \$200; P_3 = \quad ?$$
$$P = P_1 + P_2 + P_3$$
$$P_2 = R(\text{pwf–}12\%\text{–}6) = \$1,500(4.111) = \$6,166$$
$$P_3 = g(\text{gpwf–}12\%\text{–}6) = \$200(8.93) = \$1,786$$
$$P = \$6,000 + \$6,166 + \$1,786 = \$13,952$$

Comments on Examples 5–24 and 5–25. Having obtained the equivalent annual cost in Example 5–24, the present worth could have been found by multiplying that amount by the series present worth factor (pwf–12%–6), or, having found the present worth in Example 5–25, the equivalent annual cost could have been found by multiplying the present worth by the capital recovery factor (crf–12%–6). Thus,

$$R = P(\text{crf–}12\%\text{–}6) = \$13,952(0.24323) = \$3,394$$

The slight difference in the final results is due to the rounding off of the factors in both the gradient and regular interest tables.

EXAMPLE 5–26

A bank offers the following personal loan plan called "The Seven Per Cent Plan."

The bank adds 7% to the amount borrowed; the borrower pays back one-twelfth of this total at the end of each month for a year. On a loan of $1,000, the monthly payment is $1,070/12 = $89.17.

What is the true interest rate per month? What are the nominal and effective rates per annum?

Solution:

$$n = 12; P = \$1,000; R = \$89.17; i = ?$$
$$R = P(\text{crf–}i\%\text{–}n)$$

Solve by interpolation.

$$(\text{crf–}i\%\text{–}12) = \frac{R}{P} = \frac{\$89.17}{\$1,000} = 0.08917$$

Try $i = 0.01$

$$(\text{crf--}1\%\text{--}12) = 0.08885$$

Try $i = 0.0125$

$$(\text{crf--}1.25\%\text{--}12) = 0.09026$$

Interpolating,

$$i = 0.01 + \left(\frac{0.08917 - 0.08885}{0.09026 - 0.08885}\right)(0.0025)$$

$$= 0.01 + \left(\frac{0.00032}{0.00141}\right)(0.0025)$$

$$= 0.01 + 0.00057 = 0.01057 \text{ or } 1.057\%$$

The *nominal interest rate per annum* corresponding to this monthly rate is:

$$12(0.01057) = 0.1268 \text{ or } 12.68\%$$

The *effective interest rate per annum* corresponding to this monthly rate is:

$$(1.01057)^{12} - 1 = 0.1345 \text{ or } 13.45\%$$

Deferred Annuities. Frequently it is necessary to deal with a series of uniform annual payments or receipts that begin sometime in the future and continue for some number of years. Such a deferred series of uniform annual payments or receipts is known as a *deferred annuity.* It may be desired to convert a deferred annuity to a present worth, to an equivalent annual series over some different period of years, or to a compound amount at some future time. Two methods of solving such a problem are illustrated in Example 5–27.

EXAMPLE 5–27

How much could you afford to spend each year for the next 6 years to avoid spending $500 a year for 10 years, beginning 5 years hence, if money is worth 8%?

or

What is the equivalent annual cost over the period of the next 6 years of spending $500 a year for 10 years beginning 5 years hence, if interest is at 8% per annum?

Solution:

$$i = 0.08; \ n_1 = 6; \ R_1 = \ ?$$

$$n_2 = 10; \ R_2 = \$500$$

$$n_3 = 5;$$

Method 1: Subtract uniform series present worth factor for 4 years from uniform series present worth factor for 14 years and multiply by the capital recovery factor for 6 years.

$$R_1 = \$500[(\text{pwf--}8\%\text{--}14) - (\text{pwf--}8\%\text{--}4)](\text{crf--}8\%\text{--}6)$$

$$= 500(8.244 - 3.312)(0.21632)$$

$$= 500(4.932)(0.21632) = \$533.40$$

Method 2: Multiply the uniform series present worth factor for 10 years by the single payment present worth factor for 4 years and multiply that by the capital recovery factor for 6 years.

$$R_1 = \$500(\text{pwf--}8\%\text{--}10)(\text{pwf}'\text{--}8\%\text{--}4)(\text{crf--}8\%\text{--}6)$$
$$= 500(6.710)(0.7350)(0.21632)$$
$$= \$533.40$$

Summary. The general technique for solving a problem in compound interest equivalence is to determine first which elements of the problem are known and which element is unknown. If the problem is one to which available interest tables apply, it will usually be most convenient to use them in its solution. Otherwise, it is necessary to substitute the known elements of the problem in the appropriate interest formula, and to solve for the unknown one.

Problems

5-1. Solve the following, assuming interest at 4% compounded annually:

(a) $100 at the end of each year for 13 years will repay a present debt of how much? (*Ans.* = $998.60.)

(b) A payment of how much now is acceptable in place of a payment of $1,500 18 years hence? (*Ans.* = $740.)

(c) A present investment of $10,000 will secure a perpetual income of how much a year? (*Ans.* = $400.)

(d) An annual end-of-year investment of how much is required to provide $22,000 at the end of 30 years? (*Ans.* = $392.30.)

(e) The present worth of $5,000 37 years hence is how much? (*Ans.* = $1,171.)

5-2. Solve the following with interest at 6% compounded annually:

(a) If $2,500 is deposited now, what uniform amount could be withdrawn at the end of each year for 15 years and have nothing left at the end of the 15th year? (*Ans.* = $257.40.)

(b) What present investment is necessary to secure a perpetual income of $1,000 a year? (*Ans.* = $16,667.)

(c) How much will be accumulated in a fund at the end of 25 years if $2,000 is invested now? (*Ans.* = $8,584.)

(d) What annual saving for 20 years must be expected to justify a present expenditure of $5,000? (*Ans.* = $435.90.)

5-3. On January 1, 1960, $100 is deposited in a fund drawing 4% interest compounded annually. Another $100 is to be deposited on each January 1 up to and including January 1, 1970. The purpose of the fund is to provide a series of uniform annual withdrawals starting January 1, 1975. The final withdrawal on January 1, 1980, will exhaust the fund. How much can be withdrawn each year during the period 1975–80? (*Ans.* = $301.)

5-4. (a) A man is to receive an annuity of $1,000 a year for 15 years, the first payment being made on March 1, 1971. He offers to sell the annuity on March 1, 1968. With interest at 3½% compounded annually, what is a fair price? (*Ans* = $10,751.)

(b) Black borrows $10,000 at 6% compounded semiannually, agreeing to repay it in 30 equal semiannual payments. How much of the principal of the loan is still unpaid immediately after he has made the 8th payment? (*Ans.* = $8,131.)

5–5. (a) A proposed product modification to avoid production difficulties will require an immediate expenditure of $14,000 to modify certain dies. What annual savings must be realized to recover this expenditure in 4 years with interest at 10%? (*Ans.* = $4,416.)

(b) What must be the prospective saving in money 6 years hence to justify a present investment of $2,250? Use interest at 7% compounded annually. (*Ans.* = $3,377.)

(c) What extra semiannual expenditure for 5 years would be justified for the maintenance of a machine in order to avoid an overhaul costing $3,000 at the end of that period? Assume interest at 8% compounded semiannually. (*Ans.* = $250.)

(d) What present expenditure would be justified by the prospect of an annual saving of $500 a year for 12 years? Assume interest at 15%. (*Ans.* = $2,710.)

5–6. Using interest tables and interpolation as far as possible, determine the approximate rates of interest indicated by the following valuations for prospective series of future payments:

(a) $2,000 for $160 a year for 15 years (*Ans.* = 2.4%.)
(b) $4,000 for $700 a year for 10 years (*Ans.* = 11.7%.)
(c) $5,000 for $250 a year for 20 years (*Ans.* = 0.0%.)
(d) $50,000 for $2,700 a year forever (*Ans.* = 5.4%.)
(e) $1,050 for $40 a year for 15 years and $1,000 at the end of the 15th year (*Ans.* = 3.6%.)

5–7. Maintenance expenditures for a structure with a 20-year life will come as periodic outlays for overhaul of $1,000 at the end of the 5th year, $2,000 at the end of the 10th year, and $3,500 at the end of the 15th year. With interest at 10%, what is the equivalent uniform annual cost for the 20-year period? (*Ans.* = $262.)

5–8. Solve the following, using interest at 7% compounded annually:

(a) What is the amount that will be accumulated in a sinking fund at the end of 15 years if $200 is deposited in the fund at the *beginning* of each of the 15 years? (*Ans.* = $5,378.)

(b) Uniform deposits are to be made on January 1 of 1961, 1962, 1963, and 1964 into a fund that is intended to provide $1,000 on January 1 of 1975, 1976, and 1977. What must be the size of these deposits? (*Ans.* = $300.)

5–9. A company leased a storage yard from a city and prepaid the rent for 6 years; the terms of the lease permit the company to continue to rent the site for 6 years more by payment of $1,500 at the beginning of each year of the second 6-year period.

Two years of the prepaid period have expired and the city is in need of funds; it proposed to the company that it now prepay the rental that was to have been paid year by year in the second 6-year period. If interest is figured at 3½%, what is a fair payment to be made now in lieu of these six annual payments? (*Ans.* = $7,207.)

5–10. An investor paid $1,000 for 10 shares of stock 12 years ago. He received dividends of $6 a share at the end of each year for the first 7 years and $3 a share at the end of each of the next 5 years. He has just sold the stock for $860. What rate of return did he make on his investment? (*Ans.* = 4.0%.)

5–11. Solve the following, assuming interest at 6% compounded annually:

(a) How much must be deposited in a sinking fund on each June 1, beginning on June 1, 1961, in order to accumulate $2,000 in the fund on June 1, 1975? (No deposit is made on June 1, 1975.)

(b) How much must the annual saving in expenses be for 10 years in order to justify the expenditure of $1,500 now?

(c) What payment would be acceptable now in place of a payment of $3,000 18 years hence?

(d) An annual maintenance expenditure of $400 will be justified for 5 years if it will avoid what amount of overhaul expense at the end of the 5th year?

5–12. Solve the following assuming interest at 4% per annum, compounded semiannually:

(a) How much can you afford to pay now to avoid an expenditure of $4,000 5 years hence?

(b) What semiannual deposit in a sinking fund will be necessary in order to accumulate a fund of $10,000 in 10 years, assuming that you make the deposits at the beginning and midpoint of each year, and that the final fund is to be accumulated 6 months after the last payment?

(c) How much must be deposited on January 1, 1961, and every 6 months thereafter until July 1, 1971, in order to withdraw $500 every 6 months for 5 years beginning on January 1, 1972?

5–13. (a) A man is to receive an annuity of $1,000 a year for 10 years, beginning on March 1, 1968. He offers to sell the annuity on March 1, 1963. With interest at 5% compounded annually, what is a fair price for the annuity?

(b) Mr. White borrows $6,000 at 6% compounded annually, agreeing to repay the loan in 15 equal annual payments. How much of the principal is still unpaid after he has made the 8th payment?

5–14. Solve the following with interest at 1% per month:

(a) What present debt can be repaid by end-of-month payments of $25 for 3 years?

(b) What end-of-month expense for 4 years would be equivalent to spending $1,200 now?

(c) What is the compound amount 5 years hence of a single deposit of $400 now?

(d) What is the present worth of a payment of $300 to be made 2 years hence?

5–15. A person borrowed $500 from a small loan company to be repaid in 12 equal end-of-month payments with interest at "1% per month." His monthly payments were computed as follows:

$$
\begin{array}{lr}
\text{Principal of loan} \dots\dots\dots\dots\dots\dots\dots & \$500 \\
\text{Interest at 1\% per month} \dots\dots\dots\dots\dots & 60 \\
\text{Credit investigation} \dots\dots\dots\dots\dots\dots & 10 \\
\hline
& \$570
\end{array}
$$

$$\text{Monthly payments} = \frac{\$570}{12} = \$47.50$$

Determine by use of the interest tables and interpolation the effective interest rate and nominal interest rate per annum that he actually paid.

5–16. (a) What annual expenditure for 12 years is equivalent to spending $1,000 at the end of the first year, $1,500 at the end of the 5th year, and $2,000 at the end of the 9th year, if interest is at 8% per annum?

(b) What single amount paid at the beginning of the first year is equivalent to the series of unequal payments in (a), with interest at 8%?

5–17. Using interest tables and interpolation as far as possible, determine the approximate rates of interest indicated by the following valuations for prospective series of future payments:

(a) $4,000 now for $300 a year for 15 years
(b) $5,000 now for $575 a year for 15 years
(c) $2,000 now for $400 a year for 5 years
(d) $1,500 now and $1,500 5 years hence for $400 a year for 10 years with the first payment 1 year hence
(e) $5,000 now for $125 a year forever
(f) $6,000 now for $12,000 37 years hence

5–18. A man wants to be able to withdraw $2,000 each year for 4 years, beginning on September 1, 1978, from a fund built up by semiannual deposits beginning on September 1, 1962. The fund will earn interest at the rate of 3.5% per annum, compounded semiannually. The last deposit will be made on March 1, 1978. What must his semiannual deposits be? How much will be in the fund on September 1, 1972?

5–19. A company can either buy certain land for outdoor storage of equipment or lease it on a 15-year lease. The purchase price is $80,000. The annual rental is $4,000 payable at the start of each year. In either case the company must pay property taxes, assessments, and upkeep. It is estimated that the land will be needed for only 15 years and will be salable for $60,000 at the end of the 15-year period. What rate of return before income taxes will the company receive by buying the land instead of leasing it?

5–20. The landowner in Problem 5–19 also offers a 15-year lease for a prepaid rental of $45,000. If the company has decided to lease rather than buy, what interest rate makes the prepaid rental equivalent to the annual rental? How should this rate be interpreted as a basis for the company's choice between prepaid and annual rental?

5–21. Using an interest rate of 12%, find the equivalent uniform annual cost for a proposed machine tool that has a first cost of $10,000, an estimated economic life of 8 years, and an estimated salvage value of $2,000. Annual maintenance will amount to $200 a year and periodic overhauls costing $600 each will occur at the end of the 2nd, 4th, and 6th years.

5–22. A company owns a fleet of trucks and operates its own maintenance shop. A certain type of truck, normally used for 5 years, has a first cost of $4,500 and a terminal salvage value of $500. Maintenance costs are $300 the first year and increase by $200 each year. Assuming interest at 10%, find the equivalent annual cost of owning and maintaining the truck.

5–23. A person engaged in making small loans offers to lend $200 with the borrower required to pay $6.80 at the end of each week for 35 weeks in order to extinguish the debt. By appropriate use of your interest tables, find the approximate interest rate per week. What is the nominal interest rate per annum? What is the effective interest rate per annum?

5–24. The purchase of certain unimproved city lots is under consideration. The price is $20,000. The owner of this property must pay annual taxes of $400. It is believed that if this property is purchased, it will be necessary for the investor to wait for 10 years before he can sell it at a favorable price. What must he the selling price in 10 years for the investment to yield 6% before income taxes?

5–25. It is desired to invest a lump sum of money on a boy's 6th birthday to provide him $2,000 on each birthday from the 18th to the 22nd, both inclusive. If interest of 4% can be obtained on a tax-exempt investment, what lump sum must be invested?

5–26. Assume that in the circumstances described in Problem 5–25, it is not practicable to invest the entire lump sum indicated by your calculations. $1,500 will be invested on the 6th birthday and a uniform annual deposit in the fund will be made on the 7th to 12th birthdays, both inclusive. Assuming 4% interest, what must be the annual deposit from the 7th to 12th birthdays?

5–27. What uniform annual payment for 30 years is equivalent to spending $10,000 immediately, $10,000 at the end of 10 years, $10,000 at the end of 20 years, and $2,000 a year for 30 years? Assume an interest rate of 8%.

5–28. A purchaser of furniture on a time-payment plan agrees to pay $44 at the end of each month for 28 months. The same furniture could be purchased for cash for $1,000. By appropriate use of your interest tables, find the approximate interest rate per month. What is the nominal interest rate per annum? What is the effective interest rate per annum?

5–29. Xavier Smith was born on July 1, 1957. On July 1, 1958, an uncle starts a fund that is intended to help the boy in two ways. The fund is to be established by a payment of $1,000 on July 1, 1958, and on each July 1 thereafter up to and including July 1, 1967—a total outlay of $10,000 by the uncle. One purpose of the fund is to help the boy finance his college education; it is provided that $2,000 shall be withdrawn for this purpose each year for 4 years starting with the boy's 18th birthday, July 1, 1975—a total withdrawal of $8,000. The remainder of the fund is to accumulate until Xavier is 30 years old on July 1, 1987, and is to be paid to him at that time to help him finance the purchase of a home. If the fund earns 3% compounded annually after taxes, how much will be paid to Xavier on his 30th birthday?

6

Annual Cost

Proposed investments in industrial assets are unattractive unless it seems likely that they will be recovered with interest; the interest should be at least the minimum rate of return that is attractive in the particular circumstances. The introduction of the time value of money into economy studies reflects this need to recover capital with a return. This chapter and the two following chapters explain three good ways to compare alternative series of disbursements and receipts. These ways are:

1. Annual cost, with a stipulated minimum attractive rate of return used as an interest rate
2. Present worth, with a stipulated minimum attractive rate of return used as an interest rate
3. Prospective rate of return, with the calculated return compared with a stipulated minimum attractive rate

This chapter introduces the annual cost method as applied to relatively simple circumstances. The method is illustrated by a series of simple examples. Applications of annual costs to more complex situations are developed in later chapters.

Cash Flow. The data for all of the examples and problems in Chapters 6, 7, and 8 are given in terms of prospective cash flow associated with stated alternatives. In the examples and problems in the present chapter, the differences between the alternatives are almost entirely differences in disbursements; the only differences in receipts entering into the comparisons are in receipts from salvage values.

Many of the problems in economy that confront the engineer are of this type; the prospective receipts from the sale of a product or service are unaffected by the engineer's choice among the various alternatives available to him. Economy studies in such cases must start with estimates of the amounts and dates of the disbursements for each alternative. It also is necessary either to estimate the full period of service from each alternative or to concentrate attention in the economy study on some shorter period that might be described as the study period.

Once such estimates have been made, a mere inspection of the figures may settle the question of relative economy; one alternative may involve less disbursements both initially and subsequently. But in the many cases where this is not true, the common situation is for one alternative to involve a higher first cost that leads to some future advantages, such as lower annual disbursements or longer life or higher salvage value. The question at issue in such cases is whether these future advantages are sufficient to justify the greater initial investment.

"Annual Cost" Means Equivalent Uniform Annual Cost. To compare nonuniform series of money disbursements where money has a time value, it is necessary somehow to make them comparable. One way to do this is by reducing each to an equivalent uniform annual series of payments. In general, the phrase *annual cost* when used in connection with economy studies is simply a short way of saying *equivalent uniform annual cost*. As a practical matter, however, it often is expedient to use various approximations to equivalent uniform annual cost. These approximations may also be described as *annual cost*. A description of some common types of approximation and an evaluation of their merits is given in Appendix A.

Income Tax Considerations in the Following Examples. In private enterprise in the United States as well as in many other countries, cash flow for income taxes is likely to be influenced by the choice between alternative proposals for investments in plant and equipment. In competitive enterprise it is sometimes a fairly complex matter to predict the income tax consequences of certain decisions.

In some types of economy study a rational choice between alternatives cannot be made without a year-by-year estimate of the prospective differences in disbursements for income taxes that will result from the choice between the two alternatives. Methods of making such estimates are explained in Chapter 15, which also develops criteria for judging when it is desirable to make such specific estimates of the income tax consequences of decisions.

In the present chapter and in the intervening chapters until Chapter 15, income tax considerations are introduced in a way that is considerably simpler. In all studies dealing with alternatives in competitive enterprise, the interest rate stipulated in examples and problems is the minimum attractive rate *before* income taxes rather than *after* income taxes. It will be presumed that a stipulated rate after taxes has been converted to the rate before taxes by making use of the tax rate assumed to be applicable.

For instance, if the tax collector will take half of the net income from a proposed investment, it appears that the investment must earn 10% before taxes in order to yield 5% after taxes. If one-third of the net income before taxes must be paid to tax collectors, it seems that a stipulated return of 8% after taxes will require 12% before. Although, for reasons explained in Chapter 15, such a simple assumption is really incorrect in principle, the use of a minimum attractive return before taxes computed in this manner is good enough for practical purposes in a great many cases.

In most instances where minimum attractive rates of return *before* income taxes of 8% or more are specified in the examples and problems in this book, it is implied that the economy study is being made in competitive industry (or possibly for an individual). Generally such rates are stated without indicating either the applicable tax rate or the stipulated rate after taxes.

Where examples and problems deal with economy studies for regulated public utilities, the rates of return (usually 6% or 7%) will be stipulated *after* income taxes, and a separate percentage will be given for the ratio of annual income taxes to first cost. Chapter 9 explains the rational basis for this method of introducing income tax considerations into economy studies for public utilities; Chapter 15 tells how to compute the ratio of income taxes to first cost in any specific case.

No prospective income tax payments are involved in economy studies for governments or for nonprofit institutions. Many of the examples and problems in this book dealing with such economy studies stipulate interest rates from 3% to 5%.

EXAMPLE 6-1. A PROPOSED INVESTMENT TO REDUCE LABOR COSTS

Statement of Alternatives. At present a certain materials handling operation in the warehouse of a manufacturing company is being done by hand labor. Annual disbursements for this labor and for certain closely related expenses (such "labor extras" as social security taxes, industrial accident insurance, paid vacations, and various employees' fringe benefits) are $8,200. The proposal to continue materials handling by the present method is called Plan A.

An alternative proposal, Plan B, is to build certain equipment that will reduce this labor cost. The first cost of this equipment will be $15,000. It is estimated that the equipment will reduce annual disbursements for labor and labor extras to $3,300. Annual payments for power, maintenance, and property taxes and insurance are estimated to be $400, $1,100, and $300 respectively.

It is expected that the need for this particular operation will continue for 10 years and that because the equipment in Plan B is specially designed for the particular purpose, it will have no salvage value at the end of that time. It is assumed that the annual disbursements for labor, power, maintenance, and so forth will be uniform throughout the 10 years. The minimum attractive rate of return before income taxes is 10%.

Annual Cost Comparison. Everything but the initial $15,000 is already a uniform annual cost. The only compound interest calculation needed is a conversion of this $15,000 to its equivalent uniform annual cost of capital recovery. The annual costs may then be tabulated for each plan and their totals may be compared.

	Plan A		*Plan B*	
Labor and labor extras	$8,200	CR = $15,000(crf–10%–10)		
		= $15,000(0.16275) =	$2,441	
		Labor and labor extras	3,300	
		Power	400	
		Maintenance	1,100	
		Property taxes, insurance	300	
Total annual cost	$8,200	Total annual cost	$7,541	

Plan B is therefore more economical than Plan A.

Simplicity of a Uniform Annual Series of Disbursements.

Experience indicates that it is almost inevitable that certain disbursements will vary from year to year. Maintenance costs fluctuate and tend to increase with age; wage rates change; property tax rates and assessed valuations change; and so forth. Nevertheless, it often happens that there is no rational basis for making different estimates for each year. Even where there is some basis for making separate year-by-year estimates, the prospective differences in year-by-year totals may be so small that it is good enough for practical purposes merely to estimate average annual disbursements and to treat the average figures as if they were uniform.

Whatever may be the reason for estimates of uniform annual disbursements, it is evident that such estimates simplify the comparison of equivalent uniform annual costs; only the capital costs require conversion by appropriate compound interest factors.

Tabulation of Cash Flow. A useful tool in many economy studies is a year-by-year tabulation of estimated disbursements and receipts associated with each of two alternatives, followed by a tabulation of the differences in cash flow between the alternatives. Table 6–1 shows such a tabulation for Example 6–1.

Many such tabulations appear throughout this book. In all of them a net disbursement is preceded by a minus sign and a net receipt is preceded by a plus sign. The final column of Table 6–1 recognizes that a reduction of disbursements is, in effect, an increase in receipts. That is, spending $3,100 less has the same effect on the company's cash as receiving $3,100 more.

The figures for totals at the bottom of cash flow tables provide a check on the arithmetic in the table. Although this check seems unnecessary in Table 6–1, it will prove useful in more complicated types of circumstances such as are discussed later in this book. It should be noted by the reader that the totals from any such cash flow tables disregard the time value of money; therefore, these totals do not by themselves provide a satisfactory basis for choosing between the alternatives being compared. Such totals may be thought of as giving the present worth of the cash flow using an interest rate of 0%.

TABLE 6–1

TABULATION OF CASH FLOW, EXAMPLE 6–1

Year	Plan A	Plan B	B − A
0		−$15,000	−$15,000
1	−$8,200	−5,100	+3,100
2	−8,200	−5,100	+3,100
3	−8,200	−5,100	+3,100
4	−8,200	−5,100	+3,100
5	−8,200	−5,100	+3,100
6	−8,200	−5,100	+3,100
7	−8,200	−5,100	+3,100
8	−8,200	−5,100	+3,100
9	−8,200	−5,100	+3,100
10	−8,200	−5,100	+3,100
Totals	−$82,000	−$66,000	+$16,000

In a tabulation such as Table 6–1 that is intended to show how receipts and disbursements will be influenced by a particular decision, the source of an estimated receipt or disbursement is immaterial. For example, a dollar spent for one purpose in a particular year has the same effect on cash flow as a dollar paid out for some other purpose; in a cash flow analysis, it is a matter of indifference whether the dollar is spent for labor, for power, for property taxes, or for anything else. Although this point seems obvious in Example 6–1, it is not always so evident; we shall have need to mention it again when we discuss increment costs and sunk costs (introduced in Chapter 14) and when we take a more critical look at the income tax effects of decisions.

Moreover, in a tabulation such as Table 6–1 showing expected cash flow for two alternatives, it is the right-hand column—the column of differences in cash flow—that is significant. This column of differences serves to clarify the question at issue in the choice between the alternatives. In Example 6–1, the question—quite obviously—is whether it will pay to spend $15,000 at once in order to save $3,100 a year (before income taxes) for the next 10 years.

Interpretation of Annual Cost Comparison in Example 6–1.
Our annual cost comparison has answered the foregoing question in the affirmative. The smaller equivalent annual cost computed for Plan B means "Yes, it will pay to spend the proposed $15,000."

This answer should properly be viewed as a qualified "Yes," subject to the appropriateness of the 10% interest rate used in the annual cost calculation. If a 10% return before income taxes is sufficient, all things considered, Plan B is clearly better than Plan A.

It should also be recognized that the answer "Yes, it will pay" refers only to the relative merits of Plans A and B. Conceivably there may be some other possible plan which, if considered, would prove to be superior to both A and B.

The Borrowed Money Point of View. Assume that all the $15,000 to be invested in the new equipment is to be borrowed at 10% interest. Assume also that this borrowing will be repaid by uniform annual end-of-year payments over the 10-year life of the equipment in the manner illustrated in Plan III, Chapter 3, page 36. These annual payments would then be $2,441, the computed capital recovery cost for Plan B in our solution of Example 6–1. Thus the total annual cost of $7,541 for Plan B may be thought of as the total annual disbursement that would be needed if the equipment were to be financed by money borrowed in this way.

Although this point of view is helpful in understanding the calculation of equivalent uniform annual costs, it is only rarely that borrowing takes place in this manner. Moreover, for reasons that will be explained in Chapter 9, the appropriate minimum attractive rate of return for use in an economy study is nearly always higher than the bare cost of borrowed money. But regardless of whether the first cost is to be borrowed 100%, or to be financed 100% out of the funds of the prospective owner, or to be financed by some combination of borrowed funds and of owner's funds, and regardless of the plans for repayment of any borrowed funds, the calculated equivalent annual costs provide an entirely valid method of comparing the long-run economy of the two alternatives, once a particular interest rate is accepted as a standard.

Nevertheless, questions of financing, separate from those of long-run economy, arise whenever proposed assets are to be financed by borrowing that must be paid back rapidly. Here a separate question is always whether the repayment obligation can be met. This topic is discussed in Chapter 17.

The End-of-Year Convention in Economy Studies. In Plan B the $2,441 capital recovery cost was an end-of-year series for 10 years. If the date of the $15,000 investment is designated as zero (0) date, the ten $2,441 figures apply to dates 1 to 10 respectively.

When we add this $2,441 year-end figure to the $5,100 that we expect will actually be paid out each year, we are, in effect, assuming that the $5,100 is also a year-end figure. As a matter of fact the disbursements included in the $5,100 are expected to occur throughout each year. Some of the disbursements (such as wages of labor) will doubtless take place at a fairly uniform rate during the year; others (such as property taxes) will occur at regular intervals; still others (such as maintenance) will occur irregularly.

It is convenient in economy studies to treat receipts and disbursements that occur throughout a year as if they took place at year end. This end-of-year convention is used in nearly all of the examples and problems in this book; unless otherwise stated, it is implied in cash flow tables and in calculations of annual costs, present worths, and rates of return. The convention greatly simplifies the required compound interest conversions. In most cases the assumption is good enough for practical purposes in the sense that it will not lead to errors in decisions between alternatives.

If continuous compounding of interest is assumed, a different convention may be adopted—namely, that all receipts and disbursements occur uniformly throughout each year. This latter convention is discussed and illustrated in Appendix B. Its chief advantages occur where the study period is short and the prospective rate of return is high.

EXAMPLE 6–2. A PROPOSED INVESTMENT
THAT HAS A SALVAGE VALUE

Statement of Alternatives. Plan C, an alternative to Plan B in Example 6–1, calls for the purchase of certain general-purpose materials handling equipment. The first cost of this equipment will be $25,000, a considerable increase over the $15,000 first cost in Plan B. However, it is estimated that this general-purpose equipment will have a $5,000 net salvage value at the end of the 10-year period of service. (The net salvage value may be defined as the gross receipts from the sale of the equipment minus any disbursements required by its removal and sale.) This equipment, which has more automatic features than the equipment in Plan B, is expected to reduce annual disbursements for labor and labor extras to $1,700. Estimated annual disbursements for power, maintenance, and property taxes and insurance are $600, $1,500, and $500 respectively. It is desired to compare Plans B and C using a minimum attractive rate of return of 10%.

Annual Cost Comparison. The annual cost of Plan B has already been calculated as $7,541. Annual costs for Plan C are as follows:

Plan C

CR = ($25,000 − $5,000)(crf–10%–10) + $5,000(0.10)
   = $20,000(0.16275) + $5,000(0.10) = $3,255 + $500 = **$3,755**

Labor and labor extras	1,700
Power	600
Maintenance	1,500
Property taxes, insurance	500
Total annual cost	$8,055

It is evident that Plan B is more economical than Plan C. The savings in operating disbursements promised by Plan C are not enough to offset its higher capital recovery costs.

The Influence of Salvage Value on the Annual Cost of Capital Recovery.

Let P = first cost of a machine or structure, n = the life or study period in years, L = prospective net salvage value at the end of n years, and i = interest rate or minimum attractive return. The annual cost of capital recovery may then be expressed as follows:

$$CR = (P - L) \left[\frac{i(1+i)^n}{(1+i)^n - 1} \right] + Li$$

or

$$CR = (P - L)(\text{crf–}i\text{–}n) + Li$$

This formula, considered algebraically, is also applicable with a zero salvage value or a negative salvage value.

The borrowed money viewpoint may be helpful in examining the rational basis of this formula. Let us apply this viewpoint to the $25,000 first cost, $5,000 salvage value, 10-year life, and 10% interest rate in Plan C. Assume that the $25,000 is borrowed at 10% interest and that it is anticipated that $5,000 of the debt will be repaid from the proceeds of the salvage value. In effect, the $25,000 debt may be divided into two parts. One part of the debt, $20,000 (i.e., $P - L$ or $25,000 − $5,000), must be repaid by uniform annual payments of $3,255 for 10 years (obtained as the product of $20,000 and the 10-year crf, 0.16275). On the other part of the debt, $5,000, it is necessary merely to pay interest of $500 each year because the investment itself will generate the $5,000 salvage necessary to repay the principal. The total annual payment on the debt is therefore $3,255 + $500 = $3,755.

In general, where there is a prospective salvage value after n years, the annual cost of capital recovery may be computed as the sum of two figures. One figure is the product of first cost minus estimated salvage, $(P - L)$, and the crf for n years and interest rate i.

The other figure is the product of salvage, (L), and interest rate i. The foregoing method of calculation is the one used in examples throughout this book.

Two other correct methods of computing capital recovery cost are described and illustrated in the following paragraphs.

In one method the capital recovery cost is calculated as the sum of the product of first cost and interest rate, and the product of the difference between first cost and salvage value and the sinking fund factor. This may be expressed algebraically as

$$CR = Pi + (P - L)\left[\frac{i}{(1+i)^n - 1}\right]$$

or

$$CR = Pi + (P - L)\,(\text{sff–}i\text{–}n)$$

As applied to the data of Plan C

$$CR = \$25,000(0.10) + (\$25,000 - \$5,000)(0.06275)$$

$$= \$2,500 + \$1,255 = \$3,755$$

Another method converts the salvage value to its present worth at zero date by multiplying salvage by the single payment present worth factor. The difference between the first cost and the present worth of the salvage is then multiplied by the capital recovery factor. This may be expressed algebraically as

$$CR = \left[P - \frac{L}{(1+i)^n}\right]\left[\frac{i(1+i)^n}{(1+i)^n - 1}\right]$$

or

$$CR = [P - L(\text{pwf}'\text{–}i\text{–}n)]\,(\text{crf–}i\text{–}n)$$

As applied to the data of Plan C, the present worth of the salvage is $\$5,000(0.3855) = \$1,927.50$.

$$CR = (\$25,000 - \$1,927.50)(0.16275) = \$3,755$$

Cash Flow for Example 6–2. Table 6–2 compares cash flow in Plans B and C. The tabulation makes it evident that the question at issue is whether it will pay to spend $10,000 at once in order to avoid spending $800 a year for 10 years and to receive $5,000 at the end of the 10th year. Although the extra $10,000 investment required for Plan C over Plan B will ultimately be recovered in the combination of cost savings and salvage value, our comparison of annual costs tells us that the recovery will not be rapid enough to yield a 10% return before income taxes.

TABLE 6–2

TABULATION OF CASH FLOW, EXAMPLE 6–2

Year	Plan B	Plan C	C − B
0	−$15,000	−$25,000	−$10,000
1	−5,100	−4,300	+800
2	−5,100	−4,300	+800
3	−5,100	−4,300	+800
4	−5,100	−4,300	+800
5	−5,100	−4,300	+800
6	−5,100	−4,300	+800
7	−5,100	−4,300	+800
8	−5,100	−4,300	+800
9	−5,100	−4,300	+800
10	$\left\{ -5{,}100 \right.$	$\left\{ \begin{array}{l} -4{,}300 \\ +5{,}000 \end{array} \right.$	$\left\{ \begin{array}{l} +800 \\ +5{,}000 \end{array} \right.$
Totals	−$66,000	−$63,000	+$ 3,000

EXAMPLE 6–3. COMPARING ALTERNATIVES THAT HAVE DIFFERENT LIVES

Statement of Alternatives. In the design of certain industrial facilities, two alternate structures are under consideration. These are referred to here as Plans D and E. The receipts from the services of the industrial organization will not be affected by the choice between the two plans. Estimates for the two plans are as follows:

	Plan D	Plan E
First cost	$50,000	$120,000
Life	20 years	40 years
Salvage value	$10,000	$20,000
Annual disbursements	$9,000	$6,000

The estimated annual disbursements include operation, maintenance, property taxes, and insurance.

It is desired to compare these alternatives using a minimum attractive rate of return of 8% before income taxes.

Annual Cost Comparison. The annual costs may be compared as follows:

Plan D

$$\text{CR} = (\$50{,}000 - \$10{,}000)(\text{crf–8\%–20}) + \$10{,}000(0.08)$$
$$= \$40{,}000(0.10185) + \$10{,}000(0.08) = \$4{,}074 + \$800 \qquad = \$\ 4{,}874$$

Annual disbursements   9,000

Total annual cost $13,874

Plan E

$$\text{CR} = (\$120{,}000 - \$20{,}000)(\text{crf–8\%–40}) + \$20{,}000(0.08)$$
$$= \$100{,}000(0.08386) + \$20{,}000(0.08) = \$8{,}386 + \$1{,}600 = \$\ 9{,}986$$

Annual disbursements   6,000

Total annual cost $15,986

Plan D is more economical.

Some Considerations in Annual Cost Comparisons When Two Alternatives Have Different Lives. When annual cost comparisons such as the preceding one are made, an objection along the following lines is sometimes raised: "Plan E has an important advantage over Plan D in that it has a much longer prospective life. How is this advantage reflected in your annual cost comparison? Doesn't your $13,874 a year give you service for only 20 years, whereas your $15,986 a year gives you service for 40 years?"

Such an objector doubtless missed a fundamental point in the mathematics of compound interest. Nevertheless, he has introduced an interesting and important topic. We shall discuss various facets of this topic in different places throughout this book.

A direct answer to our objector may be made by pointing out that the 20-year estimated life in Plan D was reflected by the use of the 20-year capital recovery factor, 0.10185, in obtaining the $4,874 CR cost, and the 40-year estimated life in Plan E was reflected by the use of the 40-year crf, 0.08386, in obtaining the CR cost of $9,986. The answer may be amplified by pointing out that the estimate of a 40-year life in Plan E implied that a service of at least this long would be required. Although the $13,874 a year for Plan D is for 20 years only, the service must be continued after the 20-year structure is retired. Presumably, although not necessarily, the annual costs of continuing the service will be of the same order of magnitude. If it is assumed that as good an estimate as any is that the replacement structure will have the same first cost, life, salvage value, and annual disbursements as the initial structure, the $13,874 annual cost in Plan D will be repeated during the second 20 years.

A somewhat more sophisticated view of the matter recognizes that the present decision between a long-lived and a short-lived alternative is simply a decision as to what to do *now*. In aiming to have the decision now turn out to be the best decision in the long run, it is appropriate to consider what may happen after the end of the life of the shorter-lived alternative. In Example 6–3, a forecast that the replacement structure in the second 20 years will have much higher annual costs than the initial structure is favorable to Plan E. Similarly, the prospect that a replacement structure with much lower annual costs will be available should be given weight in the present choice as a factor favoring Plan D. In general, prospects for price increases and for extra costs incident to replacement are favorable to the selection of longer-lived alternatives; prospects for technological improvements, changes in service requirements, and price reductions are favorable to the selection of shorter-lived alternatives. The extent to which such prospects may be evaluated numerically in the cost comparison and the extent to which they must be considered only as irreducible data will naturally depend on circumstances. This topic is explored further in Chapter 13 and thereafter. In this chapter and in the two that follow, wherever some specific assumption is necessary for the cost comparison, it will be assumed that replacement assets will repeat the costs that have been forecast for the initial asset.

Cash Flow Tabulations When Alternatives Have Different Lives. If cash flow for Plans D and E is to be compared for a 40-year period, some assumptions must be made regarding disbursements in the final 20 years of Plan D. In Table 6–3 it is assumed that the final 20 years will repeat the costs of the first 20. The table has been shortened by using a single line for each series of years in which cash flow is uniform.

TABLE 6–3

TABULATION OF CASH FLOW, EXAMPLE 6–3

Years	Plan D	Plan E	E − D
0	−$50,000	−$120,000	−$70,000
1–19	−9,000 per year	−6,000 per year	+3,000 per year
20	$\left\{\begin{array}{l} -9,000 \\ +10,000 \\ -50,000 \end{array}\right.$	$\left\{\begin{array}{l} -6,000 \end{array}\right.$	$\left\{\begin{array}{l} +3,000 \\ +40,000 \end{array}\right.$
21–39	−9,000 per year	−6,000 per year	+3,000 per year
40	$\left\{\begin{array}{l} -9,000 \\ +10,000 \end{array}\right.$	$\left\{\begin{array}{l} -6,000 \\ +20,000 \end{array}\right.$	$\left\{\begin{array}{l} +3,000 \\ +10,000 \end{array}\right.$
Totals	−$440,000	−$340,000	+$100,000

The final column of the table shows that the initial extra outlay of $70,000 will ultimately be recovered plus an additional $100,000. Nevertheless, our annual cost comparison has indicated that this recovery of capital is too slow to yield 8% before income taxes and that, by the standard we have set, this extra $70,000 outlay for Plan E is undesirable.

Because 20 years is evenly divisible into 40 years, it was a simple matter to tabulate prospective cash flow for a period that would give the same number of years of service for the two plans. All that was required was our assumption regarding the disbursements during the second 20 years. In most comparisons of alternatives with different lives, the matter is more complicated than in Example 6–3; the total years tabulated must be the least common multiple of the estimated lives of the two alternatives. For example, if one alternative had a 10-year life and the other a 25-year life, it would be necessary to consider a 50-year period, with 5 life cycles for one alternative and 2 for the other. If lives were, say, 13 and 20 years, a 260-year period would have to be tabulated before reaching the point where the alternatives gave equal years of service.

We shall see that a disparity in lives of alternatives creates the same difficulty in present worth comparisons and in calculation of rates of return that we now observe in the tabulations of comparative cash flow. Various methods of dealing with this difficulty are developed in subsequent chapters. Because no one method is completely satisfactory, the method selected is properly influenced by the circumstances of the economy study.

EXAMPLE 6–4. COMPARING ALTERNATIVES THAT HAVE PERPETUAL LIVES

Statement of Alternatives. In the design of an aqueduct that is assumed to have a perpetual period of service, two alternative locations are proposed for a certain section.

Location J involves a tunnel and flume. The tunnel is estimated to have a first cost of $200,000 and is assumed to be permanent. Its annual upkeep costs are estimated as $500. The flume will cost $90,000, has an estimated life of 20 years, and is expected to have annual maintenance costs of $2,000.

Location K involves a steel pipe line and several miles of concrete-lined earth canal. The pipe line has an estimated first cost of $70,000, an estimated life of 50 years, and an estimated annual maintenance cost of $700. The earth canal will cost $80,000 and is assumed to be permanent. During the first 5 years it is estimated that maintenance on the earth canal will be $5,000 a year; thereafter, it is estimated as $1,000 a year. The concrete lining will cost $40,000; it has an estimated life of 25 years with annual maintenance cost of $300.

All salvage values are assumed to be negligible. The interest rate is 5%.

Annual Cost Comparison. Annual costs may be compared as follows:

	Location J	
Tunnel		
Interest = $200,000(0.05)		= $10,000
Maintenance		500
Flume		
CR = $90,000(crf–5%–20) = $90,000(0.08024)		= 7,222
Maintenance		2,000
Total annual cost		$19,722

	Location K	
Pipe line		
CR = $70,000(crf–5%–50)		
= $70,000(0.05478)		= $ 3,835
Maintenance		700
Earth canal		
Interest on first cost = $80,000(0.05)		= 4,000
Interest on PW of extra early maintenance		
= $4,000(pwf–5%–5)(0.05) = $4,000(4.329)(0.05)		= 866
Maintenance		1,000
Concrete lining		
CR = $40,000(crf–5%–25) = $40,000(0.07095)		= 2,838
Maintenance		300
Total annual cost		$13,539

Selection of Location K will result in a saving of nearly $6,200 in annual costs.

Two new points arise in this solution. One deals with the annual cost associated with a perpetual life for a structure. Here interest (or return) on investment takes the place of capital recovery; as n approaches infinity, the capital recovery factor approaches the interest rate. If one adopts the borrowed money point of view, it is as if the $200,000 for the tunnel, for example, were borrowed under terms that permitted a perpetual debt with $10,000 interest paid every year.[1]

The extra maintenance of $4,000 a year for the first 5 years for the earth canal is a nonrecurring expenditure somewhat comparable to first cost. To translate this into an equivalent perpetual annual cost, it first must be converted into its present worth of $17,316 on zero date. Then, like the $80,000 investment in the canal itself, it is converted into an equivalent perpetual series by multiplying by the interest rate.

The Small Difference in Annual Cost Between Very Long Life and Perpetual Life. Forever is a long time! Past experience suggests that even the projects that appear likely to be longest-lived will eventually reach the end of their usefulness, despite the difficulty of estimating the specific cause and date of termination of life. The estimator whose economy studies imply permanence of certain constructions does not really have the illusion that his projects will last forever; he merely expects that they will last a very long time, possibly 100 years or more.

In an economy study the difference between 100 years and forever is very small indeed. For example, at 5% interest the capital recovery factor for 100 years is 0.05038. That is, an increase of the interest rate from 5% to 5.04% would have the same effect on annual cost as reducing the estimated life of a structure from forever to 100 years. Even with interest at 3%, the difference between 100 years and forever has the same influence on annual cost as a difference of $\frac{1}{6}$ of 1% in the interest rate.

In many long-lived projects, economy studies are made and costs are computed as if the expected life were 50 years. This is common both in public works projects, such as federal river basin projects in the United States (see Chapter 18) and in private projects.

EXAMPLE 6–5. COMPARING ALTERNATIVES IN WHICH ANNUAL
DISBURSEMENTS HAVE A UNIFORM GRADIENT

Statement of Alternatives. Many tractors of a particular type but of different ages are being used by a company engaged in large-scale farming operations. Although there have been no formal rules on replacement policy, the usual

---

[1] Because of the common practice of bond refunding in the public utility industry, many business debts are, in effect, perpetual. This matter is discussed in Chapter 17. But if this were an aqueduct for a municipal water supply or for an irrigation district, there would nearly always be a public requirement that the debt be paid off within a specified number of years, possibly 40 or less. Such a requirement would not affect the validity of the annual cost calculations based on perpetual life. However, as brought out in Chapter 17, it would create an additional question of the actual total disbursements for debt service and other purposes with each of the proposed alternative locations.

practice has been to replace tractors when they were about 10 years old. The first cost of a tractor is $12,000. Records have been kept of maintenance costs under conditions of fairly uniform use from year to year. There is clearly a marked upward tendency in maintenance costs as tractors get older, even though the maintenance costs at a given age differ from tractor to tractor. An analysis indicates that, on the average, maintenance costs will be $1,600 the first year, $1,930 the second, $2,260 the third, and will increase by $330 a year for each year of age.

It is desired to compare the equivalent annual costs for an average tractor assuming a 7-year life with such costs for an average tractor assuming a 10-year life. Estimated salvage value will be $4,000 for a 7-year-old tractor and $2,800 for a 10-year-old one. It is believed that costs other than maintenance and capital recovery costs can be disregarded in this comparison as these costs will be practically the same whether tractors are retired after 7 years or after 10 years. The minimum attractive return is 8% before income taxes.

Annual Cost Comparison. The year-by-year maintenance costs may be treated as if they are made up of two parts. The first part is a uniform series of $1,600 a year. The second part is $0 the first year, $330 the second, $660 the third, and so on, increasing $330 each year. The second part constitutes a gradient series which may be converted to an equivalent uniform annual series by use of the appropriate gradient factor (gf) from Table E–23.

Tractor Retired After 7 Years

CR = ($12,000 − $4,000)(crf–8%–7) + $4,000(0.08)
　 = $8,000(0.19207) + $4,000(0.08) = $1,537 + $320　　　　　　= $1,857
Equivalent annual maintenance cost
　 = $1,600 + $330(gf–8%–7)
　 = $1,600 + $330(2.69) = $1,600 + $888　　　　　　　　　　= 2,488
Total of annual costs compared　　　　　　　　　　　　　　= $4,345

Tractor Retired After 10 Years

CR = ($12,000 − $2,800)(crf–8%–10) + $2,800(0.08)
　 = $9,200(0.14903) + $2,800(0.08) = $1,371 + $224　　　　　= $1,595
Equivalent annual maintenance cost
　 = $1,600 + $330(gf–8%–10)
　 = $1,600 + $330(3.87) = $1,600 + $1,277　　　　　　　　　= 2,877
Total of annual costs compared　　　　　　　　　　　　　　= $4,472

The equivalent annual costs over the life of the 7-year tractor will be somewhat lower than those over the life of the 10-year one.

Comments on Example 6–5.

Where it seems reasonable to estimate that disbursements (or receipts) will increase or decrease by a uniform amount each year, the gradient factor is helpful in computing equivalent uniform annual costs. It often happens that the estimate of a uniform gradient is as good an estimate as it is practicable to make in cases where upward or downward trends are expected.

Where disbursements are expected to vary irregularly from year to year and the figures for each year are predicted for use in the economy study, the gradient approach is not suitable; it is necessary first to convert all disbursements to present worth before converting to equivalent uniform annual cost. This type of calculation is illustrated in the next chapter.

Although Example 6–5 introduces the subject of the time at which it is economical to replace an asset that is physically capable of being continued in service, this example omits consideration of a number of matters that are important in replacement economy. A more adequate consideration of this interesting and important subject is deferred until Chapter 16 and thereafter.

The Usefulness of Annual Cost Calculations Is Not Limited to Comparisons of Alternatives Involving Different Series of Disbursements. Although the examples given in this chapter have all dealt with comparisons of alternatives of the "Why this way?" type, a number of other uses of annual costs will be illustrated in Part III. Where the question is whether a proposed investment involving certain prospective revenues is justified, annual costs may be computed for comparison with the expected revenues. Where for some reason, such as agreement between the parties concerned or public regulation of certain prices, the pricing of a product or service is to be based on annual cost, the purpose of computing such a cost may be to find the justified selling price. In economy studies for public works, as illustrated in Chapter 18, annual costs may be computed for comparison with annual benefits.

Omission of Mention of Irreducibles in This Chapter. Economy studies are generally undertaken to arrive at a decision on action or at a recommendation for action. In so far as possible, it is helpful to reduce alternative courses of action to money terms in order to have a common unit to measure the differences between alternatives. Nevertheless, as pointed out in Part I, it often happens that important matters for consideration simply cannot be reduced to terms of money in any satisfactory way. Such irreducibles should be considered along with the money figures in arriving at any decision among alternatives. In those borderline cases where the money comparisons are close, the irreducibles are likely to control the decision.

In this chapter and the two that follow, we deal chiefly with the calculations necessary to reflect the time value of money in comparing alternatives that involve different estimated cash flows. It is desirable that persons responsible for decisions on matters of economy understand the principles involved in such interest conversions. These are definite principles that exist regardless of the irreducibles entering into any particular situation. Experience shows that they frequently are not clearly understood by engineers and other persons who need to understand them. In order to permit concentration of attention on these principles, the subject matter has been deliberately de-emotionalized in these three chapters by references to Plans A and B, Locations J and K, and so forth, and by the omission of irreducibles as far as possible. A more complete discussion of economy studies in a realistic setting involving irreducibles is deferred until Part III of this book.

Summary. One way of reflecting in economy studies the desirability of recovering invested capital with a return is to compare alternatives on the basis of equivalent uniform annual cost, using as an interest rate the minimum attractive rate of return. Because many of the estimated disbursements are the same year after year, such annual cost comparisons are likely to be convenient. The basic data for such comparisons consist of estimated cash flows associated with the alternatives being compared. Conversions into equivalent annual cost require the use of appropriate factors obtained from compound interest tables or formulas.

Problems

6–1. Compare the annual costs of Pumps Y and Z for a 12-year service using a minimum attractive rate of return of 10% before income taxes.

	Pump Y	Pump Z
First cost	$2,500	$4,000
Estimated salvage value	none	$1,000
Annual pumping cost	$550	$400
Annual repair cost	$250	$120

(*Ans.* = Pump Y, $1,167; Pump Z, $1,060.)

6–2. An 18-in. pipe considered for a certain service has a first cost of $21,000 and annual pumping costs of $6,700. A 24-in. pipe in the same location will have a first cost of $32,000 and annual pumping costs of $3,850. The expected period of service is 7 years after which the pipe will be removed with an expected salvage value of 50% of its first cost. The minimum attractive return is 8% before income taxes. Compare the annual costs. (*Ans.* = $9,557 for 18-in.; $8,203 for 24-in.)

6–3. Two temporary structures are to be compared for a given 9-year service. Both will have negative net salvage values at the end of the 9 years; the cost of removal will exceed the receipts from salvaged materials. Compare annual costs using a minimum attractive return of 12% before income taxes.

	Structure W	Structure X
First cost	$9,000	$13,000
Estimated salvage value	−3,000	−1,000
Annual maintenance cost	800	300

(*Ans.* = Structure W, $2,692; Structure X, $2,808.)

6–4. A proposed material for covering the roof of a building will have an estimated life of 10 years and will cost $1,850. A heavier grade of this roofing material will cost $785 more but will have an estimated life of 15 years. Installation costs for either material will be $1,200. Compare the annual costs for the two roofs using a minimum attractive return of 8% before income taxes. (*Ans.* = lighter grade, $455; heavier grade, $448.)

6–5. Compare annual costs of the following types of pipe for a given service, using an interest rate of 5%.

	Wood Pipe	Cast Iron Pipe
First cost	$10,000	$23,000
Life	20 years	60 years
Salvage value	none	$3,000
Annual upkeep	$600	$100

(*Ans.* = wood, $1,402; cast iron, $1,307.)

6–6. A university that purchases its electric energy for 1.7 cents per kw-hr is to buy a number of 10-kw capacity distribution transformers. Two competing makes compare as follows:

	Cherokee	Seminole
First cost	$260	$232
Iron loss in watts (continuing 24 hours a day regardless of the size of the load)	57	71
Copper loss in watts at full load	188	204

The copper loss varies as the square of the load. Although the load on a transformer will actually vary throughout all values from 0 to 10 kw, it is sufficiently accurate to assume that the transformers carry a full load 1,000 hours a year, a half load 2,000 hours a year, and no load the remainder of the time. The iron loss continues for the full 8,760 hours per year. The estimated life of a distribution transformer is 28 years. The probable salvage value of a 10-kw transformer is $30. With interest at 4½% compare the annual costs of the two transformers. (*Ans.* = Cherokee, $29.24; Seminole, $29.95.)

6–7. A school district considers two alternative plans for an athletic stadium. An engineer makes the following cost estimates for each:

Concrete Bleachers. First cost, $350,000. Life, 100 years. Annual upkeep cost, $2,000.

Wooden Bleachers on Earth Fill. First cost of entire project, $200,000. Painting cost every 3 years, $10,000. New seats every 12 years, $40,000. New bleachers every 36 years, $100,000. Life of earth fill is permanent.

Compare the annual costs of the two plans assuming perpetual service and an interest rate of 5%. (*Ans.* = concrete, $19,633; wooden, $16,736.)

6–8. Annual disbursements (other than driver's wages) for operation and maintenance of certain trucks under particular operating conditions tend to increase by $300 a year for the first 5 years of operation; first-year disbursements are $2,200. The first cost of a truck is $4,800. The estimated salvage value after 4 years is $1,400; after 5 years it is $1,000. Compare the equivalent uniform annual costs for a truck held for 4 years and for 5 years. Use a minimum attractive return of 10% before income taxes. (*Ans.* = $3,827 for 4 years; $3,845 for 5 years.)

6–9. It is desired to determine whether to use insulation 1 in. thick or 2 in. thick in insulating a steam pipe. The steam loss from this pipe without insulation would cost $3.00 per year per foot of pipe. A 1-in. insulation will cut out 89% of the loss and will cost 96 cents per foot. A 2-in. insulation will cut out 92% of the loss and will cost $2.04 per foot. Compare the total annual costs of insulation per 1,000 feet, including cost of lost steam, for the two thicknesses, using a life of 15 years for the insulation with no salvage value. The minimum attractive return is 8% before income taxes.

6–10. A certain service can be performed satisfactorily either by Machine M or N. Machine M has a first cost of $6,000, an estimated life of 12 years, no salvage value, and annual disbursements (for all purposes except income taxes) of $4,000. The corresponding figures for Machine N are $14,000, 18 years, 20% salvage value, and $2,400. Compare the annual costs assuming a minimum attractive return of 15% before income taxes.

6–11. Compare the equivalent annual cost of perpetual service for Plans I and II using interest at 5%.

Plan I involves an initial investment of $150,000. Of this, $75,000 is for land (assumed to be permanent) and $75,000 is for a structure that will require renewal, without salvage value, every 30 years. Annual disbursements will be $10,000 for the first 10 years and $7,000 thereafter.

Plan II involves an initial investment of $250,000. Of this, $100,000 is for land and $150,000 is for a structure that will require renewal, with a $30,000 salvage value, every 50 years. Annual disbursements will be $4,000.

6–12. For a certain service in a manufacturing plant, a centerless grinder must be purchased. A secondhand machine that will be satisfactory will cost $5,000; a new machine of more up-to-date design will cost $12,000. Annual disbursements for labor and labor extras are estimated as $9,200 with the secondhand machine and $8,300 with the new one. Annual maintenance costs are estimated to be $600 the first year and to increase $150 each year with the secondhand machine and to be $400 the first year and to increase $100 each year with the new machine. Annual property taxes and insurance will be 3% of the investment for each machine. The expected period of service is 12 years. At the end of this period, it is estimated that the secondhand machine will have a negligible salvage value and that the new one will have a $4,000 salvage value. Prepare a tabulation of cash flow for each machine and tabulate the differences in cash flow as influenced by the choice. Compare the annual costs of the two machines assuming a 12% minimum attractive return before income taxes.

6–13. A manufacturer proposes to build a new warehouse. A reinforced concrete building will cost $58,000 whereas the same amount of space can be secured in a frame and galvanized metal building for $30,000. The life of the concrete building is estimated as 50 years; average annual maintenance cost is estimated as $500. The life of the frame building is estimated to be 25 years; average annual maintenance cost is estimated as $900. Fire insurance would be carried on the building and its contents in either case; the annual rate would be $1.50 per $1,000 of insurance for the concrete building and $4.00 per $1,000 of insurance for the frame building. Assume that the average amount of insurance carried will be on contents of $400,000 plus 60% of first cost of the building. Average annual property taxes are estimated as 1.4% of the first cost. Compare annual costs of the two types of warehouse using a minimum attractive return of 8% before income taxes. Neglect any possible salvage values at the end of the lives of the buildings.

6–14. A manufacturer wishes to compare two electric motors for a given service. The service requires a 100-horsepower motor that is to be operated at full load 800 hours per year and at half load 1,600 hours per year.

The Gadget Electric Co. offers a motor with a guaranteed full-load efficiency of 91% and half-load efficiency of 87% at a price of $2,520. The Whoosit Electric Co. offers a motor with a guaranteed full-load efficiency of 89.5% and half-load efficiency of 85% at a price of $2.210. (Efficiency is the ratio of energy output to energy input. Motors are rated on output. One horsepower equals 0.746 kilowatts.) Energy costs 2.2 cents per kw-hr.

If each motor makes exactly its guaranteed efficiency and the motors are assumed to have a life of 25 years with zero salvage value, and to be equal in all respects except efficiency and first cost, compare their economy on the basis of annual cost. The minimum attractive return is 8% before income taxes.

6–15. Compare the annual costs of the following two types of power plant to be used for an isolated mine. The expected period of service is 10 years. The minimum attractive return is 15% before income taxes.

	Steam Plant	Diesel Plant
First cost	$20,000	$30,000
Salvage value after 10 years	1,000	5,000
Annual operation and repair cost	9,200	6,000

6–16. Two methods of heating a small temporary building are being considered. Cost estimates for the two methods are as follows:

	Method S	Method T
First cost	$4,200	$2,800
Salvage value	600	1,000
Annual fuel cost	200	450
Annual maintenance cost	125	300

The building is to be used for 6 years. Compare the annual costs of the two plans using a minimum attractive return of 12% before income taxes.

6–17. Machine J has a first cost of $50,000, an estimated service period of 12 years, and an estimated salvage value of $20,000 at the end of the 12 years. Estimated annual disbursements for operation and maintenance are $6,000. A major overhaul costing $10,000 will be required at the end of 6 years. An alternate is Machine K, which has a first cost of $30,000 and an estimated zero salvage value at the end of the 12-year service period. Estimated disbursements for operation and maintenance will be $8,000 for the first year, $8,500 the 2nd year, and will increase $500 each year thereafter. Using an interest rate of 10%, compare the equivalent uniform annual costs of a 12-year service from Machines J and K.

7

Present Worth

Two uses of present worth calculations in engineering economy are explained and illustrated in this chapter, namely:

1. Comparison of alternative series of estimated money disbursements
2. Placing a valuation on prospective money receipts

A third important use of present worth, discussed in Chapter 8, is for trial-and-error calculations to determine unknown rates of return.

Use of Present Worth To Compare Plans A, B, and C of Examples 6–1 and 6–2. It will be recalled that Plans A, B, and C involved, respectively, annual disbursements of $8,200, $5,100, and $4,300 for a 10-year period. Plan A had no first cost; Plan B had $15,000 first cost and zero salvage value; Plan C had $25,000 first cost and $5,000 salvage value. The interest rate was 10%. The data for the following calculations consist of these estimates of cash flow for the three plans; no use is made of the annual costs that were calculated in Chapter 6.

Plan A

PW of annual disbursements = $8,200(pwf–10%–10) = $8,200(6.144)	= $50,380

Plan B

PW of annual disbursements = $5,100(pwf–10%–10) = $5,100(6.144)	= $31,330
First cost	15,000
PW of all disbursements for 10 years	$46,330

Plan C

PW of annual disbursements = $4,300(pwf–10%–10) = $4,300(6.144)	= $26,420
First cost	25,000
PW of all moneys paid out for 10 years	$51,420
Less	
PW of salvage value = $5,000(pwf'–10%–10) = $5,000(0.3855)	= 1,930
PW of net disbursements for 10 years	$49,490

Present worths are calculated as of the zero date of the series of payments being compared. Because first costs are already at zero date, no interest factors need to be applied to first cost. Where an estimated salvage value occurs, as in Plan C, the present worths of the salvage value must be subtracted to obtain the present worth of the net disbursements.

Simplicity of Conversion from Present Worth to Annual Cost and Vice Versa. In Chapter 6 the equivalent uniform annual costs for these three plans were calculated directly from the estimated cash flows. An alternate way to find annual costs would be to calculate them from the present worths. Each present worth can be converted into an equivalent uniform annual series by multiplying it by 0.16275, the crf for 10% and 10 years.

$$\text{Annual cost, Plan A} = \$50,380(0.16275) = \$8,200$$
$$\text{Annual cost, Plan B} = \$46,330(0.16275) = \$7,541$$
$$\text{Annual cost, Plan C} = \$49,490(0.16275) = \$8,055$$

These figures, of course, are identical with the annual cost figures obtained in Chapter 6. In a similar manner an alternate way to have computed the present worths for the three plans would have been to multiply each annual cost calculated in Chapter 6 by 6.144, the series present worth factor for 10% and 10 years.

The general statement may be made that annual cost can be calculated from present worth by multiplying present worth by the appropriate capital recovery factor; present worth can be calculated from annual cost by multiplying annual cost by the appropriate series present worth factor (or dividing by the capital recovery factor). The alternative that is favored in an annual cost comparison is also favored in a present worth comparison, and by the same proportion. For example, the annual cost of Plan B is 6.4% below the annual cost of Plan C; the present worth of B is also 6.4% below C. Of course this convertibility between annual cost and present worth depends on the use of the same interest rate in both calculations and on the use of identical cash flow estimates for the same period of years.

Where alternatives involve irregular series of payments, the first step in computing annual costs should be to find the present worths.

EXAMPLE 7–1. COMPARISON OF ALTERNATIVES INVOLVING IRREGULAR SERIES OF DISBURSEMENTS

Statement of Alternatives. Engineers for a public utility company have proposed two alternate plans to provide a certain service for the next 15 years. Each plan includes sufficient facilities to take care of the expected growth of the demand for the particular utility service during this period.

Plan F calls for a three-stage program of investment in facilities; $60,000 will be invested at once, $50,000 more after 5 years, and $40,000 more after 10 years. Plan G, a two-stage program, calls for a $90,000 immediate investment followed by a $30,000 investment at the end of 8 years. In both plans estimated annual income taxes are 3% of the investment that has been made up to date and estimated annual property taxes are 2% of the investment to date. Annual maintenance costs in Plan F are estimated as $1,500 for the first 5 years, $2,500 for the second 5 years, and $3,500 for the final 5 years. For Plan G, annual maintenance costs are estimated as $2,000 for the first 8 years and $3,000 for the final 7 years. Salvage value at the end of 15 years is estimated to be $45,000 for Plan F and $35,000 for Plan G.

Table 7–1 presents the foregoing estimates as a tabulation of cash flows. For purposes of the economy study, a minimum attractive rate of return of 7% is to be used.

Comparison of Present Worths. The present worths of the respective net disbursements for 15 years may be computed as follows:

Plan F

Initial investment	$ 60,000
PW of investment made after 5 years = $50,000(pwf'–7%–5) = $50,000(0.7130)	= 35,650
PW of investment made after 10 years = $40,000(pwf'–7%–10) = $40,000(0.5083)	= 20,330
PW of annual disbursements, years 1 to 5 = $4,500(pwf–7%–5) = $4,500(4.100)	= 18,450

PW of annual disbursements, years 6 to 10
  = $8,000(pwf–7%–10 minus pwf–7%–5)
  = $8,000(7.024 − 4.100) = $8,000(2.924)
	= 23,390

PW of annual disbursements, years 11 to 15
  = $11,000(pwf–7%–15 minus pwf–7%–10)
  = $11,000(9.108 − 7.024) = $11,000(2.084)
	= 22,920

PW of all moneys paid out for 15 years	$180,740

Less
  PW of salvage value
  = $45,000(pwf'–7%–15)
  = $45,000(0.3624)
	= 16,310

PW of net disbursements for 15 years	$164,430

Plan G

Initial investment	$ 90,000
PW of investment made after 8 years = $30,000(pwf'–7%–8) = $30,000(0.5820)	= 17,460
PW of annual disbursements, years 1 to 8 = $6,500(pwf–7%–8) = $6,500(5.971)	= 38,810

PW of annual disbursements, years 9 to 15
  = $9,000(pwf–7%–15 minus pwf–7%–8)
  = $9,000(9.108 − 5.971) = $9,000(3.137)
	= 28,230

PW of all moneys paid out for 15 years	$174,500

Less
  PW of salvage value
  = $35,000(pwf'–7%–15) = $35,000(0.3624)
	= 12,680

PW of net disbursements for 15 years	$161,820

TABLE 7–1

TABULATION OF CASH FLOW, EXAMPLE 7–1

Year	Plan F	Plan G	G − F
0	−$ 60,000	−$ 90,000	−$30,000
1	−4,500	−6,500	−2,000
2	−4,500	−6,500	−2,000
3	−4,500	−6,500	−2,000
4	−4,500	−6,500	−2,000
5	{ −4,500 { −50,000	{ −6,500 {	{ −2,000 { +50,000
6	−8,000	−6,500	+1,500
7	−8,000	−6,500	+1,500
8	{ −8,000 {	{ −6,500 { −30,000	{ +1,500 { −30,000
9	−8,000	−9,000	−1,000
10	{ −8,000 { −40,000	{ −9,000 {	{ −1,000 { +40,000
11	−11,000	−9,000	+2,000
12	−11,000	−9,000	+2,000
13	−11,000	−9,000	+2,000
14	−11,000	−9,000	+2,000
15	{ −11,000 { +45,000	{ −9,000 { +35,000	{ +2,000 { −10,000
Totals	−$222,500	−$200,000	+$22,500

Comparison of Annual Costs. To compute equivalent uniform annual costs for the 15-year period, the respective present worths must be multiplied by the crf for 7% and 15 years.

Plan F

Annual cost = $164,430(0.10979) = $18,050

Plan G

Annual cost = $161,820(0.10979) = $17,770

Which Plan Should Be Selected? The present worth (and annual cost) of Plan G is only slightly less than that of Plan F. Here is a case where a small change in the basic estimates for the two plans (either in amount or timing of cash flows) could have altered the present worths enough to shift the balance in favor of Plan F. Generally speaking, when a comparison is as close as this one, the decision should be made on the basis of any differences between the plans that have not been reduced to money estimates—on the so-called irreducible data entering into the problem of choice.

Present Worth Comparisons When Alternatives Have Different Lives. There is no point in converting two or more alternative cash flow series into present worth and then comparing the present worths unless the cash flow series relate to a provision of a needed service for the same number of years.

Some of the difficulties arising in comparing alternatives with different lives were discussed in Chapter 6. In our discussion there it was pointed out that a convenient simple assumption is that replacement assets will repeat the costs that have been forecast for the initial asset. In the present chapter we shall continue to make this assumption; a more critical look at the matter will be deferred until Chapter 13 and thereafter.

If the assumption is made that costs will be repeated for replacement assets, a decision must then be made regarding the length of the study period for which present worths will be compared. Sometimes it is convenient to use the least common multiple of the lives of the two alternatives. Otherwise, the present worth study must be for a perpetual period. Usually present worths for an assumed perpetual period of service are referred to as *capitalized costs*.

Illustration of a Comparison of Present Worths for a Least Common Multiple of the Lives of the Alternatives. It will be recalled that in Example 6–3, Plan D had $50,000 first cost, 20-year life, $10,000 salvage value, and $9,000 annual disbursements; Plan E had $120,000 first cost, 40-year life, $20,000 salvage value, and $6,000 annual disbursements. Table 6–3, page 87, shows estimated cash flow for a 40-year period. The interest rate was 8%. A comparison of the present worths of a 40-year service, computed directly from the cash flow data, is as follows:

Plan D

First cost	$ 50,000
PW of net disbursement for renewal in 20 years	
$\quad = (\$50,000 - \$10,000)(\text{pwf}'\text{-}8\%\text{-}20)$	
$\quad = \$40,000(0.2145)$	= 8,580
PW of annual disbursements	
$\quad = \$9,000(\text{pwf-}8\%\text{-}40) = \$9,000(11.925)$	= 107,320
Total PW of disbursements	$165,900
Less	
$\quad$ PW of receipt from final salvage value after 40 years	
$\quad\quad = \$10,000(\text{pwf}'\text{-}8\%\text{-}40)$	
$\quad\quad = \$10,000(0.0460)$	= 460
PW of net disbursements for 40 years	$165,440

Plan E

First cost	$120,000
PW of annual disbursements	
$\quad = \$6,000(\text{pwf-}8\%\text{-}40) = \$6,000(11.925)$	= 71,550
Total PW of disbursements	$191,550
Less	
$\quad$ PW of receipt from salvage value after 40 years	
$\quad\quad = \$20,000(\text{pwf}'\text{-}8\%\text{-}40)$	
$\quad\quad = \$20,000(0.0460)$	= 920
PW of net disbursements for 40 years	$190,630

It will be noted that in Plan D, the $10,000 receipt from salvage of the first asset was subtracted from the $50,000 investment in the renewal asset in order to find the net disbursement required after 20 years; the $40,000 figure thus obtained was then multiplied by the 20-year present worth factor. However, it was necessary to make a separate calculation of the present worth of the receipt from the final salvage value after 40 years and to subtract this present worth from the present worth of all disbursements.

In Chapter 13, we shall discuss the subject of the sensitivity of the conclusions of an economy study to moderate changes in the estimates. It is evident from the present worth comparison of Plans D and E that the estimates of salvage values after 40 years have very little influence on the choice between the plans; a dollar 40 years hence is equivalent to only 4.6 cents today when interest is at 8%. In general, it may be stated that comparisons of economy are not sensitive to changes in estimated distant salvage values unless the interest rate used is very low.

Moreover, in comparing Plans D and E, the choice is relatively insensitive to the estimated cost of the renewal asset in Plan D. For example, if the estimated net disbursement for the renewal asset 20 years hence should be doubled, the total present worth for Plan D would be increased by only $8,580; Plan D would still be considerably more economical than Plan E.

The present worths for Plans D and E may be converted into annual costs by multiplying them by the crf for 8% and 40 years:

$$\text{Annual cost, Plan D} = \$165,440(0.08386) = \$13,874$$

$$\text{Annual cost, Plan E} = \$190,630(0.08386) = \$15,986$$

Of course, these annual cost figures agree with the ones that were computed directly from the cash flow series in Example 6–3 (page 85).

Capitalized Cost. The calculation of the present worth of perpetual service may be illustrated by comparing Plans D and E, as follows:

Plan D

First cost	$ 50,000
PW of infinite series of renewals	
$\quad = (50,000 - \$10,000)(\text{sff}-8\%-20) \div 0.08$	
$\quad = \$40,000(0.02185) \div 0.08 = \$874 \div 0.08$	= 10,925
PW of perpetual annual disbursements	
$\quad = \$9,000 \div 0.08$	= 112,500
Total capitalized cost	$173,425

Plan E

First cost	$120,000
PW of infinite series of renewals	
$= (\$120{,}000 - \$20{,}000)(\text{sff-8\%-40}) \div 0.08$	
$= \$100{,}000(0.00386) \div 0.08$	= 4,825
PW of perpetual annual disbursements	
$= \$6{,}000 \div 0.08$	= 75,000
Total capitalized cost	$199,825

The calculation of the present worth of an infinite series of renewals starts with the conversion of the periodic renewal cost into an equivalent perpetual uniform annual series. Thus $40,000 at the end of any 20-year period is multiplied by the 20-year sinking factor to convert it to $874, a uniform annual figure throughout the 20-year period. Therefore, $40,000 at the end of every 20th year is equivalent to $874 a year forever. The present worth of this infinite series in Plan D is then $874 ÷ 0.08 = $10,925.

It will be noted that the figures for the present worths of perpetual service in Plans D and E are only slightly greater than the previous figures for the present worths of 40 years' service. The $26,400 advantage for Plan D in capitalized cost is not much more than the $25,190 advantage in present worth of 40 years' service. Considered from the viewpoint of present worth, the difference between 40 years and forever is small.

Capitalized costs are simply annual costs divided by the interest rate. The annual cost in Plan D was $13,874; the capitalized cost is $13,874 ÷ 0.08 = $173,425.

Annual Cost vs. Present Worth for Comparing Alternative Series of Disbursements. Historically, present worth methods have been advocated by a number of writers on engineering economy.[1] Capitalized costs were widely used for many years, particularly by civil engineers. The widespread use of capitalized costs probably had its origin in Wellington's classic work *The Economic Theory of Railway Location* (1887). This—in a day in which most engineers worked for railways during at least part of their careers—influenced the thinking of the entire engineering profession. Wellington—considering that many elements of the railway had perpetual life—would divide an expected saving by the interest rate to determine the justifiable increase in first cost to bring about that estimated saving.

[1] Goldman's *Financial Engineering* (New York: John Wiley & Sons, Inc., 1921) developed the subject of engineering economy through capitalized cost comparisons; the term coined for capitalized cost in this book was "vestance." Johannesson in his *Highway Economics* (New York: McGraw-Hill Book Co., Inc., 1931) based nearly all his comparisons on capitalized cost, assuming perpetual life for most highway improvements.

For most economy studies, the authors of this book prefer annual cost comparisons to present worth comparisons. The most important advantage is that, generally speaking, people seem to understand annual costs better than they understand present worths. A relatively minor advantage is that annual costs are usually somewhat easier to compute except in circumstances such as Example 7–1 where irregular series of disbursements are involved.

It already has been emphasized that, given the same interest rate and the same estimated series of disbursements, comparisons by annual cost lead to the same conclusions as comparisons by present worth. Nevertheless, certain serious errors in the basic data of the economy study seem to be more common when analysts use present worth methods.

Some Common Errors When Present Worth Comparisons Are Used. Three errors that the authors have often observed in present worth studies are as follows:

1. Perpetual lives are assumed, particularly in capitalized cost comparisons, even though the observed facts indicate that the lives of the proposed machines and structures are likely to be fairly short.

2. The dates when accounting charges are to be made are substituted for the dates of expected disbursements before the present worths are computed. As an example, assume a proposed structure with a first cost of $100,000 and an estimated life of 50 years with zero salvage value. If straight-line depreciation accounting (explained in Chapter 10) is used, the annual depreciation charge in the accounts will be $2,000 (i.e., $100,000 ÷ 50) for 50 years. An uncritical analyst might add this $2,000 a year to the expected disbursements during each year and then convert his annual total to present worth at zero date at, say, 5% interest. As the present worth of $2,000 a year for 50 years at 5% is $36,500, he has, in effect, converted $100,000 at zero date to $36,500 at zero date. This peculiar result comes from the use of two interest rates in a series of conversions, one forward through 50 years at 0%, the other backward through the same years at 5%. By such confused conversions using two interest rates, it is possible to appear to prove that three is equal to one—or to any other figure!

3. Interest rates used in present worth comparisons are frequently too low.

The pointing out of these common errors is an indictment of analysts using present worth methods rather than of the methods themselves. But the evidence obtained from examination of many economy studies is that many of the cost comparisons that are made by present worth methods do, in fact, lead to incorrect conclusions for the reasons that have been outlined.

What Is a "Conservative" Interest Rate To Use in a Present Worth Comparison? The purpose of the interest calculations in economy studies is to determine whether proposed investments are justified—whether it seems likely that they will be recovered with at least a stipulated minimum attractive rate of return. For reasons that are explained in Chapter 9, this rate often should be considerably higher than the bare cost of borrowed money.

If the question were asked, "How large an endowment fund is required to endow a scholarship of $1,000 a year?" it is obvious that the answer should be obtained by capitalizing $1,000 a year at an interest rate that can be obtained on securities involving a minimum risk of loss. This will be a low interest rate, perhaps 3% or 4%.

The present worth of the disbursements required for a given service may be described as the sum of money necessary to endow that service. This description of present worth sometimes leads analysts to the selection of an interest rate appropriate to an endowment fund; such a rate is viewed as a "conservative" one. Such analysts fail to recognize that the economy-study calculations are made to guide a decision between alternatives and that no actual endowment is contemplated.

The use in economy studies of a low interest rate appropriate to endowment funds has the effect of making alternatives requiring higher investments appear to be desirable even though they show the prospect of yielding a relatively small return. The interest rate used for present worth conversions in economy studies usually should be considerably higher than an endowment-type rate; it should be the rate of return required to justify an added investment considering all of the circumstances of the case.

An Estimate of the Value of an Income-Producing Property to a Present or Prospective Owner Implies a Present Worth Calculation. Many different kinds of property are acquired for the purpose of securing prospective future money receipts in excess of the future disbursements, if any, associated with the ownership of the property.

To determine the maximum amount that it is reasonable to pay for any such income-producing property, the following are required:

1. An estimate of the amounts and dates of prospective money receipts resulting from ownership of the property
2. An estimate of the amounts and dates of prospective money disbursements resulting from ownership of the property

3. A decision on the minimum attractive rate of return required to justify this investment in the light of its risk and in the light of returns available from other prospective investments
4. A calculation to determine the net present worth, that is, the excess of the present worth of the prospective receipts over the present worth of the prospective disbursements

If the purchase price of the income-producing property is greater than this computed net present worth, the estimates indicate that the property will fall short of earning its minimum attractive return. Hence if reliance is to be placed on these estimates, the purchase of the property is not attractive.

The same set of estimates and calculations is appropriate in judging the value of a property to its present owner. Generally speaking, a property is worth to its owner at least the net amount for which he can sell it (i.e., the amount to be received from the sale minus the disbursements incident to the sale). In other words, market value in the sense of the net price for which a property could actually be sold tends to place a *lower* limit on the value of a property to its owner. If the sole service of a property to its owner is to produce future net money receipts, an *upper* limit on the value of a property to its owner is generally placed by the excess of present worth of prospective receipts over prospective disbursements. If this present worth is less than the net price for which the property can be sold, it will ordinarily pay to sell the property.

Other factors entering into the estimate of the value of a property to its owner are discussed in later chapters. One important factor is the cost of replacement with an equally desirable substitute.

The remainder of this chapter gives examples of the calculation of net present worth for four different types of income-producing property, as follows:

1. A series of uniform annual payments for a limited number of years
2. A perpetual series of uniform annual payments
3. A typical corporation bond
4. A commercial rental property

The general subject of the present worth aspects of valuation is explored further by a number of problems and examples throughout the remainder of this book.

Valuation of Uniform Annual Series. It was shown in Plan III of Table 3–1 that the present worth of $1,358.68 a year for 10 years was $10,000 with interest at 6%. The influence of interest rate on value may be observed if we consider the question of how much an investor would be willing to pay for the prospect of these payments if he required a 7% return on his investment. Here $P = \$1,358.68$-(pwf–7%–10) = \$1,358.68(7.024) = \$9,543. If he were satisfied with a 5% return, he would pay \$1,358.68(pwf–5%–10) = \$1,358.68-(7.722) = \$10,492.

Valuation of Perpetual Annual Series. As has already been pointed out in Chapter 5, the present worth of a perpetual uniform annual series is the annual payment divided by the interest rate; this stretches the definition of present worth to mean the investment that will provide—as interest on it—a desired annual payment forever.

Whenever an investment is made where the termination of the income series at a definite time is not contemplated, valuation calculations are likely to be made on this basis. Thus, a stock paying an annual dividend of \$6 would be valued at \$120 on a 5% basis. The implications of such valuations should be recognized by those who make them; it is unlikely that the corporation will continue its existence forever—or that dividends will always be paid at exactly the present rate—or that a given investor's ownership of the stock will continue indefinitely. Consideration should be given to the question of whether or not the assumption of perpetuity is a fairly close approximation to what is anticipated, before using calculation methods that assume perpetuity.

This comment is also pertinent with respect to comparisons of economy on the basis of capitalized cost, such as are described in this chapter. This limitation particularly applies to the determination of the investment that may be justified by a prospective annual saving.

Valuation of a Bond. Most corporate bonds and many bonds issued by governmental units are promises to pay interest, usually semiannually, at a given rate, and to pay the principal of the bond at some definite future date. For example, a 3%, \$1,000 bond due 20 years hence calls for payments of \$15 every 6 months for 20 years plus a payment of \$1,000 at the end of this time. Assume this bond is first to be valued to yield 4% compounded semiannually and then valued to yield 3.6% compounded semiannually.

At an interest rate of 3% compounded semiannually, the present worth of these payments is obviously \$1,000. At any other interest rate, the value of the bond is the sum of the present worth of the uniform series of interest payments and the present worth of the ultimate principal payment. These present worths are of course calculated at the interest rate that the investor at the calculated value is to receive, not at the coupon rate on the bonds.

To find the present worth of the payments at 4% compounded semiannually, the 2% interest table should be used with the following result:

PW of 40 interest payments
$= \$15(\text{pwf-}2\%\text{-}40) = \$15(27.255)$ = \$410.30
PW of principal payment
$= \$1,000(\text{pwf'-}2\%\text{-}40) = \$1,000(0.4529) =$ 452.90
_____
Value of bond to yield 4%   = \$863.20

An alternative method of valuation is to note that at 4% the present worth of a 4%, 20-year, \$1,000 bond is obviously \$1,000. The 3% bond to be valued differs from this because it carries \$15 semiannual payments rather than \$20 payments. Its value to yield 4% will be the present worth of the payments on a 4% bond minus the present worth of the deficiency in its interest coupons below those of a 4% bond. This is

$$\$1,000 - (\$20 - \$15)(\text{pwf-}2\%\text{-}40) = \$1,000 - \$5(27.355) = \$863.20$$

To find the value of the bond to yield 3.6% compounded semiannually, it is necessary to make a solution by logarithms, using the present worth formulas. The results of such a calculation are as follows:

$$\text{PW of interest} = \$15 \left[\frac{(1.018)^{40} - 1}{0.018(1.018)^{40}} \right] = \$425.09$$

$$\text{PW of principal} = \frac{\$1,000}{(1.018)^{40}} \quad = \quad 489.89$$

Value of bond to yield 3.6%   = \$914.98

or

$$\$1,000 - (\$18 - \$15) \left[\frac{(1.018)^{40} - 1}{0.018(1.018)^{40}} \right] = \$1,000 - \$85.02 = \$914.98$$

There are published bond value tables which give the relation between price and yield to the investor for bonds with various coupon rates and years to maturity. Where such tables are available, calculations of the type just illustrated are unnecessary.

Approximate Calculation in Bond Valuation. Sometimes bond values are desired involving interest rates that are not given in available interest tables. A rough approximation to such values may be found by a linear interpolation between values obtained for the available interest rates on either side of the desired one. Thus to find the value of the 3% bond to yield 3.6%, it may first be valued at 3.5% (using the 1¾% interest table) and then at 4%, and the value at 3.6% then interpolated as follows:

Value of bond to yield 3.5% = \$928.50
Value of bond to yield 4%   =   863.20

Approximate value to yield 3.6% = $928.50 $- \dfrac{0.10}{0.50}$ ($928.50 − $863.20)

$$= \$914.40$$

This checks fairly well with the correct figure of $914.98.

It may also be noted that the difference between semiannual and annual compounding may be neglected without great error, if it is assumed that interest is paid only once a year and that the stipulated yield is based on annual compounding. With these assumptions the approximate value of the 3% bond to yield 4% is

PW of interest = $30(pwf–4%–20) = $30(13.590)   = $407.70
PW of principal = $1,000(pwf′–4%–20) = $1,000(0.4564) = 456.40

Value of bond to yield 4%   = $864.10

This checks closely with the correct method; it will be noted the errors in present worths of interest and principal are of opposite signs and thus tend to compensate.

EXAMPLE 7–2. VALUATION OF A COMMERCIAL RENTAL PROPERTY

Statement of Money Estimates. A commercial rental property is offered for sale for $58,000. This property consists of a two-story building in the business district of a small city. The building contains two stores on the first floor and a number of offices on the second floor.

A prospective purchaser estimates that if he buys this property he will hold it for about 10 years. He estimates the average annual receipts from rentals during this period to be $7,000, and the average annual disbursements for all purposes in connection with its ownership and operation (maintenance and repairs, janitor service, utilities, taxes, insurance, etc.) to be $2,700. He believes the property can be sold for a net $40,000 at the end of 10 years. He considers the minimum attractive rate of return on this type of investment to be 7%. On the basis of these estimates, what price for this property would just permit him to recover his investment with a 7% return before income taxes?

Calculation of Present Worths. The estimated annual excess of receipts over disbursements is $7,000 − $2,700 = $4,300. According to the estimates, the purchaser of this property is buying the prospect of net money receipts of $4,300 a year for 10 years plus a lump sum of $40,000 at the end of the 10th year. At 7% the present worth of this set of receipts is

PW of $4,300 a year = $4,300(pwf–7%–10) = $4,300(7.024) = $30,200
PW of $40,000, 10 years hence
    = $40,000(pwf′–7%–10) = $40,000(0.5083)   = 20,330

Value to yield 7%   = $50,530

If receipts and disbursements turn out as estimated, it is evident that a purchaser of this property for $58,000 will not realize a 7% return on his investment.

Compound Amount Comparisons in Economy Studies. At the start of this chapter it was stated that money time series might be compared by converting them to equivalent single payments at some specified date, and that the present was usually the most convenient date. With respect to economy studies regarding proposed investments, the "present" is usually the beginning of the period of time under consideration. An alternative possible date is the end of this period; this requires compound amount conversions rather than present worth conversions.

Although such compound amount comparisons are occasionally used in economy studies, the use of compound amount would seem to have no merit not possessed by present worth. On the other hand, small changes in the interest rate have a deceptively large effect on the differences in compound amount. Hence the chances of misinterpretation of a compound amount study would seem much greater than the chances of misinterpretation of a study based on present worth.

Summary. Valuation of prospective future series of net money receipts is a problem in present worth. In economy studies the comparison of estimated disbursements for alternative plans may be done by present worth conversions. If such comparisons are for a limited number of years of service, the present worth of the cost of the same number of years of service should be calculated for each alternative. When such comparisons are of the present worth of the cost of perpetual service, they are termed capitalized cost comparisons.

The interest rate used in conversions for economy studies should be the rate of return required to justify an investment; this applies to present worth conversions as well as to annual cost conversions. For various reasons, present worth comparisons in economy studies seem more difficult to interpret than annual cost comparisons. Except in certain special situations to which present worth comparisons seem particularly adapted, it is recommended that annual cost comparisons be preferred.

Problems

7–1. For a given pumping service for a regulated public utility, it is proposed to use either a 10-in. or a 12-in. pipe. The 10-in. pipe has a first cost of $4,500 and the annual pumping cost is estimated as $900. The 12-in. pipe has a first cost of $6,000 and the annual pumping cost is estimated as $550. The service will be required for 15 years; no salvage value is expected for either pipe at the end of this period. Annual property taxes are estimated as 2% of first cost and annual income taxes as 3% of first cost. Compare the present worths of the cost of 15 years' service, using an interest rate of 6%. (*Ans.* = $15,426 for 10-in.; $14,256 for 12-in.)

7–2. The following two alternatives are being considered for a governmental service. Compare the present worths of the cost of 24 years' service, using an interest rate of 5%.

	Structure Y	Structure Z
First cost	$4,500	$10,000
Estimated life	12 years	24 years
Estimated salvage value	none	$1,800
Annual disbursements	$1,000	$720

(*Ans.* = Structure Y, $20,805; Structure Z, $19,377.)

7–3. Two alternate plans are being considered in a growth situation for a regulated public utility. Compare the present worths of the costs of 20 years' service, using a minimum attractive return of 7% after income taxes.

Plan I requires an immediate investment of $30,000. The life of this plant is 20 years with a $3,000 salvage value at the end of the life. Annual maintenance cost is $2,000. Annual property taxes are 2.5% of first cost and annual income taxes are 4.5% of first cost.

Plan II requires an immediate investment of $20,000 which has a life of 20 years, a $2,000 salvage value at the end of the life, and annual maintenance cost of $1,600. Tax rates are the same as in Plan I. This will be supplemented by an additional investment of $12,000 10 years hence. This latter plant will have a life of 10 years, a $3,000 salvage value, annual maintenance cost of $1,200, property taxes of 2.5% of first cost, and income taxes of 5.0% of first cost. (*Ans.* = Plan I, $72,660; Plan II, $64,090.)

7–4. Two possible types of road surface are being considered with cost estimates per mile as follows:

	Type A	Type B
First cost	$8,000	$12,000
Resurfacing period	12 years	18 years
Resurfacing cost	$5,000	$5,000
Average annual upkeep cost	$400	$300

The periodic resurfacings will involve replacement of only the wearing surface and not of the base or subsurface. Compare these two types on the basis of the capitalized cost of perpetual service, using interest at 3½%. (*Ans.* = Type A, $29,210; Type B, $26,400.)

7–5. A promissory note is offered for sale on which the yearly payments are $587. There are 11 annual payments still due, the first one of these due one year from now. How much should an investor pay for this note in order to get 8% interest, compounded annually, before income taxes? To get 7%? To get 6%? (*Ans.* = 8%, $4,191; 7%, $4,402; 6%, $4,630.)

7–6. Interest on a 3½%, $1,000 bond due in 25 years is payable semiannually with the first payment 6 months hence. What will be the price of this bond to yield 5%, compounded semiannually? (*Ans.* = $787.30.)

7–7. An investor is considering the purchase of a rental property. The excess of receipts over disbursements is estimated as $4,000 a year for 10 years. It is estimated that the property can be sold for $25,000 at the end of 10 years. At what price for this property would the investor just recover his investment with a return of 8% before income taxes? (*Ans.* = $38,420.)

7–8. The PQR Manufacturing Co. has a contract that gives it the exclusive right to manufacture a certain patented article. By the terms of the contract the company pays the inventor $300 per year plus 4 cents for each article manufactured. The inventor is now offering his patent, which has 8 years yet to run, for sale to the company for $4,000. If the minimum attractive return on this investment is 8% before income taxes, what annual production of this article for the next 8 years must be expected to make it a good investment for the company to purchase the patent now rather than to continue with its contract with the inventor? (*Ans.* = 9,900 units.)

7–9. Estimates for two alternate plans in the design of certain industrial facilities are:

	Plan I	Plan II
First cost	$25,000	$50,000
Life	20 years	30 years
Salvage value	$5,000	none
Annual disbursements	$5,500	$2,800

Using a minimum attractive return of 10% before income taxes, compare the present worths of the net disbursements for 60 years with the two plans. Assume that the replacement facilities in both plans will have the same first costs, lives, salvage values, and annual disbursements as the initial facilities.

7–10. Compare Plan C and Plan D on the basis of the capitalized cost of perpetual service using interest at 5%. Plan C calls for an initial investment of $500,000, and expenditures of $20,000 a year for the first 20 years and $30,000 a year thereafter. It also calls for the expenditure of $200,000 at a date 20 years hence and every 20th year thereafter. Plan D calls for an initial investment of $800,000 followed by a single investment of $300,000 30 years hence. It also involves annual expenditures of $10,000.

7–11. A county is planning to build a 3-story office building. It is expected that some years later 3 more stories will be added to the building. Two alternate designs have been made, as follows:

Design A is a conventional design for a 3-story building of this type. The estimated first cost is $420,000.

Design B assumes the initial building to be the first 3 stories of a 6-story building. This increases the initial construction cost to $490,000.

With Design A, it is estimated that it will cost $500,000 to add the 3 more stories at a later date. With Design B, the addition of 3 more stories will cost only $400,000. The estimated total life of the building is 60 years with zero salvage value at the end of that time. It is estimated that maintenance costs will be $1,000 a year lower with Design B than with Design A throughout the entire 60 years. It is believed that other annual disbursements, including insurance, will be the same with the two designs. As this is a government project, there will be no property taxes or income taxes.

With interest at 3%, how soon must the additional stories be needed to justify the selection of Design B?

7–12. A full development of part of a certain water supply project is to be compared with a stepped program of development. The full development involves a first cost of $1,400,000 for properties that are believed to be permanent. Annual operation and upkeep costs are $120,000. The stepped program involves an investment of $800,000 now and $1,000,000 15 years hence; both investments are for properties believed to be permanent. Annual operation and upkeep will be $100,000 for the first 15 years and $150,000 thereafter. With interest at 5%, compare the capitalized costs of these alternatives.

7–13. Two plans are under consideration to provide certain public utility facilities. Each plan is designed to provide enough capacity during the next 18 years to take care of the expected growth of load during that period. Regardless of the plan chosen now, it is forecast that the facilities will be retired at the end of 18 years and replaced by a new plant of a different type.

Plan I requires an initial investment of $50,000. This will be followed by an investment of $25,000 at the end of 9 years. During the first 9 years, annual disbursements will be $11,000; during the final 9 years, they will be $18,000. There will be a $10,000 salvage value at the end of the 18th year.

Plan II requires an initial investment of $30,000. This will be followed by an investment of $30,000 at the end of 6 years and an investment of $20,000 at the end of 12 years. During the first 6 years annual disbursements will be $8,000; during the second 6 years they will be $16,000; during the final 6 years they will be $25,000. There will be no salvage value at the end of the 18th year.

With interest at 6%, compare the present worths of the net disbursements for the two plans.

7–14. Interest on a 2½%, $1,000, 20-year bond is payable semiannually with the first payment 6 months hence. What will be the price of this bond to yield 4%, compounded semiannually?

7–15. Interest on a 4¼%, $1,000 bond due in 16 years is payable semiannually with the first payment 6 months hence. Determine by calculation, using the interest tables, and by interpolation the approximate price of this bond to yield 3¼% compounded semiannually.

7–16. An investor is considering the purchase of a rental property. The excess of receipts over disbursements is estimated as $2,540 a year for 15 years. It is estimated that the property can be sold for $10,000 at the end of 15 years. At what price for this property would the investor just recover his investment with a 10% return before income taxes?

7–17. The owner of a patent has made a contract with a corporation that is given the exclusive right to use the patent. The corporation has agreed to pay him $1,000 a year at the end of each of the first 4 years during the period of developing a market for the invention, $5,000 at the end of each year for the next 8 years, and $2,000 at the end of each year for the final 5 years of the 17-year life of the patent. The owner of this patent is offering it for sale. At what price would the purchaser receive exactly a 7% return before income taxes?

7–18. Two schemes of federal subsidy of public works projects have been used in the United States. In PWA projects, outright grants were made to cities for a portion of the construction cost of approved projects, with the remainder of the cost to be repaid by the cities at interest over a period of years. For example, a grant of 30% might be made, with the remaining 70% to be paid at interest over a 20-year period. Another plan of subsidy has been to require the repayment of all the construction cost without any interest. This latter plan is suggested for a proposed college dormitory project. The government is asked to put up $1,000,000 for this project, with the college paying back this amount at $25,000 a year for 40 years.

Assume that money really costs the government 3½%. On this assumption, this plan really amounts to an outright subsidy of how many dollars?

7–19. The XYZ Tile Co. secures its tile clay from property owned by John Doe, adjacent to the tile plant. Some years ago the company made a royalty contract with Doe on which it pays royalties of 50 cents per ton for all clay removed from his property. This contract has 5 years to run. It is estimated that Doe's holdings will supply the company's needs of 20,000 tons a year for the next 15 years before the clay is exhausted. The company owns a large deposit of clay at some distance from the plant; in relation to the company's needs, the deposit may be viewed as practically inexhaustible. Costs of removing the clay would be substantially the same as from Doe's holdings; however, the cost of transporting the clay to the plant would be greatly increased. Doe is aware of this fact; it is believed that a new royalty contract (5 years hence) for the final 10 years would need to provide a royalty rate of $1 per ton. At this royalty rate, it will still be advantageous to use Doe's clay rather than the company's more distant holdings.

The president of the XYZ Tile Co. has just learned that Doe would consider an outright sale of his land to the company. By purchasing this land, the company would no longer have to pay royalty for the clay removed. The company's minimum attractive return is 10% before income taxes. What is the maximum amount it could afford to pay Doe for his land? Assume that at the end of 15 years the land can be sold for $10,000.

7–20. An advertisement of a periodical read by farmers started as follows: "At a prominent western university, the Professor of Agricultural Economics has figured that a definite price tag can be placed on farmers' grade A wives. It seems that farmers who said that their womenfolk cooperated extensively in the operation of their farms earned, on the average, $2,760 more than those who did not have such cooperation. And this sum represents an investment of $69,000 at 4%. At that rate we have no hesitancy in saying that our magazine reaches $179,400,000,000 worth of the nation's very best farm wives. These 2,600,000 women . . ."

Reproduce the calculation on which this $69,000 figure is evidently based. What unlikely event is implied by this "valuation" of a "grade A" farm wife?

7–21. The construction cost of a certain federal reclamation project is to be repaid without interest over a period of years. Assume that costs are $125 an acre for a certain farm of 80 acres, a total of $10,000 to be repaid. No payments at all are to be made for the first 5 years. Then $250 is to be paid at the end of each year for 40 years to pay off the $10,000 without interest.

It is evident that the omission of interest by the government is, in effect, a subsidy to the farmer. It has been suggested that in this case a measure of the subsidy is the difference between the $10,000 construction cost paid by the government and the present worth of the deferred annuity paid by the farmer. Accepting this suggestion and computing interest at $3\frac{1}{2}\%$, what appears to be the amount of the subsidy in this case?

7–22. Using an interest rate of 5%, compute the capitalized cost of perpetual service of the following stadium project. Initial investment is $2,000,000. The service period is assumed to be perpetual and certain elements of the investment (e.g., land, earth fill) are assumed to have perpetual life. Estimated future disbursements are as follows:

Annual maintenance, $20,000
Seat replacement, $500,000 every 20 years
Replacement of major structural elements, $800,000 every 40 years

7–23. What is the present worth of the cost of 18 years of service from a machine that has a first cost of $22,000, a life of 18 years, an estimated salvage value of $2,000 at the end of the life, and annual operation and maintenance costs of $5,000? Assume an interest rate of 12%.

7–24. What is the capitalized cost of perpetual service from a structure that has a first cost of $60,000, a life of 30 years, an estimated salvage value of $10,000, and annual operation and maintenance costs of $7,000? Use an interest rate of 5% and assume that replacement structures will have the same first costs, lives, salvage values, and annual operating costs as the original structure.

8

Calculating a Prospective Rate

of Return

Our examples in Chapters 6 and 7 started with the assumption of an interest rate or minimum attractive rate of return. Calculations were then made to provide a basis for judgment as to whether proposed investments would meet this standard.

Often it is appropriate to compute the prospective rate of return on an investment rather than merely to determine whether or not the investment meets a given standard of attractiveness. Usually this calculation is carried out to best advantage by a trial-and-error method. Two or more interest rates are assumed, present worths or equivalent annual costs are calculated, and the rate of return is found by interpolation.

Although economy studies necessarily deal with prospective investments, an example of the finding of the rate of return on a terminated investment may throw light on certain aspects of the subject that need to be understood. Our first example is of this type. It is followed by a number of examples dealing with prospective investments.

EXAMPLE 8–1. RATE OF RETURN ON A PAST INVESTMENT

Facts of the Case. This example relates to a completed 7-year period. Our assumed zero date is January of the first year when an investor purchased a residential rental property for $9,950. As the investor immediately spent $950 for various improvements to the property, his total initial outlay was $10,900. In late December at the end of the seventh year, the property was sold for a gross sales price of $22,000. From this was deducted a 5% broker's commission of $1,100, leaving a net receipt from the sale of $20,900. The second column of Table 8–1 shows the receipts that occurred during the period of ownership. The third column shows all disbursements (other than income taxes), including maintenance costs, property taxes, and insurance. The fourth column combines these figures to give the year-by-year net cash flow before income taxes. Two lines are devoted to the final year (year 7), one showing the receipts and disbursements in connection with rentals and the other showing receipts and disbursements in connection with the sale of the property.

TABLE 8–1

CASH FLOW FROM A TERMINATED INVESTMENT IN RENTAL PROPERTY

Year	Receipts	Disbursements	Net Cash Flow
0		−$10,900	−$10,900
1	+$1,500	−500	+1,000
2	+1,800	−550	+1,250
3	+1,800	−570	+1,230
4	+1,800	−450	+1,350
5	+1,800	−360	+1,440
6	+1,800	−430	+1,370
7	+1,700	−410	+1,290
7	+22,000	−1,100	+20,900
Totals	+$34,200	−$15,270	+$18,930

Calculation of Rate of Return. The rate of return is the interest rate at which the present worth of the net cash flow is zero. Here this is the interest rate at which the present worth of the net receipts that occurred in years 1 to 7 is just equal to the $10,900 disbursement that was made at zero date.

In the present worth calculations in Table 8–2, the end-of-year convention has been used. (It will be recalled that this convention has been used throughout

TABLE 8–2

PRESENT WORTH CALCULATIONS FOR TRIAL-AND-ERROR DETERMINATION OF RATE OF RETURN ON A TERMINATED INVESTMENT IN RENTAL PROPERTY

Year	Net Cash Flow	pwf′–15%	PW at 15%	pwf′–20%	PW at 20%
0	−$10,900	1.0000	−$10,900	1.0000	−$10,900
1	+1,000	0.8696	+870	0.8333	+833
2	+1,250	0.7561	+945	0.6944	+868
3	+1,230	0.6575	+809	0.5787	+712
4	+1,350	0.5718	+772	0.4823	+651
5	+1,440	0.4972	+716	0.4019	+579
6	+1,370	0.4323	+592	0.3349	+459
7	+22,190	0.3759	+8,341	0.2791	+6,193
Totals	+$18,930		+$ 2,145		−$ 605

Chapters 6 and 7.) The cash flow figures for each year have been multiplied by the respective present worth factors for interest rates of 15% and 20%. The sum of the present worths is +$2,145 at 15% and −$605 at 20%. The following linear interpolation between these values indicates that this investment yielded a return of a little less than 19% before income taxes.

$$\text{Rate of return} = 15\% + \frac{\$2,145}{\$2,750}\,(20\% - 15\%) = 18.9\%$$

EXAMPLE 8–2. RATE OF RETURN ON A PROSPECTIVE INVESTMENT IN A RENTAL MACHINE

Estimates Relative to a Proposed Investment. John Smith has received an inheritance of $12,000. A friend engaged in the business of rental of construction machinery suggests that Smith invest this $12,000 in a tractor of a certain type. The friend will serve as Smith's agent in the rental of this asset on a commission basis and will remit to Smith the net receipts from each year's rentals at the end of the year. He estimates that for rental purposes the machine will have a useful life of 8 years, with a 10% final salvage value. His estimates of year-by-year receipts from rentals and of disbursements for all purposes are shown in Table 8–3. Disbursements are chiefly for repairs and maintenance but also include storage, rental commissions, property taxes, and insurance.

TABLE 8–3

ESTIMATED CASH FLOW FROM PURCHASE AND OWNERSHIP
OF A RENTAL MACHINE

Year	Receipts	Disbursements	Net Cash Flow
0		−$12,000	−$12,000
1	+$4,200	−500	+3,700
2	+3,900	−900	+3,000
3	+3,600	−1,200	+2,400
4	+3,500	−1,400	+2,100
5	+3,100	−1,400	+1,700
6	+3,000	−1,500	+1,500
7	+2,800	−1,500	+1,300
8	+2,650	−1,500	+1,150
8*	+1,200		+1,200
Totals	+$27,950	−$21,900	+$ 6,050

* Receipt from salvage value.

Calculation of Rate of Return. Table 8–4 indicates that if the friend's estimates of cash flow turn out to be correct, Smith's return before income taxes will be 12%. In Table 8–4 and in subsequent tables of this type, the present worth factors are omitted. In Table 8–2 these factors were shown for each year and for each interest rate.

In deciding whether or not to undertake this particular investment, Smith should compare the prospective return of 12% before income taxes with the prospective return before income taxes obtainable from alternative investments that he believes are of comparable risk. (At this stage in our discussion, we are assuming that return *before* income taxes is a satisfactory criterion for comparing alternatives.) He must also decide whether he is willing to undertake the risks associated with this type of investment.

TABLE 8–4

PRESENT WORTH CALCULATIONS TO DETERMINE PROSPECTIVE RATE OF RETURN, EXAMPLE 8–2

Year	Estimated Cash Flow	Present Worth at 10%	Present Worth at 12%	Present Worth at 15%
0	−$12,000	−$12,000	−$12,000	−$12,000
1	+3,700	+3,364	+3,304	+3,218
2	+3,000	+2,479	+2,392	+2,268
3	+2,400	+1,803	+1,708	+1,578
4	+2,100	+1,434	+1,335	+1,201
5	+1,700	+1,056	+965	+845
6	+1,500	+847	+760	+648
7	+1,300	+667	+588	+489
8	+2,350	+1,096	+949	+768
Totals	+$ 6,050	+$ 746	+$ 2	−$ 985

Some Comments on Examples 8–1 and 8–2. Example 8–1 is an actual case with receipts and disbursements rounded off to multiples of $10. Example 8–2 makes use of assumed data with figures that were chosen to be useful in illustrating several different facets of engineering economy. From time to time throughout this book we shall refer to the data of these two examples to illustrate a number of matters. Such references occur later in this chapter and also in Chapter 10 (in presenting depreciation accounting) and in Chapter 15 (in illustrating the calculation of rate of return after income taxes).

It will be noted that the method used for finding rate of return is the same in both examples, even though Example 8–1 deals with a past investment and Example 8–2 deals with a proposed investment.

One aspect of both examples is that a single asset constitutes a separate business enterprise for which all receipts and disbursements are identifiable. It is rarely true of the capital goods of modern industry that specific receipts can be identified with individual machines or structures. For example, the receipts from the sale of a manufactured product cannot be identified with, say, the factory building, or with a specific machine used in a sequence of operations, or with a specific item of materials handling equipment. In this particular respect these two examples are not typical of the usual rate-of-return analysis for purposes of decision making in industry. Subsequent examples throughout this book will continue to emphasize the point brought out in earlier chapters that it is the prospective differences in cash flow between alternatives that need to be forecast and analyzed as a basis for choosing between the alternatives.

Different Names Applied to the Computation of Rate of Return by the Methods Illustrated in This Chapter. Rate of return calculations of the type illustrated in Examples 8–1 and 8–2 are as old as writings on the mathematics of finance. Since the early 1950's, however, the use of such calculations by industrial companies in the United States has greatly increased. Various names have been applied to this method of calculation. One name is the *discounted cash flow method;* another is the *Investor's Method.* Rate of return calculated in this way has been called the *Profitability Index* (sometimes abbreviated to PI) and the *interest rate of return.*[1]

Of the four phrases mentioned, "discounted cash flow" seems to be the one most widely used in industry. It describes the data required and the method of calculation illustrated in Tables 8–2 and 8–4. *Cash flow* refers to the fact that the required data must be given as the amounts and dates of receipts and disbursements. *Discounted* applies to the calculation of present worth; calculating the present worth of a future payment is often described as discounting the payment to the present date.

But many circumstances arise where the calculation of rate of return by correct methods is done without the use of present worth; often the use of equivalent uniform annual figures is equally satisfactory. For this reason the phrase "discounted cash flow" (which seems to imply the use of present worth) is not used throughout the remainder of this book. In general, the phrase "rate of return" used in this book means a rate computed by applying appropriate compound interest analysis to past or prospective cash flow.

There are a number of methods in common use in industry that give figures purporting to be rates of return. The most common of these methods are described in Chapter 10. Because these methods so often give figures that differ widely from one another as well as from the rate that would be computed by correct compound interest techniques, the rates computed by these methods are referred to in Chapter 10 as "so-called rates of return."

Calculations such as were illustrated in Tables 8–2 and 8–4 require a fair amount of arithmetic; it is necessary to multiply each

---

[1] The phrase "discounted cash flow" is associated with the name of Joel Dean, management consultant. The phrase "Investor's Method" (usually capitalized) is associated with the names of Horace G. Hill, Jr., and John C. Gregory, both of The Atlantic Refining Company. The phrase "Profitability Index" (also usually capitalized) is associated with the name of Ray I. Reul of the Chemicals Divisions of Food Machinery and Chemical Corporation. The phrase "interest rate of return" is associated with the names of J. B. Weaver and R. J. Reilly of Atlas Powder Company. References to specific writings by these gentlemen are made in Chapters 9, 10, and 19.

year's cash flow by the single payment present worth factor for two or more interest rates. Where uniform series of payments are involved, the arithmetic is somewhat simpler; capital recovery factors or series present worth factors may be used. In some problems calculations may be simplified by the use of gradient factors or gradient present worth factors.

The examples in the remainder of this chapter illustrate methods of computing rates of return where the facts are simpler than in Examples 8–1 and 8–2.

EXAMPLE 8–3. DETERMINING THE PROSPECTIVE RATE OF RETURN ON A BOND INVESTMENT

Facts of the Case. A certain 4%, $1,000 bond due 20 years hence may be bought for $950. Interest on this bond is payable every 6 months. It is desired to know the rate of return to be received by a purchaser of this bond if he holds it to maturity. In accordance with the usual practice in stating bond yields, this rate is to be expressed as a nominal interest rate assuming semiannual compounding.

Calculation of Bond Yield. Before the nominal interest rate per annum can be found, it first is necessary to find the rate per 6-month period. The n in the interest calculations will apply to the number of 6-month periods. The prospective cash flow is −$950 at zero date, +$20 for each of the 40 periods, and +$1,000 at the end of the 40th period. At 2% interest per 6-month period, the present worth of the receipts is obviously $1,000. The present worth of the cash flow at 2% is, therefore, −$950 + $1,000 = +$50.

To find the present worth at any other rate, the present worths of the $20 series and of the final $1,000 must be computed separately:

$$\text{PW at } 2\tfrac{1}{2}\% = -\$950 + \$20(\text{pwf-}2\tfrac{1}{2}\%\text{-}40) + \$1,000(\text{pwf}'\text{-}2\tfrac{1}{2}\%\text{-}40)$$
$$= -\$950 + \$20(25.103) + \$1,000(0.3724) = -\$75.50$$

By interpolation,

$$i = 2\% + \frac{\$50}{\$125.50}(2\tfrac{1}{2}\% - 2\%) = 2.2\%$$

The nominal rate per annum, compounded semiannually, is $2(2.2\%) = 4.4\%$.

Tables of bond yields may be obtained giving the rate of return on bonds as a function of the bond interest rate, price, and number of years to maturity. Such tables generally give the yield to the nearest hundredth of a per cent. If such a table were available, the foregoing type of approximate calculation would be unnecessary.

EXAMPLE 8–4. DETERMINING THE PROSPECTIVE RATE OF RETURN FROM A UNIFORM ANNUAL SERIES OF NET RECEIPTS

Data from Example 6–1. The final column of Table 6–1 (page 80) showed that the differences in cash flow between Plans B and A consisted of a disbursement of $15,000 at zero date and receipts of $3,100 a year for 10 years.

Calculation of Rate of Return. The present worth of the net cash flow may be computed for various interest rates using the series present worth factors for 10 years.

$$\text{PW at } 15\% = -\$15,000 + \$3,100(\text{pwf}-15\%-10)$$
$$= -\$15,000 + \$3,100(5.019) = +\$559$$

$$\text{PW at } 20\% = -\$15,000 + \$3,100(\text{pwf}-20\%-10)$$
$$= -\$15,000 + \$3,100(4.192) = -\$2,005$$

Interpolation indicates a return of about 16%.

In the special case where the prospective net receipts from an investment, P, constitute a uniform annual series, R, an alternate solution is to compute P/R or R/P and to interpolate between the appropriate factors in the interest tables (pwf or crf, as the case may be) to find the rate of return. In this instance, P/R = $15,000/$3,100 = 4.839. Interpolation between 5.019, the pwf for 15% and 10 years, and 4.192, the pwf for 20% and 10 years, indicates the rate of return to be about 16%.

A comment on the use of the capital recovery factor in this type of calculation is made later in this chapter in connection with the discussion of the errors introduced by linear interpolation.

EXAMPLE 8-5. PROSPECTIVE RATE OF RETURN IN EXAMPLE 6-2

Data from Example 6-2. Plan B in Example 6-2 had a first cost of $15,000, annual disbursements of $5,100, a 10-year life, and zero salvage value. Plan C had a first cost of $25,000, annual disbursements of $4,300, a 10-year life, and a $5,000 salvage value. The difference in cash flow between C and B (shown in the final column of Table 6-2, page 85) was −$10,000 initially, +$800 a year for 10 years, and +$5,000 at the end of 10 years.

Calculation of Rate of Return. A calculation of present worth of the net difference in cash flow using 3% and 4% interest indicates that the extra $10,000 investment in Plan C will be recovered with a return of about 3.8%.

$$\text{PW at } 3\% = -\$10,000 + \$800(\text{pwf}-3\%-10) + \$5,000(\text{pwf}'-3\%-10)$$
$$= -\$10,000 + \$800(8.530) + \$5,000(0.7441) = +\$544$$

$$\text{PW at } 4\% = -\$10,000 + \$800(\text{pwf}-4\%-10) + \$5,000(\text{pwf}'-4\%-10)$$
$$= -\$10,000 + \$800(8.111) + \$5,000(0.6756) = -\$133$$

In Example 8-4 and in the foregoing calculation, we dealt only with the differences in cash flow between the two alternatives that were being compared. Of course the same conclusion would be reached regarding rate of return on extra investment if the present worths of all disbursements were computed for both alternatives. The following tabulation shows that the two alternatives have the same present worth at about 3.8%.

	Plan B	Plan C	Difference (B − C)
PW at 3%	$58,503	$57,959	+$544
PW at 4%	$56,366	$56,499	−$133

The rate of return on extra investment must also be the interest rate at which the alternatives have the same equivalent uniform annual cost. The following tabulation shows that this occurs at about 3.8%.

	Plan B	Plan C	Difference (B − C)
Annual cost at 3%	$6.858	$6,795	+$63
Annual cost at 4%	$6,949	$6,966	−$17

It will be noted that although the elements of cash flow common to Plans B and C have been included in the foregoing present worth and annual cost figures, it is only the differences in cash flow that have any influence on the conclusion regarding rate of return. The common elements of cash flow will contribute equally to the present worths (or to the annual costs) of both alternatives regardless of the interest rate assumed.

A Possible Misinterpretation of Rate of Return When Three or More Alternatives Are Being Compared. It will be recalled that in Examples 6–1 and 6–2, Plan A was to continue the present method of carrying out a certain materials handling operation. Plan B required a $15,000 investment in equipment intended to reduce labor costs; Plan C required a $25,000 investment in such equipment. The minimum attractive rate of return before income taxes was 10%. Plan B was favored by the annual cost comparison in Chapter 6 and by the present worth comparison in Chapter 7.

Our calculations of rate of return should also lead us to the conclusion that Plan B is the best of the three plans. The $15,000 investment in Plan B promises a 16% return before income taxes as compared to the present method, Plan A. As 16% is higher than our 10% standard, B is superior to A. On the other hand, the additional $10,000 investment required for Plan C will yield only 3.8% before income taxes as compared to B. As 3.8% is less than our 10% standard, the $10,000 investment is not justified and Plan C should be rejected.

Once a particular minimum attractive rate of return is selected as the criterion for comparing alternatives, a correct analysis of rates of return will invariably lead to the same conclusion that will be obtained from a correct annual cost comparison or a correct present worth comparison.

However, incorrect conclusions are sometimes reached by computing rates of return from the wrong pairs of alternatives. For example, if Plan C is compared with Plan A, the prospective return on the $25,000 investment is 10.8% before income taxes. Someone favoring Plan C might argue that because it promises 10.8% as compared to the present method of doing things and because 10.8% exceeds the 10% minimum attractive return, the full $25,000 investment is justified.

If Plan B were not available, it is true that the 10.8% return would indicate the justification of Plan C. But because of the availability of B, C is unattractive. The $10,000 increment of investment in C over B will not pay its way, yielding only 3.8% before income taxes. In general, each separable increment of proposed investment ought to be considered separately in relation to its justification. Unsound proposals often appear to be justified because they are improperly combined with sound ones from which they may be separated.

The prospective return on Plan C as compared to Plan A has no useful meaning as a guide to decision making in this case. The viewpoint presented here is expanded in Chapter 12 which deals with comparisons of multiple alternatives.

Demonstrating the Validity of a Rate of Return Computed by Compound Interest Methods. In our introductory discussion of compound interest in Chapter 3, Table 3–1 illustrated four cases where an investment of $10,000 was recovered in 10 years with a return of 6%. The four cases involved four quite different series of year-end cash receipts by the investor of the original $10,000. The figures in Table 3–1 showed the year-by-year unrecovered balances in each case and demonstrated that the four cases were alike in providing complete capital recovery of the original $10,000 with interest at 6%.

Whenever correct compound interest methods are used to compute a rate of return, a similar tabulation may be used to show the validity of the computed rate. For example, it will be recalled that in Example 8–2 our discounted cash flow calculations indicated capital recovery with a return of 12%. Table 8–5 demonstrates the correctness of this 12% figure by year-by-year calculations of unrecovered balances assuming an interest rate of 12%. All but 59 cents of the initial $12,000 investment turns out to be recovered with 12% interest.

TABLE 8–5

A Demonstration That the Flow of Cash Receipts in Example 8–2
Leads to a Recovery of Capital with a 12% Return

End of Year	Year's Interest at 12% on Unrecovered Balance	Unrecovered Balance Plus Year's Interest	End-of-year Cash Receipts	End-of-year Unrecovered Balance Assuming 12% Interest
0				$12,000.00
1	$1,440.00	$13,440.00	$3,700	9,740.00
2	1,168.80	10,908.80	3,000	7,908.80
3	949.06	8,857.86	2,400	6,457.86
4	774.94	7,232.80	2,100	5,132.80
5	615.94	5,748.74	1,700	4,048.74
6	485.85	4,534.59	1,500	3,034.59
7	364.15	3,398.74	1,300	2,098.74
8	251.85	2,350.59	2,350	0.59

Where someone questions the meaning of a computed rate of return, a tabulation such as Table 8–5 will sometimes help to clarify matters. Where persons are suspicious of compound interest methods and prefer some other "approximate" method of computing rate of return (such as one of those discussed later in Chapter 10), such a tabulation may be useful in demonstrating the correctness of the compound interest method and the incorrectness of the other methods.

Rate of Return Calculations Assume the Termination of the Consequences of an Investment Decision. Example 8–1 viewed an investment in retrospect: that is, it considered a past investment in income-producing property from the date of acquisition of the property until the date of its final disposal. With full information about the money receipts and disbursements that were associated with this investment, it was possible to compute the rate of return obtained. Although Examples 8–2 to 8–5 dealt with prospective investments rather than with past ones, the viewpoint was really the same as in Example 8–1; the transactions were viewed from the date of prospective acquisition to the prospective date of termination of ownership.

Although an economy study regarding the desirability of a proposed investment may properly take the point of view of a terminated transaction, this viewpoint is hardly possible with regard to a past investment not yet terminated. For this reason, all judgments regarding profits or losses in business enterprises not yet terminated should really be thought of as preliminary estimates that in the long run may turn out to be either too favorable or not favorable enough. For example, the relatively high return of 18.9% in Example 8–1 was caused by the sale of the rental property for approximately twice its cost; if there had been accounts for this enterprise, a conventional analysis of the accounts at any time before the property was sold would have indicated a return of much less than 18.9%.

Conclusions regarding the profitability of investments not yet terminated are usually drawn from the accounts of business enterprises. Some aspects of the difference in viewpoint between an economy study to determine whether or not to make a proposed investment and the accounting procedures relating to the same investment once it is actually made are explored in Chapter 10.

Chapters 6 and 7 explained that when alternatives deal with aspects having different estimated lives, a convenient simple assumption is that replacement assets will repeat the cycle of disbursements and receipts that have been forecast for the initial asset. Example 8–6 illustrates the use of this assumption in computing rate of return.

EXAMPLE 8–6. RATE OF RETURN CALCULATIONS WHEN ALTERNATIVES HAVE DIFFERENT LIVES

Data from Example 6–3. This example determines the rate of return (before income taxes) on the extra investment in Plan E as compared to Plan D. Annual costs for these plans were compared in Example 6–3. Present worths and capitalized costs were compared in Chapter 7. The comparisons in Chapters 6 and 7 were based on a minimum attractive rate of return of 8% before income taxes.

It will be recalled that Plan D had a first cost of $50,000, a life of 20 years, a $10,000 salvage value, and annual disbursements of $9,000. Plan E had a first cost of $120,000, a life of 40 years, a $20,000 salvage value, and annual disbursements of $6,000.

Calculation of Rate of Return. To compute a prospective rate of return on the $70,000 extra investment in Plan E, it is necessary that the two plans apply to service for the same number of years. Assume that the disbursements for Plan E forecast for the first 20 years will be repeated in the second 20 years as shown in the cash flow tabulation, Table 6–3 (page 87).

One way to compute the rate of return on extra investment is to compute the present worth of 40 years' service assuming different interest rates. Interpolation between the following differences in present worth shows that the two plans have the same present worth at about 4.8%.

	Plan D	Plan E	Difference (D − E)
PW at 4%........	$244,310	$234,592	+$9,718
PW at 5%........	$218,087	$220,114	−$2,027

The same 4.8% return is found by interpolating between the differences in equivalent uniform annual costs using different interest rates.

	Plan D	Plan E	Difference (D − E)
Annual cost at 4%......	$12,343	$11,852	+$491
Annual cost at 5%......	$12,710	$12,828	−$118

Still another method, not illustrated here, would be to compute the capitalized costs of perpetual service using interest rates of 4% and 5% and to interpolate between the differences.

Although any of the foregoing methods of solution will give the correct answer, the point that 4.8% is really the prospective return on *extra* investment may be somewhat clearer if the problem is approached using only the differences in cash flow between the two plans. These differences were tabulated in the final column of Table 6–3 (page 87). Plan E requires an extra disbursement of $70,000 at zero date, offset by reduced disbursements of $3,000 a year for 40 years and $40,000 at the end of the 20th year and by an increased receipt of $10,000 from the larger salvage value at the end of the 40th year. Present worths of the differences in cash flow are as follows:

$$PW \text{ at } 4\% = -\$70,000 + \$3,000(\text{pwf–4\%–40}) + \$40,000(\text{pwf}'–4\%–20)$$
$$+\$10,000(\text{pwf}'–4\%–40)$$
$$= -\$70,000 + \$3,000(19.793) + \$40,000(0.4564) + \$10,000(0.2083)$$
$$= +\$9,718$$

PW at 5% = −$70,000 + $3,000(17.159) + $40,000(0.3769)
$$+ \$10,000(0.1420)$$
$$= -\$2,027$$

Again interpolation gives us the 4.8% figure. If a year-by-year calculation should be made similar to Table 8–5, it would show that if a person invested $70,000 and as a result of this investment received $3,000 a year for 40 years plus single payments of $40,000 and $10,000 at the end of 20 and 40 years respectively, he would recover his $70,000 with interest at approximately 4.8%.

Guessing the Rate of Return Before a Trial-and-Error Calculation.

In computing unknown rates of return by compound interest methods, it usually is necessary to compute present worths (or equivalent uniform annual costs) at two or more interest rates. The time needed for calculation will be minimized if the first interest rate tried is fairly close to the correct rate. Frequently a simple inspection of the cash flow series will tell whether to start by guessing a fairly low rate or a fairly high one.

Where the cash flow series is irregular, it sometimes saves time to make a preliminary calculation before deciding on the first guessed rate. In such a calculation the cash flow series being analyzed may be changed in a way that makes it possible to find the interest rate quickly with the help of interest tables. The following paragraphs illustrate how such preliminary calculations might have been made for the cash flow series of Examples 8–1, 8–2, and 8–6.

In Example 8–1 most of the positive net cash flow is concentrated in the 7th or final year. A first guess might assume the entire amount, +$29,830, in the 7th year. In effect, the cash flow series is changed so that a P of $10,900 leads to an S of $29,830 at the end of 7 years. The corresponding single payment present worth factor is then $P \div S = \$10,900 \div \$29,830 = 0.365$. For $n = 7$, pwf′–15% is 0.376 and pwf′–20% is 0.279. If all the net positive cash flow had actually been concentrated in the 7th year, it is evident that the return would have been slightly over 15%. Because some of the net positive cash flow occurred in years 1 to 6, the actual return must be higher than this figure. Good tactics in this case would be to make the first trial at 20%; the second trial could then be at either 15% or 25%, depending on the result of the first trial.

In Example 8–2 the net positive cash flow is not concentrated at the end of the period; it is well distributed throughout the 8 years. Substitute a cash flow series with the same net positive cash flow spread uniformly over the 8 years. In such a series, R is $18,050 \div 8 = \$2,256$. The corresponding series present worth factor is then $P \div R = \$12,000 \div \$2,256 = 5.32$. For $n = 8$, pwf–10% is 5.33 and pwf–12% is 4.97. With uniform cash flow the return would have been about 10%. Because there is more positive cash flow in the early years than in the later years, the return must be more than 10%. Good tactics in this case would be to make the first trial at 12%; the second trial could then be at either 10% or 15%, depending on the result of the first trial.

In Example 8–6, let us consider only the series of differences in cash flow between Plans D and E (the series shown in the final column of Table 6–3, page 87). In this series the average net positive cash flow throughout years 1 to 40 is $170,000 ÷ 40 = $4,250. If the cash flow had been uniform, $P \div R$ would have been $70,000 ÷ $4,250 = 16.47. For $n = 40$, pwf–5% is 17.16 and pwf–6% is 15.05. With uniform cash flow the return would have been about 5.3%. Because the net positive cash flow is less than $4,250 a year for the early years, a reasonable guess is that the return is less than 5.3%. Good tactics would be to make the first trial at 5%; the second trial could then be at 4% or 6%, depending on the result of the first trial.

Minor Errors Introduced by Linear Interpolation in Computing Rates of Return. Suppose that in Example 8–2 we had computed the present worth of net cash flow only at 10% and 15%. The respective present worths at these rates, as shown in Table 8–4, are +$746 and −$985. A linear interpolation between these figures is as follows:

$$\text{Estimated rate of return} = 10\% + \frac{746}{1,731}(15\% - 10\%) = 12.2\%$$

We already know from Example 8–2 that the return is 12%. It is evident that the foregoing interpolated value is a little too high. It is obvious that all such relationships between interest rate and present worth must be curvilinear. Where present worths have been computed for interest rates separated by 1% (such as the 3% and 4% rates in Example 8–5), the possible error from linear interpolation is relatively small. This error naturally can be larger where present worths are computed for rates separated by 5% (such as the 15% and 20% rates in Example 8–1). The possible error from linear interpolation is greatest when the rate of return is midway between the two interest rates used in the calculation.

Some analysts use graphical methods in finding unknown rates of return. In order to show the curvature of the present worth curve, graphical methods usually require calculation of present worths assuming three or more interest rates.

In this book the practice is to use linear interpolation and to state the interpolated rates of return to the nearest tenth of a per cent. Advantages of linear interpolation are that the calculation can be made quickly by slide rule and that present worths need be calculated at only two interest rates. Analysts should recognize that linear interpolation sometimes causes an error in the rate of return of one or two tenths of a per cent.

In general, the calculations of rates of return in economy studies are made to influence decisions among alternatives. The errors introduced by a linear interpolation in any compound interest method are usually so small as to have no appreciable influence on the decision making.

The errors, if any, introduced by linear interpolation, using present worth methods usually tend to give computed rates of return a little above the true rate. In contrast, the errors, if any, introduced by linear interpolation in annual cost methods usually tend to give computed rates of return slightly below the true rate. This point is illustrated by the following simple example. Consider a $10,000 investment that is expected to result in an end-of-year net positive cash flow of $1,259 a year for 12 years. P is $10,000; R is $1,259. Therefore the series present worth factor is $P \div R = 7.943$, and the capital recovery factor is $R \div P = 0.12590$. It can be seen from the 7% table that the return is exactly 7%. But assume that no 7% table is available and that it is necessary to interpolate between figures from 6% and 8% tables. In these tables the series present worth factors are 8.384 and 7.536 respectively; a linear interpolation to hundredths of a per cent indicates a return of 7.04%. The capital recovery factors are 0.11928 and 0.13270 respectively; a linear interpolation indicates a return of 6.99%. However, if interpolated values had been stated only to the nearest tenth of a per cent, both methods would have given 7.0%, the correct figure.

Use of Interest Tables Based on Continuous Compounding in Computing Unknown Rates of Return. The end-of-year convention in economy studies was explained in Chapter 6. This convention has been employed in the calculations of rates of return in the present chapter and is used in such calculations throughout the main body of this book.

In some economy studies in industry, a different convention is used; it is assumed that all prospective receipts and disbursements during each year will occur uniformly throughout that year. To use this alternate convention, it is necessary to assume continuous compounding of interest (explained in Chapter 4) and to have interest tables based on continuous compounding and on the uniform flow of funds throughout each year.

Tables E–25 and E–26 (in Appendix E) are such tables. Their use in connection with rate of return calculations is explained in Appendix B. This appendix also discusses the circumstances under which the uniform-flow convention may be preferable to the end-of-year convention.

Certain Cases in Which Two or More Solutions Are Possible in Computing Rates of Return. The calculation of rate of return may be expressed by an algebraic equation in which the interest rate is the unknown. Certain of these equations have two or more roots. This topic is discussed in Appendix C.

Although persons responsible for economy studies should be aware of the circumstances under which two or more different rates of return may be computed from the same cash flow, such circumstances are rarely a source of difficulty in actual studies.

Rate of Return from a Combination of Two Separable Proposed Investments That Have Different Prospective Rates of Return. A certain mining property is for sale for $1,500,000. The engineer for the prospective purchaser estimates the remaining life of the mine as 8 years. For each of these years he estimates that the excess of receipts over disbursements will be $391,000. He desires to compute the prospective rate of return.

In mining enterprises there is a traditional method of determining rate of return known as Hoskold's method. In this method it is assumed that uniform annual deposits will be made into a conservatively invested sinking fund that will earn interest at a relatively low rate. The annual deposits are to be just sufficient to replace the original investment at the end of the life of the property. The rate of return is computed by dividing the investment into the annual amount remaining after setting aside the sinking fund deposit.

To illustrate Hoskold's method, assume 4% interest on the sinking fund. The annual deposit in the fund to recover $1,500,000 at the end of 8 years is $1,500,000(sff–4%–8) = $1,500,000(0.10853) = $162,800. The annual cash remaining for the owners of the property after they have made the sinking fund deposit will be $391,000 − $162,800 = $228,200. As $228,200 ÷ $1,500,000 = 0.152, this project is viewed as one promising a 15.2% return.

If the same proposal is analyzed by correct compound interest methods, the computed rate of return is 20%; $391,000(pwf–20%–8) = $391,000(3.837) = $1,500,000. The difference between the viewpoints underlying these 15.2% and 20.0% figures deserves some comment here, particularly because the viewpoint leading to the 15.2% figure is by no means restricted to the mineral industries.

If the purchaser of the mining property actually makes the two investments contemplated in the 15.2% calculation and if receipts and disbursements turn out as forecast, it is true that his combined return will be 15.2%. From the combination of the two investments he will have a cash flow of −$1,500,000 at zero date, +$228,200 a year for 8 years, and +$1,500,000 at the end of the 8th year.

The important point to recognize here is that this 15.2% return is the result of *two* separate investments, one yielding 20% and the other yielding only 4%. Presumably the decision to make the investment with the 20% yield does not require that there also be a decision to make the 4% investment. If not, the 4% investment has no relevance in making the decision about the proposed investment with the 20% yield. It is the 20% figure, not the 15.2% one, that should be used as the index of attractiveness of the proposed investment in the mining property.

This Hoskold-type viewpoint on computing rate of return is rarely, if ever, appropriate as a basis for decision making on proposed investments. It seems particularly indefensible in the common case where it is used when no actual sinking fund is contemplated. Further comment on this topic is made in Appendix A and Appendix C.

Determining the True Cost of Borrowed Money. In finding the true interest rate paid by a corporation that borrows money by the sale of bonds, the calculations are similar to those indicated for computing rate of return on a bond investment. However, it is necessary to recognize that borrowing causes the corporation to make certain disbursements that are not receipts to the bond investor.

For instance, a $10,000,000 bond issue of 4.5%, 20-year bonds that was sold by investment bankers to the ultimate investor at 95 (i.e., $950 per $1,000 bond) might have been sold by the issuing corporation to an investment banking syndicate at 91½. Thus the corporation would receive $9,150,000 for its promise to pay $450,000 a year for 20 years and $10,000,000 at the end of that time. These payments would repay the amount received with interest at about 5.2%.

If the initial expenses to the corporation in connection with the bond issue were $200,000 (for such items as engraving bonds, preparing a registration statement for the Securities and Exchange Commission, accounting and legal expenses in connection with the issue), and if the annual disbursements involved in fees for registrar and trustee, costs of making interest payments, and the like were $30,000, the true cost of this borrowed money would be even greater. The corporation is really receiving a net sum of $8,950,000 now in exchange for an obligation to pay $480,000 a year for 20 years and $10,000,000 20 years hence. Present worth calculations and interpolation indicate that the true cost of this borrowed money is about 5.7%.

Thus a given loan may appear to have different interest rates, depending on the point of view. In this illustration the coupon rate on the bonds was 4.5%; the yield to the bond investors was 4.9%; the bonds were sold by the corporation to the investment bankers at a price giving a yield of 5.2%; considering the cost incidental to the borrowing of money, the actual cost of money to the corporation was 5.7%.

The foregoing analysis disregards income tax considerations. The usual result of income taxation in the United States is—in effect— to reduce the cost of borrowed money to private borrowers below a figure obtained from the foregoing type of calculation. Certain aspects of the relationship between income taxes and borrowing are discussed in Chapters 15 and 17.

Interest Rates Are Not Always What They Seem. There are many situations in which a superficial examination of the facts may lead to an underestimate of the interest rate being paid by a borrower. One such situation has just been described. Another was described in Chapter 5 in which a "Seven Per Cent Plan" turned out to involve an interest rate of nearly 14% per annum.

Another such situation exists whenever, in a purchase of a property "on terms," there is a difference between the selling price to a cash buyer and one to a buyer who agrees to pay the purchase price in periodic installments with interest.

For instance, a residential property is for sale for $12,000 under the following arrangements: $2,000 cash and the balance of $10,000 to be repaid with interest at 5½% in uniform installments for 15 years. Investigation discloses that a buyer on these terms must also pay $300 immediately for appraisal fee, title insurance, and similar charges. It also appears that the same property can be purchased for $10,500 cash.

For the sake of simplicity in our calculations, let us assume uniform *annual* payments rather than monthly payments as would customarily be required. The uniform payment, R, to repay a P of $10,000, with $i = 0.055$ and $n = 15$, is $10,000(0.09963) = $996.

It is evident that a buyer for cash will pay $10,500 now and thus conclude the transaction. A buyer on borrowed money will pay out $2,300 now and $996 a year for 15 years. This $996 a year is clearly an alternative to an $8,200 immediate cash payment; if the buyer had the $8,200 he could substitute it for the promise to pay $996 a year for 15 years. To find the real cost of borrowed money to him, it is necessary to find the interest rate at which his annual payments for 15 years would repay $8,200. As $R/P = \$996/\$8,200 = 0.1215$, interpolation between the capital recovery factors for 8% and 10% shows this interest rate to be approximately 8.6%.

The difference between the apparent $5\frac{1}{2}\%$ interest and the actual 8.6% interest paid by the buyer on credit was concealed in the difference between the cash price and credit price, and in the initial charges incident to the loan.

Another Meaning for "Rate of Return on Investment." Throughout this book, the phrase "rate of return on investment" is used in the meaning illustrated in this chapter, as the rate of "interest" at which an investment is repaid by revenues or savings. However, it should be pointed out that another meaning is sometimes given to this phrase. In this other use, "rate of return" is taken to mean the excess of the return over the current interest rate on borrowed capital, or the excess of the return over the going interest rate on conservative investments. A return described in this book as 9% would be described as a 3% return in a case where the going rate of interest was assumed to be 6%.

This other meaning for "rate of return" corresponds somewhat to the economic theorist's concept of "profit," just as the meaning adopted in this book corresponds more closely to the accountant's concept of profit. Either meaning is a possible one, but it is obvious that both cannot be used without confusion. The meaning used here has been chosen because it seems better adapted to practical business situations. Thus, wherever "rate of return" is used throughout these pages, it means a figure to be compared with the interest paid on borrowed capital or obtainable on investments elsewhere, rather than a figure in excess of such interest.

Summary. A comparison between alternatives involving money payments and receipts of different amounts at different dates may be expressed by an interest rate, the rate that makes the two alternatives equivalent. When one alternative involves a higher present investment and higher future net receipts (possibly as a result of lower future disbursements), this interest rate may be called the prospective rate of return on the extra investment. Its calculation provides one of the several methods of determining in an economy study whether a proposed investment will be recovered with a return commensurate with the risk—in other words, one of the methods of considering the time value of money in economy studies.

The actual rate of return realized by an investor from an investment cannot be determined until his association with the investment has terminated; it may differ substantially from the apparent rate of return at some intermediate period. The viewpoint of an engineering economy study for a proposed investment, involving, as it does, estimates for the full expected economic life of a machine or structure, implies calculations of rate of return of the same type as would be required to judge the actual return realized from terminated investments.

In a loan transaction the true cost of money to the borrower, which should be obtained by viewing the transaction as the difference between the net present cash provided by the borrowing and the future money outlays that the borrowing necessitates, will often be much greater than the apparent or contract rate of interest.

Problems

General Notes Regarding Problems for Chapter 8. Unless otherwise stated, the end-of-year convention is to be assumed for receipts and disbursements occurring during a year. All problems are to be interpreted as asking for rates of return *before* income taxes. Where alternative assets have different lives, it is to be assumed that replacement assets will have the same first costs, lives, salvage values, and annual disbursements as the assets they replace. Answers to Problems 8–1 to 8–12 are approximate, determined by interpolation to the nearest tenth of a per cent.

8–1. An unimproved city lot was purchased for $1,700 in January, 1948. Taxes on it were paid as follows:

1948.......$20	1952.......$30	1956.......$40
1949........ 20	1953........ 30	1957........ 40
1950........ 20	1954........ 30	1958........ 50
1951........ 20	1955........ 40	1959........ 50

At the end of 1959 the lot was sold for $3,500, less a 5% commission to the real estate broker. What rate of return was obtained on this investment? (*Ans.* = 4.4%.)

8–2. The purchase of an unimproved residential lot in a city is under consideration as a speculation. The purchase price of the lot is $2,000. It is believed that if this lot is held for 8 years it can be sold for $3,200. From this must be deducted a 5% sales commission of $160 and a $40 payment for title insurance, leaving a prospective net receipt of $3,000 on the date of the sale. Throughout the 8 years there will be no receipts from the ownership of the lot. Annual disbursements for property taxes are estimated to be $60 throughout the period of ownership. What is the prospective rate of return on the investment? (*Ans.* = 2.7%.)

8–3. A project has a first cost of $120,000 and an estimated salvage value after 25 years of $20,000. Estimated average annual receipts are $25,900; estimated average annual disbursements are $15,060. Assuming that annual receipts and disbursements will be uniform, compute the prospective rate of return. (*Ans.* = 8.0%.)

8–4. A promissory note calling for payments of $1,100 at the end of each year for the next 13 years is offered for sale for $10,400. What is the prospective rate of return? (*Ans.* = 4.9%.)

8–5. Project Y involves a present investment of $50,000. Estimated annual receipts for 20 years are $20,000; estimated annual disbursements are $12,500. An alternative is Project Z that involves a present investment of $75,000, annual receipts for 20 years of $28,000, and annual disbursements of $18,000. Assuming that there will be no value remaining in either project at the end of 20 years, what is the prospective rate of return on the investment in each project? What is the prospective rate of return on the extra investment required by Project Z? (*Ans.* = Y, 14.0%; Z, 11.9%; extra investment, 7.8%.)

8–6. Interest on a 4½%, $1,000 bond due in 15 years is payable semiannually with the first payment 6 months hence. The bond is for sale for $850. If a buyer at this price holds the bond till maturity, find the nominal rate of interest compounded semiannually that he will receive. (*Ans.* = 6.0%.)

8–7. In Problem 6–1 (page 92), what is the prospective rate of return on the extra investment required for Pump Z? (*Ans.* = 17.9%.)

8–8. In Problem 6–5 (page 93), what is the prospective rate of return on the extra investment required for the cast iron pipe? (*Ans.* = 5.7%.)

8–9. In Problem 7–11 (page 111), assume that the extra 3 stories will be required in 15 years. What is the rate of return on the extra investment of $70,000 required for Design B? (*Ans.* = 2.5%.)

8–10. A subdivider offers lots for sale at $2,500, $500 to be paid down and $500 to be paid at the end of each year for the next 4 years with "no interest" to be charged. In discussing a possible purchase, you find that you can get the same lot for $2,250 cash. You also find that on a time purchase there will be a service charge of $50 at the date of the purchase to cover legal and handling expenses and the like. What rate of interest will actually be paid if the lot is purchased on this time plan? (*Ans.* = 6.8%.)

8–11. A corporation receives $8,750,000 as a result of an issue of $10,000,000 of 4%, 30-year bonds. If annual expenditures for trustee's and registrar's fees and clerical and other expense in connection with interest payments amount to $25,000, what is the interest rate that expresses the true cost of this borrowed money to the corporation? Assume interest payable annually. (*Ans.* = 5.1%.)

8–12. It is proposed to purchase a machine to be used for rental purposes. The first cost is $20,000. It is estimated that in the first year of ownership receipts will exceed disbursements by $5,000. Considering declining rental receipts with age and increased upkeep costs, it is believed that this figure will decline by $300 each year and will be $4,700 in the second year, $4,400 in the third, and so on. It is estimated that the machine will be retired after 15 years with a $2,000 salvage value. What is the prospective rate of return? (*Ans.* = 17.1%.)

8–13. The first cost of a piece of business property containing stores and offices is $90,000. A prospective investor estimates that annual receipts from rentals will be $11,800 and that annual disbursements will be $4,700. He also estimates that the property will be salable for a net $60,000 at the end of 20 years. What is the prospective rate of return?

8–14. An investor purchased a piece of vacant property in 1944 for $5,300. He paid taxes of $70 a year for 15 years and finally sold the property in 1959 for $9,200. What was his rate of return?

8–15. An investor purchased 100 shares of stock in the PQR Corporation for $3,500. He received no dividends for the first 2 years, $2 a share dividends each year for the next 4 years, and $4 a share dividends each year for the next 3 years. After holding the stock for these 9 years, he sold it for $7,500. What was his rate of return?

8–16. A promissory note calling for payments of $1,810 a year for the next 13 years is offered for sale for $15,000. What is the prospective rate of return?

8–17. Two pumps are being considered for a certain service of 25 years. The Toltec pump has a first cost of $3,000 and an estimated annual cost of $2,200 for electric energy used for pumping purposes. The Mandan pump has a first cost of $2,550. Because it is less efficient, its annual costs for pumping energy will be $60 higher than those of the Toltec pump. It is anticipated that there will be no other cost differences and no salvage values. What is the prospective rate of return on the extra investment required to purchase the Toltec pump?

8–18. Plan T involves a first cost of $25,000, a life of 15 years, zero salvage value, and annual disbursements of $6,000. Plan V involves a first cost of $45,000, a life of 30 years, a salvage value of $10,000, and annual disbursements of $4,500. Find the rate of return on the extra investment required by Plan V.

8–19. A corporation sells an issue of $5,000,000 of 3½%, 20-year bonds to an investment banking concern for $4,700,000. The corporation's initial disbursements for fees of lawyers, accountants, trustee, and other expenses in connection with the bond issue are $200,000. Each year the disbursements for fees to the trustee and registrar of the bonds and the clerical and other expenses in connection with interest payments are $35,000. What is the actual cost of this borrowed money expressed as an interest rate? To simplify calculations, assume that interest is payable annually.

8–20. A home is offered for sale for $20,000, the purchaser to make a $3,500 down payment and to pay the balance in uniform end-of-year payments for 18 years with interest at 5½%. Or the property may be purchased for cash for $18,200. A prospective purchaser is undecided whether to buy this home on the installment plan or to withdraw cash from another investment in order to take advantage of the cash price. It is evident to him that because the cash price is lower than the installment price, he will, in effect, be paying more than the apparent 5½% interest for his loan. Compute for him the true cost of this borrowed money expressed as an interest rate.

8–21. The subscription rates to *The Saturday Evening Post* are $6 for 1 year, $10 for 2 years, $14 for 3 years, and $18 for 4 years, payable in advance in all cases. Consider a person who expects to subscribe for the next 12 years. Conceivably he might take 12 subscriptions for 1 year each, 6 for 2 years each, 4 for 3 years each, or 3 for 4 years each. At what interest rate do the 1-year and 2-year subscription plans have equal present worths? One and 3 years? One and 4 years? Two and 3 years? Two and 4 years? Three and 4 years? Discuss the significance of these six interest rates you have computed as a guide to a decision on the length of the subscription period.

8–22. A magazine offers three types of subscription, payable in advance, as follows:

1 year	$ 4.50
2 year	7.50
Life	50.00

(a) In comparing the economy of a 1-year subscription with that of a 2-year subscription, what is the rate of return on the extra investment in the 2-year subscription?

(b) A subscriber to this magazine is convinced that he wants to subscribe to it for the rest of his life. He desires to compare the economy of a life subscription with that of continuing to renew a 2-year subscription. According to a standard mortality table his remaining life expectancy is 30 years. If he takes the life subscription and lives exactly 30 years more, what will be his rate of return on his extra investment in the life subscription?

8–23. A 15-year loan from Sweden to U.S.S.R. provided for no interest to be paid during the first 3 years and for 3% interest to be paid from the 4th to the 15th year. Assume $100,000,000 to be borrowed on a basis such as this, with the borrower agreeing to pay $3,000,000 interest at the end of each year from the 4th to the 15th, both inclusive, and to pay the principal of $100,000,000 in a lump sum at the end of the 15th year. What is the true interest rate paid by such a borrower? Determine this as closely as you can by the use of your interest tables.

8–24. Project X requires a present investment of $250,000. Estimated annual receipts for 25 years are $50,000; estimated annual disbursements are $20,000. An alternative is Project Y, which involves a present investment of $350,000. Estimated annual receipts for 25 years are $70,000; estimated annual disbursements are $30,000. Each project is estimated to have a $50,000 salvage value at the end of 25 years. The minimum attractive rate of return is 10%. Make the necessary calculations to determine whether to recommend Project X, Project Y, or neither. Make a specific recommendation and explain why you made it.

8–25. An investor purchased a piece of unimproved city property for $7,000 in 1944. He paid taxes of $150 a year on this for 10 years. Then in 1954 he sold a part of this property for $5,000. He paid taxes of $100 a year on the remainder for 5 more years and in 1959 sold it for $15,000. Using your interest tables, make the necessary calculations to find out as accurately as possible the rate of return that he made on this investment. For the sake of simplicity in your calculations, assume that the transactions occurred on January 1, 1944, 1954, and 1959, respectively, and assume the taxes were end-of-year payments.

8–26. An investor bought 10 shares of C, B, & A Co. stock for $10,000. He held this stock for 15 years. For the first 4 years he received annual dividends of $500. For the next 3 years he received annual dividends of $400. For the final 8 years he received annual dividends of $300. At the end of the 15th year, he sold his stock for $7,000. What rate of return did he make on his investment?

8–27. It is proposed to purchase a machine to be used for rental purposes. The first cost is $50,000. It is estimated that in the first year of ownership, receipts will exceed disbursements by $10,000. Considering declining rental receipts with age and increased upkeep costs, it is believed that this figure will decline by $500 each year and will be $9,500 in the second year, $9,000 in the third, and so on. It is estimated that the machine will be retired after 12 years with a $13,000 salvage value. What is the prospective rate of return?

8–28. In Problem 6–10 (page 94), what is the rate of return on the extra investment required by Machine N?

8–29. In Problem 6–12 (page 94), what is the rate of return on the extra investment required by the new centerless grinder?

8–30. In Problem 6–15 (page 95), what is the rate of return on the extra investment required by the diesel plant?

8–31. In Problem 7–17 (page 112), the asking price for the patent is $35,000. What rate of return would be received by a purchaser at this price?

8–32. In Problem 7–19 (page 112), Doe's asking price for his land is $140,000. What rate of return will be received by the XYZ Tile Co. if it purchases at this price?

8–33. A certain rental property has a first cost of $50,000. If this property is purchased, it is believed that the property will be held for 10 years and then sold. It is estimated that after 10 years the property will be salable for $30,000. The estimated receipts from rentals are $10,000 a year throughout the 10 years. Estimated annual disbursements in connection with ownership and operation of the property (maintenance, property taxes, insurance, etc.) will be $3,000 the first year and will increase $300 each year thereafter to a figure of $5,700 in the 10th year. In addition, it is estimated that there will be a single nonrecurrent outlay of $2,000 for a maintenance overhaul at the end of the 5th year. What is the prospective rate of return before income taxes?

9

What Interest Rate?

The title of Part II of this book is "Interest—the Time Element in Economy." In Chapters 3, 4, and 5 much of the discussion dealt with loan transactions in which the interest rate was determined by agreement between lender and borrower. In Chapters 6, 7, and 8, however, the emphasis was on economy studies to guide decisions on the design and purchase of machines and structures; in such studies it is necessary for someone responsible for the study to make a decision regarding the interest rate to be used. It was pointed out that the selection of a particular interest rate for use in an economy study implies that the rate selected is believed to be the minimum attractive rate of return, all things considered.

But what matters ought to be considered in setting a minimum attractive rate of return? And how should this rate be determined in each case? These are important questions that are not always easy to answer. They are discussed in this chapter with reference to decisions in competitive industry, in regulated public utilities, in governmental organizations, and in personal finance. Some comments are also made on the relationship between the public welfare and the interest rates used in economy studies.

The Concept of Capital Rationing in Relation to the Minimum Attractive Rate of Return.[1] In business enterprises engaged in competitive industry, the funds available for investment in capital assets during any given period of time usually are limited. For example, assume that in the ABC Manufacturing Company, $90,000 is the most that can be made available for the coming year.

Because of technological progress and our expanding economy, it also is common that the total of the proposals for productive in-

---

[1] In his various writings, Joel Dean has presented this concept with particular skill. For example, see his *Capital Budgeting* (New York: Columbia University Press, 1951), particularly chap. iv; *Managerial Economics* (Englewood Cliffs, N.J.: Prentice-Hall, Inc., 1951), particularly chap. x; and "Measuring the Productivity of Capital," *Harvard Business Review* (January–February, 1954).

vestments in new capital assets will be considerably greater than the total of the available funds. Assume that Table 9–1 shows the investment proposals for the ABC Manufacturing Company, arrayed in order of prospective rate of return after income taxes.

TABLE 9–1

PROPOSALS FOR EXPENDITURES IN ABC MANUFACTURING COMPANY
FOR THE COMING YEAR

(Available funds limited to $90,000)

Project	Investment Required	Prospective Rate of Return	Cumulative Total of Investments
U	$12,000	40%	$ 12,000
Y	45,000	20%	57,000
Z	8,000	18%	65,000
S	25,000	15%	90,000
X	22,000	12%	112,000
T	30,000	10%	142,000
V	55,000	9%	197,000
W	10,000	8%	207,000

In this simple example it is evident that the $90,000 of available funds will be exhausted by Projects U, Y, Z, and S. It follows that the minimum rate of return that is attractive is 15%, the prospective return on Project S. If an investment is made in any project yielding less than 15% (X, T, V, W, or some other project not tabulated), the effect will be to eliminate the possibility of investing in some project that will yield 15% or more.

Validity of the Capital Rationing Concept. Matters are rarely as simple as implied by the foregoing discussion. For example, it may be impracticable to array all of the proposals for capital expenditures during the coming year and to be sure that no other good proposals—now unforeseen—will develop during the year. The total funds that can be made available for capital expenditures may not be fixed absolutely but may be related to the attractiveness of the proposed projects. In choosing among available projects, it often is desirable to apply supplementary criteria in addition to prospective rate of return. Various aspects of these topics are discussed throughout the remainder of this book and the whole subject is considered more critically in the final chapter.

Nevertheless, the principle is entirely sound that the minimum attractive rate of return ought to be chosen with the objective of making the best possible use of a limited resource. This resource is, of course, the money that can be made available for investment in capital assets and closely related items. If the consequence of making an investment yielding 10% is to forego some other investment that would yield 20%, it is not sensible to make the 10% investment. The high figures for minimum attractive return that so often are used in competitive industry are based in part on this principle.

Why Consider the Time Value of Money in Economy Studies? Objections are sometimes raised to the giving of any consideration whatsoever to interest in the making of decisions between technical alternatives. A brief answer to the question "Why recognize interest in connection with engineering economy studies?" may be phrased as follows: "Interest exists as a business fact; if you borrow money it is necessary to pay interest; if you have money you can earn a return by investing it. Where a choice is to be made between alternatives that involve different money receipts and disbursements at different times, it therefore is essential to consider interest. Engineering economy studies generally involve decisions between such alternatives."

This statement of the reason for recognizing interest in decision making seems to imply a slight difference in the explanation between the situation in which money is actually borrowed and the situation in which it is available without borrowing. Since businessmen sometimes reason differently about these two situations, it is worth while to examine them separately at this point.

Distinction Between Equity Funds and Borrowed Funds. Assume that you buy a $12,000 home by paying $3,000 in cash and securing a long-term loan for the remaining $9,000. Your *equity* in the $12,000 property is then $3,000. Your home ownership has been financed one-fourth by equity funds and three-fourths by borrowed funds.

In business the equity funds are the funds provided by the owners of the enterprise. In corporate business the owners are the stockholders of the corporation. A corporation may also finance in part by long-term borrowings, frequently through the sale of bonds. The bondholders are *creditors* of the corporation; their legal relationship to the corporation differs greatly from that of the stockholders. Where funds are borrowed, there is generally an agreement to pay interest and principal at stipulated dates. No such obligation exists in connection with equity funds.

Some of the problems caused by doing business on borrowed money are discussed briefly in Chapter 17. At the present point in our discussion, it needs to be brought out that the less stable the earning power of a prospective borrower, the less desirable it is to borrow. Many business enterprises in competitive industry are financed largely or entirely from equity funds. Authorities on finance recognize that it is appropriate for many regulated public utilities to secure from one-third to one-half of their capital from long-term borrowing. In certain types of government projects the entire first cost of a project is financed by borrowing.

Considering the Time Value of Money for Proposals To Be Financed by Equity Funds. Engineering structures and machines may be built or acquired by individuals, partnerships, private corporations, and governmental bodies. Unless they are financed by borrowing, they must necessarily be financed out of money belonging to the owners of the enterprise.

These equity funds may come from various sources. In private corporations, for instance, they may come from the sale of stock, or from profits that are "plowed back" into the business rather than paid out as dividends to the stockholders, or from the recovery of capital previously invested in other machines and structures. In governmental bodies, equity funds may come from direct assessments or taxation (e.g., the gasoline tax used to finance highway improvement).

Where capital assets are financed entirely by equity funds, it is not necessary to pay out interest to any creditor. Here interest is a cost in the economists' sense of *opportunity cost*. When funds are invested in any particular capital goods, the opportunity is foregone to obtain a return from the investment of the funds elsewhere. Interest is a cost in the sense of an opportunity foregone.

In deciding whether to invest equity funds in specific capital assets, an important question is how good an opportunity will be foregone. In other words, if the investment in the specific capital assets is not made, what return is likely to be obtainable from the same funds invested elsewhere? In principle the interest rate (minimum attractive rate of return) used in an economy study ought to be the rate of return obtainable from the opportunity foregone, as nearly as can be determined.

What Investment Opportunity Is Being Foregone? The opportunity foregone may be either within the business enterprise or outside of it. In Table 9–1 earlier in this chapter, the minimum attractive rate of return was 15% because any investment yielding less than 15% would cause the ABC Manufacturing Company to forego the opportunity to earn 15% in Project S.

The appropriate figure for minimum attractive rate of return is generally higher when the opportunity foregone is within the enterprise. Two circumstances, both illustrated in Table 9–1, are generally present when a within-the-enterprise figure is controlling. One circumstance is the presence of many good opportunities for investment within the enterprise. The other circumstance is the limitation of available funds. High minimum attractive rates of return are common in competitive industry because both of these circumstances occur so frequently.

If new equity capital cannot be secured for a business enterprise and no new money is to be borrowed, the available funds for investment in new fixed assets are usually limited to current earnings retained in the business (if any) and to capital recovered from previous investments in fixed assets. (This latter source of funds is discussed in Chapter 17.) But even where new equity funds *can* be secured, the management of a business enterprise may deem it unwise to obtain them. In many small and moderate-sized enterprises that are owned by a few individuals, the securing of new equity capital may involve a sacrifice of control by the present owners. In large corporations in competitive industry where no question of control is involved, boards of directors often find other reasons that influence them against the raising of new equity capital.

In determining a minimum attractive rate of return in a given business enterprise or other sphere of activity, it always is appropriate to consider possible opportunities for return that may be foregone outside of the enterprise as well as within it. For example, corporate stockholders have opportunities for personal investments outside of their corporation; the board of directors should not withhold part of the current earnings from the stockholders unless the prospective return from the reinvestment of these earnings within the enterprise is as great as the return the stockholders could obtain from personal investments elsewhere. A similar line of reasoning may be applied to government projects financed by current taxation; the collection of these taxes requires the taxpayers to forego an opportunity to earn a return from personal investment of the moneys collected.

Representative Costs of Borrowed Money. Interest rates paid by borrowers vary from time to time.[2] The variations in the general

[2] The funds of life insurance companies are representative of diversified investments of a highly conservative type. The Institute of Life Insurance reports the net rate of interest earned on invested funds by all United States life insurance companies as follows: 1916—4.80%; 1926—5.09%; 1936—3.71%; 1946—2.93%; 1956—3.63%. There was a fairly steady decline in return from 1923 to 1947 and a steady increase thereafter. The figures for 1946 and 1956 are reported as "rate before Federal income taxes." See *Life Insurance Fact Book—1957*, p. 55.

level of interest rates reflect changes in the supply and demand for loanable funds. In modern society the level of interest rates is greatly influenced by governmental fiscal policies.

Interest rates also vary from one class of borrower to another. Thus, in 1959, many states, cities, school districts, and other local governmental units were borrowing at from 3.5% to 4.5%; the United States government was borrowing at about 4%; large well-known corporations were borrowing at from 4% to 6%; individuals buying automobiles and household appliances on time payments were paying rates that were, in effect, from 12% to 15%; in certain states the legal maximum rate on certain small loans, paid by some borrowers, was 2½% a month (an effective rate of 34½% per annum); rates on home loans, considering all charges, ranged from 5% to over 10%.

To a large extent, differences in interest rates from one borrower to another reflect the judgment of lenders as to the relative risk of loss in the various loans. In certain cases—particularly in personal loans—differences in interest rates may also reflect large differences in the administrative costs of loan contracts. Interest rates on bonds of states and local governmental units in the United States are influenced by their tax-exempt status; because interest received by the holders of such bonds is not subject to the federal income tax, states and municipalities can borrow money at lower interest rates than would otherwise be possible.

The point has been emphasized in earlier chapters that the true cost of borrowed money is often much greater than the borrower believes it to be. Sometimes, as illustrated in Chapter 5, loan plans are described in a way that misleads borrowers as to the actual interest rate. Frequently, as explained in the discussion near the end of Chapter 8, there are various expenses and other adverse conditions associated with borrowing that cause the true cost of borrowed money to be considerably more than the contract interest rate.

Relationship of the Minimum Attractive Rate of Return to the Cost of Borrowed Money. Consider an economy study to judge the justification of a project to be financed entirely by borrowing.

Persons who have not given the matter much critical thought often assume that the interest rate to be used in such a study ought to be the bare cost of borrowed money. Although this view is particularly common in governmental projects and in personal economy studies, the same view is sometimes advanced in connection with projects in competitive industry. The following paragraphs relate solely to competitive industry.

The reasons why the minimum attractive rate of return to be used in such an economy study should be greater than the cost of borrowed money may be summarized as follows:

1. Decisions made for business enterprises engaged in competitive industry are presumably made from the viewpoint of the owners of the enterprise. If the prospective return to be obtained from investing borrowed funds in capital assets is just equal to the cost of the borrowed money, the owners will gain no advantage from the borrowing. The prospective return needs to be greater than the cost of borrowed money in order to justify the risks and other disadvantages to the owners associated with fixed obligations to pay interest and to repay principal at stated dates. This topic is explored further in Chapter 17.

2. Even though it may *seem* as if certain types of assets can be financed entirely by borrowing (e.g., certain machinery purchased on the installment plan), the amount of possible borrowing by any business enterprise depends on the amount of equity capital in the enterprise. Generally speaking, the cost of new capital to an enterprise ought to be viewed as a weighted average of the cost of borrowed capital and equity capital. This weighted average will nearly always be considerably higher than the cost of borrowed money.

3. If there is a limit on the total funds available for investment in capital assets from all sources including borrowing, and if there are many proposals for investments in assets that seem likely to yield high returns, the type of reasoning illustrated in Table 9–1 is applicable. If the $90,000 of available funds in Table 9–1 had come entirely from borrowing at, say, 5%, rather than from equity sources, the minimum attractive rate of return for the ABC Manufacturing Company would still have been 15% after income taxes. The controlling element in determining the minimum attractive rate would still have been the fact that the selection of any project yielding less than 15% would cause the elimination of some project that would yield 15% or more; the 5% cost of the borrowed money would not have been relevant.

The Element of Risk in Relation to the Minimum Attractive Rate of Return. In some types of loan transactions the risk of loss is recognized to be greater than in other types. (A good measure of risk of loss would be obtained by finding the actual losses sustained by lenders on different types of loans over a long period of years.) It has been pointed out that the risk of loss influences the interest rate. Generally speaking, the poorer the credit rating of a borrower, the greater the interest rate he will have to pay.

In a similar way the standard of attractiveness applied to proposals for capital expenditures in industry may be related to estimated risk of loss. For example, there are four major divisions in the petroleum industry, production, refining, transportation, and marketing. There are obvious differences in risk associated with investment proposals in the different divisions. One large integrated oil company has recognized these differences by requiring a minimum attractive rate of return of 18% after income taxes for certain types of proposals in the production division, 14% for proposals in the refining division, and 10% for proposals in the transportation and marketing divisions.

Often the element of risk is recognized at the level of decision making by top management without the use of any such formal rules. For example, in Table 9–1 the management of the ABC Manufacturing Company might deem Project X to be considerably less risky than Project S. Project X might therefore be preferred even though its rate of return is only 12% compared to the 15% estimated for Project S.

Analysts disagree on the question of whether it is better to recognize this element of risk of loss in setting a minimum attractive rate of return or to introduce the matter into economy studies in some other way. This topic is discussed further in Chapter 13.

Shall Minimum Attractive Rate of Return in Competitive Industry Be Before or After Income Taxes? Decisions in business enterprises engaged in competitive industry are presumably made from the viewpoint of the owners of the enterprise. Obviously it is to the owners' advantage to obtain the best possible rate of return *after* income taxes rather than *before* income taxes.

Where analysts responsible for economy studies in competitive industry make studies before income taxes, along the lines illustrated in Chapters 6 to 8, the implication is that the same choices among alternatives will be made by studies made before taxes or after taxes. This point may be illustrated by a reference to Table 9–1, which gave prospective rates of return after taxes for eight projects. Assume that a table is made showing rates of return before income taxes rather than after, and that all prospective rates of return before taxes are approximately double the after-tax rates shown in Table 9–1. The new table would array the projects in the same order as Table 9–1, and the same four projects—U, Y, Z, and S—would be selected. The minimum attractive rate would appear to be 30% before income taxes rather than 15% after taxes, but there would be no difference in the action resulting from the economy studies.

If it were invariably true that an array of projects in order of rate of return would be the same before and after income taxes, the conclusions of economy studies would not depend on whether the studies were made before or after taxes. Under such circumstances the greater simplicity of making studies before taxes would be a valid basis for always using before-tax studies and merely increasing the minimum attractive rate of return (or interest rate used) enough to recognize the effect of income taxes. In this book the foregoing simple method will continue to be used through Chapter 14.

However, it frequently happens that the best projects after income taxes are not the same as the best ones before income taxes. Usually this circumstance arises because of differences in rate of write-off for tax purposes applicable to different investments or because of different tax rates applicable to different investments. A number of such cases are described in Chapter 15 and thereafter. For this reason, it is desirable that many economy studies in competitive industry be made after income taxes. A critical look at the question of when to make studies before taxes and when after taxes is deferred until Chapter 15.

Need for a Uniform Criterion of Attractiveness of Proposed Investments at All Levels of Decision Making Throughout an Enterprise. A common condition in industry is described by Robert F. Barrell as follows: [3]

Most companies have some definite sum of money available for investment purposes. Since the amount of available capital is limited, decisions must be made with respect to alternative uses such that the company will maximize its earnings on this added investment. Furthermore, a company's budget director and executives must set up some base for evaluating the returns on alternative uses for capital before such decisions can be made. Generally, a company will establish some minimum acceptable rate of return, below which it feels the return is insufficient to justify the risk assumed by the company on that particular venture.

It has been observed that under present practices in industry, decision making pertaining to investments is based upon time-rate-use of money only in the higher echelons of top management. For example, decisions pertaining to amounts set aside for expansion programs, research and development, are usually made on this basis. However, the decisions which are made by the lower echelons of management and by engineering, scientific and manufacturing personnel, pertaining to the actual expenditure of these funds, are not based on time-rate-use of money, but rather on hunch decisions and value judgments. Although these decisions may be fortified by rough computations based upon reasonable assumptions, they

---

[3] In an unpublished paper, "Analog Computers for Calculating the Rate of Return on Added Investment," submitted to fulfill the requirements of the management training program of the University of Buffalo. Mr. Barrell is an engineer for a large manufacturing company.

often yield misleading results. Furthermore, due to the lack of uniformity in such approximations from one person to the next, these decisions cannot possibly reflect top management policy for the optimum use of invested capital.

It would appear that this is a serious defect in our industrial planning structure. Decisions are based on sound calculations up to the point where the detailed expenditures are made, and at this point the basis for decision making suddenly changes. What would it mean to a company if each of the purchases of machines, tools, molds, dies, or plant modifications were all judged on a minimum acceptable rate of return for the additional investment set by top management for that particular plant or division?

Our Table 9–1 represented an analysis of a group of separate projects such as might be prepared by a budget director for submission to top management. As pointed out in the foregoing quotation, it is desirable that the economic decisions within each project be made on substantially the same basis as the top management decisions among the projects. Otherwise, desirable elements that would yield high returns may be eliminated from some projects and other projects may be overdesigned in the sense that they include unjustifiable increments of investment.

(The reader may recall Examples 8–4 and 8–5 in which it was proposed to modernize present materials handling methods. One possible way to do this was by a $25,000 investment in Plan C, yielding a return of 10.8% as compared to present methods. The minimum attractive rate of return was stipulated as 10%. If Plan C had been submitted for budgetary approval without mention of any alternative plan and the 10% standard had been applied, Plan C presumably would have been approved. Nevertheless, as explained in Example 8–5, the final increment of $10,000 of investment in Plan C—as compared to an alternate scheme for improving materials handling—would yield only 3.8%.)

This topic of obtaining uniformity in criteria for investment decisions at all levels of decision making within an organization is explored further in Chapters 12 and 19.

The Regulation of Privately Owned Public Utilities. In the United States and elsewhere, certain types of privately owned business enterprises are subject to regulation as public utilities. These include suppliers of electricity, gas, water, telephone service, and other communications services, and various types of transportation services. Regulation is conducted by various state and federal commissions, with certain decisions by regulatory commissions subject to review by the courts. Matters regulated include the general level of rates, specific rate structures, certain standards of service, the issuance of securities, and classifications of accounts.

With certain exceptions in the case of transportation utilities, regulated utilities tend to be monopolistic in character with their monopoly protected by public regulation. There are a number of good reasons why the public both restricts and to some extent protects the activity of public utilities. Many utilities require a franchise from the community to put their pipes or poles or conduits or tracks in the streets and require the exercise of the state's privilege of eminent domain to secure certain needed rights of way. All public utilities clearly perform a service that is of great importance to the community. Moreover, most utilities require a very high investment in plant and equipment in comparison to their annual revenues and annual operating costs.

Perhaps this relatively high plant investment is the most distinguishing characteristic of the public utility field. A large proportion of public utility costs are so-called fixed costs such as taxes, depreciation, and cost of capital. For this reason, a monopoly in the public utility field is highly economical. For example, if we have two competing electric light and power companies in a community, they must duplicate each other's distribution systems with a resulting higher total investment than would exist if there were but one system. If both had enough revenues to earn a fair return on their respective investments, the aggregate revenues of the two would be much more than the revenues of a single company that earned a fair return on the investment in only one distribution system. In certain types of utilities particularly telephone utilities and urban transportation utilities, the service available from either of two competing utilities is less satisfactory than that obtainable from a monopolistic company covering the entire area. Moreover, there is often a nuisance factor to having an extra set of poles or an extra pipe line in a given street that makes monopoly desirable.

In most industries competition tends to regulate rates and service in the public interest. Before the days of public utility regulation in the United States, experience indicated that competition was not an adequate regulator in the utility field. What is likely to happen where competing utilities exist with no regulation is cutthroat competition with a tendency to cut rates down to increment costs of production. This is likely to be followed by a consolidation and unregulated monopoly with a price that is set on a monopoly price basis.

Relationship Between Regulatory Policies and the Rapid Growth of the Need for Public Utility Service. The general experience in the United States and other industrialized countries has been one of continuous increase in demand for utility service. Since 1900 this has been particularly true of electric, gas, water, and telephone utilities. There are high social costs caused by inadequate capacity of utility plant. The public interest therefore requires that utility companies be in a position to finance necessary expansion and modernization of plant. If new capital to finance expansion is to be secured, a utility must have the prospect of earnings sufficient to attract such capital.

Rates, therefore, should be high enough to attract capital. At the same time they should be low enough so that the charges to the public are reasonable, all things considered. A common method used by commissions to accomplish these two ends has been to set rates at a level so that the prospective total revenues received by a utility from the sale of its public utility services will equal its prospective operating expenses including an allowance for depreciation, plus income taxes, plus a "fair return" on the investment in the property employed in the utility service.[4]

The appropriate fair return to be allowed in any given instance should reflect the over-all cost of money to the utility being regulated, considering both the interest that must be paid for borrowed money and the dividend rate needed to attract new equity capital. The fair return will properly be higher for a relatively risky utility enterprise (such as an urban transportation company) than for a relatively secure one (such as a large electric light and power company). The rate of return necessary to attract capital will also be influenced by the size of the utility and the extent to which it is well known to investors. The appropriate fair return will change from time to time with changes in the general level of interest rates. In recent years regulatory commissions have generally allowed rates of return somewhere in the range from 5% to 8%.

Occasionally one hears the statement that public utilities are *guaranteed* a return on their investments. Any such statement is incorrect. The most that a regulatory commission can do is to allow a rate schedule that gives the utility a chance to earn a fair return *if it can get it*. Certain utilities (such as some urban transportation companies) find it impossible to earn an adequate return with any schedule of rates.

The complexities of the actual regulation of utility rates are beyond the scope of this book; we shall not attempt to examine the

---

[4] The rules governing rate regulation have been laid down in a series of decisions by the United States Supreme Court and other courts. These decisions have taken place over a period of years. The viewpoint of the Supreme Court on underlying principles has changed from time to time. Later court decisions permitted regulatory bodies to exercise much more latitude than was allowed in earlier years. See particularly *Federal Power Commission v. Hope Natural Gas Co.,* 320 U.S. 591 (1944).

numerous controversial issues involved in this interesting and important subject. For the purposes of our present discussion, it is sufficient to note that in the United States the usual condition has been for utilities to expand rapidly and to be able to raise new capital when needed. This has been particularly true of electric, gas, water, and telephone utilities. It is common for approximately half of new funds to come from long-term borrowings and the remainder from the sale of equity securities (preferred and common stocks).

Some Differences Between Economy Studies in Regulated Public Utilities and in Competitive Industry. Some contrasts between public utilities and competitive industry that bear on the central theme of this chapter are as follows:

1. As already pointed out, the funds available for investment in new fixed assets are often limited in enterprises engaged in competitive industry. In contrast, a public utility is likely to be raising new capital for expansion at frequent intervals and decisions made by the utility management ordinarily are not controlled by a limitation on funds that can be made available for plant investment. For this reason, the considerations of capital rationing that often are so important in competitive industry do not usually enter into the selection of a minimum attractive return in public utilities. (Exceptions to this statement occur in certain utilities where it is difficult or impossible to raise new capital, for example, the urban transportation utilities already mentioned.) It follows that justifiable figures for minimum attractive return in public utilities are generally lower than in competitive industry; figures such as 15% or more after income taxes that are common in competitive industry are rarely appropriate in public utilities.

2. Just as in competitive industry, the over-all cost of money to a public utility, considering both borrowed money and equity capital, tends to establish an appropriate *lower limit* for the minimum attractive return to be used in economy studies. However, unlike competitive industry, the *upper limit* for minimum attractive return in a public utility should rarely be much greater than this cost of money. The "fair return" on investment permitted under the policies of many regulatory commissions in the United States is based on the over-all cost of money to the utility. It can be shown that, under certain common procedures in rate regulation, the long-run effect of decision making using a minimum attractive return either more or less than this fair return is to increase the cost of utility service to the customers. When the return that the regulatory authorities allow on a utility's investment is used as the minimum attractive return in the utility's economy studies, these studies are

—in effect—being made from the viewpoint of the utility's customers. That is, decisions between alternative types of plant are being made in a way that will minimize the rates that will be charged for the utility's service. Thus the objective of economy studies in a regulated public utility should be to minimize the utility's revenue requirements.

3. It has been pointed out that the common rate-making formula for utilities is designed to permit the utility to earn a fair return *after* income taxes. In effect the rate-making authorities view prospective income taxes as an element of expense to be included in the rates charged for utility service.

It is explained in Chapter 15 that under certain assumptions regarding rate making the income taxes resulting from any plant investment may be expressed as a percentage of that investment. The appropriate percentage will depend on the income tax rate, on the life and per cent salvage value of the fixed assets, and on the average interest rate paid on long-term borrowings and the proportion of capital raised by borrowing. The great differences between a rational treatment of income tax considerations in economy studies for competitive industry and for public utilities are brought out in Chapter 15.

A common minimum attractive return used in utility economy studies is 7%. Common annual income tax percentages for utility economy studies in the United States are from 2% to 6% of first cost, depending on matters explained in Chapter 15.

Selecting an Interest Rate for Personal Economy Studies. Many personal decisions call for recognition of the time value of money. Sometimes the question at issue in choosing an interest rate may be the straightforward one of the rate obtainable on a conservative investment. (For example, several of the problems following Chapter 5 called for determining the periodic deposits in a fund to provide a desired sum of money for educational purposes at a future date.) In other cases the issue may be the true cost of money to be borrowed. (Examples where true cost exceeded apparent cost have been given in Chapters 5 and 8.)

In relation to the subject matter of this book, a more interesting group of personal decisions are those that call for the same type of analysis needed in many engineering economy studies. In this group of personal decisions a choice is to be made among alternative courses of action, and criteria for rational decision making cannot be established without selecting a minimum attractive rate of return. Representative examples are a choice between home ownership and renting, a decision whether to convert a personal home into a rental property, a choice between job opportunities that have different pension arrangements, and a decision whether to make an investment aimed to reduce future personal expenditures (e.g., the insulation of a personal residence).

Such personal decisions are likely to be made more sensibly with the help of an economy study. This is true even though—as pointed out in Chapter 1—matters of personal taste are important elements in this type of decision. An economic analysis sometimes shows that it is very costly to indulge certain personal tastes and that there is an economic advantage in indulging certain others.

In selecting a minimum attractive return for personal decision making, the relevant questions may be phrased as follows: "What investment opportunities, if any, are likely to be foregone as a result of the proposed decision?" and "What is the cost of money, all things considered?" The reader will note that these are the same questions that arise in economy studies for business enterprise. In personal decisions, just as in business decisions, it may be the answer to the first question that should establish the minimum attractive return, or it may be the answer to the second one.

For persons with adequate funds to invest, the investment opportunity foregone will often be a conservative one yielding a relatively low interest rate. For many such persons in the United States, it is desirable to make personal economy studies in a way that recognizes the income-tax aspects of the proposed decision; in such studies it may be appropriate to assume that the investment opportunity foregone is a tax-free investment. The tax-free yield on such an investment might be from $2\frac{1}{2}$ to $4\frac{1}{2}\%$.

For persons who owe money at interest, the outlay of funds presently available may mean that the opportunity is foregone to reduce the debt. A debt reduction should be thought of as a gilt-edge investment, certain to yield a definite return through the saving of interest. For many persons who have borrowed money to finance homes, a debt reduction will be, in effect, an investment at 5% or 6%.

Where one or both of the alternatives in a personal economy study call for the borrowing of money, the cost of money may be influenced by the purpose of the loan. The same person who can finance a home by a loan costing 6% may pay 12% or 15% to finance the purchase of an automobile or home appliance. As already mentioned, certain unsecured personal loans may carry very high interest rates of 30% or more.

Under certain circumstances, the cost of money on a personal loan may be less after income taxes than before taxes. This topic is mentioned briefly in Chapter 15.

Minimum Attractive Rate of Return in Economy Studies for Governments. Where economy studies are made for government projects, the most common practice is to use an interest rate equal to the bare cost of borrowed money to the particular government agency. Although this practice is justifiable in certain instances, its uncritical use in all cases may cause the investment in many governmental projects to be unjustifiably high and may cause the approval of other governmental projects that ought to be disapproved.

This controversial subject of the minimum attractive rate of return on governmental investments is explored further in Chapter 18. Along the lines of the discussion in the present chapter, two reasons why this rate often should exceed the interest rate on governmental borrowings are:

1. Governments are frequently in a situation similar to the one illustrated in Table 9–1 for a competitive enterprise. That is, there are often many good opportunities for the productive investment of funds for a particular governmental activity or governmental unit and the amount of funds available to that activity or unit are limited. Under these circumstances the minimum attractive rate of return should be determined in a way that makes the best possible use of the limited resource of available funds. The same problems of capital rationing that arise in competitive enterprise also occur in governments.

2. Where governmental projects are being carried out for the benefit of a particular group of taxpayers and are being financed from taxation, the investment opportunities foregone by the taxpayers should be considered in setting a minimum attractive rate of return. To illustrate this point by an extreme example, it may be noted that highway improvements are financed largely by taxes on highway users. Economy studies for highway improvements based on an interest rate of, say, 3%, tend toward the justification of all project elements that yield 3% or more in savings of highway user costs. However, if the moneys used for these project increments were not collected as taxes but remained in the hands of the highway users, they could be invested much more productively by the large fraction of highway users who finance their automobiles by borrowing at interest rates of 12% or 15%.

Explanation of Interest in Economic Theory. We have answered the practical question, "Why consider the time value of money in decision making?" by saying that interest is a business fact. It is also desirable to consider the answer to the more fundamental question, "Why does interest exist as a business fact?"

In answering this question, the economist explains interest, as he explains any other sort of price, by examining the supply and demand situations for investment funds. On the supply side he points out that interest is necessary as an incentive to saving; on the demand side he points out that interest is possible because capital is productive.

Explanation of the Necessity of Interest. On the supply side the economist points out that if you lend money at interest you deprive yourself of immediate satisfactions. You cannot use your money to buy consumers' goods now if you lend it to somebody else, or if you spend it yourself on engineering machines or structures (i.e., producers' goods), or if you buy stock in a corporation that spends it this way, or if you pay it to the government, which uses it for public works. We all of us have a low present estimation of the utility of future goods; for instance, the prospect of a square meal next year does not look as good to us as a square meal today. Thus we need some sort of incentive to defer consumption, a compensation for waiting or putting off immediate satisfactions.

However, in recent years it has been recognized that this explanation is not quite complete, and that the desire for security might serve as an incentive for a good deal of saving even though there were no interest. Moreover, there are numerous individuals with sufficiently large personal incomes so that the incentive to spend all their incomes immediately for consumers' goods is so small that they will invest a substantial part of their incomes regardless of the size of the interest rate. Nevertheless, the higher the interest rate, the greater the motive for putting off consumption in order to earn a return on invested money; it is reasonable to believe that if the prospect of a return (i.e., interest) on invested capital were removed, the stimulus for its investment would also disappear.

Explanation of the Possibility of Interest. On the demand side, how is it possible to pay interest? That is, how can business enterprises find it profitable to borrow money and pay the interest required by lenders; how is it possible for corporations to pay dividends that are in effect a return upon the stockholders' invested capital? The answer is that capital goods (i.e., producers' goods such as engineering machines and structures) are productive.

The economist in his explanation of interest will take you back to primitive society and illustrate the productivity of capital by the situation of primitive man trying to hunt and fish without any tools other than his hands. He finds that by making tools (such as spears, canoes, bows and arrows) he may greatly increase his catch. These capital goods are not anything that can be eaten; he must defer consumption for a while when he makes these instruments of production. But after he has gone hungry for a time while making these "producers' goods," he can catch more fish and kill more game, thus, he makes a return on the investment of his time.

In the same sense present-day engineering machines and structures are productive. It is possible to invest money in plant and machinery, in the fixed-capital goods of business enterprise, and to do things better than could be done otherwise. It is because of this that enterprises can borrow money and pay interest, or can secure money for the investment of ownership funds and pay dividends that are greater than the interest that the stockholder could otherwise receive by lending them.

So we have the twofold explanation of interest. Interest can exist because capital is productive, and it is probably necessary that interest exist if there is to be any substantial incentive for voluntary saving.

Implications of the Theoretical Explanation of Interest. It has been stated that interest is possible because capital goods (i.e., producers' goods) are productive. A better statement might be that under favorable circumstances specific capital goods may be sufficiently productive to earn a return.

Whether in fact specific capital goods in a given set of circumstances promise to be productive enough to earn a return is a problem in engineering economy. Each situation must be examined with respect to the specific prices that apply to the given circumstances. The technical considerations that usually enter into such a problem make an engineering training necessary for its solution.

For instance, consider the selection of the steam pressure for a steam-electric power plant. The higher the pressure the greater the initial investment in boilers, valves, piping, etc.; but—within limits—the less the amount of fuel required to produce a given quantity of electric energy. The point beyond which it is not a productive investment of capital to increase steam pressure depends on many circumstances (such as the extra cost of the equipment necessary for higher pressures, the cost of fuel, and the amount and time distribution of the load). There is no particular pressure that is inherently the most economical regardless of circumstances. And the question of just what pressure is economical in a given set of circumstances cannot be decided apart from the technical considerations involved.

The engineer is thus in a position where he is called upon to make recommendations as to the economic wisdom of specific capital expenditures for machines and structures; he determines whether they are likely to be productive enough under the circumstances to earn a return (interest) sufficient to justify an investment in them.

Engineering Economy Studies from the Social Viewpoint. Because engineers are in a position to propose some capital expenditures and veto others, they indirectly exercise a considerable influence in the distribution of the social energies between consumers' goods and producers' goods; and they directly exercise an influence in the distribution of the social energies between various alternative producers' goods. Decisions between alternatives are necessarily dependent on the expression of otherwise incommensurable quantities (e.g., hours of unskilled labor, hours of various kinds of skilled labor, pounds of steel, tons of coal, barrels of fuel oil, board feet of lumber, acres of land) in a common unit—money value. Each money value is a result of a complex interaction of forces of supply and demand that reflects the utility and the scarcity of the commodity involved. To the extent that the price system so arrived at may be defended as weighing, as well as can be done, the sacrifices involved in the production of various commodities and the satisfactions obtainable from their use, the requirement that any capital goods to be created show the prospect of earning a return (interest) on the investment in them should tend toward a wise distribution of our social energies. In other words, not only is the recognition of the time value of money in economy studies by private individuals and corporations the only sensible policy for such individuals and corporations, but it is also sound policy from the collective viewpoint.

Differences Between Engineering and Accounting Viewpoints on the Time Value of Money. Engineering economy studies generally deal with *proposed* investments in machines or structures. As long as an investment is only proposed but not yet made, it is necessary to recognize interest in any calculations relative to the decision whether or not to make it; there is always offered the alternative of an investment at interest.

The engineer's usual viewpoint here is in contrast to that of the accountant. Accounting records deal generally with *past* investments, receipts, and disbursements. Once money is invested in machines and structures it is not necessarily true that the alternative exists of investing the money productively elsewhere; in fact, there is generally no such alternative. Thus in calculations relative to past expenditures and disbursements the time value of money may or may not be considered, depending upon the questions that it is desired to answer by means of the calculations. Many of the questions that the accounts of a business are called on to answer do not require the consideration of interest; thus interest on ownership capital (i.e., where there is no actual interest payment to a creditor) is not generally considered as a cost in accounting, although there are some exceptions.

This difference between the engineer's viewpoint before the event and the accountant's viewpoint after the event often creates problems in trying to reconcile the calculations made for engineering economy studies with accounts of a concern; some of these problems are discussed in Chapter 10, others, in later chapters. Often controversies arise between the engineers and the accountants of a concern owing to their conflicting views of cost; such controversies generally reflect a mutual misunderstanding of the legitimate objectives of procedures designed to serve different purposes. What is needed is a recognition by both engineers and accountants of the difference in the objectives of their calculations.

A Concluding Statement on Part II. In studies to determine a prospective rate of return (the subject matter of Chapter 8), the lowest rate of return deemed sufficient to justify a proposed investment may obviously be described as the minimum attractive rate of return. In annual cost comparisons (Chapter 6) or present worth comparisons (Chapter 7), the interest rate selected for use in equivalence calculations is—in effect—a minimum attractive rate of return regardless of whether or not it is so described.

In the remaining chapters of this book, annual cost studies and rate-of-return studies will be used more frequently than present worth studies. Generally speaking, the choice of one of these three methods of analysis for a particular example indicates that the authors feel that the method selected is preferable for the type of case being illustrated. However, it is desirable always to remember that the three methods correctly used will all indicate the same decision between alternatives once a particular minimum attractive return has been chosen. A summary statement of recommendations on the selection of a technique of comparison is given in Chapter 19, the final chapter of this book.

The choice of a minimum attractive rate of return obviously has a great influence on decision making at all levels at which decisions are made between alternative investments in fixed assets. Proposed investments that look attractive at 3% appear to be undesirable at 7%; proposals that look good at 7% are properly vetoed at 15%. Further comments on the choice of a minimum attractive rate of return are made at various places in Part III. In the meantime the major point to keep in mind is that the controlling element in the choice of a minimum attractive return should ordinarily be either the return on the investment opportunity foregone or the over-all cost of money, all things considered. There is no one figure for minimum attractive rate of return that is appropriate to all circumstances; it is reasonable that this figure should be much higher in some cases than in others.

Problems

9–1. Examine the financial page of the daily newspaper or current issues of some financial journal to determine the current yields on United States government bonds and on representative municipal, public utility, and industrial bonds. What are current rates of interest on home loans and on loans on commercial property in your locality? Discuss possible reasons for the differences in these interest rates.

9–2. Find some index of the yield of high-grade corporate bonds that has been in existence for 25 years or more. Find a comparable index for medium-grade corporate bonds. Plot the two indexes on coordinate paper, showing the year-by-year figures for the past 25 years. Note the variations in the general level of interest rates and also the differences between the variations of the rates of high-grade and medium-grade bonds.

9–3. A number of years ago, some leading citizens of the town of Q agreed that their community was badly in need of a modern hotel that would cost approximately $250,000. To meet this need they organized the Civic Hotel Company. By strenuous solicitation they were able to raise $150,000 by selling 1,500 shares of stock at $100 a share. The other $100,000 necessary to build the hotel was provided by a building and loan association on a 10-year, 8% mortgage that called for uniform annual payments sufficient to pay interest and extinguish the debt at the end of the 10 years.

After the hotel was completed, the board of directors of the Civic Hotel Company leased it to a company that operated a national chain of hotels. The lease ran for 20 years and contained a clause permitting the operating company to purchase the hotel for $100,000 at the end of the 20-year period. The operating company agreed to furnish the hotel and pay all taxes (including income taxes) and operating expenses, and was to receive all revenues from the operation of the hotel. It also agreed to meet the rather high interest and repayment obligations on the mortgage during the first 10 years of the lease. During the last 10 years of the lease, the operating company agreed to make payments sufficient to permit annual dividends of $8 per share. No payments at all were to be made to the stockholders during the first 10 years. This was the most favorable operating contract that the directors of the Civic Hotel Company were able to secure anywhere.

When the local stockholders, many of whom had bought stock under considerable pressure, learned that there was no prospect of dividends for 10 years, they were very much disappointed, and a number of them were anxious to sell their stock. Henry Smart, one of the businessmen in the original group that promoted the project, was reported to be buying stock from some of these disgruntled stockholders at $75 a share.

This resulted in local comment to the effect that Henry Smart was a "shrewd old skinflint" who was taking advantage of his public-spirited fellow citizens. There were remarks regarding the "fat dividends" he would be receiving after the mortgage was paid off. One man was reported to have turned down Smart's offer of $75 a share and to have commented publicly to the effect that the "old Shylock" would not get his stock unless he paid him what it was worth.

Was $75 a share really too low a price for this stock? Make the necessary assumptions and the necessary financial calculations to place a value on this stock. Discuss your conclusions.

9–4. The management of the BCD Company has concluded that no more than $200,000 of new investment funds can be made available during the coming year. There are 5 investment proposals, A, B, C, D, and E, that together would require $300,000 of funds.

Make the necessary calculations to determine which proposals should be selected if the choice is made to obtain the highest possible rate of return before income taxes. If you recognize the necessity of capital rationing in these circumstances, what appears to be the minimum attractive rate of return before income taxes?

A. A project for cost reduction of certain manufacturing operations requires an investment of $50,000. The estimated life of the equipment is 12 years with zero salvage value. The expected annual reduction in net operating disbursements for the next 12 years is $14,000.

B. A project for cost reduction of certain distribution operations requires an additional investment of $50,000 in inventory of product in branch warehouses. This inventory is expected to have 100% salvage value at all times. The expected annual reduction in net operating disbursements is $9,000.

C. Facilities to produce certain parts now purchased will require a $50,000 investment. It is estimated that these facilities will have a 50% salvage value at the end of 8 years. Annual disbursements of $20,000 are required to continue to purchase these parts; annual disbursements for production of the parts are estimated to be $12,000.

D. Additional plant to expand the production of a certain product requires an investment of $50,000. This plant is estimated to have a $10,000 salvage value at the end of 15 years. It is estimated that annual receipts from the sale of this product will be increased by $18,500 and annual disbursements for its production and sale will be increased by $11,800.

E. A proposed new product requires $100,000 of immediate investment. Estimated excess of receipts over disbursements in connection with the production and sale of this product is $10,000 the first year, $15,000 the 2nd, and increases by $5,000 a year to $30,000 in the 5th year. This estimated positive cash flow is again $30,000 in the 6th year and is expected to decrease by $5,000 a year to $10,000 in the 10th year. The estimated salvage value at the end of 10 years is $25,000.

PART III

TECHNIQUES FOR ECONOMY STUDIES

10

Some Aspects of Depreciation Accounting

The examples of economy studies in Chapters 6, 7, and 8 started with estimates of the effect on cash flow of proposed decisions between alternatives. No mention was made of the effect on the accounts of an enterprise. The topic of the relationship between accounting and economy studies is introduced in the present chapter. This chapter deals primarily with one facet of accounting, namely, accounting for depreciable fixed assets (such as buildings, structures, machinery, and equipment).

Why Should Students of Engineering Economy Learn About Depreciation Accounting? Persons responsible for decisions on the acquisition and retirement of fixed assets need a general understanding of depreciation accounting for a variety of reasons. Two of these reasons are developed in the present chapter:

1. Often it is necessary to reconcile economy studies with the accounts of an enterprise. This need arises in various ways. Some data for economy studies come from the accounts and must be modified by conversion to cash flow before they are suitable for use in the economy studies. Frequently it is necessary that economy studies be related to the accounts for presentation to colleagues, to management personnel, or to the general public. The follow-up (if any) of decisions based on economy studies must be based in part on figures from the accounts.
2. There are in common use several methods of making so-called rate of return studies that depend on the depreciation accounts. The student of engineering economy needs to understand these methods in order to be aware of their deficiencies.

This book deals with depreciation accounting primarily in relation to engineering economy; there are many aspects of the subject that are not presented at all or that are discussed only briefly and superficially. Some other aspects of depreciation accounting referred to later in the book are as follows:

1. Chapters 14 and 16 point out certain common errors made in economy studies for retirements and replacements—errors that are related in part to a misunderstanding of depreciation accounting.
2. Chapter 15 shows how it is necessary to use depreciation accounting in estimating how disbursements for income taxes will be influenced by choices among alternative investments in fixed assets. The authors believe that this relationship between depreciation accounting and income taxes makes it essential that persons responsible for economy studies have some understanding of depreciation accounting.
3. Chapter 17 shows the relationship between depreciation accounting and one source of funds for investment in fixed assets. It also discusses the relationship between depreciation accounting and the provision of funds for the replacement of assets.
4. Chapter 19 discusses a common misuse of depreciation accounting in computing so-called payoff periods.
5. Appendix A discusses certain methods based on the depreciation accounts that are sometimes used for approximate calculations of equivalent uniform annual costs.

A Useful Definition. The accounting concept of depreciation is well described in a report of the Committee on Terminology of the American Institute of Certified Public Accountants as follows: [1]

Depreciation accounting is a system of accounting which aims to distribute the cost or other basic value of tangible capital assets, less salvage (if any), over the estimated useful life of the unit (which may be a group of assets) in a systematic and rational manner. It is a process of allocation, not of valuation. Depreciation for the year is the portion of the total charge under such a system that is allocated to the year. Although the allocation may properly take into account occurrences during the year, it is not intended to be a measurement of the effect of all such occurrences.

This definition will be referred to from time to time throughout our discussion of the subject.

The Balance Sheet and Profit and Loss Statement. Any presentation of the elements of accounting must focus attention on two important types of statements obtained from the accounts.

One of these, the *balance sheet,* describes the condition of an enterprise at a particular moment, for example, at the close of business on the final day of a fiscal year. The balance sheet shows what the enterprise owns (its assets), what it owes (its liabilities), and shows the "value" of the owners' equity in the enterprise as the excess of assets over liabilities. All balance sheet valuations are

[1] Accounting Research Bulletin 22, American Institute of Certified Public Accountants, 1944.

arrived at using the formal and systematic rules of accounting and sometimes differ greatly from market values of the same properties.

The other statement, the *profit and loss statement,* also called the *income statement,* gives the incomes and expenses of an enterprise as shown by the books of account for a period of time and states whether the enterprise has made a profit or loss and how much. The longest period of time covered by the usual profit and loss statement is a fiscal year. (A business fiscal year does not always coincide with the calendar year, as it may start on some date other than January 1.) The figures in the profit and loss statement, like those in the balance sheet, are determined using the formal and systematic rules of accounting.

Example 10–1 illustrates the relationship between depreciation accounting and the balance sheet and profit and loss statement in an extremely simple case. This example describes an actual investment from which certain complicating factors have been omitted. Example 10–2 deals with another actual case that is relatively simple, illustrating a common method of estimating year-by-year return on investment from the accounts. Both examples deal with terminated business enterprises. It will be noted that in Example 10–1 the enterprise finally turned out to be unsuccessful even though the initial indication from the accounts was that the enterprise was extremely profitable. In contrast, Example 10–2 deals with an enterprise that finally turned out to be much more profitable than it first seemed to be from an analysis of the accounts.

EXAMPLE 10–1. DEPRECIATION IN THE ACCOUNTS OF A MINIATURE GOLF COURSE

Facts of the Case. During the early days of so-called miniature golf courses during the depression years in the United States, an individual whom we shall call George Spelvin built the first such course in his home city. He rented a vacant lot in a strategic central location and spent $4,500 to construct his golf course. When he shut down for the winter at the end of his first year, he had taken in $5,000 in admission fees and had paid out $1,500 for various operating expenses. At this time he refused an offer of $8,500 from an amusement syndicate for his golf course and lease. When he commenced operations again in the spring of his second year, the local interest in miniature golf had declined to the point where his receipts barely covered his operating disbursements. He continued operations for a few months on this unsatisfactory basis and then abandoned his venture.

Financial Statements for the First Year and Their Relationship to Depreciation Accounting. At the time of completion of the construction of the golf course, the balance sheet for this enterpise (if one had been prepared) would have been as follows:

Assets		*Liabilities and Owner's Equity*	
Golf Course	$4,500	G. Spelvin, Invested Capital.....	$4,500

At the close of his first season, if Spelvin had not recognized that part of the service life of his golf course had expired, he would have believed that his profit was $3,500, the excess of his receipts over his disbursements. Under this unrealistic assumption, his balance sheet before his withdrawal of any of this "profit" would have been:

Assets		Liabilities and Owner's Equity	
Cash	$3,500	G. Spelvin, Invested Capital.....	$4,500
Golf Course	4,500	G. Spelvin, Retained Earnings...	3,500
	$8,000		$8,000

Actually he estimated a 5-year life for his golf course and decided to allocate $900, one-fifth of his $4,500 outlay, as the depreciation expense of the first year's operations. (We shall see that this is the straight-line method of depreciation accounting.) The book value of his golf course was reduced by $900 as a result of his accounting entry for this depreciation, and the figure for profit shown by his accounts was $900 less than it would have been if no depreciation had been recognized. His year-end balance sheet after giving recognition to this depreciation write-off was:

Assets			Liabilities and Owner's Equity	
Cash		$3,500	G. Spelvin, Invested Capital.....	$4,500
Golf Course	$4,500		G. Spelvin, Retained Earnings...	2,600
Less				
Allowance for Depreciation	900	3,600		
		$7,100		$7,100

His profit and loss statement for the year was:

Receipts from admissions...		$5,000
Less		
Operating Expenses:		
Disbursements for rent, taxes, attendance, upkeep...............	$1,500	
Depreciation on golf course...................................	900	2,400
Profit from first year's operations.......................................		$2,600

This profit shown by the books was 58% of Spelvin's original $4,500 investment.

Comment on the Foregoing Financial Statements. This simple example illustrates several important points regarding depreciation accounting, as follows:

1. The operation of making the $900 depreciation charge on the books of account involved no cash flow. In effect, the $900 depreciation entry was an allocation to the first year of operation of a portion of a previous $4,500 cash flow that the accounts had viewed as causing the acquisition of an asset rather than as the incurring of an expense.

(In Chapter 15, we shall see that even though the act of making a depreciation entry on the books does not in itself change the cash on hand, a depreciation entry in an income tax return influences the cash flow for income taxes. If Spelvin had paid income taxes and if the depreciation figure in his tax return had been based on his books of account, his tax payments would have been influenced by the depreciation charge entered in his books.)

2. The profit as shown by the books of account depends on the depreciation charge and therefore is influenced by the estimated life and salvage value and by the depreciation accounting method selected. Thus Spelvin's use of straight-line depreciation accounting and his assumption of a 5-year life and no salvage value gave him a profit figure of $2,600. If he had assumed a 2-year life and charged half of the $4,500 cost of the golf course as depreciation, his profit figure would have been only $1,250. If he had assumed that the golf course would always have 100% salvage value, his profit figure would have been $3,500. Although, as the quoted definition said, depreciation accounting requires the writing off of cost "in a systematic and rational manner," there are many different systematic and rational ways to write off cost, and these different ways give different figures for profit.

3. The valuation of assets on the balance sheet is similarly influenced by the depreciation charge. The so-called book value of an asset is merely that portion of the cost of the asset that has not yet been charged off as depreciation expense. The book value of the golf course was $3,600 at the end of the first year because $900 of depreciation had been charged against the year's operations and deducted from the $4,500 cost of the course. If the depreciation charge had been less than $900, the book value would have been higher; if the depreciation charge had been more than $900, the book value would have been lower.

The quoted definition of depreciation accounting pointed out that "it is a process of allocation and not of valuation." The valuation shown for a depreciable asset on the books of account is not influenced by unpredicted fluctuations in market value. Thus the $3,600 book value for the golf course was not influenced by the fact that the syndicate's offer, turned down by Spelvin, indicated that the course had a market value of $8,500 on the year-end date when the balance sheet was prepared.

EXAMPLE 10–2. YEAR-BY-YEAR ESTIMATES OF RATE OF RETURN FROM AN INVESTMENT IN RENTAL PROPERTY

Facts of the Case. Example 8–1 (page 114) described an investment in rental property. The cash flow series from this investment was shown in Table 8–1. The rate of return on the investment was 18.9% before income taxes, as computed in Table 8–2 by appropriate compound interest methods. Because a property costing $10,900 was sold for a net $20,900 after 7 years of ownership, the actual rate of return from the terminated investment was considerably higher than the rate of return had appeared to be during the period of ownership.

Table 10–1 shows the figures for annual profits as shown by the accounts of this enterprise for its first 6 years of operation. For purposes of accounting, the $10,900 investment was broken down as follows:

Land	$1,500
Buildings	8,000
Furniture	1,400

TABLE 10–1

ACCOUNTING FIGURES FOR ANNUAL PROFITS AND CURRENT ESTIMATES
OF RATE OF RETURN FOR DATA OF EXAMPLE 8–1

Year	Book Value at Start of Year	Receipts for Year	EXPENSES FOR YEAR		Profits for Year	Apparent Rate of Return on Investment
			Repairs, Taxes, etc.	Depre- ciation		
1	$10,900	$1,500	$500	$340	$ 660	6.1%
2	10,560	1,800	550	340	910	8.6
3	10,220	1,800	570	340	890	8.7
4	9,880	1,800	450	340	1,010	10.2
5	9,540	1,800	360	340	1,100	11.5
6	9,200	1,800	430	340	1,030	11.2

In accordance with the conventions of accounting, no prospective decrease (or increase) in the value of land was considered in the accounts. For purposes of depreciation accounting, the buildings were assumed to have a 40-year life with no salvage value, and the furniture was assumed to have a 10-year life with no salvage value. Straight-line depreciation was charged in the accounts at $200 a year for the buildings and at $140 a year for furniture, a total of $340 a year. The profit figures for each year shown in the next-to-last column of Table 10–1 are the years' positive cash flows diminished by the $340 depreciation charge.

The table also shows the book value of the property at the start of each year. In the first year this was the investment of $10,900; each year it was diminished by the $340 depreciation charge made in the books of account. The final column of the table shows the profit for each year expressed as a percentage of the start-of-year book value. This latter figure may be thought of as a current esti-mate of rate of return on investment computed by a method that often is used in relation to the accounts of an enterprise.[2]

Weakness of Certain "Approximate" Methods of Computing Rate of Return on Investment.

An incidental aspect of Examples 10–1 and 10–2 is that both examples illustrate the point that inter-mediate judgments of rates of return may be considerably in error. In fact, the two actual cases used in these examples are extreme cases deliberately selected to emphasize this point. In Example

[2] An alternate method, also frequently used, is to express the year's profit as a percentage of the average of the book values at the start and the finish of the year. For example, the 5th year's profit, $1,100, would be divided by $9,370 (the average of $9,540 and $9,200) to obtain an apparent return of 11.7%.

10–1 the rate of return appeared to be 58% at the end of the first year even though when the investment was terminated it turned out that there was not even a 0% return. In Example 10–2, the rates of return for the first three years appeared to be less than 9% even though the over-all rate of return on the terminated investment turned out to be approximately 19%.

Of course the true over-all rate of return obtained over the life of an investment cannot be known until ownership has been terminated. Nevertheless, year-by-year figures for profit are essential in the conduct of a business (and in the collection of income taxes); it is not practicable to wait until the termination of a business enterprise to draw conclusions regarding its profitability. It is natural to compute year-by-year rates of return by relating the profit figures taken from the accounts to some investment figure also taken from the accounts.

At this point in our discussion a clear distinction needs to be made between the problem of computing a single figure for rate of return on an investment based on the full period of consequences of the investment and the problem of estimating year-by-year figures for rate of return. As explained in Chapter 8 (and demonstrated in Table 8–5), compound interest methods are required to find the correct figure for rate of return over the life of an investment. The foregoing statement applies both to the calculation of rate of return from a terminated past investment and to the calculation of estimated rate of return from estimates of cash flow for the entire period of service of a proposed investment.

It is rarely, if ever, of much importance to find the rate of return on a terminated past investment (such as the one in Example 10–2). Although the rate of return may be of historical interest, nothing can be done about terminated investments.

In contrast, the estimation of rate of return on a proposed investment is a matter of great practical importance. Generally speaking, the best criterion of attractiveness of a proposed investment is the single figure that expresses the prospective rate of return over the life of the investment. It needs to be emphasized that it is this over-all rate of return that is significant for proposed investments, not year-by-year estimates of rates of return of the type illustrated in Table 10–1.

In the opinion of the authors of this book, there is seldom any valid reason for not using correct compound interest methods in analyzing proposed investments. A great deal of time and effort often goes into the making of estimates for economy studies relative to proposed investments. Only a few minutes more time are needed to apply methods of computing rate of return that are correct in principle than are needed to apply any of the various competing incorrect methods.

However, several incorrect methods of computing prospective rates of return on proposed investments are in common use in industry. Although these methods all have their origins in the type of calculations of rate of return on past investment illustrated in Examples 10–1 and 10–2, we shall see that the methods give results that differ greatly from one another. Sometimes these methods are used in the belief that they are good approximations to correct compound interest methods; sometimes they are used under the illusion that they are correct in principle.

Before we can describe and evaluate these "approximate" methods, we must first examine the most common methods of depreciation accounting.

General Comment on All Methods of Depreciation Accounting. As brought out in the quoted definition of depreciation accounting, it is the *cost* of tangible assets, less prospective salvage value, that is written off on the books of account. In effect, the cost of capital assets is viewed as a prepaid expense to be apportioned among the years of service of the assets "in a systematic and rational manner."

There are many different methods of writing off cost that obviously are "systematic." Moreover, methods that differ greatly from one another have been advocated as being "rational." In the United States the methods in common use have been influenced by changes in income tax laws and regulations, particularly by changes in 1934 and 1954 that will be mentioned in the following discussion.

One way to classify depreciation accounting methods is as follows:

1. Methods that aim to give a greater write-off in the early years of life than in the final years of life
2. Methods that aim to give a uniform write-off throughout the entire service life
3. Methods that aim to give a smaller write-off in the early years of life than in the final years

In class (1) we shall discuss the declining-balance method, the sum-of-the-years-digits method, and certain multiple-straight-line methods. In class (2) we shall discuss the straight-line method. In class (3) we shall discuss the sinking-fund method. Because of its historical importance, the straight-line method is discussed first.

Straight-Line Depreciation Accounting. In the straight-line method, the full service life of the asset is estimated. The prospective net salvage value at the end of the life is also estimated and expressed as a percentage of first cost. The annual depreciation rate to be applied to the first cost of the asset being written off is computed as follows:

$$\text{Straight-line rate} = \frac{100\% \text{ minus estimated salvage percentage}}{\text{estimated service life in years}}$$

Consider a machine tool with a first cost of $35,000, an estimated life of 20 years, and an estimated net salvage value of $3,500. The salvage percentage is $3,500 ÷ $35,000 = 0.10 or 10%.

$$\text{Straight-line rate} = \frac{100\% - 10\%}{20} = \frac{90\%}{20} = 4.5\%$$

With this straight-line depreciation rate, the depreciation charge every year will be $1,575 (i.e., 4.5% of the $35,000 first cost).

The same $1,575 may be computed without the use of the 4.5% figure, as follows:

Straight-line depreciation charge

$$= \frac{\text{first cost minus estimated salvage value}}{\text{estimated service life in years}}$$

$$= \frac{\$35,000 - \$3,500}{20} = \frac{\$31,500}{20} = \$1,575$$

Prior to 1934, it was common in the manufacturing industries of the United States for cost to be written off in a much shorter period than full service life. For example, the cost of machinery often was written off by a uniform annual charge during the first 10 years of its life. At the expiration of this period the machinery was carried on the books of account as "fully depreciated." It was not uncommon for the full service lives of machines so written off to be 20 or 25 years or even longer. Although in pre-1934 days, this method of write-off was described as "straight-line," we shall see that the method is more accurately described as a special case of multiple-straight-line depreciation accounting.

A change in policy of the U. S. Treasury Department in 1934 and thereafter was intended to force the writing off of cost for tax purposes over the full service life. With the straight-line method applied over full service life, the final years of life receive exactly the same depreciation charges as the initial years of life.

Declining-Balance Depreciation Accounting. It is common for assets to be used for stand-by or other inferior uses during the final years of their lives. The contribution of assets to income often is much greater in the early years of life than in the final years. For these reasons and for other reasons brought out in Chapter 15, it usually is sensible to write off the cost of assets more rapidly in the early years of life than in the later years.

Several ways of making this more rapid write-off in the early years were authorized for income tax purposes in the United States in 1954. The use of these new methods for tax purposes was restricted to assets having lives of three years or more that were acquired new by the taxpayers in 1954 or thereafter. One of these methods was the so-called double-rate declining-balance method.

In any declining-balance depreciation accounting, a given depreciation rate is applied each year to the remaining book value, that is, to that portion of the cost of an asset (or assets) that has not already been written off in a previous year. For example, if a 10% rate is applied to an asset that cost $35,000, the depreciation charge in the first year is 0.10($35,000) = $3,500. In the second year the charge is 0.10($35,000 − $3,500) = 0.10($31,500) = $3,150. In the third year it is 0.10($31,500 − $3,150) = 0.10($28,350) = $2,835. And so on.

In the double-rate declining-balance method authorized for income tax purposes in the United States in 1954, the depreciation rate is computed as $\dfrac{200\%}{\text{estimated life in years}}$. This rate is double the straight-line rate that would be allowed for an asset that has an estimated zero salvage value and the given estimated life. In computing the permissible declining-balance rate, the prospective terminal salvage value, if any, is disregarded.

Consider, for example, the $35,000 machine tool for which we computed the 4.5% straight-line rate. This had a 20-year estimated life and a $3,500 estimated salvage value. The permissible declining-balance rate for this asset is 200% ÷ 20 = 10%. The application of a 10% rate for 20 years will lead to a book value of $4,255 at the end of the 20th year.

If P represents the first cost of an asset and f represents the declining-balance rate expressed as a decimal, the book value at the end of r years obviously will be $P(1 - f)^r$. At this point in our discussion, the so-called textbook method of computing a declining-balance rate requires a brief mention. Assume that a rate f is desired that will make the book value at the end of an n-year life exactly equal to an estimated terminal salvage value, L. Then

$$L = P(1 - f)^n$$

and

$$f = 1 - \sqrt[n]{\frac{L}{P}}$$

However, this method of setting a declining-balance rate is rarely if ever used. It cannot be used with zero salvage value. Small differences in estimated salvage value make a great difference in the computed rate. For example, consider two $1,000 assets each with a 20-year estimated life, both with small prospective salvage values. Asset X has an estimated salvage value of $50; asset Y has an estimated salvage value of $1. The declining-balance percentage computed for X is 13.91% and for Y is 29.20%.

In the actual use of the declining-balance method, it is better to select a depreciation rate that seems appropriate, all things considered, than to compute a rate from the textbook formula. The declining-balance rates permitted by the 1954 tax laws and regulations in the United States are intended to permit a write-off of about two-thirds of the cost of an asset in the first half of the service life.

Sum-of-the-Years-Digits Depreciation Accounting.

This method, authorized in the United States by the 1954 tax law, apparently was never used in actual accounting practice before that date. The digits corresponding to the number of years of estimated life are added together. For example, consider our $35,000 machine tool with its estimated life of 20 years. The sum of the digits from 1 to 20 is 210. The depreciation charge for the first year is 20/210 of the depreciable cost (i.e., of the first cost minus the estimated salvage value). This is $20/210(\$35,000 - \$3,500) = 20/210(\$31,500) = \$3,000$. In the second year the charge is $19/210(\$31,500) = \$2,850$. In the third year it is $18/210(\$31,500) = \$2,700$. And so on. The charge decreases by $150 (i.e., by 1/210 of $31,500) each year until it is $150 in the 20th year.

This method writes off about three-fourths of the depreciable cost in the first half of the life.

Sinking-Fund Depreciation Accounting.

This method visualizes an imaginary sinking fund established by uniform end-of-year annual deposits throughout the life of an asset. These deposits are assumed to draw interest at some stated rate, such as 6%, 4%, or 3%, and are just sufficient so that the fund will equal the cost of the asset minus its estimated salvage value at the end of its estimated life. The amount charged as depreciation expense in any year consists of the sinking-fund deposit plus the interest on the imaginary accumulated fund. The book value at any time is the first cost of the asset minus the amount accumulated in the imaginary fund up to date. The sinking-fund method is also known as the present-worth method; the book value at any time is equal to the present worth of the uniform annual cost of capital recovery for the remaining years of life plus the present worth of the prospective salvage value.

For example, assume that our $35,000 machine tool is to be depreciated by the 6% sinking-fund method. The annual sinking-fund deposit is ($35,000 − $3,500)(sff–6%–20) = ($31,500)-(0.02718) = $856.2. This will also be the depreciation charge in the first year. In the second year the depreciation charge will be $856.2 + $856.2(0.06) = $907.6. In the third year it will be $856.2 + ($856.2 + $907.6)(0.06) = $962.0. And so on.

The book value at any age can be computed without year-by-year calculations by finding the amount in the imaginary sinking fund and subtracting this amount from the first cost. For instance, the sinking fund at the end of 12 years will amount to $856.2(caf–6%–12) = $856.2(16.870) = $14,444. The book value at this time is therefore $35,000 − $14,444 = $20,556. This book value may be checked by computing the present worth at date 12 of the annual cost of capital recovery for the remaining 8 years plus the present worth of the terminal salvage value. The annual capital recovery cost is ($35,000 − $3,500)(crf–6%–20) + $3,500(0.06) = ($31,500)-(0.08718) + $3,500(0.06) = $2,746.2 + $210.0 = $2,956.2. The sum of the present worths of remaining capital recovery and terminal salvage value is $2,956.2(pwf–6%–8) + $3,500(pwf'–6%–8) = $2,956.2(6.210) + $3,500(0.6274) = $18,358 + $2,196 = $20,554. (The interest tables in this book are not carried to enough significant figures for this calculation to check to the nearest dollar.)

Book values with the sinking-fund method are always greater than they would be with the straight-line method. The difference is greater for long-lived assets than for short-lived ones, and is greater with high interest rates than with low ones. The straight-line method has sometimes been described as the limiting case of the sinking-fund method in which the interest rate has been assumed to be 0%.

Although the sinking-fund method was used in certain industries a few decades ago, it has ceased to be of much importance in actual accounting practice. It is explained here primarily because of the use of so-called sinking-fund depreciation in certain engineering economy studies in a manner explained in Appendix A.

An Illustration of Depreciation Charges and Book Values by Various Methods. Table 10–2 shows the year-by-year write-offs that would be made for our $35,000 machine tool by the four methods that have been explained. The table also shows end-of-year book values. In the declining-balance and the 6% sinking-fund methods, the book values have been rounded off to the nearest dollar for listing in the table; the figures shown in the table for yearly depreciation charges have been made consistent with the figures shown for book value.

TABLE 10–2

COMPARISON OF DEPRECIATION CHARGES AND BOOK VALUES BY FOUR METHODS OF DEPRECIATION ACCOUNTING

(Asset has first cost of $35,000, estimated life of 20 years, and estimated salvage value of $3,500.)

Year	Depreciation Charge for Year				End-of-Year Book Value			
	Declining Balance	Years Digits	Straight Line	6% Sinking Fund	Declining Balance	Years Digits	Straight Line	6% Sinking Fund
0					$35,000	$35,000	$35,000	$35,000
1	$3,500	$3,000	$1,575	$ 856	31,500	32,000	33,425	34,144
2	3,150	2,850	1,575	908	28,350	29,150	31,850	33,236
3	2,835	2,700	1,575	962	25,515	26,450	30,275	32,274
4	2,551	2,550	1,575	1,020	22,964	23,900	28,700	31,254
5	2,297	2,400	1,575	1,081	20,667	21,500	27,125	30,173
6	2,067	2,250	1,575	1,146	18,600	19,250	25,550	29,027
7	1,860	2,100	1,575	1,215	16,740	17,150	23,975	27,812
8	1,674	1,950	1,575	1,287	15,066	15,200	22,400	26,525
9	1,506	1,800	1,575	1,365	13,560	13,400	20,825	25,160
10	1,356	1,650	1,575	1,447	12,204	11,750	19,250	23,713
11	1,221	1,500	1,575	1,533	10,983	10,250	17,675	22,180
12	1,098	1,350	1,575	1,626	9,885	8,900	16,100	20,554
13	998	1,200	1,575	1,723	8,897	7,700	14,525	18,831
14	890	1,050	1,575	1,827	8,007	6,650	12,950	17,004
15	801	900	1,575	1,936	7,206	5,750	11,375	15,068
16	720	750	1,575	2,052	6,486	5,000	9,800	13,016
17	649	600	1,575	2,175	5,837	4,400	8,225	10,841
18	584	450	1,575	2,306	5,253	3,950	6,650	8,535
19	525	300	1,575	2,444	4,728	3,650	5,075	6,091
20	473	150	1,575	2,591	4,255	3,500	3,500	3,500

It is evident that "systematic" ways of writing off cost can differ greatly from one another. Comment on the rational basis of a choice among the different methods is deferred until later in the chapter.

Some Other Methods of Depreciation Accounting. Some types of capital assets can be identified with the production of specific units of output. For such assets, depreciation can be charged in proportion to units of production provided it is reasonable to estimate life in production units. The method has been used for assets associated with exhaustible natural resources where the factor limiting the life of the assets is the quantity of the natural resource in question. Thus the cost of a sawmill might be depreciated at so much per thousand board feet sawed, or the cost of a coal mine tipple might be depreciated at so much per ton of coal mined. Frequently the unit-of-production method is used for motor vehicles with depreciation charged in proportion to miles of operation. The method is rarely used in diversified manufacturing because of the difficulty of finding any suitable production unit.

It is possible to use depreciation accounting methods where two or more straight lines are needed to show the decline in book value from first cost to estimated salvage value. Such a scheme may be described as a multiple-straight-line method. Under the United States 1954 tax law, multiple-straight-line methods may be used for tax purposes subject to the restriction that the amount written off at any time during the first two-thirds of life is not more than would have been permitted under the declining-balance method. For example, our $35,000 machine tool might be written off at $2,250 a year for the first 10 years and at $900 a year for the final 10 years.

A special case of the multiple-straight-line method is the one in which the entire first cost (less estimated salvage value, if any) is written off on a straight-line basis in some period shorter than the life. As previously stated, this was the common situation in the United States before 1934. When an asset with a 25-year life was written off at 10% a year for 10 years and 0% for the remaining 15 years, this was really a multiple-straight-line method with one of the straight-line rates as 0%.

Under the 1954 tax law in the United States, it is permissible to switch from the declining-balance method to the straight-line method at any time before an asset is retired. For example, Table 10–2 shows the book value of our machine tool by the declining-balance method to be $8,897 at the end of 13 years. If the estimated remaining life on this date is still 7 years and the estimated salvage value is still $3,500, a straight-line write-off of $\dfrac{\$8,897 - \$3,500}{7}$ = $771 a year could be used for the final 7 years.

Three Common Methods of Computing So-Called Rates of Return on Proposed Investments. There are many different ways in which prospective figures from the accounts are used to compute ratios that are alleged to be prospective rates of return. George Terborgh in the chapter entitled "Popular Rule-of-Thumb Tests of Investment Merit," in *Business Investment Policy* [3] reports attending a conference where 14 companies reported 14 different methods of this type of calculation.

----

[3] George Terborgh, *Business Investment Policy* (Washington, D.C.: Machinery and Allied Products Institute, 1958), p. 33.

The numerous schemes that the authors of this book have observed all seem to be variants of the following three methods:

1. The ratio of prospective average annual profit after depreciation to original investment is alleged to be the prospective rate of return on investment. Often this is referred to as the "original book" method.
2. The ratio of prospective average annual profit after depreciation to the average book value is alleged to be the prospective rate of return on investment. Often this is referred to as the "average book" method. In many instances it gives a figure for rate of return that is double the figure given by the original book method.
3. The figures for prospective profit after depreciation for each year are divided by the prospective book value figures for the start of the respective year in the way that was illustrated in Table 10–1. This division gives a series of ratios that are alleged to be year-by-year prospective rates of return. Conceivably, these rates might be averaged to give an over-all figure for rate of return.

All these methods may be used to compute so-called rates of return either before or after income taxes. Because the calculation of income tax payments is not discussed in this book until Chapter 15, our present illustrations must deal with the computation of rates of return *before* income taxes. The same objections that will be raised to the use of these methods to calculate rates of return before income taxes are equally applicable to their use for after-tax calculations.

Two Competing Investment Proposals. To illustrate these three methods and to demonstrate that all of them are inferior to correct compound interest methods, it is helpful to use some numerical examples. The following is adapted with some modifications from an illustration used by Horace G. Hill, Jr.,[4] for many years Budget Director of The Atlantic Refining Company.

Two investment proposals, a vacuum still and a product terminal, are competing for limited funds in an oil company. Each requires an immediate disbursement of $110,000, all of which will be capitalized on the books of account. In both cases the expected life is 10 years with zero salvage value. Straight-line depreciation will be used in the accounts.

The estimated positive cash flow resulting from the vacuum still will be $38,000 the first year, $34,000 the second, and will diminish by $4,000 a year until it is $2,000 in the tenth year. The estimated positive cash flow resulting from the product terminal will be

[4] Horace G. Hill, Jr., *A New Method of Computing Rate of Return on Capital Expenditures,* a pamphlet published privately by the author (Berwyn, Pa., 1953).

$5,000 in the first year, $9,000 in the second, and will increase by
$4,000 a year until it is $41,000 in the tenth year. With a trial-and-
error present worth solution and with the aid of Table E–24, the
respective rates of return are computed as follows:

Vacuum Still

$$\text{PW at } 15\% = -\$110,000 + \$38,000(\text{pwf-}15\%\text{-}10) - \$4,000(\text{gpwf-}15\%\text{-}10)$$
$$= -\$110,000 + \$38,000(5.019) - \$4,000(16.98) = +\$12,800$$
$$\text{PW at } 20\% = -\$110,000 + \$38,000(\text{pwf-}20\%\text{-}10) - \$4,000(\text{gpwf-}20\%\text{-}10)$$
$$= -\$110,000 + \$38,000(4.192) - \$4,000(12.89) = -\$2,260$$

Interpolation indicates a return of slightly over 19%.

Product Terminal

$$\text{PW at } 10\% = -\$110,000 + \$5,000(\text{pwf-}10\%\text{-}10) + \$4,000(\text{gpwf-}10\%\text{-}10)$$
$$= -\$110,000 + \$5,000(6.144) + \$4.000(22.89) = +\$12,280$$
$$\text{PW at } 12\% = -\$110,000 + \$5,000(\text{pwf-}12\%\text{-}10) + \$4,000(\text{gpwf-}12\%\text{-}10)$$
$$= -\$110,000 + \$5,000(5.650) + \$4,000(20.25) = -\$750$$

Interpolation indicates a return of slightly less than 12%.

As a 19% return is considerably better than a 12% one, it is evident that the vacuum still is the more attractive project.

The straight-line depreciation for each project will be $11,000 a
year for 10 years, 10% of the original $110,000 investment. Let us
assume that all cash flow except the original investment will affect
the profit or loss figure on the books of account in the year when
the cash flow occurs. Then the influence of each project on the
prospective enterprise profit each year will be the positive cash flow
minus the $11,000 depreciation charge. A tabulation of the esti-
mated year-by-year influences of the two projects on the profit to
be shown by the accounts is as follows:

Year	Vacuum Still	Product Terminal
1	+$27,000	−$ 6,000
2	+23,000	−2,000
3	+19,000	+2,000
4	+15,000	+6,000
5	+11,000	+10,000
6	+7,000	+14,000
7	+3,000	+18,000
8	−1,000	+22,000
9	−5,000	+26,000
10	−9,000	+30,000
Total profit	+$90,000	+$120,000
Average annual profit	+$ 9,000	+$ 12,000

Rate of Return (So-Called) by Original Book Method. In this
method the average annual estimated profit is divided by the esti-

mated original investment. The calculations for the two projects are:

$$\text{``Rate of return'' on vacuum still} = \frac{\$9,000}{\$110,000} = 0.082 \text{ or } 8.2\%$$

$$\text{``Rate of return'' on product terminal} = \frac{\$12,000}{\$110,000} = 0.109 \text{ or } 10.9\%$$

It is evident that this method of calculation ranks our two projects in the wrong order. This error is due to the failure of the method to give any weight whatsoever to the *timing* of the consequences of a project. The figure for "average profit," the *numerator* of the fraction, fails to reflect the difference between a dollar in the near future and one in the distant future.

It also is evident that the method has given us figures for rates of return that are less than the rates that we computed by correct compound interest methods. In most cases the original book method will understate the true rate of return. The difficulty here is that the *denominator* of the fraction, the full original investment, is too large since it fails to reflect the concept that the year-by-year positive cash flow should be viewed in part as a recovery of the money originally disbursed.

Rate of Return (So-Called) by Average Book Method. In this method the average annual estimated profit is divided by the average book value over the life of the project (or possibly over the period of the economy study). As the book value in both of our projects declines uniformly from \$110,000 to \$0 over the 10-year period, the average book value in each is \$55,000. The calculations for the two projects are:

$$\text{``Rate of return'' on vacuum still} = \frac{\$9,000}{\$55,000} = 0.164 \text{ or } 16.4\%$$

$$\text{``Rate of return'' on product terminal} = \frac{\$12,000}{\$55,000} = 0.218 \text{ or } 21.8\%$$

This method also ranks our projects in the wrong order, making the better project appear to be the poorer one. Just as in the original book method, the numerator of the fraction gives no weight to the timing of the consequences of a project.

The difference between the average book and original book methods is entirely in the denominator of the fraction that gives the computed rate of return. The use of an average figure in the denominator recognizes the viewpoint that the investment is being recovered throughout the life of a project rather than on the date the project terminates.

In our example, the denominators in the average book method are half those in the original book and the computed rates of return are double those of the original book. However, this two-to-one relationship between the two methods does not always exist. For example, it will not exist for a project that does not have zero salvage value. In the special case where the salvage value is 100%, the two methods give the same figure for rate of return.

Rates of Return (So-Called) from Year-by-Year Estimated Profits and Book Values. In this method the estimated profit to be shown by the books for each year is divided by the computed book value for the start of the year in question (or in some cases by the average of the start-of-year and end-of-year book values). Both the profit figures and the book values depend on the method of depreciation accounting to be used. This point is illustrated in Tables 10-3 and 10-4, which show the application of this method of computing rate of return to our two competing projects. The tables show calculations using straight-line depreciation and also using years-digits depreciation.

Several aspects of this method of computing prospective rate of return make its use undesirable for economy studies. Some objections to this method, illustrated by Tables 10-3 and 10-4, are as follows:

1. Even if the year-by-year computed rates of return had any validity as a guide to decision making on proposed investments, the

TABLE 10-3

APPARENT YEARLY RATES OF RETURN FROM VACUUM STILL PROJECT
ASSUMING TWO METHODS OF DEPRECIATION ACCOUNTING
(All dollar figures in thousands)

Year	Profit Before Depreciation	Straight-Line Depreciation				Years-Digits Depreciation			
		Year's Depreciation	Profit	Start-of-Year Book Value	Rate of Return	Year's Depreciation	Profit	Start-of-Year Book Value	Rate of Return
1	$ 38	$ 11	+$27	$110	+24.5%	$ 20	+$18	$110	+16.4%
2	34	11	+23	99	+23.2%	18	+16	90	+17.8%
3	30	11	+19	88	+21.6%	16	+14	72	+19.4%
4	26	11	+15	77	+19.5%	14	+12	56	+21.4%
5	22	11	+11	66	+16.7%	12	+10	42	+23.8%
6	18	11	+7	55	+12.7%	10	+8	30	+26.7%
7	14	11	+3	44	+6.8%	8	+6	20	+30.0%
8	10	11	−1	33	−3.0%	6	+4	12	+33.3%
9	6	11	−5	22	−22.7%	4	+2	6	+33.3%
10	2	11	−9	11	−81.8%	2	0	2	0.0%
Totals	$200	$110	+$90		+17.5%	$110	+$90		+222.1%
		Average rate of return....			+1.7%	Average rate of return..			+22.2%

TABLE 10–4

APPARENT YEARLY RATES OF RETURN FROM PRODUCT TERMINAL PROJECT
ASSUMING TWO METHODS OF DEPRECIATION ACCOUNTING

(All dollar figures in thousands)

Year	Profit Before Depre- ciation	Straight-Line Depreciation				Years-Digits Depreciation			
		Year's Depre- ciation	Profit	Start- of-Year Book Value	Rate of Return	Year's Depre- ciation	Profit	Start- of-Year Book Value	Rate of Return
1	$ 5	$ 11	— $ 6	$110	—5.5%	$ 20	— $ 15	$110	—13.6%
2	9	11	—2	99	—2.0%	18	—9	90	—10.0%
3	13	11	+2	88	+2.3%	16	—3	72	—4.2%
4	17	11	+6	77	+7.8%	14	+3	56	+5.4%
5	21	11	+10	66	+15.2%	12	+9	42	+21.4%
6	25	11	+14	55	+25.5%	10	+15	30	+50.0%
7	29	11	+18	44	+40.9%	8	+21	20	+105.0%
8	33	11	+22	33	+66.7%	6	+27	12	+225.0%
9	37	11	+26	22	+118.2%	4	+33	6	+550.0%
10	41	11	+30	11	+272.7%	2	+39	2	+1,950.0%
Totals	$230	$110	+$120		+541.9%	$110	+$120		+2,879.0%
		Average rate of return..			+54.2%	Average rate of return...			+287.9%

rates would be difficult to interpret. The many different rates computed for a single project are confusing; it is much better to have
a single figure indicating an over-all rate of return. It is evident
from Tables 10–3 and 10–4 that this difficulty cannot be resolved in
a satisfactory manner by taking an average of the year-by-year
rates. The vacuum still project, shown by correct methods to have
a 19% return, has an average return of less than 2% when straight-
line depreciation is assumed; the product terminal project, shown
by correct methods to have a 12% return, has an average return of
nearly 290% when years-digits depreciation is assumed.

2. A method of computing rate of return before income taxes
should not be influenced by the arbitrary time-allocation of the
investment among accounting periods. Both Tables 10–3 and 10–4
bring out the point that the foregoing principle is violated by this
method of computing rate of return. Both of our projects seem to
look much better with the years-digits method than with the
straight-line method of depreciation accounting.

(In Chapter 15 we shall see that when years-digits or declining-
balance depreciation is used for income tax purposes, the rate of
return *after* income taxes usually will be a little higher than when
straight-line depreciation is used for tax purposes. This after-tax
difference in rate of return results from the influence of the depreciation accounting method on the *timing* of cash flow for income

taxes. However, the effect of a depreciation accounting method on the timing of tax payments is an entirely different topic from the analysis of various methods of computing so-called rates of return.)

3. Like the original book and average book methods, the method of computing year-by-year rates of return fails to array proposals correctly in the order of their merit. All three methods make the inferior project, the product terminal, seem to be better than the superior project, the vacuum still.

General Comment on the Foregoing Three Methods of Computing Rate of Return. Our calculations of rates of return for our two projects have demonstrated that these methods, sometimes described as "approximate," may give figures that actually are very poor approximations to the rate of return that would be computed by correct compound interest methods. We have also seen that the various methods give quite different answers. Although the correct figure for the vacuum still project was about 19%, our different calculations gave us answers of 8.2%, 16.4%, 1.7%, and 22.2%. Although the correct figure for the product terminal project was about 12%, our answers here were 10.9%, 21.8%, 54.2%, and 287.9%.

We also noted that all of the methods ranked our two projects in the wrong order; the inferior project seemed to be better than the superior one. Of course it is not always true that these methods will give an incorrect ranking of proposed investments. Ordinarily the chief cause of an incorrect ranking is the failure of the methods to give proper weight to the timing of cash flow. Our example comparing the vacuum still with the product terminal was chosen to stress this particular weakness of these common methods of computing rates of return; the vacuum still had most of its positive cash flow in the early years of its life whereas the product terminal had the largest part of its positive cash flow in the final years of its life.

However, our example comparing the vacuum still and the product terminal did not illustrate a quite different weakness of these three methods. In a correct calculation of rate of return before income taxes by compound interest methods, it is immaterial whether a cash disbursement is to be capitalized on the books of account or whether it is to be charged as an expense in the year when it occurs. But the three methods that we have discussed all use book value (original or average or the current year's) as the denominator in a fraction stated to be the rate of return. "Book value" ordinarily refers only to items that are capitalized on the books of account. Thus two projects having identical cash flows might appear to have quite different rates of return if the two projects are to be treated differently in the accounts. This type of error may lead to incorrect ranking of projects and may also increase the inherent errors in the rates of return computed by these three methods.

Why Are Incorrect Methods of Computing Rate of Return in Common Use? A reader of this book who is not already employed in an organization using one of these methods may well ask why methods of analysis that are so erratic and unreliable are so widely used. This is a good question to which the authors are unable to give a fully satisfactory answer. George Terborgh [5] refers to these and similar methods of analysis as "really industrial folklore, handed down from one generation of management to the next. They have no scientific rationale, no legitimate intellectual parentage."

In some instances it doubtless is true that the methods are used because the people who use them are not aware that any better methods are available. But there are many cases where analysts consciously reject compound interest methods of computing rates of return in favor of the original book or average book method. The choice of book methods usually is defended by the following arguments:

1.   Book methods are alleged to be easier to apply.
2.   Book methods are alleged to be easier to explain to others.

The greater ease of application of book methods is not a valid argument for their use. There are many economy studies in which compound interest methods can be applied as easily as book methods, once the compound interest methods are understood by the analyst. Moreover, even where compound interest methods require, say, an extra half-hour of an analyst's time, this extra time usually is trivial in relation to the many hours of time that have been spent on the gathering of data to be used in the economy study.

In many organizations it is true that the book methods are easier to explain. Unless managers and engineers have some understanding of compound interest, methods that seem to be tied to the books of account can be explained more readily than methods that use the mathematics of compound interest. The answer to this argument is that, as we have pointed out, book methods lead to erratic and unreliable answers that cannot be trusted as a basis for action; com-

[5] Terborgh, *op. cit.*, p. 28.

pound interest methods should be used in spite of the greater difficulty of explaining them.

A pertinent comment on this subject is made by Ray I. Reul of the Chemical Divisions of Food Machinery and Chemical Corporation, as follows: [6]

Another obstacle to the acceptance of an objective method (of computing rate of return) is the desire of nearly all business executives to find a method of evaluation that will be directly comparable to accounting evaluations of current operations. I would like to, too! But I know it cannot be done. It is time the inevitable was faced. The search for such a method is like looking for a pot of gold at the end of the rainbow—foredoomed to failure. It is an impossibility which has been given the cloak of plausibility by the use of the same words, "rate of return on investment," to describe . . . entirely different concepts.

What Meaning Shall Be Attached to the Phrase "Rate of Return" as Applied to Proposed Investments? In our initial discussion of equivalence in Chapter 3, we examined a loan transaction in which an investor exchanged an initial cash disbursement of $10,000 for the prospect of end-of-year cash receipts of $1,358.68 a year for 10 years. It was shown (in the tabulation for Plan III, Table 3–1) that this series of receipts enables the investor to recover his investment with exactly 6% interest per annum. It might also be stated that he is scheduled to recover his investment with a 6% rate of return.

This is the only sense of rate of return that is a sound and consistent guide to action regarding proposed investments, and it is the only sense in which the phrase is used in this book. Where one of the methods based on the depreciation accounts is employed, we use the phrase "so-called rate of return."

(It may be of interest to apply the various methods based on the books of account to our simple case of the $10,000 investment recovered at 6% interest by $1,358.68 a year for 10 years. By the original book method, the rate of return appears to be 3.59%. By the average book method, it appears to be 7.17%. The year-by-year method depends on the scheme used for a time allotment of the investment among the 10 years; if a straight-line allotment is used, the return appears to vary from 3.59% the first year to 35.87% the 10th year.)

Arguments on the silly and unanswerable question "What does rate of return really mean?" have been so heated in some industries that certain industrial writers have tried to avoid the question by coining other phrases for rate of return obtained by correct compound interest methods. Thus Reul uses the phrase "Profitability Index" or "PI" in this meaning. Weaver and Reilly of Atlas Powder Company have suggested the phrase "interest rate of return" to be used in this same sense.[7]

A Classification of Reasons for Retirement. Property units are generally retired for one or more of the following reasons:

1. *The availability of improved machines or structures for performing the same service.* Research and development work by scientists and engineers is continually leading to new and more economical ways of doing existing jobs. If the prospective economies from new methods are sufficient, it will pay to replace old assets with new ones or to relegate the old assets to stand-by purposes or other inferior uses.

2. *Changes in the amount and type of service requirements.* This includes such changes as increase or decrease in the amount of service required from the old asset, due to an increase or decrease in the demand for its product or service. It also includes changes in the product or service required. These changes frequently arise from competitive situations, either from competition among producers in a single industry or from competition with substitute products or services. They may also be caused by acts of public authority.

3. *Changes in the existing machines or structures themselves.* Machines and structures wear out, corrode, and decay as the result of age and use. Often this increases maintenance costs and decreases the quality and reliability of performance to the extent that it pays to replace assets that are still capable of continuing to render service. In some circumstances wearing out, corrosion, and decay may make retirement imperative rather than merely economical.

4. *Changes in public requirements regarding the machine or structure.*

5. *Casualties.*

These reasons for retirement are not mutually exclusive, but in most cases operate in combination with one another. Thus an old machine might be replaced by a new one that (1) incorporated new automatic features that reduced unit labor costs, (2) provided increased capacity to meet an increased demand for the product, and (3) had the prospect of initial maintenance costs considerably lower than the current high maintenance costs of the old machine.

Reasons Why Economical Replacements Are Often Deferred. In modern industrial society most retirements are made because

---

[7] J. B. Weaver and R. J. Reilly, "Interest Rate of Return for Capital Expenditure Evaluation," *Chemical Engineering Progress,* LII, No. 10 (October, 1956), 405–12.

someone decides that it will pay to make them. They are made even though the assets to be retired are still capable of rendering service at a cost for many years more.

However, many causes operate to defer the retirement of assets beyond the date when retirement is really economical. These causes operate particularly when retirements are associated with replacements. Some of them are:

1. In general, decisions regarding replacements tend to be made on a very conservative basis, with the result that many replacements that would really turn out to be economical are put off.

2. The necessary funds may not be available to finance the purchase of replacement assets.

3. Even though the financing of replacements may be possible, the conditions of the financing may make it seem undesirable from the viewpoint of the people who must make the decisions. For example, if corporate profits are retained in the business beyond a limited point, a corporation in the United States may be subject to a special federal surtax on "improper accumulation of surplus." (See Chapter 15 for a discussion of this.) Or, as another example, the controlling stockholders in a closed corporation will naturally be reluctant to undertake financing that may result in the loss of their control.

4. There may be uncertainty about the continuation of the present demand for the product or service. Such uncertainty is particularly common whenever there is a belief that a business recession is imminent. This uncertainty naturally operates to defer replacements.

5. The existence of any considerable book value for an existing asset unfortunately may operate as a barrier to its replacement. As explained in Chapter 14, this is an illogical barrier. Nevertheless, it is an important one in fact and does prevent many economical replacements.

It should be noted that all of these causes operate in the same direction. They all tend to lengthen the actual lives of industrial property units beyond the point where it would really be economical to make replacements. There are no such common causes operating in the opposite direction.

Mortality Dispersion for Physical Property Units. Not all human beings die at the same age. Some die young and others live to a ripe old age. Nevertheless, it is possible to analyze human mortality experience to determine curves and tables that give satisfactory estimates of average life and of the percentage of survivors at any age. Thus a life insurance company can predict with confidence what percentage of 100,000 healthy white native males 20 years old will survive to the ages of 27 or 49 or 65, even though it is not possible to say with respect to any individual whether he will survive any given number of years.

Physical property units are like human beings in having a mortality dispersion. Of a number of property units that seem identical, some will be retired at an early age and others will serve many years

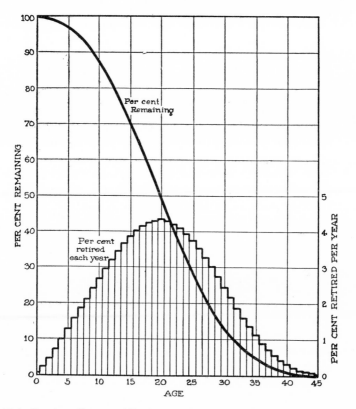

FIGURE 10–1. Survivor Curve and Retirement-Frequency Curve for Certain Telephone Underground Cable

before retirement. This fact of mortality dispersion is illustrated in Figure 10–1. This figure shows two curves that have been derived in the analysis of the retirement experience of telephone exchange underground cable.

The reversed curve starting in the upper left-hand corner of the diagram is called a *survivor curve*. It shows the percentage of this type of plant that, in the particular group of cable studied, may be expected to be in service at any given number of years after its installation. For instance, 70% will be in service after 15 years of life.

The lower stepped curve is a *retirement frequency curve*. It shows the annual retirements expressed as a percentage of the original amount installed. Although the maximum number of retirements is at age 20, retirements are taking place from the 1st year of life to the 44th year.

These curves are mathematically fitted ideal curves derived from a certain group of actual data involving several million dollars' worth of exchange underground cable. Curves of this type have been developed in connection with the requirements of depreciation accounting.

Estimating Service Life. Certain types of assets, such as automobiles, may have several owners before reaching the scrap heap. For each owner, the "life" for accounting purposes should be the expected period of service to the owner himself. In general, service life for accounting purposes is viewed as the number of years elapsing from an asset's acquisition to its final disposal by the particular owner, regardless of the different uses to which the asset may have been put during these years. Since 1934, the foregoing view of service life has governed the administration of income tax laws in the United States.

Where sufficient data are available, various types of statistical studies may be made to estimate average service lives. In many cases such studies lead to survivor curves of the type illustrated in Figure 10–1. Statistical studies made year after year for a particular class of assets often indicate that the average realized life has been changing.[8]

In the absence of statistical studies, published compilations of average service lives are available for guidance. A document developed for income tax purposes in the United States contains estimated average useful lives for several thousand different types of industrial assets.[9]

In many cases an economy study to guide a decision on whether or not to acquire an asset should use a shorter estimated life than the one that will be used in the accounts if the asset is acquired. It is the economic life that is relevant in decision making, not the full service life—which, for reasons already stated, may be considerably longer than economic life. Moreover, an economy study usually relates to the primary or initial type of service of an asset; it is rarely appropriate in an economy study to give much consideration

---

[8] For a concise explanation of the various statistical methods of estimating average service life, see E. L. Grant and P. T. Norton, Jr., *Depreciation* (New York: The Ronald Press Co., 1955), chap. v.

[9] U. S. Treasury Department, Internal Revenue Service, *Bulletin F, Estimated Useful Lives and Depreciation Rates* (Washington, D.C.: Government Printing Office).

to possible stand-by or other inferior services during the final years of an asset's life.

Certain Types of Assets Not Subject to Depreciation Charges in the Accounts. It is a convention of accounting that land is carried on the books at its original cost regardless of changes in its market value. No depreciation or appreciation on land is shown in the books of account. Of course, if land is finally sold at a price above or below its original cost, a "gain" or "loss" assigned to the year of the sale is shown on the books. But for accounting purposes, it is not necessary to make an estimate of the future sale price of land.

In the absence of any basis for a different forecast, some economy studies may follow the lead of orthodox accounting and assume—in effect—that investments in land will have 100% salvage values. But cases occur where this is not an appropriate assumption. Sometimes there is good reason to forecast that at the end of a study period land will be sold for much more or much less than its original cost. If so, this forecast is relevant in any analysis to guide the decision on whether or not to invest in the land; the estimated future sale price of the land is one element of cash flow to include in the economy study.

Many economy studies relate to the investment in plant to permit the sale of a new product or expanded sale of an existing product. In addition to the investment in physical plant, such a project usually requires an outlay for *working funds*. The working fund investment will usually include inventories of materials, work in process, and finished goods. It will also include the excess of accounts receivable associated with the project over accounts payable similarly associated. For certain types of product there may also be an inventory of returnable containers.

The working fund investment is not subject to depreciation on the books of account. For purposes of an economy study an outlay for working funds should ordinarily be treated as if it were an investment that had a prospective 100% salvage value at the end of the study period. That is, it usually is reasonable to expect that when a product is discontinued the accounts receivable will be collected and the inventories will be liquidated. Comments on certain aspects of the estimation of working fund requirements are made in Chapter 14.

The Various Meanings of "Depreciation." The meanings of words develop out of their use. Many words are used in a number of different meanings. Depreciation is such a word. In any use of the word, there needs to be a clear differentiation among these various meanings.

In his outstanding book, *Valuation of Property,* Professor J. C. Bonbright [10] points out that substantially all the different technical meanings attached to the word *depreciation* are variants of four basic concepts. These are:

1. DECREASE IN VALUE. This concept implies that the value of one asset is in some way computed at two different dates. The value at the later date subtracted from the value at the earlier date is the *depreciation* regardless of what combination of causes may have been responsible for the value change. When depreciation is used in everyday speech, this is the meaning generally implied; it is also implied by most dictionary definitions.

Like depreciation, *value* is a word with many meanings. As pointed out by Professor Bonbright, the two most important and useful of these meanings in the economic sense of the word are *market value* and *value to the owner.* These two concepts are discussed briefly later in this chapter. Depreciation in the sense of decrease in value may apply to either of these two concepts of value. Values may be determined by actual market price, by appraisal, or in any other appropriate way.

2. AMORTIZED COST. This is the accounting concept of depreciation, which has been explained in the present chapter. From the viewpoint of accounting, the cost of an asset is a prepaid operating expense to be apportioned among the years of its life by some more or less systematic procedure. It should be emphasized that it is cost, not value, that is apportioned in orthodox accounting.

Although we have used the common phrase *book value* to describe the difference between the cost of an asset and the total of the depreciation charges made to date against the asset, this difference is more accurately described as *unamortized cost.*

3. DIFFERENCE IN VALUE BETWEEN AN EXISTING OLD ASSET AND A HYPOTHETICAL NEW ASSET TAKEN AS A STANDARD OF COMPARISON. This is the appraisal concept of depreciation. Many appraisals of old assets are based on replacement cost. A replacement cost appraisal should answer the question "What could one afford to pay for this asset in comparison with the most economical new one?"

An upper limit on the value to its owner of an old asset may be determined by considering the cost of reproducing its service with

[10] J. C. Bonbright, *Valuation of Property* (New York: McGraw-Hill Book Co., Inc., 1937), chap. x.

the most economical new asset available for performing the same service. This most economical new substitute asset may have many advantages over an existing old asset, such as longer life expectancy, lower annual disbursements for operation and maintenance, increased receipts from sale of product or service. The deduction from the cost of the hypothetical new substitute asset should be a measure in money terms of all of these disadvantages of the existing old asset.

In the language of appraisal, this deduction is called *depreciation*. Appraisal depreciation, therefore, should mean the value inferiority at some particular date (the date of the appraisal) of one asset, the existing old one being appraised, to another asset, a hypothetical new one used as the basis of valuation. This concept implies two assets and the measurement of their values at one date.

4. IMPAIRED SERVICEABLENESS. As machines become older they are often unable to hold as close tolerances as when they were new. Similarly, the strength of structures may be impaired by the decay of timber members or the corrosion of metal members. Engineers have sometimes used the word *depreciation* to refer to such impaired functional efficiency.

It should be emphasized that this is not a value concept at all. Impaired serviceableness may result in decrease in value, but there are many other common reasons for decrease in value. Assets that are physically as good as new are not necessarily as valuable as when they were new. They may have higher operation and maintenance costs; they will nearly always have shorter life expectancy; service conditions may have changed; more economical alternative methods may have become available. As the use of depreciation in the sense of impaired serviceableness has generally led to confusion in valuation matters, the word is not used in this sense elsewhere in this book.

Concepts of Value.[11] As previously stated, the most useful economic concepts of value are *market value* and *value to the owner*.

Market value properly refers to the price at which a property could actually be sold. For certain types of valuation this is not an appropriate concept to use. Often only one owner is in a position to make effective use of a given item of property; although continued possession of this property may be of great monetary importance to its owner, the property might bring only a negligible price if sold to someone else.

---

[11] For an authoritative and thorough discussion of value concepts, see *ibid.*, chaps. iii, iv, and v.

Hence the concept of value to a specific owner is of great importance in the valuation of property. Value to the owner may be defined as the money amount that would be just sufficient to compensate the owner if he were to be deprived of the property. Generally speaking, this value will not be greater than the money amount for which the owner could soon replace the property with the best available substitute, with due allowance for the superiority or inferiority of that substitute. And, generally speaking, value to the owner will not be less than the market price for which the property could be sold. The concept of value to the owner may properly be applied to a prospective owner as well as to a present owner.

The word *value* is also sometimes used in what might be called a neutral sense as any money amount that is associated with specific items of property for some given purpose. An example of this is the use of the phrase *book value* to describe the unamortized cost of property as shown by the books of account.

Relationship Between the Annual Cost of Capital Recovery with a Return and the Depreciation Charge in the Accounts. Consider our first illustration of an annual cost comparison in Chapter 6. In Example 6–1, we analyzed a proposal to invest \$15,000 in certain materials handling equipment. This equipment had an estimated life of 10 years with a zero terminal salvage value. As the minimum attractive rate of return was 10%, we computed the equivalent uniform annual cost of capital recovery as follows:

$$CR = \$15,000(crf{-}10\%{-}10) = \$2,441$$

This calculation told us that \$2,441 a year for 10 years was required to recover a \$15,000 investment with a 10% rate of return. To recover the same investment in 10 years with a 0% rate of return would obviously have required only $\$15,000 \div 10 = \$1,500$ a year. The difference of \$941 between the \$2,441 and the \$1,500 was due to the difference between a 10% rate of return and a 0% rate.

If the same 10-year life and zero salvage value used in the economy study are to be used in the accounts if the \$15,000 investment is made, and if straight-line depreciation is used, the annual depreciation charge will be \$1,500. Moreover, regardless of the depreciation accounting method, \$1,500 is the *average* depreciation charge required to write off \$15,000 in 10 years. Thus in reconciling an economy study based on equivalent uniform annual cost with the books of account, the depreciation charge may be thought of as capital recovery with a 0% return. Or capital recovery with a stated rate of return may be thought of as average depreciation plus enough extra to yield the stated rate of return (or to yield a stated interest rate).

The foregoing view of the matter may help the reader to avoid an error sometimes made by persons who are introduced for the first time to the calculation of equivalent annual costs. This error is to add depreciation and capital recovery cost. Someone making this error in Example 6–1 would have added the $1,500 average depreciation and the $2,441 capital recovery cost to obtain a total of $3,941. It should be obvious that such an addition provides for a double recovery of the $15,000 investment during the 10-year period—one recovery at 0% interest and the other at 10%.

In some of the literature of engineering economy, the figure we have described as capital recovery with a return is described as depreciation plus interest. Where this description is employed, depreciation and interest are usually computed separately and then added together to obtain an annual cost figure. Different methods of defining "depreciation" and "interest" may be employed. The most common combinations are sinking-fund depreciation plus interest on first cost, straight-line depreciation plus interest on first cost, and straight-line depreciation plus average interest. The different combinations will, of course, give different totals. Appendix A illustrates these three methods of computing annual cost of capital recovery and discusses their good and bad points.

It should be noted that in the frequent cases where the estimate of life or salvage value to be used in the economy study differs from the estimate to be used in the accounts, there is no point in trying to reconcile the economy study with the accounts. Moreover, decision making on proposed investments (the usual objective of an economy study) should be concerned with prospective change in market value or value to the owner (depreciation or appreciation in the popular sense) rather than with amortization of cost (depreciation in the accounting sense). This particular aspect of the difference in viewpoint between engineering economy and accounting is brought out in Chapters 14 and 16 in connection with our discussion of economy studies for retirements and replacements.

Distinction Between Single-Asset and Multiple-Asset Depreciation Accounting.[12] Assume a group of assets that have the mortality distribution shown in Figure 10–1. Although the average service life of these assets is 20 years, retirements occur all the way from the first to the 45th year. For the sake of simplicity in the following illustration, assume that the expected salvage value is zero and that each asset, when retired, actually has a zero salvage value. Assume that straight-line depreciation is to be used; the

---

[12] For a more complete discussion of this topic, see Grant and Norton, *op. cit.*, particularly chaps. vi, vii, viii, x, and xix.

20-year average service life and zero salvage value requires a 5% depreciation rate.

Now assume that each asset has its own account and that the depreciation on each asset is computed separately. (This is referred to as *single-asset* or *item* depreciation accounting.) Approximately half of the assets will be retired before they are 20 years old. Every such asset will have some book value when retired; with no realized salvage value, the books of account will show a "loss" for each retirement. The half of the assets that survive for more than 20 years will be fully written off at age 20; no further depreciation charges will be made against them during their period of service from years 20 to 45.

In contrast, assume that one account is used to include the investment in all of these assets; each year the depreciation charge is made against the group of assets rather than against the individual assets and the book value at any time applies to the group with no identifiable separate figure applicable to each asset. With the assets considered in a group and with the fact of mortality dispersion recognized, it will be evident that the retirements at ages short of 20 years are not "premature" in the sense that they are inconsistent with the estimate of a 20-year *average* service life. If a set of unequal numbers are averaged, some of the numbers must be less than the average and others must be greater. The recognition of this point in multiple-asset depreciation accounting eliminates the "loss on disposal" entry under normal circumstances. However, in multiple-asset accounting, depreciation charges continue beyond the average service life.

In the language used in publications of the U. S. Internal Revenue Service, a distinction is made among three general types of multiple-asset accounts, as follows:

1. *Group accounts.* Examples of such accounts would be passenger automobiles, punch presses, office desks.
2. *Classified accounts.* Some examples are transportation equipment, machinery, furniture and fixtures.
3. *Composite accounts.* As an example, transportation equipment, machinery, and furniture and fixtures might be included in a single account.

Particularly in the manufacturing industries, the most common practice is to use classified accounts. Often, the use of item accounts is limited to such assets as buildings and structures.

In this book the most important use of depreciation accounting is in connection with the calculation of cash flow for income taxes. In most of our examples and problems illustrating such calculations (starting with Chapter 15), our computations of the tax aspects of depreciation are made as if item accounts were to be used. This assumption of single-asset accounting is made chiefly for reasons of simplicity—to avoid the need to devote space to an explanation of the numerous technical details of multiple-asset accounting. In many studies, particularly those relative to proposed new assets, it makes no difference whether single-asset or multiple-asset accounting is assumed.

An economy study for a proposed retirement is one type of study in which the timing of cash flow for income taxes with single-asset accounting may differ greatly from the timing with multiple-asset accounting. Usually the critical point in this type of study is whether a "loss on disposal" will be allowable for tax purposes. This topic is discussed in Chapter 16.

Some Aspects of Depreciation Accounting Not Developed in This Book. We have already mentioned that the various types of statistical analysis of physical property mortality are not explained here, and that most of the technicalities of multiple-asset accounting have been avoided. Some other topics that we have omitted are as follows:

1. Assets generally are acquired during a fiscal year rather than exactly at the start of a year. For example, consider an asset acquired on March 31 in a business enterprise having the calendar year as its fiscal year. The question arises regarding the depreciation charge to be made for the remainder of the year. Because 9 months of the year remain, it might seem reasonable to charge 9/12 of the depreciation computed for the first full year of life under the depreciation accounting method selected. However, such a practice would require the application of a different fraction to each new asset, depending on its date of acquisition.

A more common practice is to use some type of *averaging convention*. The so-called half-year convention is a common one; all assets are given a half-year's depreciation charge during their acquisition year regardless of the time of the year when they were acquired. Another convention is to charge a full year's depreciation for the acquisition year for the assets acquired during the first half of the year and no depreciation for those acquired during the second half.

In our examples we have, in effect, assumed that all assets are acquired at the start of a fiscal (and tax) year and that a full year's depreciation is charged during the year of acquisition.

2. There are various possible accounting treatments of gross amounts realized from salvage values and of costs of removing

assets when retired. The way these matters are to be treated may influence the depreciation rate to be used and will determine the type of entry to be made on retirement.

3. There are differences between depreciation accounting where each year's acquisitions of a particular class of asset are kept in a separate account and where all year's acquisitions of the class of asset are merged together in a so-called open-end account.

4. It will rarely be true that average lives and salvage values will turn out exactly as estimated. Various problems arise associated with re-estimates of remaining lives and salvage values for existing assets. These problems differ with different depreciation accounting methods.

One purpose of mentioning the foregoing topics is to make it plain to our readers that our approach to depreciation accounting here is necessarily a simplified one—that there are many facets to the subject that we do not have space to explore. Another purpose is to suggest depreciation accounting and the tax aspects of depreciation as appropriate subjects for study by persons who are responsible for making or reviewing economy studies. Although an introduction to engineering economy can be made with simplified assumptions about depreciation accounting, a more sophisticated understanding of the subject will be helpful in certain types of economy studies.

The authors' views regarding the selection of a method of depreciation accounting are briefly stated in Chapter 15, following the discussion of certain income tax aspects of depreciation.

Problems

10–1. An asset has a first cost of $13,000, an estimated life of 15 years, and an estimated salvage value of $1,000. Using the straight-line method, find (a) the annual depreciation charge, (b) the annual depreciation rate expressed as a percentage of first cost, and (c) the book value at the end of 9 years. ($Ans. =$ (a) $800; (b) 6.15%; (c) $5,800.)

10–2. An asset has a first cost of $22,000, an estimated life of 30 years, and an estimated salvage value of $2,000. Using the sinking-fund method with a 4% interest rate, find (a) the depreciation charge in the first year, (b) the depreciation charge in the 6th year, and (c) the book value at the end of 20 years. ($Ans. =$ (a) $356.60; (b) $433.85; (c) $11,381.)

10–3. An asset has a first cost of $5,000. It is to be depreciated by the declining-balance method using a rate of 12.5%. (a) What will be the book value at the end of 5 years? What will be the depreciation charge (b) in the first year, and (c) in the 6th year? ($Ans. =$ (a) $2,564.55; (b) $625; (c) $320.57.)

10–4. An asset has a first cost of $9,000, an estimated life of 12 years, and an estimated salvage value of $1,200. It is to be depreciated by the sum-of-the-years-digits method. What will be the depreciation charge (a) in the first year and (b)

in the 7th year? (c) What will be the book value at the end of 6 years? (*Ans.* =
(a) $1,200; (b) $600; (c) $3,300.)

10–5. Project A has an initial investment in depreciable property of $100,000.
The prospective life is 10 years with zero salvage value. Estimated excess of receipts over disbursements before income taxes is $33,000 the first year, $29,500
the second, and decreases uniformly by $3,500 each year to $1,500 in the 10th
year. Straight-line depreciation will be used in the accounts. Estimate the rate
of return before income taxes by the following methods:

  (a) Interest rate that makes the present worth of net cash flow equal to zero
  (b) Ratio of average annual book profits to initial investment
  (c) Ratio of average annual book profits to the average of the start-of-year
      book values
  (d) Ratio of average annual book profits to the average of the book values
      throughout the 10-year period
  (e) Average of the year-by-year profit rates computed from each year's esti-
      mated book profits divided by the start-of-year book value for the year in
      question.

(*Ans.* = (a) +17.4%; (b) +7.25%; (c) +13.2%; (d) +14.5%; (e) −0.1%.)

10–6. Like Project A in the preceding problem, Project B has a first cost of
$100,000, an estimated life of 10 years, zero salvage value, and will be subject to
straight-line depreciation. The total estimated excess of receipts over disbursements for the 10-year life is the same as in Problem 10–5. However, the first year's
positive cash flow is only $1,500 and this increases by $3,500 a year to $33,000 in
the 10th year. Estimate the rate of return before income taxes by the same five
methods used in Problem 10–5. (*Ans.* = (a) +8.3%; (b) +7.25%; (c) +13.2%;
(d) +14.5%; (e) +42.6%.)

10–7. What generalizations about the four methods of finding so-called rates
of return used in parts (b) to (e) of Problems 10–5 and 10–6 are suggested by a
comparison of the results of the two problems?

10–8. An asset has a first cost of $17,500, an estimated life of 18 years, and
an estimated salvage value of 5% of first cost. Using the straight-line method,
find (a) the annual depreciation charge, (b) the annual depreciation rate expressed as a percentage of first cost, and (c) the book value at the end of 10 years.

10–9. An asset acquired by a manufacturing company has a first cost of
$50,000, an estimated life of 9 years, and an estimated salvage value of $5,000.
Compute the depreciation charge for each of the first 2 years of life as it would be
made in the company's accounts by each of the following four methods. (Assume
that a full year's charge is made in the first year of ownership.)

  (a) Straight-line method
  (b) Years-digits method
  (c) Double-rate declining-balance method
  (d) 4% sinking-fund method

10–10. A machine has a first cost of $90,000, an estimated life of 6 years, and
an estimated salvage value of $6,000. How much depreciation will be written off
during the second year of life by the (a) straight-line method, (b) years-digits
method, (c) double-rate declining-balance method?

10–11. A building has a first cost of $180,000, an estimated life of 40 years,
and an estimated salvage value of $16,000. Compute the depreciation charge for
each of the first 2 years and the book value at the end of 20 years by the (a)
straight-line method, (b) years-digits method, (c) double-rate declining-balance
method, and (d) 6% sinking-fund method.

10–12. In Problem 8–3 (page 132), compute the so-called rate of return by (a) original book method and (b) average book method. How do these rates compare with the 8.0% rate of return computed by compound interest methods in Problem 8–3?

10–13. In Problem 8–5 (page 133), compare the rates of return computed by compound interest methods with so-called rates of return computed by original book method and average book method for Projects Y, Z, and for the extra investment in Z.

10–14. In Problem 8–12 (page 133), compare the 17.1% rate of return computed by compound interest methods with so-called rates of return computed by original book and average book methods.

10–15. A manufacturer has the policy of paying the delivery costs on certain parts that a group of good customers order for emergency replacements. Many of these deliveries are by air express. An increased inventory of parts kept in a certain branch warehouse will require an investment of $50,000. It is estimated that this investment will make it possible to reduce annual delivery costs by $4,000. Assume that this increased inventory will be maintained for 10 years and then disposed of for 100% salvage value. Show your computations for prospective rate of return on investment (before income taxes) by (a) compound interest methods, (b) original book method, (c) average book method, and (d) method of year-by-year rate of return. What important point regarding these different methods of computing rate of return is illustrated by your answers in this problem?

10–16. What declining-balance rates will give a book value of (a) 30%, (b) 10%, and (c) 1% of the first cost at the end of 20 years?

10–17. Example 8–2 analyzed a proposed investment in a rental machine having a first cost of $12,000, an estimated life of 8 years, and an estimated $1,200 salvage value. Table 8–3 (page 116) gives the year-by-year estimates of receipts and disbursements. Prepare a table similar to Table 10–3 showing the apparent yearly rates of return from this investment using (a) straight-line depreciation and (b) years-digits depreciation. Compute the averages of these two sets of rates. How do these rates compare with the correct figure of 12% computed in Chapter 8?

10–18. A building has a first cost of $100,000, an estimated life of 50 years, and an estimated zero terminal salvage value. It is to be depreciated by the 6% sinking-fund method. Without computing year-by-year depreciation charges, find its book value at the end of 30 years. Using 6% interest, compute its annual capital recovery cost over its 50-year life. Assume that when it is 30 years old, a purchaser buys it for a price equal to its then existing book value and that he estimates its remaining life to be 20 years. Using 6% interest, compute the capital recovery cost over this remaining life. Comment on the results of these two calculations of capital recovery cost.

11

A Pattern for Economy Studies

Chapter 1 emphasized the desirability of comparing all the promising alternatives in making engineering decisions and stressed the advantages of converting alternatives into money terms. Chapter 2 emphasized the importance of recognizing *differences* between alternatives. Chapters 3 to 9 explained techniques for judging whether proposed investments were attractive; particular stress was laid on calculations involving the time value of money.

Subsequent chapters discuss various types of economy studies. At this point it is worth while to consider the general sequence of steps in an economy study and to note some of the problems that may arise in the different steps.

Some Basic Concepts Useful in Making Economy Studies. When making an economy study, it is helpful to keep the following ideas in mind:

1. The study is made from the viewpoint of the owner or owners of an enterprise. (Exceptions to this were discussed in Chapter 9 and will be discussed further in Chapters 15 and 18.)
2. The study is a comparison of alternatives and deals with prospective differences between the alternatives.
3. The effects of the decision are in the future and begin at the time of the decision.
4. In so far as possible, the differences between alternatives should be reduced to differences in money receipts and disbursements.

The Sequence of Steps in an Economy Study. In discussing economy studies, it is helpful to think of the following steps that may be necessary in any study:

1. The recognition of a problem requiring study
2. The identification of the possible alternatives to be compared, and the preliminary estimates of the prospective differences between the alternatives with monetary differences expressed as receipts and disbursements on specific dates

3. The analysis of the preliminary estimates to determine which alternatives justify the expense of further study
4. A detailed examination of the alternatives selected for final consideration to establish estimates of the differences of both monetary and nonmonetary factors and dates and amounts of receipts and disbursements
5. Determination of the interest rate or minimum attractive rate of return and the calculations, of the type described in Chapters 6 to 8, to place the money time series on a comparable basis
6. A choice between the alternatives, considering the monetary comparison and also the prospective differences that were not reduced to money terms

These Steps Are Not Always Distinct. In many economy studies two or three of these steps may be telescoped together so that they are not immediately distinguishable. This is particularly likely to be true of those "thumbnail" estimates which engineers use for the purpose of determining whether a particular alternative suggested for the solution of a given problem justifies detailed study.

For instance, an engineer discussing the proposed installation of a small industrial diesel electric power plant stated that "fixed charges" [1] on the plant would be about $25 a kw. This statement telescoped together steps in his reasoning which were somewhat as follows:

1. *Estimates in nonmonetary terms.* A diesel installation (engine, generator, and accessories) with a capacity in the neighborhood of 200 kw. will be required. The economic life of such a plant will be about 20 years. At the end of that period there will be little, if anything, about the plant which can be sold. It will be necessary to pay local property taxes on this plant and to carry fire insurance on it.

2. *Translation into amounts and times of money receipts and disbursements.* A preliminary guess at the over-all investment in a plant of this capacity is $150 a kw. The realizable salvage value at the end of 20 years may be assumed as $0. Average annual taxes during the 20-year period will be 2% of the investment. Average annual expenditures for insurance during the period will be 0.8% of the investment.

3. *Financial calculations to permit comparing this alternative with some other one on the basis of annual cost.* The minimum attractive rate of return before income taxes was set at 12%. The

---

[1] The term "fixed charges" which is so commonly used by engineers is an ambiguous one. As pointed out in Chapter 2, charges that may be fixed as between two alternatives may be decidedly variable as between two other alternatives. "Investment charges" is a more accurately descriptive term for what the engineer meant in this instance.

annual cost of capital recovery in 20 years with a 12% return is 13.4% of the investment. This capital recovery cost is added to the average percentage of 2.8 to be disbursed each year for taxes and insurance. This gives annual investment charges of 16.2%. This percentage multiplied by the investment, $150 per kw., gives $24.30, which is, roughly, $25 a kw.

Economy Studies Involve Forecasting. The basic concepts enumerated at the beginning of this chapter emphasized the fact that economy studies are based on the prospective differences among alternatives and that the effects of the decisions are in the future. Thus, the estimator who makes an economy study is making a prophecy, whether he realizes it or not. He must predict certain kinds of events, some of which can be predicted with a fairly high degree of confidence in the forecast and others of which must be forecast with much less assurance.

Alternatives are defined in physical terms involving designs, selection of machines and structures, and estimates of goods and services required for their construction and operation. To the extent that such estimates are based upon fundamental laws such as those of mechanics or electricity or thermodynamics, confidence in their accuracy should be high. An estimate based upon Ohm's law may be expected to be as good in 2060 as it is in 1960, and is made with confidence. Estimates based in part on theory and in part on experimental results, or entirely upon experiments, may vary considerably from the actual facts (when at some later time the facts become known). Statistical techniques may be used to provide an estimate of the range of future values with some desired confidence provided sufficient experimental data are available. Such matters as the efficiency curve of a motor or pump, the friction loss in a hydraulic pipe line, the fuel consumption of a diesel engine, and the effects of road surface on automobile tire wear are examples of estimates that might be subject to considerable variation from the final results.

Estimates, and calculations based on them, are made to help in reaching decisions or recommendations regarding decisions among alternatives. The estimator is thus concerned about having the best and most accurate estimates of the differences among the alternatives that the available time and money will permit. Furthermore, he must recognize the degree of confidence that he can place in his estimates and test his estimates to see how sensitive they are to slight changes in the conditions or parameters employed in their computation.

Difficulties in Obtaining Information for Forecasting Purposes.
In most economy studies the calculations are much easier than the
process by which the estimates used in the computations are obtained. Very frequently the internal sources of data have been set
up for other purposes and consequently do not have readily available the information in the desired form. The estimator must be
cautious regarding the information that he uses to be sure that it is
relevant to his problem. For example, the books of account are kept
according to a set of accounting rules that have been agreed upon
by the interested management personnel. Frequently arbitrary
groupings or allocations are made so that the estimator cannot use
the accounting data for an economy study without first determining
how he can eliminate the nonrelevant information. Overhead or
burden may have been allocated to the cost of a product as a percentage of the direct labor cost. In such cases the estimator must
be sure that, in proposing another method of producing the product
with less direct labor, he determines the actual effects on the burden
costs rather than assuming that they will be the same percentage
of direct labor. Using such a percentage figure will distort his estimates and could lead to the wrong decision.

Many sources of information, both internal and external, are
available to the person making an economy study. In the United
States the federal government provides many statistical studies of
numerous subject areas that are useful in predicting events or
trends in the future. Similarly, state and local agencies, chambers
of commerce, journals, professional organizations, and foundations
perform and report on special studies that may be useful to the
forecaster. The warning sounded in the previous paragraph about
the hazards of using internal source data without understanding
the bases on which they accumulated is equally applicable to external source data.

**Check Lists of Costs That May Be Influenced by Choice of
Alternatives Are Useful Tools.** Just as it is imperative that *all*
alternatives be considered in an economy study, it is also imperative
that *all* the prospective differences be identified and evaluated in
money terms, if possible. A list of cost items to be examined in connection with any economy study is a convenient tool that helps
prevent the oversight of important differences. Such a list will vary
from one concern to another, but it should be the result of careful
analysis of the cost elements that are encountered in common problems. Several different lists may be prepared to cover different types
of problems.

A suggested list to be used in economy studies for machinery selection and replacement in manufacturing enterprises is as follows:

Investment
Expected economic life in years (or capital recovery period specified
   by management to be used for economy studies)
Estimated salvage value at end of life
Annual cost of taxes
Annual cost of insurance
Annual cost of materials
Annual cost of direct labor
Annual cost of indirect labor
Annual cost of maintenance and repairs
Annual cost of power
Annual cost of supplies and lubricants
Annual cost associated with space occupied by machine
Other annual indirect costs

Some organizations prepare standard forms on which estimates of cost items and the computations of the equivalent annual cost, rate of return, or other comparable monetary amounts are shown. Examples of two such forms are shown in Figures 19–1 and 19–2 in Chapter 19. Figure D–3 in Appendix D illustrates a computation form developed by the Machinery and Allied Products Institute, which contains an extensive check list of items to be estimated in studies for proposed replacement of machinery.

EXAMPLE 11–1. USE OF CHECK LIST OF COSTS IN A GOING CONCERN

This example shows how the foregoing check list might be used to assure that all the relevant cost items were included in the economy study.

A furniture manufacturer plans to purchase machinery to be used in the production of office chairs. One decision that must be made is a choice between hand shapers and automatic shapers. Data on the performance of these machines in other plants indicate that it will be necessary to buy either two hand shapers or one automatic shaper.

The estimated installed cost of $5,450 for the automatic machine compared with $1,875 for a hand shaper is based upon the manufacturers' quotations plus estimates of the freight and installation costs. The economic life assumed for each —5 years—is based on an arbitrary judgment by the management as to the desired capital recovery period in view of possible obsolescence or changing conditions of demand; this is in spite of the likelihood that these machines would be physically serviceable for 20 years or more. Any possible salvage value at the end of 5 years is to be neglected in the economy study.

The annual tax rate of 1.8% is determined by examining the tax bills and the ratio between the assessed value and the book value of the plant. The insurance rate is determined by inspecting the insurance policy, and is 0.7% of installed cost.

The choice between the hand and the automatic shapers will not affect the material cost in this case. (If one produced more defective parts than the other, the materials would be a consideration in the study.)

Direct labor costs are based upon time studies, estimated annual production, and estimated wage rates. By determining the parts that will be produced on the shapers and making allowances for setup times, personal needs, etc., it is estimated that the time per chair on the automatic shaper will be 4.72 minutes and on the hand shaper will be 8.62 minutes. The hand shaper requires a higher degree of skill, and the hourly rate, including fringe benefits, will be $1.95, while that for the automatic shaper will be only $1.78. Annual production will be 20,000 chairs.

An examination of the duties of the various factory employees normally included under the classification of "indirect labor" indicates that this item will be unaffected by the choice.

Estimates of annual cost of maintenance and repairs are based upon average charges for similar machines, and indicate $45 for the hand shaper and $25 for the automatic. Average power consumption will be 3 kw. for each hand shaper and 10 kw. for the automatic shaper. The average cost of purchased energy is 2.0 cents per kw-hr. Annual supplies and lubricants for each machine are estimated to be $5 per year.

Space charges (based on investment charges on land and buildings plus building upkeep costs) as used in the accounting system of this factory are 40 cents per sq. ft. of floor area per year. A hand shaper will use 50 sq. ft. and an automatic will use 75 sq. ft. of floor space. Any space saved in this part of the factory can be used to advantage for other purposes. Despite the practice in this factory of allocating indirect manufacturing expense (burden) in proportion to direct labor costs, it is apparent that no other indirect expenses will be altered by the choice between the two types of shaper.

From these estimates, the annual cost comparison based upon a minimum attractive rate of return before taxes of 15% is as follows:

	Hand Shaper	Automatic Shaper
Capital recovery	$1,118	$1,627
Taxes and insurance	94	136
Direct labor	5,600	2,800
Maintenance and repairs	90	25
Power	172	315
Supplies and lubricants	10	5
Space expenses	40	30
	$7,124	$4,938

Treatment of Investment and Interest During Construction.

In most economy problems involving investment in a piece of equipment or purchased items, the investment is actually made about the same time that the capital equipment is acquired and put into service. In this case it is usual to assume during the economy study computations that time zero is the time the item is put into service. On the other hand, when the investment is made in a building or some other structure, there may be a substantial lapse of time between the time at which the first payments are made and the time the structure is put into use. Payments may be spread over the construction period lasting from one to several years. The longer the construction period the more money probably involved, and the treatment of the investment and interest on the investment becomes important.

For economy studies involving large investments and substantial periods of time, it is most appropriate to assume that the study begins on the date of completion of the project. This dictates that the interest foregone on the payments made prior to the completion should be computed and added to the cost of the project. Thus the total investment at the time the economy study starts is the actual investment plus the interest that could have been accumulated on those payments up to the time of completion of the project. If the payments are few in number, it is most convenient to compute the interest lost on each by using the single payment compound amount factors. If, however, many payments are made over the construction period, it may be more realistic to use continuous compounding interest factors (explained in Appendix B). Thus, it is desirable to estimate the times as well as the amounts of investment outlays in large projects in order to obtain a better basis for comparing alternative proposals.

Separable Decisions Should Be Made Separately. It sometimes happens that a proposal that is unsound and uneconomical is made to look attractive by merging it with another separable proposal that is sound and economical. Such merging of separable proposals is an obstacle to the making of good decisions.

An illustration of this kind of error in relation to separable increments of investment was given in Chapter 8 following Example 8–5. Further illustrations of this type are given in Chapter 12 in connection with the discussion of the analysis of multiple alternatives by the method of rate of return.

A quite different example of possible error through the merging of separable matters is given in Chapter 17 in our discussion of the relationship between economy studies and sources of investment funds. Generally speaking, the choice among alternative types of physical plant is separable from the choice of alternative methods of financing such plant. A merging of an analysis for decision making on plant selection with an analysis for decision making on financing may lead to uneconomical decisions on both matters.

Use the Systems Viewpoint Whenever Applicable. In attempting to consider separable matters separately, some engineers tend to divide a problem into parts when it should not be so divided. This usually occurs when the engineer is dealing with a system of some kind and he tries to treat the parts as completely independent parts. Chapter 1 introduced the idea of a complex system in which it is very difficult if not impossible to analyze the complete system as one unit. It suggested that in such cases "suboptimization" might be practiced; a complex system might be broken up into several parts and an analysis made to determine which of the available alternatives is best for each particular part without regard to the effects on the other parts of the system. It is always advisable to study the entire system before resorting to suboptimization. This concept does not violate the principle of making separable decisions separately. In this case the selection of all of the parts of a system so that the over-all cost is minimized or so that the rate of return is maximized is just one problem, and does not involve mixing two dissimilar problems together. The only reason for dividing the system into parts is that the interrelationships are so complex that we cannot identify all of the possible alternatives in a reasonable time nor calculate the comparisons in a reasonable time. In some cases the interrelationships are of a variable nature so that mathematical models must be used to represent the interaction of costs or revenues. Sometimes it is necessary, in order to derive a mathematical model, to assume so many things that the model does not truly represent the actual economic elements of the system.

The following example illustrates the systems viewpoint and shows some of the difficulties that may be encountered in using it. The reader will note that the systems viewpoint is maintained even when it becomes necessary to resort to suboptimization. The systems viewpoint requires that one not lose sight of the problem as a whole even when it is necessary to deal with the parts separately.

EXAMPLE 11–2. A MATERIALS HANDLING SYSTEM FOR A WHOLESALE DRUG DISTRIBUTOR

Facts of the Case. One of the nation's largest independent drug distributors has 8 distribution centers covering a major part of the country. It is now planning to remodel one of its warehouses that serves a population center of about 10 million people in an area about 200 miles wide by 500 miles long.

Each distribution center carries about 30,000 items in stock from which it fills several thousand orders per day. Most of the orders involve less-than-case lots of 10 to 50 different items. About 2,000 items account for 50% of its volume and another 2,000 items account for the next 30% of its volume. The company maintains its own fleet of trucks on which it delivers all its orders within a radius of 50 miles (about 6 million people) on a daily basis. Daily shipments are made to more distant points by way of commercial carriers. About 80% of its volume is delivered by its own trucks.

The company has experimented with a number of different materials handling systems for filling orders and has warehouses in which the order selection is performed entirely by hand, others involving some mechanization, and one in which the most important 2,000 items are stored in a completely automatic, electronically controlled order-picking machine, with the other items being picked by hand and placed on a conveyor system for accumulating orders. The company is now trying to decide just what combination of methods to use in this installation.

The majority of the orders to this distribution center are telephoned in by the individual drugstores. A clerk types out a temporary invoice as she takes the order over the telephone. The items on the preliminary invoice must be picked from the stock in the warehouse and moved to the packing area. The items are checked against the invoice and any unfilled items are marked off. A final invoice in four copies is typed, with one copy serving as a shipping list, one as a receipt to be signed by the receiving clerk at the drugstore, one for the accounts receivable office for billing purposes, and the fourth for the inventory control section for use in maintaining stock levels.

It is important to visualize the interrelationships of the various activities. Prompt and complete shipments are essential for customer satisfaction. Errors, short shipments, and delays drive customers to competing distributors. Drugstores typically maintain only limited stocks of drug items and expect to be able to replace stock within 5 to 10 hours from local distributors.

This example deals primarily with the materials handling system, but it was found that the paperwork systems were so closely tied to the materials handling system that they must be considered simultaneously. Three major systems must be integrated: (1) the materials handling (receiving, storing, order picking, and packing); (2) customer paperwork (taking order, preparation of invoice and shipping list, and end-of-month billing); and (3) inventory control (maintaining perpetual inventory, determination of order points, and writing purchase orders).

Identification of the alternatives available can best be done for the different subsystems individually. The physical handling system can be subdivided into three subsystems:

A. Receiving and storing
B. Order picking and assembly
C. Packing for shipment

Subsystem A. The products are always received in cases or in multi-case lots, and must be transported to the proper storage area in the warehouse and stacked in the shelves and bins. The alternative methods that appear feasible are:

A1. A completely manual system, using 4-wheeled shop trucks for transportation
A2. A pallet-fork truck system. Manually palletize at the dock. Small-volume items would require manual separation and stacking at point of storage.
A3. Under floor tow chain towing 4-wheeled trucks through the warehouse. Requires manual loading, unloading, and stacking.
A4. Powered belt or roller conveyors running from dock to storage area. Requires manual loading, unloading, and stacking
A5. Completely automatic conveyorized system, employing live storage of cases on gravity roller conveyors and electronic dispatching and control

Subsystem B. A typical order consisting of from 1 to 12 bottles, jars, tubes, small boxes, etc., of 10 to 25 items. Most of the items are relatively small. The order picking and assembly can be performed in a number of ways:

B1. Completely manual system, employing 4-wheeled shop trucks, with one person picking all the items for one order

B2. A belt conveyor system, nonautomatic, with manual picking and manual regulation of the placement of orders on the belt for transport to the packing tables

B3. Under floor tow chain with 4-wheeled shop trucks, performing in same way as conveyors in B2

B4. Overhead chain conveyor system with independent, dispatchable carriers, but with manual picking

B5. Completely automatic order picking of the large-volume items and any of the other alternatives for the low-volume items

Subsystem C. The packing function is basically a manual job, allowing only minor variations in the arrangement of the work places to accommodate the order-picking system selected. The packing operation should include the final accuracy check on the shipment and the initiation of the customer paperwork.

Subsystem D. The records system dealing with the customer can be operated in a number of different ways, with a wide choice of actual equipment under each general alternative:

D1. Completely manual system

D2. Basically manual, but including a duplicating process to eliminate the retyping of invoices in multiple copies

D3. Basically manual, but including semiautomatic accounting machine to prepare invoices, shipping lists, and monthly bills

D4. An automatic system involving electronic data processing equipment, punched cards, automatic printers, etc.

Subsystem E. The inventory control system must maintain a perpetual inventory for each item and see that an adequate supply is on hand at all times. Thus, it must not only have daily records of receipts and sales of each item, but must continuously analyze sales trends, market fluctuations, and prices in order to set the best purchasing policies. The available methods are similar to those dealing with the customer:

E1. Completely manual system

E2. Basically manual, but including some semiautomatic accounting machines to summarize daily sales and receipts, compute inventories, and compare balances with order points

E3. Fully automatic system, using electronic data processing equipment to perform the operations

The complete system in this warehouse must contain one of the alternatives from each of the five subsystems. With 5 alternatives each for subsystems A and B, 1 for C, 4 for D, and 3 for E, there are a total of 300 possible combinations from which the most economical should be chosen. It is theoretically possible to estimate the expenses involved and the effects on receipts of each of the 300 possible alternatives, but it is doubtful that attempting to do so would be worth the effort.

In the first place, many of the 300 combinations can be eliminated as impracticable. For example, it would obviously be foolish to install subsystem A3, the under floor tow chain, for handling incoming materials and then use subsystem B2, the belt conveyor, for order picking. This would involve two separate systems covering the same floor area, two large investments in equipment, and would increase the complications of layout, because the conveyor would permanently occupy space and interfere with the layout of the tow chain system. Similarly, the choice of subsystem D3, the use of semiautomatic accounting machines for processing customers' orders and invoices, would make system E1 a foolish choice, because a great deal of the information needed by inventory control would be readily available from subsystem D3 in a form that could best be handled by semiautomatic machines rather than by hand. Furthermore, the selection of a fully automatic order-picking system for the large-volume items, subsystem A5, would practically demand the use of either subsystem D3 or D4 and either E2 or E3, because the information to the order-picking machine would have to be in a form that the machine could understand and be available at speeds that could not be possible with manual insertion.

Consequently, the selection of the system for this remodeled distribution center can best be made by making up a set of combinations for the materials handling problem and another set for the paperwork. Each alternative combination for the materials handling should be chosen so that the two subsystems will be compatible and so that the specific information needs (restrictions imposed by the handling system on the information system) will be known. Then the alternative combinations for the information and paperwork systems should be selected to make most economical use of whatever equipment is involved in that combination. One or more combinations should be devised to meet the information needs of each handling alternative. Thus, suboptimization can be employed to simplify the problem. Equivalent annual costs can be computed for each alternative combination, and the best pair of alternatives can be selected.

Comments on Example 11–2. This example illustrates a number of important concepts that must be understood by the person undertaking a complex economy study. The systems viewpoint is important to this case. If an attempt had been made at the beginning to identify only those complete systems that would be feasible, it is unlikely that all the alternatives would have been recognized. By breaking the whole system into subsystems and examining each individually, the analyst helped assure that he would not overlook some important alternative. Furthermore, the analysis of the subsystems tends to bring the requirements of an acceptable whole system into proper focus.

The company had other distribution centers and many of the alternatives had been used in various forms. Cost data were available from the other centers, but the data could not be used in the existing form. Differences in such items as taxes, labor rates, insurance rates, and volumes to be handled among the different locations required adjustment of the cost data to suit the conditions at this location. None of the other distribution centers have a system that is considered to be ideal, and this remodeling presents another opportunity to try to develop the best possible system. Consequently, the new system will be a composite of many of the ideas from different plants and entirely new ideas. This is really a new problem and requires a complete analysis rather than dependence on past solutions. The determination of the data to be used in the analysis will be a major problem.

This example will be used again in Chapter 12 to illustrate the analysis of a problem dealing with multiple alternatives.

Improved Analytical Procedures as a Possible Alternative to Investments. As emphasized in Chapter 1, misleading conclusions may be drawn from economy studies if an alternative that is really superior to all the others is omitted from consideration. Sometimes when an unsatisfactory condition is under review and an investment in fixed assets is proposed to correct this condition, no thought is given to possible methods of improving the condition without a substantial investment.

For example, new machinery may be proposed to reduce high labor costs on a certain operation. Work simplification methods based on motion study may provide an alternative way to reduce these costs. As another example, new machinery may be proposed in order to reduce the percentage of spoilage in the production of a manufactured product that must meet close tolerances. An alternative way to accomplish this result may be through the use of the techniques of statistical quality control.

A number of organizations have reported that the analysis of procedural problems preparatory to the purchase or lease of a large, high-speed computer has resulted in the improvement of existing procedures to the point that the computer could not be justified. The introduction of a computer always requires the careful analysis of the problems to be solved on it in order to translate the problem into language the computer can understand. Such analysis frequently reveals flaws in the current procedures that could have been solved without waiting until the lease or purchase of a computer was proposed.

In the public works field, also, proposed investments may have alternatives that are not obvious at first glance. For instance, the cost of flood damage may be reduced by investment in flood protection reservoirs, levees, and channel improvement. This cost may also be reduced by an improved system of flood forecasting accompanied by an effective system of transmitting the forecasts to people in the area subject to flood.

Comment on an Objection Sometimes Raised to the Making of Economy Studies. Occasionally when an economy study is proposed, the objection is raised that the particular circumstances are such that there is no reasonable basis for making any estimates in money terms. For this reason the objector concludes that the decision on the action to be taken must be made intuitively. Although the limitations of "hunch" decisions between engineering alternatives were brought out in Chapter 1, further comment on this matter seems appropriate at this point.

In choosing between engineering alternatives, an effort to make a formal economy study is frequently justified even in those cases where a first impression makes it appear that no satisfactory basis exists for estimating the money receipts and disbursements influenced by the choice. Before alternatives can be translated into money terms, they must be clearly defined. An attempt to make a clear definition of alternatives is a great help in arriving at sensible decisions. Moreover, it often happens that the process of defining alternatives results in the disclosure of an alternative superior to any that had previously been thought of.

The point was brought out in Chapter 1 that unless alternatives are translated into money terms, they cannot be expressed in commensurable units. This point can hardly be overemphasized. Often the attempt to translate alternatives into money units shows that certain differences between the alternatives that had seemed to be important are really trivial. This separation of the elements that should control the decision from the unimportant elements may be evident even though the money estimates are subject to a considerable range of uncertainty. Without a translation into common units, the various elements in the comparison of alternatives cannot be placed in their proper relationship to one another.

Engineering Reports. The results of engineering economy studies are usually expressed in one or more of the following ways:

1. By the preparation of an engineering report. The report in the case of consulting engineers will be addressed to the client for whom the investigation was conducted, but many reports are simply made by a subordinate engineer to a superior officer in his own organization.
2. By the establishment of standards, usually expressed by specifications or instructions of some sort
3. As a part of a program of budgetary control

Engineering reports frequently need to recognize the existence of three possible classes of readers:

1. The executive who wants the conclusions immediately without any of the surrounding evidence
2. The reader (possibly the same executive in a more leisurely mood) who wants a general picture of the reasoning employed in reaching the conclusions and the general methods of procedure used in collecting the information on which the conclusions are based

3. The technical expert who wishes to check the report in its technical details

To meet the needs of these three classes of readers, there has evolved a more or less standard form of organization for an engineering report.

1. A report will start with a brief statement of the questions that have been investigated and the conclusions that have been reached. These matters are often covered in the letter of transmittal.
2. The main body of the report will include a general discussion giving a connected story of the methods and procedures employed and the reasoning used in reaching the conclusions.
3. Technical details (tables, maps, and diagrams, and such material), which represent supporting data for the general discussion, will be included in a series of appendixes.

Of course, all reports do not follow this form. We must recognize the difference in content and mode of expression between routine reports and special reports, according to the familiarity of the prospective reader with the technical aspects of the problem under investigation. No unqualified general rules for the form of the report may be laid down except to say that a report should always be designed with the convenience of the reader and the intended purpose in mind.

Standards. Results of studies of the most economical methods may be expressed in the form of standards. Such standards may serve to make generally effective the best practices as determined by expert study.[2] In this age of standardization, standards are of many sorts. The National Bureau of Standards classifies them into standards of measurement, standard constants, standards of quality, standards of performance, and standards of practice. Economy studies for a particular corporate organization are most likely to result in standards that control only the activities of that organization, although in some cases the standards adopted may be more general in their scope. Particularly important in this connection are standard operating practices and methods and standards for selection of materials and machines. A discussion of the general subject of standardization with its many angles is beyond the scope of this volume.

Specifications. Engineering economy studies may be made for the specific purpose of determining how to write the specifications for an engineering project. In the preparation of specifications, care

---

[2] Standards may frequently represent a compromise between conflicting ideas. They may often be reached simply by bringing together the individuals who have had the greatest experience with the things they are to cover and who are most interested in their application.

should be taken to see that every item included results from an intelligent study of the conditions to be met. Too frequently specification clauses are simply copied from previously used specifications without consideration of whether the same conditions or objectives are to be met, and the new specifications are not only not appropriate but increase the cost of the project unnecessarily. The engineering economy study is an excellent means of determining the actual requirements for a set of specifications.

Budgets. A budget involves estimates or forecasts of expenditures and revenues for the various operations of a business. Estimates for each department depend upon the expected activities of other departments; for instance, the estimated expense of the various departments of an electric utility would depend upon the anticipated growth of load. A system of budgetary control may be made the major coordinating agency for the varied activities of a large organization.

The two major types of budgets used by business organizations are the operating budget and the investment or capital budget. These may give rise to derived or subsidiary budgets. Thus, estimates of operating revenues and expenses and estimates of investment expenditures by months will serve to define cash requirements. The cash flow techniques employed in this book tend to assist in the preparation of budgets by detailing the expected revenues and expenditures each year. The resulting cash budget will make possible the intelligent planning of bank loans and new security issues.

An operating budget involves estimates of operating revenues and expenses by departments [3] or divisions, and is an instrument of control over the department or division managers. The budget period is frequently one year, though sometimes less, and the budget items are usually estimated by months. After the adoption of a budget, comparisons of actual and estimated figures will usually be made monthly.

The investment budget aims to control capital expenditures. Investment budgets are usually prepared for a much longer period of time than operating budgets, and the engineers should be required to consider all of the plant additions of various sorts that are likely to be necessary for several years in advance. This consideration should involve approximate estimates of their cost and should include studies regarding their economy. Engineering economy studies are most useful in relation to investment budgets, but the

[3] To facilitate budgetary control, it is important that the accounting system be so designed that the classification of accounts follows the lines of departmental responsibility for expenditure. No account should exist which is likely to involve charges incurred by more than one department.

results of the proposed investments will affect the operating budgets of the departments involved in the capital additions.

An investment budget should make the engineering department initiate the plant expansion and improvement program and tell the business executives how much financing they need to do. It cannot be too strongly emphasized that this will result in much more effective planning than exists in the more usual situation where the financial men first decide how much financing they are going to do and then say to the engineer, "You may have so much money to spend." This is a fundamental administrative difference between two types of organization.

Some other aspects of capital or investment budgeting will be discussed in Chapter 19.

Summary. This chapter has outlined a sequence of steps that are required in an engineering economy study, and has introduced the difficulties in making estimates of disbursements and revenues that affect the economy of the proposed project. The concepts of the systems viewpoint and suboptimization as they may affect the economy study were illustrated, and the relationship between economy studies and budgetary control was discussed.

Problems

11-1. Select a situation familiar to you in which the selection of one from a number of engineering alternatives is required. Explain what estimates, in non-monetary terms, must be made in order to evaluate the alternatives. What differences between the alternatives would be convertible to prospective money receipts and disbursements for definite dates? What other differences would not be readily reducible to terms of money and time?

11-2. What estimates and calculations would you consider necessary to determine the commercial feasibility of one of the following projects? List the estimates and information that you would need, indicate how you would obtain the data, and show what use you would make of the different estimates:

(a) The construction of a number of small apartments near your campus for married students, to be financed by the sale of bonds, the principal and interest of which will be repaid from rental income

(b) The proposal to lease a fleet of trucks for use in delivering bread from a bakery to the grocery stores in the area served

(c) A golf driving range in your college community

(d) The establishment of an equipment rental business to provide rental tools for "do-it-yourself" fans

(e) The establishment of a "do-it-yourself" automobile repair shop near your campus to serve students who want to customize their cars

(f) The purchase of a fast, six-place airplane to be used to transport field service personnel to construction sites where the company's large diesel engines are being used to supply power to large construction equipment

(g) The construction of a toll bridge at an assigned site financed by private capital

12
Dealing with Multiple Alternatives

Many decisions involve the choice among a large number of possible courses of action. Nevertheless, a first step in learning how to reason clearly about choosing between many alternatives is to learn how to choose between *two* alternatives. Moreover, general principles of decision making often are clearer when only two alternatives are involved. For these reasons, most of the examples and problems up to this point have dealt with alternatives in pairs. Many of the examples and problems in later chapters also deal with only two alternatives.

The present chapter deals with certain special aspects of comparisons of three or more alternatives, particularly where the alternatives relate to different proposed levels of investment in physical assets.

EXAMPLE 12–1. COMPARISON OF DIFFERENT LEVELS OF INVESTMENT HAVING DIFFERENCES IN PROSPECTIVE ANNUAL NET RECEIPTS

Facts of the Case. A number of different possible plans are under consideration for the construction of a building for commercial rentals on a piece of city property. Table 12–1 shows the six alternative plans under consideration. Lines A, B, and C of Table 12–1 show the estimated total investment in land and building for each plan and the estimates of annual receipts and disbursements. It is assumed that regardless of which plan is adopted, the property will be held for 10 years and at the end of that period will have a resale value equal to the original investment in the land and building.[1] This assumption is made here to simplify the calculation of prospective rates of return. The minimum attractive rate of return before income taxes is considered to be 12%. That is, this is believed to be the prospective rate of return that could be obtained from other investments having the same risk.

[1] As brought out in Chapter 10, it is appropriate in an economy study to make the best possible estimate of the holding period and the prospective resale price of a property to be held a shorter period than its full life. It might well be true that an investor in urban property would expect increases in land value in 10 years to offset the decline in value of his building during that period. Or perhaps he might expect that building costs would rise sufficiently during this period so that at the end of the period a 10-year-old building would be salable at its original cost. Or possibly a combination of both of these factors might enter into a forecast of 100% resale value.

Line D of Table 12–1 gives annual net receipts, that is, gross receipts minus disbursements. As the expected salvage value is 100%, no portion of the net receipts needs to be considered as a partial recovery of capital. Hence the figure in line E for rate of return on total investment is obtained by dividing the annual net receipts (line D) by the total investment (line A).

TABLE 12–1

COMPARISON OF THE RELATIVE ECONOMY OF SIX PLANS FOR CONSTRUCTION OF A COMMERCIAL RENTAL PROPERTY

(All plans are assumed to have 100% resale value after 10 years.)

Plan	I	II	III	IV	V	VI
A. Total investment..	$100,000	$130,000	$152,000	$184,000	$220,000	$260,000
B. Annual receipts...	$ 22,300	$ 34,000	$ 40,200	$ 46,900	$ 53,700	$ 58,200
C. Annual disbursements	14,100	17,700	18,300	21,000	24,500	27,000
D. Annual net receipts	$ 8,200	$ 16,300	$ 21,900	$ 25,900	$ 29,200	$ 31,200
E. Rate of return on total investment	8.2%	12.5%	14.4%	14.1%	13.3%	12.0%
F. Extra investment above next lower investment		$ 30,000	$ 22,000	$ 32,000	$ 36,000	$ 40,000
G. Increase in annual net receipts		8,100	5,800	4,000	3,300	2,000
H. Rate of return on extra investment		27.0%	26.4%	12.5%	9.2%	5.0%

Lines F, G, and H relate to the calculation of the rate of return on the extra investment above the next lower investment under consideration. For example, consider the comparison of Plan IV with Plan III. Plan IV increases the investment from $152,000 to $184,000, an increment of $32,000. It increases prospective annual net receipts from $21,900 to $25,900, an increment of $4,000. This increment in annual net receipts constitutes a 12.5% rate of return on the increment in investment.

Interpretation of Prospective Rates of Return on Several Levels of Investment in an Income Property. If all of the calculated rates of return in line E had been less than the minimum attractive rate of return of 12.0%, it would have been evident that none of the plans were attractive. But when two or more plans show a rate of return that meets this standard, the choice among them calls for the calculation of the rate of return on the extra investment, such as shown in line H. This permits the application of the principle that each avoidable increment of investment must pay its own way by meeting the standard of attractiveness. This principle was first introduced in Chapter 8 and then illustrated again in Chapter 11. In this example an increment of investment is not attractive unless it shows a prospective rate of return of 12% before income taxes.

The application of this principle to the data of Table 12–1 leads to the selection of Plan IV. Even though the rate of return on the total investment is reduced from 14.4% in Plan III to 14.1% in Plan IV, the 12.5% rate of return on the extra investment of $32,000 in Plan IV is better than a 12% investment elsewhere that has equal risk.

On the other hand, Plan V is unattractive despite its prospective 13.3% rate of return on total investment. It contains $36,000 of avoidable investment yielding a prospective rate of return of only 9.2%.

Two types of errors are often made in interpreting prospective rates of return on several levels of investment. The first type is the error of selecting the alternative that gives the highest prospective rate of return on the total investment. In Example 12–1, this error would have resulted in the selection of Plan III, with its prospective rate of return of 14.4%. This error has the effect of preventing the investment of an additional $32,000 at a prospective rate of return of 12.5%, which is greater than would be obtained if the $32,000 is invested in some alternative investment at 12%.

The second type of common error is that of selecting the maximum investment on which the prospective rate of return is equal to or greater than the minimum attractive rate of return. In Example 12–1, Plan VI shows a rate of return of 12.0% on the total investment, and therefore would be chosen if this type of error is made. Examination of Table 12–1 reveals that if Plan VI is chosen, the last $40,000 of the investment earns only 5% and the $36,000 before that earns only 9.2%. Since the minimum attractive rate of return, 12%, was based on the assumption that other opportunities for investment with equal risk exist that will earn 12%, then these amounts ($40,000 and $36,000) could be invested at 12% instead of the prospective 5.0% and 9.2%, respectively, that would be earned by Plan VI.

The effects of these two types of errors are shown in Table 12–2. Line A shows the annual net receipts from the 6 plans shown in Table 12–1. Line B shows the annual net receipts obtained by investing the remainder of the total of $260,000 at 12% in the alternative investment. Line C shows the total annual net receipts from the $260,000. Plan IV produces the maximum net receipts. It is $160 greater than Plan III, which would be chosen if the first type of error is made. It is $3,820 greater than the net receipts if the second type of error is made and Plan VI is chosen.

TABLE 12-2

COMPARISON OF TOTAL ANNUAL RECEIPTS FROM SIX PLANS
FOR THE INVESTMENT OF $260,000

Plan	I	II	III	IV	V	VI
A. Annual net receipts from rental property	$ 8,200	$16,300	$21,900	$25,900	$29,200	$31,200
B. Annual receipts from the remainder of $260,000 invested at 12%	19,200	15,600	12,960	9,120	4,800	0
C. Total annual net receipts	$27,400	$31,900	$34,860	$35,020	$34,000	$31,200

Dealing with Irregular Pattern of Rates of Return on Increments of Investment.

A presentation of prospective rates of return such as that shown in Table 12–1 may sometimes be misinterpreted, particularly where the rates of return on extra investment follow an irregular pattern. To illustrate this, assume an additional plan, IVa, involving an investment of $200,000 and annual net receipts of $23,800. The section of the table relative to Plans IV, IVa, and V would then contain the following misleading figures:

Plan	IV	IVa	V
A. Total investment	$184,000	$200,000	$220,000
D. Annual net receipts	25,900	26,400	29,200
E. Rate of return on total investment	14.1%	13.2%	13.3%
F. Extra investment above next lower investment	$ 32,000	$ 16,000	$ 20,000
G. Increase in annual net receipts	4,000	500	2,800
H. Rate of return on extra investment	12.5%	3.1%	14.0%

At first glance it might appear that Plan V now meets the standard of attractiveness by showing a 13.3% rate of return on the total investment and a 14.0% rate of return on the extra investment.

On more critical examination, however, it is clear that the 14.0% rate of return on the $20,000 extra investment in Plan V over Plan IVa has no significance as a guide to the choice among the alternatives. The showing of a 3.1% rate of return on the $16,000 extra investment in Plan IVa should eliminate Plan IVa from consideration. Plan V should therefore be judged by comparison with the next lower investment that meets the required standard, namely, Plan IV.

Stated somewhat differently, the $20,000 extra investment in Plan V over Plan IVa yielding 14.0% cannot be made without also making a $16,000 investment yielding only 3.1%. The sum of these two is a $36,000 investment, which, as already pointed out, yields only 9.2%, and is therefore unattractive.

Multiple-Alternative Problems Where Differences in Receipts Are Not Involved. Many problems confronting the engineer involve choices among alternatives where the prospective receipts from the sale of a product or service are not affected by the alternative chosen. In such cases the money differences between the alternatives are simply differences in the prospective disbursements. Where different levels of investment are involved, the most convenient method of comparison of such alternatives is by annual costs. The fact that there is less chance of misinterpretation where comparisons are made by the annual cost method (or present worth method) was first brought out in the discussion following Example 8–5, in Chapter 8.

As brought out in Chapter 8, the interest rate used in annual cost comparisons should be the minimum attractive rate of return. Where there is no difference in the prospective receipts, the selection of the alternative having the lowest annual cost will then insure that no extra investment will be made that does not show the prospect of earning at least the minimum attractive rate of return.

Examples 12–2 and 12–3 illustrate annual cost comparisons where there are several alternatives and where differences in receipts are not involved.

EXAMPLE 12–2. PRELIMINARY STUDY TO DETERMINE THE ECONOMIC DIAMETER OF AN OIL PIPE LINE

Facts of the Case. Table 12–3 shows preliminary estimates and calculations of annual costs in connection with a proposed pipe line. Four diameters of pipe are under consideration. The larger the diameter of the pipe, the lower the friction loss in the line. An increased size of pipe therefore reduces the necessary investment in pumping stations and reduces the amount of energy necessary to overcome friction in the line.

In this preliminary study the estimated life of both the pipe line and pumping stations was taken as 15 years with zero salvage value. The minimum attractive rate of return was 15% before income taxes. Investment charges of 20.3% were the sum of the resulting annual capital recovery cost of 17.1% and estimated average annual taxes and insurance of 3.2%.

The table indicates that the 10-in. and 12-in. pipes have approximately equal annual costs. Both are clearly more economical than the 8-in. and 14-in. sizes. The choice between the 10-in. and 12-in. sizes should not be made without careful detailed cost estimates for each. If such estimates continue to show the two sizes as having substantially equal annual costs, the choice should be made on the basis of the irreducible data. One important matter to consider would be the prospect of an increase or decrease in flow during the life of the pipe line.

TABLE 12–3

COMPARISON OF ANNUAL COSTS FOR DIFFERENT DIAMETERS
OF PROPOSED OIL PIPE LINE

(All figures in thousands of dollars)

Pipe Diameter	8-in.	10-in.	12-in.	14-in.
A. First cost of pipe line....................	$ 9,600	$12,000	$14,300	$16,900
B. Number of pumping stations	10	7	4	2
C. Cost per pumping station	$ 360	$ 350	$ 340	$ 350
D. First cost of pumping stations	3,600	2,450	1,360	700
E. Total investment	$13,200	$14,450	$15,660	$17,600
F. Investment charges at 20.3%	$ 2,680	$ 2,933	$ 3,179	$ 3,573
G. Annual pipe line maintenance	294	325	364	390
H. Annual pumping station maintenance and attendance	320	225	108	70
I. Average annual fuel cost for pumping	780	450	290	140
J. Total equivalent annual cost	$ 4,074	$ 3,933	$ 3,941	$ 4,173

This example illustrates a characteristic of many design problems involving alternative levels of investment. It will be noted that the larger the investment in the pipe line, the smaller the investment required for the pumping plant. It is common experience that an increased investment in one place will reduce the necessary investment somewhere else. Whenever possible, this should be indicated directly in the cost estimates of total investment as has been done here.

EXAMPLE 12–3. THE SELECTION OF A MATERIALS HANDLING
SYSTEM FOR A WHOLESALE DRUG DISTRIBUTOR

Facts of the Case. In Example 11–2, Chapter 11, the systems viewpoint was discussed in connection with the selection of a materials handling system for a wholesale drug distributor. It was pointed out that the materials handling equipment and the data handling systems are so closely interrelated that they should be considered simultaneously in order to obtain the best over-all system. It was suggested that a number of feasible combinations of the various possible subsystems be selected for detailed study.

This example presents a rather typical case in which the choice among the alternatives does not affect the revenue, but does affect the cost of providing a given service to the customers. Furthermore, the example involves increasing levels of investment and decreasing operating costs, and employs the annual cost method of comparison based upon a minimum attractive rate of return before income taxes. The company employs an interest rate of 15% before taxes for engineering economy analyses.

Eight different combinations of the subsystems were subjected to preliminary economic analysis, and five combinations that showed the most promise of being economical were selected for detailed cost analysis. These five combinations were as follows:

Combination 1 consists of manually operated 4-wheel shop trucks for both handling incoming shipments and order picking, along with a manual system for records keeping and inventory control. It includes a duplicating process for multiple copies.

Combination 2 consists of underfloor tow chain with 4-wheel shop trucks for both handling operations and semiautomatic accounting equipment for all records keeping and inventory control.

Combination 3 employs an underfloor tow chain with 4-wheel trucks for incoming materials, an overhead chain conveyor with independent dispatchable carriers for order picking, and an automatic electronic data processing system for records keeping and inventory control.

Combination 4 employs fork lift trucks for handling incoming materials, a completely automatic order-picking system for the 2,000 high volume items and manual picking for all other items, and an automatic electronic data processing system.

Combination 5 is the same as *combination 4* except that it has automatic order picking for 4,000 high volume items.

Table 12-4 shows the cost information, life, salvage value, and operating expenses for the five combinations. It is assumed that the same service will be rendered by all five combinations. There are, however, some irreducibles that must be considered in the final decision. With combinations 3, 4, and 5 the invoices,

TABLE 12-4

COST COMPARISON OF ALTERNATIVE MATERIALS HANDLING SYSTEMS
FOR WHOLESALE DRUG DISTRIBUTOR

Combination	1	2	3	4	5
A. Total first cost	$ 5,000	$ 22,320	$ 42,160	$200,000	$250,000
B. Estimated economic life, years	15	10	10	10	10
C. Estimated salvage value at end of economic life	0	$ 5,000	$ 7,000	$ 25,000	$ 30,000
D. Capital recovery factor, $i = 15\%$	0.17102	0.19925	0.19925	0.19925	0.19925
E. Equivalent annual cost of capital recovery	$ 855	$ 3,900	$ 8,060	$ 38,650	$ 48,400
F. Average annual labor cost ...	158,400	123,200	110,000	52,800	44,000
G. Average annual fuel and power costs	100	600	800	1,600	1,900
H. Average annual maintenance costs	900	1,500	1,800	3,600	4,500
I. Average annual taxes and insurance	150	669	1,265	6,000	7,500
J. Annual rental on data processing equipment	0	1,200	12,000	18,000	20,500
K. Total equivalent annual costs	$160,405	$131,069	$133,925	$120,650	$126,800

bills, purchase orders, and reports will be available earlier than with a manual system. The combinations 4 and 5 will provide capacity to handle more orders per day with very little added expense, while all the other combinations can only be expanded by adding additional people (and increasing labor costs). The automatic systems will no doubt require a somewhat greater development and "debugging" period than the other systems. Also, a greater number of errors will probably be made in both order filling and billing during the initial period, but eventually the automatic systems should operate with fewer errors than the other combinations.

Table 12–4 reveals that combination 4 has the lowest prospective annual cost with a minimum attractive rate of return of 15% before income taxes. Combination 4 is only $6,150 better than combination 5, however, and consideration of such irreducibles as prospective increases in business, less dependence on labor, and the prospect of fewer errors might lead the management to select combination 5.

Multiple-Alternative Problems Where Time Value of Money Is Not Involved.

In some comparisons of the economy of a number of alternatives, only immediate expenditures are involved. In such cases it is not necessary to consider the time value of money. One such case is given in the following example.

EXAMPLE 12–4. ECONOMIC SPAN LENGTH FOR A BRIDGE

Facts of the Case. An example of a multiple-alternative comparison that does not involve the time value of money is the determination of the economic span length of a bridge that must necessarily consist of a number of spans. Here the greater the span length used, the greater the weight of steel that is required in the superstructure per foot of bridge. The cost of a pier will be almost independent of the span length used, up to a certain point. Thus the greater the span length, the fewer the piers that will have to be used, and the lower the substructure cost per foot of bridge.

TABLE 12–5

EFFECT OF SPAN LENGTH ON ESTIMATED FIRST COST OF A 1,200-FT. BRIDGE

Span Length	Weight in Lb. per Ft.	Steelwork Cost	No. of Piers and Abutments	Cost of Substructure	Total Cost
150	4,000	$1,056,000	9	$1,980.000	$3,036,000
200	5,000	1,320,000	7	1,540,000	2,860,000
240	5,800	1,531,000	6	1,320.000	2,851,000
300	7,000	1,848,000	5	1,100,000	2,948,000
400	9,000	2,376,000	4	960,000	3,336,000

Consider the selection of span length under the following conditions: A low-level, double-track railroad bridge is to be constructed for a 1,200-ft. crossing. The weight of steel in the superstructure in pounds per lineal foot is estimated to vary (between span lengths of 150 to 400 ft.) in accordance with the equation

$$\text{Weight per foot} = 20(\text{span length}) + 1,000$$

Steel work is estimated at 22 cents per pound erected cost. The piers and abutments, which are to be 50 ft. deep on rock foundations, are estimated to cost $220,000 each for span lengths of 150 to 300 ft., and $240,000 each for a span length of 400 ft. Flooring cost is constant regardless of span length, and may be neglected in the comparison. A comparison of costs for different span lengths is shown in Table 12–5.

The economical span length is evidently 240 ft.

Formulas for Minimum-Cost Point. Examples 12–2 and 12–4 describe situations in which cost varies with some variable of design. In both examples, one or more elements of cost increased as the value of the design variable increased, and one or more elements of cost decreased with an increase in the value of the design variable. In each example, there was one value of the design variable that made the sum of all costs a minimum.

Wherever the variation of cost as a function of the design variable can be expressed by an algebraic equation, it is possible to use calculus to find the value of the design variable that results in minimum cost. The literature of engineering economy is full of formulas for minimum-cost points arrived at in this way.

The simplest case is one in which one element of cost varies in direct proportion to the variable of design, a second element of cost varies inversely as the variable of design, and all other costs are independent of this variable. Although minimum-cost point formulas may, of course, be developed for situations much more complex than this, many of those that are in common use by engineers do actually deal with situations of this type. A general solution of the problem of finding the minimum-cost point in such circumstances is as follows:

Let
$$y = \text{total cost}$$
and let
$$x = \text{the variable of design}$$

The situation of cost variation just described may be expressed by the equation

$$y = ax + \frac{b}{x} + c$$

Taking the first derivative, we find

$$\frac{dy}{dx} = a - \frac{b}{x^2}$$

Equating this to zero, and solving for x,

$$x = \sqrt{\frac{b}{a}}$$

This is the value of the design variable that makes cost a minimum.

When $x = \sqrt{\dfrac{b}{a}}$, the directly varying costs equal the inversely varying costs. This may be demonstrated as follows:

$$ax = a\sqrt{\frac{b}{a}} = \sqrt{ab}$$

$$\frac{b}{x} = \frac{b}{\sqrt{\dfrac{b}{a}}} = \sqrt{ab}$$

The formula, $x = \sqrt{\dfrac{b}{a}}$, can be applied to a number of different kinds of problems, but it should be obvious that certain precautions should be taken in the applications. For example, the statement that the minimum-cost point occurs when the directly varying costs equal the inversely varying costs is not correct unless the line representing the directly varying costs goes through the origin. Also, the cost represented by ax must actually vary directly with a and the cost represented by $\dfrac{b}{x}$ must actually vary inversely. In the following example the cost per pound of wire must be the same for all different sizes of wire (which usually is not true), and the energy losses must vary inversely with the wire size. A variable rate for electric energy or the existence of leakage loss and Corona loss (such as occur in high voltage transmission lines) interfere with the second assumption. Moreover, the analysis disregards any possible adverse consequences of voltage drop on the operation of electrical equipment.

EXAMPLE 12–5. ECONOMICAL SIZE OF AN ELECTRICAL CONDUCTOR

Facts of the Case. The greater the size of an electrical conductor, the less the energy loss that will take place in it. (Power loss in watts is I^2R, where $I =$ current in amperes and $R =$ resistance in ohms. This may be converted to kilowatts by dividing by 1,000. Power loss in kw. multiplied by the number of hours it occurs in a given period will give energy loss in kw-hr.) Thus an increased investment in conductor metal will save an operating expense for electric energy.

Assume that a conductor is to be selected to carry 30 amperes for 2,800 hours per year, with the cost of wire at 32 cents per pound and electrical energy purchased at 2.3 cents per kw-hr. The life is estimated as 25 years with zero salvage value. The minimum attractive rate of return before taxes is 12%, and average annual taxes are estimated at 1.75% of first cost. These charges proportional to investment—namely, capital recovery cost of 12.75% and taxes of 1.75%—are lumped together as investment charges of 14.5%.

The cross-sectional area of a copper conductor is expressed in circular mils, and the weight of the conductor is directly proportional to the cross-sectional area and the resistance to the flow of current is inversely proportional to the area. Therefore, let x represent the cross-sectional area in circular mils, and x_e represent the most economical size for the stated conditions. The resistance, R, for a conductor of 1,000 ft. in length and 1 circular mil in cross-sectional area is approximately 10,580 ohms at 25°C, and the same conductor will weigh approximately 0.00302 pounds.

The investment in the conductor will be

$$\$0.32(0.00302)x$$

The annual cost will be $\$0.32(0.00302)(0.145)x$. Let

$$\$0.32(0.00302)(0.145) = a = \$0.000140$$

The annual cost of power loss is

$$\frac{I^2R\,(2,800)\,(\$0.023)}{1,000}$$

but

$$R = \frac{10,580}{x}$$

Therefore, the cost of power loss is

$$\frac{(30^2)\,(2,800)\,(\$0.023)\,(10,580)}{1,000x}$$

Let

$$b = \frac{(30^2)\,(2,800)\,(\$0.023)\,(10,580)}{1,000} = \$613,200$$

From the formula developed in the previous article we know that the most economical value of x, x_e, occurs when

$$x = \sqrt{\frac{b}{a}}$$

$$x_e = \sqrt{\frac{\$613,200}{\$0.000140}} = 66,180 \text{ circular mils}$$

By examining a table of wire sizes (American Wire Gage, B & S) the closest available conductor is Gage No. 2, with 66,400 circular mils. The next smaller size is Gage No. 3, with 52,600 circular mils. Obviously, No. 2 should be selected.

Comments on Example 12–5. In this example the size of the conductor was treated as a continuous variable. In actuality, the conductors available are discrete sizes, increasing by a geometric progression at the rate of 1.123^2 for the cross-sectional area. The fact that there are specific sizes of wire available and that tables giving the resistance, weight, cross-sectional area, etc., are also available makes another method of solution attractive.

In Table 12–6 five successive wire sizes that might be used for this application have been selected and the annual cost of each size was computed. The table shows that wire size No. 2 gives the

TABLE 12–6

COMPARISON OF ANNUAL COSTS OF VARIOUS WIRE SIZES IN THE SELECTION
OF AN ELECTRICAL CONDUCTOR

(All calculations based on 1,000 ft. of copper wire)

	00	0	1	2	3
A. Size of wire (AWG)	00	0	1	2	3
B. Weight of wire in lb.	403	319	253	201	159
C. Investment at 32 cents/lb.	$129.00	$102.10	$81.00	$64.30	$50.90
D. Resistance in ohms	0.0795	0.100	0.126	0.159	0.201
E. Power loss—kw(30 amps.)	0.0716	0.090	0.113	0.143	0.181
F. Annual energy loss in kw-hr. (2,800).	200	252	316	400	507
G. Investment charges at 14.5%	$ 18.70	$ 14.80	$11.74	$ 9.32	$ 7.38
H. Cost of lost energy at 2.3 cents per kw-hr.	4.60	5.80	7.27	9.20	11.66
I. Total annual cost	$ 23.30	$ 20.60	$19.01	$18.52	$19.04

lowest annual cost. This table also emphasizes the fact that one type
of cost increases as the other decreases, as happens in many problems involving multiple alternatives. Furthermore, note that at the
most economical alternative the investment charges approximately
equal the cost of lost energy. This is characteristic of problems in
which the total costs can be represented by the equation

$$y = ax + \frac{b}{x} + c.$$

It was first pointed out by Lord Kelvin that the economical size
of conductor is that for which the annual investment charges just
equal the annual cost of lost energy. This is well known in electrical
engineering as Kelvin's Law. The costs in Figure 12–1 illustrate its
application.

**The Problem of Economic Production Quantities in Manufac-
turing.** Possibly there has been more written about methods of
determining the economic size of a manufacturing lot than about
any other single problem of engineering economy. This common
problem in manufacturing arises whenever a machine or group of
machines is capable of being shifted from one part or product to
another. A machine will be set up for a "run" on a certain product;
when the stock on that product has been built up to a desired point,
it will be shifted to the production of something else. Thus, whenever a factory production order is made out, a decision must be
made on the matter of lot size.

Ordinarily, any run on a given product will involve a preparation
cost which is independent of the number of pieces to be produced in

the lot. This will include such items as the cost of tool preparation and the cost of the machine setup. Preparation cost—expressed either as an annual total or as a unit amount per piece—will vary inversely with lot size. For instance, if the sizes of lots are doubled, annual expenditures for preparation will be cut in half.

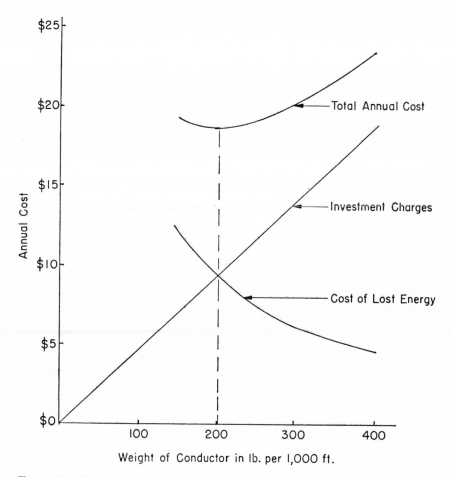

FIGURE 12–1. Comparison of Annual Costs in the Selection of an Electrical Conductor

On the other hand, a doubled lot size means a doubled inventory with resulting doubled costs of storage, taxes, and insurance for that inventory. It also means that the money outlay at the time a lot is manufactured will be doubled; thus, more of the concern's funds will be used for the financing of inventories. If such extra investment of funds is to be justified, it must yield a return commensurate with the risk. This should be reflected in the economic lot size calculations (which, in effect, are to determine whether the savings in reduced preparation costs minus the additional costs for storage, taxes, and insurance resulting from larger lot sizes, represent an adequate return on the extra investment in inventories) by an "interest" charge against the inventory investment at the desired rate of return on funds invested in working capital.

EXAMPLE 12–6. A TABULAR COMPARISON TO DETERMINE ECONOMIC LOT SIZE

Facts of the Case. The comparison of costs for various lot sizes is relatively simple if uniform demand for the manufactured product or piece is assumed. Table 12–7 shows such a comparison for the following situation:

S, the total preparation cost for each lot, is $4.60.

P, the total number of pieces which can be made per day with the machine operated at full capacity, is 100.

U, the total number of pieces used per day, is 10.

N, the number of days worked per year, is 300.

C, the variable outlay per piece, is $0.44. This consists of direct material cost per piece, $0.20; direct labor cost per piece, $0.16; and variable overhead or burden per piece, which is estimated as 50% of direct labor cost. This variable burden includes such items as indirect labor, indirect material, power, and repairs.

T, the total apportioned cost per piece, is $0.56. This includes direct material and direct labor as before, and indirect manufacturing expense apportioned by a burden rate of 125% of direct labor cost. This burden rate, which is based on the assumption of "normal" output, includes not only the "variable" indirect expenses but also those "fixed" indirect expenses which are independent of the rate of production within wide limits of variation—for instance, taxes, insurance on plant and machinery, and most of the cost of superintendence, heat, light, building upkeep, and depreciation.[2]

A, the cost of storing one piece for one year, is $0.04. (It is generally more convenient to consider storage cost on such a rental basis, than in any other way. In this case it is to be based on the maximum inventory anticipated, as with storage of the pieces produced in bins, sufficient storage space must be dedicated to the particular product to take care of the maximum requirements.)

B, the annual rate for inventory taxes and insurance, based on the book value (i.e., total apportioned cost including the full burden rate) of the inventories, is 1.5%, or 0.015.

I, the minimum attractive rate of return on investment, is 20%, or 0.20. This high rate is intended to reflect the risk of inventory obsolescence that exists whenever inventories are large.

It will be noted that Table 12–7 gives *annual* costs *variable* with lot size.

---

[2] The implications of the 125% total burden rate that includes a 50% variable burden rate, about the variation of indirect manufacturing expense with output are as follows: With a normal direct labor cost of $20,000, indirect manufacturing expense will be $25,000. Of this $15,000 is "fixed," and $10,000 "variable." With direct labor cost at $12,000, indirect manufacturing expense would, therefore, be $21,000 (i.e., $15,000 plus 50% of $12,000). While any such separation of indirect manufacturing expense into "fixed" and "variable" elements may fall short of an accurate description of how such expenses really vary, it is generally closer to the facts than the assumption that indirect expenses vary in proportion to direct expenses.

TABLE 12-7

MINIMUM-COST POINT IN THE SELECTION OF THE SIZE OF A MANUFACTURING
LOT—COMPARISON OF ANNUAL COSTS VARIABLE WITH LOT SIZE

	Q	100	200	300	400	500	600
(1) Lot size.........							
(2) Lots manufactured per year...	$\dfrac{NU}{Q}$	30	15	10	$7\frac{1}{2}$	6	5
(3) Maximum inventory-pieces......	$Q\left(1 - \dfrac{U}{P}\right)$	90	180	270	360	450	540
(4) Investment (variable) in maximum inventory..	$CQ\left(1 - \dfrac{U}{P}\right)$	\$ 39.60	\$ 79.20	\$118.80	\$158.40	\$198.00	\$237.60
(5) Interest on investment in average inventory....	$\dfrac{ICQ}{2}\left(1 - \dfrac{U}{P}\right)$	3.96	\$ 7.92	\$ 11.88	\$ 15.84	\$ 19.80	\$ 23.76
(6) Book value of maximum inventory...........	$TQ\left(1 - \dfrac{U}{P}\right)$	\$ 50.40	\$100.80	\$151.20	\$201.60	\$252.00	\$302.40
(7) Taxes and insurance on average inventory.......	$\dfrac{BTQ}{2}\left(1 - \dfrac{U}{P}\right)$	\$ 0.38	\$ 0.76	\$ 1.14	\$ 1.51	\$ 1.89	\$ 2.27
(8) Storage cost.....	$AQ\left(1 - \dfrac{U}{P}\right)$	\$ 3.60	\$ 7.20	\$ 10.80	\$ 14.40	\$ 18.00	\$ 21.60
(9) Total annual cost of carrying inventory........	$\dfrac{IC + BT + 2A}{2}Q\left(1 - \dfrac{U}{P}\right)$	\$ 7.94	\$ 15.88	\$ 23.82	\$ 31.75	\$ 39.69	\$ 47.63
(10) Annual preparation cost.......	$\dfrac{SNU}{Q}$	\$138.00	\$ 69.00	\$ 46.00	\$ 34.50	\$ 27.60	\$ 23.00
(11) Total annual cost variable with lot size...........	(9) + (10)	\$145.94	\$ 84.88	\$ 69.82	\$ 66.25	\$ 67.29	\$ 70.63

The same comparison might have been made on the basis of unit costs; in that case items (5), (7), (8), (9), (10), and (11) would all have been divided by the annual production, NU. The relative values would, of course, have been unchanged. However, it is somewhat easier to see the magnitude of the differences in cost involved in any choice, if annual costs are used rather than unit costs.

Only those costs variable with lot size have been compared. No advantage is gained by including in the comparative cost study all of the production expenses for labor, material, and overhead which are unaffected by the choice of lot size. Similarly, no carrying charges have been included for the minimum inventory required regardless of lot size.

The following comments relate to the numbered lines of Table 12-7:

1. Note the use of the symbol Q to designate lot size.

2. The number of lots per year is obviously the total annual production NU divided by the lot size.

3. If a day's production P is 100 units and a day's use U is 10 units, 90 units from each day's production remain to increase inventory; thus we get the factor $\left(1 - \dfrac{U}{P}\right)$. Where P is large in proportion to U, the omission of this factor

will simplify the calculations with little influence on the final result. Moreover, unless the use is fairly uniform from day to day, the entire lot produced may be an addition to inventory; in such cases it is better to omit the $\left(1 - \dfrac{U}{P}\right)$ entirely.

4. A point of difference between this exposition of the lot size problem and the usual treatment of the problem in management literature, lies in the "valuation" here of inventories for the purpose of calculating "interest" (i.e., minimum attractive return) at the increment cost of their production rather than at the total cost apportioned by the cost system. Like all economy studies, the determination of an economic lot size is a problem in measuring differences between alternatives. In comparing one alternative, Large Inventory, with another alternative, Small Inventory, the difference between the expenditures necessary to procure them will not include any of the "fixed" indirect manufacturing expenses. It is only this increment of expenditure necessary to get the larger inventory which is relevant in calculating "interest" or return.

5. As in all economy studies, interest should be figured at the minimum attractive rate of return on investment in the light of the risk rather than at the bare cost of borrowed money. Because the risks involved in inventory investment are substantial, the difference between these two figures may be large. Many published discussions on economic lot sizes have used an interest rate such as might be paid on bank loans (usually 6% or thereabouts); this gives a lot size that is too high.

The assumption behind the calculation of interest on *average* inventory rather than on maximum inventory is that many different items are being produced in intermittent lots. The peak inventory for one item will occur at the time of the minimum inventory for another; the net "investment" by the manufacturer will be based on the average of all peaks and minimums.

6. Both fire insurance and taxes will be based on the total allotted cost of production rather than on increment cost.

7. The same reasoning about averages used in (5) applies here.

8. Whether storage costs should be based on average inventory or on maximum inventory is a matter of fact to be determined in any specific instance. Where storage is in bins, it is generally necessary to provide space for maximum requirements. Where it is not, as in the furniture industry, it is often more reasonable to base storage costs on average inventory.

9. This is the sum of interest (i.e., return on investment), taxes, insurance, and storage cost, on the inventory.

10. The annual preparation cost is obviously the preparation cost for a lot multiplied by the number of lots manufactured per year.

11. Although a lot of 400 pieces appears to be the most economical, the difference in cost from 300 to 600 seems so small as to be negligible. This might well result in the selection of 300 as the desirable lot size for production.

The irreducibles in the lot size problem are almost always on the side of the selection of smaller lot sizes. They may include any or all of the following: (1) risk of obsolescence of part or product due to style changes or design changes, (2) desirability of conserving working capital, and (3) avoidance of risk of loss on inventory declines as a result of falling prices.

Larger lot sizes mean larger inventories. Where changes in design or style come suddenly, the manufacturer with large inventories is likely to have difficulty in disposing of them except at a loss. Moreover, where a concern's funds are not adequate to finance large inventories without substantial bank loans that may involve possible difficulties of repayment in the event of business recession, the desire to keep working capital requirements to a minimum is a motive toward small inventories.

In view of these irreducibles it is often desirable to look not for the minimum-cost point but rather for the minimum-cost range (i.e., the range through which the choice of a lot size has little effect on cost) and then to select the lot size at the lower end of that range. The selection of a lot size of 300 on the basis of the calculations of Table 12–7 would be an example of this policy.

EXAMPLE 12–7. USE OF A FORMULA TO DETERMINE ECONOMIC LOT SIZE [3]

Facts of the Case. The minimum-cost formula developed earlier in this chapter is applicable to the economic lot size problem, because one cost element varies directly with some variable under investigation and another element of cost varies inversely with this variable. The problem of finding the economic size of a manufacturing lot involves the carrying charges on inventory that vary directly with lot size, and the preparation or setup costs which vary inversely. Hence the formula for minimum-cost point developed earlier in this chapter may be used to find the lot size for which the sum of these costs is a minimum.

It was shown that the design variable, x, should equal $\sqrt{\dfrac{b}{a}}$ for minimum cost, where a is the coefficient for the directly varying costs and b is the coefficient for the inversely varying costs. Lines (9) and (10) of Table 12–7 indicate the values of these coefficients as

$$a = \frac{IC + BT + 2A}{2}\left(1 - \frac{U}{P}\right)$$

$$b = SNU$$

Q, the lot size, corresponds to x

The economic lot size is therefore given by the expression

$$Q = \sqrt{\frac{2SNU}{(IC + BT + 2A)\left(1 - \dfrac{U}{P}\right)}}$$

The application of this formula is illustrated by its use for the problem solved by direct calculation in Table 12–7, as follows:

$$Q = \sqrt{\frac{2(\$4.60)(300)(10)}{[(0.20)(\$0.44) + (0.015)(\$0.56) + 2(\$0.04)]\left(1 - \dfrac{10}{100}\right)}} = 417$$

If the factor $\left(1 - \dfrac{U}{P}\right)$ is eliminated [for reasons explained in the discussion of line (3) of Table 12–7], and the minor item of taxes and insurance on inventory is neglected, this simplifies to

$$Q = \sqrt{\frac{2SNU}{IC + 2A}}$$

[3] The symbols that have been used throughout the economic lot size discussion are those employed by Professor Paul T. Norton, Jr., in his pamphlet, *Economic Lot Sizes in Manufacturing*, Virginia Polytechnic Institute Engineering Extension Division Series, Bulletin No. 31. With minor points of variation, the formula given here is that developed by Professor Norton.

A special slide rule or nomographic chart may be devised for the rapid solution of this formula. The minimum attractive rate of return, I, will usually be fixed by company policy, leaving the four figures to be determined for each lot size situation as the preparation cost, S; the annual production, NU; the increment cost of producing one unit, C; and the cost of storing one unit for one year, A.

Multiple Variable Problems. The examples and discussions of this chapter have dealt with the simplest type of cost minimization problems of the "steady state" type. In each of these examples only one variable has been used and the assumption was made that such matters as demand, cost, and other factors were constant. In many cases this simple approach is quite adequate and provides reliable decision information, but care must be used to assure oneself that the assumptions actually fit the problem under study. For example, in the study of the most economical conductor (Example 12–4), it was assumed that the demand (30 amperes), the time (2,800 hours), and the cost of energy (2.3 cents per kw-hr) were all constant. If any one or all of these factors vary from year to year, the solution given by the Kelvin's Law model will not necessarily be the optimum solution.

Many problems need to be analyzed as problems in the best combination of a number of variables. In some cases the variables can be treated, using probabilistic mathematics in order to determine the optimal solution. In other cases some of the variables are not continuous, and the solution depends upon estimating the relevant factors in different combinations, and then computing the equivalent annual costs for each different combination. The solution of Example 11–2, in Chapter 11, was of this type. In some problems where there is no good basis for estimating the value of certain factors and no history on which to base a prediction of the probability of the future values for the factor, it is necessary to make the best estimates you can and then to test the sensitivity of the solution to changes in that factor. This technique will be discussed at greater length in Chapter 13.

The literature of operations research contains many examples of engineering economy problems involving several variables. In most of these examples the solutions are based upon probabilistic statements regarding the behavior of the variables, and the solutions usually are sets of decision rules. These solutions are "dynamic solutions" as opposed to "steady state solutions," in that they provide for varying the course of action according to the prevailing conditions at a given time in order to optimize, minimize, or maximize some parameter.

An example of a dynamic model of the economic lot size problem is given in *Dynamic Version of the Economic Lot Size Model*.[4] In this model it is assumed that the demand is known but different in each period and consequently the inventory costs vary from period to period. The time periods are assumed to be a month in practice. As in the previously stated simple model, the cost and selling price are constant. If the cost of the item were allowed to vary from period to period, as actually happens, the model would be more complex.[5] The subject of mathematical models in replacement economy is discussed at length in Appendix D.

Problems

12-1. The weight of a double-track railway half through plate girder bridge for a certain loading varies with the span length in accordance with the following formula: $W = 25S + 2,050$, which applies between span lengths of 50 and 130 ft. where W is weight in pounds per lineal foot and S is span length.

Assume cost of steel erected at 18 cents per lb. Assume cost, C, in dollars of a pier and its foundation varying with the following formula: $C = 54,000 + 90S$.

It is desired to make a 980-ft. crossing. Compute the cost of steelwork and piers for this crossing divided into 8, 9, 10, 11, and 12 equal spans. (The cost of flooring is constant regardless of span length and may be neglected in these calculations.) What is the economical span length? ($Ans. = 108.89$ ft.)

12-2. Assume that the prices and resistances of various sizes of single-core, low-tension, lead-sheathed electrical cable are as follows:

Size	Resistance in Ohms per 1,000 Ft.	Price per 1,000 Ft.
0	0.0983	$ 648
00	0.0779	724
000	0.0618	800
0000	0.0490	928
250,000 circ. mils	0.0416	1,058

The cost of electric energy to a certain user of this cable is 1.05 cents per kw-hr. The annual cost of capital recovery is to be based on a 25-year life, no salvage value, and a 7% minimum attractive return. Average annual taxes are 1.5%. What is the most economical section to transmit 200 amperes 1,800 hours per year? ($Ans. = $ Size 000.)

12-3. In a certain manufacturing plant, schemes for cost-reducing machinery are judged on the basis of the "gross return," which is computed as the ratio of the annual saving in direct material and labor to the investment. To justify the investment of funds in such projects, there must be a gross return of 30%. This 30% covers capital recovery (interest and depreciation), taxes, and insurance.

---

[4] Harvey M. Wagner and Thomson M. Whitin, *Dynamic Version of the Economic Lot Size Model*, Technical Report No. 48, Prepared under Contract N6onr–25133 for the Office of Naval Research, Department of Economics, Stanford University, Stanford, California, February 28, 1958.

[5] The reader is referred to the *Journal of the Operations Research Society of America* and *Journal of The Institute of Management Science* for numerous articles in which models for engineering economy problems involving several variables are given.

Funds are available to finance any projects that meet this standard of attractiveness. On a certain operation, six alternative proposals for cost reduction are made. Which one of these would you recommend? Why?

Proposal	Required Investment	Annual Saving in Direct Materials and Labor
A	$ 6,000	$1,500
B	8,000	2,500
C	12,000	4,100
D	13,000	4,200
E	18,000	6,000
F	25,000	7,600

(*Ans.* = Proposal E.)

12–4. A new piece of standard pumping equipment costing $7,000 installed has an estimated life of 12 years. Certain improvements could be made and auxiliary apparatus added that would increase the estimated life to 15 years and also effect a reduction of $300 in annual disbursements for operation. What additional investment would be justified to accomplish this if the minimum attractive return is 6%? Assume zero salvage values in both cases. (*Ans.* = any additional investment up to $4,023 would be justified.)

12–5. The management of a manufacturing plant has established the requirement that cost reduction proposals involving purchase of new machinery must show annual savings in direct costs of at least 22% of the investment to be accepted. This 22% "gross return" is to cover capital recovery, taxes, and insurance. Several proposals for alternative changes in one operation are as follows:

Proposal	Required Investment	Annual Savings
A	$4,800	$1,280
B	6,600	1,850
C	4,000	780
D	5,500	1,670
E	7,100	2,050

Should one of these proposals be accepted? If so, which one? Why? (*Ans.* = Proposal E.)

12–6. (a) Use the economic lot size formula to determine the economic size of a manufacturing lot under the following conditions: Preparation cost is $10; variable outlay per piece is 20 cents; annual rental of storage space per finished piece is 0.5 cents; minimum attractive rate of return is 12%; annual demand (250 working days per year) is 10,000 pieces; machine output per working day is 500 pieces. (*Ans.* = 2,529.)

(b) Calculate a table similar to Table 12–7, using lots that are multiples of 1,000.

12–7. (a) Use the economic lot size formula to determine the economic size of a manufacturing lot under the following conditions: Preparation cost is $225; variable outlay per piece is 6 cents; annual rental of storage space per finished piece is 1.5 cents; minimum attractive rate of return is 12%; annual demand (250 working days per year) is 300,000 pieces; machine output per working day is 5,000 pieces. (*Ans.* = 69,100.)

(b) Calculate a table similar to Table 12–7, using lots that are multiples of 10,000.

12–8. A group of men have purchased a large city lot on which they plan to build apartments. The architects have submitted several different proposals for the apartment development, involving different investments, annual disbursements, and annual revenues. The owners have decided that they must have the prospect of a rate of return of 15% per annum before income taxes, and are trying to decide which of the proposals to accept. The estimates relative to the four most promising plans for development are as follows:

	Plan A	Plan B	Plan C	Plan D
A. First cost of buildings and land.........	$140,000	$170,000	$190,000	$220,000
B. Estimated resale value of buildings and land 10 years hence	125,000	140,000	155,000	175,000
C. Excess of average annual revenues over average annual disbursements	$ 24,000	$ 28,000	$ 31,000	$ 41,000

Which plan of development should the owners select? Justify your solution. (*Ans.* = Plan D.)

12–9. A man of some wealth is a partner in a number of different small businesses. His practice is to supply the capital for promising new businesses for a 50% partnership in the business, so that he receives 50% of the profits. One of his partners has proposed that additional capital be put into their physical plant in order to reduce the annual disbursements. The proposals are mutually exclusive, and the estimated life of each is 10 years. All have a zero salvage value after 10 years.

Proposal	A	B	C	D	E
Investment required	$3,000	$5,000	$7,000	$10,000	$14,000
Reduction in annual disbursements	900	1,400	1,700	2,400	3,800

If the investor requires that his share of the profits have the prospect of providing a rate of return of 10% on his investment, which of the proposals should he approve?

12–10. Problem 12–1 gave the formula for the weight of a double-track, half through plate girder bridge for certain loading as $W = 25S + 2,050$ lb. for spans of 50 to 130 ft., where W is the weight in pounds and S is the span in feet.

Assume that the cost of steel erected has gone up to 24 cents per pound and that the cost in dollars, C, of a pier or an abutment is estimated by the formula: $C = 60,000 + 80S$.

Compute the cost of steelwork and piers for the crossing of 980 ft. Assume 8, 9, 10, 11, and 12 spans of equal length. What is the economical span length?

12–11. A mining company is installing a motor-driven ventilating fan for its mines at a point 8,000 ft. away from its power station. Determine the economical wire size to use to supply 20 amperes for 8,000 hr. a year. Assume that energy costs 1.4 cents per kw-hr, and copper wire is 32 cents per lb. (Weight and resistances of various wire sizes are given in Table 12–6.) Use a minimum attractive rate of return of 12% before income taxes and assume that the wire has a 20-year life with zero salvage value. Assume average taxes as 2% of first cost.

12–12. Many valves are required in a certain pipe line that carries a corrosive chemical. In the past, cast-iron valves have always been used and have required replacement every 2 years. Now valves of two corrosion-resistant alloys, A and B, are available. Estimates of installed first costs, lives, and salvage values for these three types of valve are as follows:

	Cast Iron	Alloy A	Alloy B
First cost	$2,000	$4,000	$6,000
Life	2 years	5 years	10 years
Salvage value	zero	$1,000	zero

(a) What is the rate of return on the extra investment in a valve of Alloy A as compared to a cast-iron valve?

(b) What is the rate of return on the extra investment in a valve of Alloy B as compared to a cast-iron valve?

(c) What is the rate of return on the extra investment in a valve of Alloy B as compared to one of Alloy A?

(d) In this manufacturing company the minimum attractive rate of return is 12% before income taxes. Which of the three valves should be selected? Explain your answer.

12–13. A manufacturing company has been cited by the local Smog Control Board for permitting too much smoke to issue from its chimney. Investigation reveals that there is no possibility of reducing the offensive smoking by controlling the combustion more closely, since part of the "smoke" is a form of dust inherent in the process. The answer seems to be in the installation of a precipitator to remove the solids from the hot gases before they leave the chimney. The plant engineer has compiled the following estimates:

	Precipitators			
	A	B	C	D
First cost installed	$3,000	$3,800	$4,500	$4,750
Life (years)	10	10	10	10
Salvage value	0	0	0	0
Annual operation costs				
Power and water	$ 640	$ 640	$ 500	$ 480
Cleaning	400	400	290	265
Maintenance	300	250	300	250
Labor extras	400	400	290	265
Taxes and insurance 2% first cost	60	76	90	95
	$1,800	$1,766	$1,470	$1,355

All precipitators are of the same capacity. Company policy is to use a minimum attractive rate of return before income taxes of 10%.

Which precipitators would you recommend? Show your calculations and explain the basis of your analysis.

12–14. A warehouse and terminal company is planning to build a subzero storage warehouse for frozen foods. The refrigeration engineer, employed by the architect, made a study of four different types of insulation that might be used and the effects on the cost of refrigeration equipment and operating costs to determine the most economical plan. The more money that is spent on insulation material in the walls and roof, the less money that must be spent on refrigerating equipment and power. The engineer's estimates are as follows:

Plan	A	B	C	D
First cost of insulation material	$25,000	$35,000	$50,000	$70,000
First cost of compressors.................	22,000	17,000	14,000	12,000
First cost of refrigerant piping and coils ...	20,000	18,000	14,000	10,000
Annual power cost	5,600	4,200	3,200	2,600

He estimated that the insulation materials would have a life of 20 years with a zero salvage value, and the mechanical equipment and piping would have a life of 10 years with a zero salvage value. Taxes and insurance are estimated at 2% of first cost per year. The terminal company told him to use a minimum attractive rate of return of 15% before income taxes.

Which plan of insulation should have been recommended by the engineer?

12–15. In a certain manufacturing company, decisions regarding approval of proposals for plant investment are based on a stipulated minimum attractive rate of return of 20% before income taxes. The mechanization of a certain costly hand operation has been proposed. Machines from six different manufacturers are under consideration. The estimated investment for each proposal and the estimated reduction in annual disbursements is given below. Approximate rates of return before income taxes on total investment and on each increment of investment are also given. These rates of return have all been computed assuming a 10-year life and zero salvage value for each machine.

Which one, if any, of these six mutually exclusive proposals should be accepted? Explain the reasons for your answer and show any additional calculations that are necessary to support your answer.

Machine	Investment	Reduction in Annual Disbursements	Rate of Return on Total Investment	Rate of Return on Increment of Investment
Onondaga ...	$30,000	$11,000	34.8%	
Oneida	50,000	14,100	25.2%	8.9%
Cayuga	55,000	16,300	26.9%	42.7%
Tuscarora ...	60,000	16,800	25.0%	0.0%
Seneca	70,000	19,200	24.3%	20.2%
Mohawk	75,000	21,100	25.1%	36.3%

12–16. The board of directors of a small manufacturing concern has approved the expenditure of $80,000 during the next 6 months for improvement of its manufacturing facilities, stipulating that each investment must earn a minimum attractive rate of return of 15% before income taxes. The plant manager has received proposals for facility improvements from four department heads, and is trying to decide exactly which proposals he will submit to the comptroller for final approval. The proposals he has to consider are as follows:

Department A: Four mutually exclusive proposals for improvement of the plating shop:

Proposal	Total Investment	Net Annual Savings in Disbursements
A1	$10,000	$2,000
A2	15,000	5,020
A3	25,000	7,795
A4	30,000	9,495

Department B: Three mutually exclusive proposals for improvement in heat treating:

B1	$10,000	$ 4,100
B2	20,000	7,820
B3	30,000	10,030

Department C: One proposal for a new machine:

Proposal	Total Investment	Net Annual Savings in Disbursements
C1	$15,000	$4,580

Department D: Three mutually exclusive proposals for improvement in assembly operations:

D1	$10,000	$4,000
D2	15,000	5,000
D3	20,000	7,500

If the plant manager assumes a 5-year life for each proposal and a zero salvage value, which proposals should he recommend to the comptroller for final approval? Explain the basis for your selection and show any calculations that you made to support your selections.

12–17. The XYZ Manufacturing Co. has funds available for investment in machinery and tools to reduce direct manufacturing costs. All proposals for such investments are to be judged on the basis of "gross return." It is decided that no investment is to be considered attractive that does not show a gross return of 25%. This is intended to cover complete capital recovery (interest plus depreciation over a short capital recovery period) plus taxes and insurance.

A group of engineers has analyzed six different proposals for investment in machinery and tooling to reduce costs on a certain operation. They have prepared the following table to provide a basis for comparison of these proposals:

Proposal	Investment	Annual Saving in Direct Mfg. Costs	Gross Return on Inv.	Extra Inv.	Extra Annual Saving	Gross Return on Extra Inv.
A	$ 1,000	$ 100	10.0%			
B	4,000	1,160	29.0%	$3,000	$1,060	35.3%
C	8,000	2,400	30.0%	4,000	1,240	31.0%
D	9,000	2,670	29.6%	1,000	270	27.0%
E	12,000	2,880	24.0%	3,000	210	7.0%
F	20,000	5,120	25.6%	8,000	2,240	28.0%

At this point the engineers disagree on the question of which of these proposals is to be recommended to the management. Green prefers C on the grounds that it has the greatest return on total investment. Brown chooses B because it has the greatest return on the extra investment. Black is inclined toward F as representing the maximum investment on which both the gross return on total investment and the gross return on extra investment are over 25%.

Which of these six proposals would you recommend? Explain why.

12–18. The owners of a chain of motels have leased a very desirable tract of land in a rapidly growing area for the purpose of building a modern "motor hotel." The lease on the land is for 30 years, and at that time all the structures on the land and the land revert to the landowner. Based on earnings in other motels and on opportunities to build in other areas, the managers have decided that each increment of investment must have the prospect of earning a rate of return of at least 15% before income taxes. The architects have prepared preliminary plans for five degrees of development, and the motel management has estimated the operating costs and revenues as follows:

Plan	Investment in Buildings and Equipment	Prospective Average Annual Excess of Revenues Over Disbursements
20 units, no restaurant	$ 90,000	$11,500
20 units, minimum restaurant	99,000	15,500
30 units, minimum restaurant	140,000	20,000
40 units, elaborate restaurant	180,000	28,000
60 units, elaborate restaurant	270,000	37,000

If it is assumed that the management has considered such expenditures as replacement of furniture, decorating, land rent, and maintenance in its estimates, which plan, if any, should it adopt for this location?

12–19. A small machined part is used more or less uniformly throughout a 200-day working year in a certain plant. The preparation cost for each production run is $65, and the variable cost of each piece is 48 cents. The annual rent of storage space for the finished part is 4 cents and the minimum attractive rate of return on investment in working capital is 20%. If 8,000 pieces are needed per year and the machine produces 96 pieces per day, how many pieces should be produced in each production run? Use the economic lot size formula.

Solve the same problem by calculating a table similar to Table 12–7, starting with 1,500 pieces per lot and increasing the lot size by 500 each time until the minimum cost is found.

12–20. An aircraft engine manufacturer has found that the cost of preparing, mailing, expediting, receiving, inspecting by sampling, and closing out a purchase order is approximately $25 for a typical order for small parts, supplies, etc.

The company uses approximately 100,000 machine screws of a certain type per year, and receives the screws in a standard package containing 2,500 screws. The screws cost 15 cents each and the storage space costs 1 cent per screw per year. The company works 200 days per year. It requires a minimum attractive rate of return of 15% on its working capital. How many containers of screws should be ordered on each purchase order? (Hint: Write an equation for the total cost of screws, letting x represent the number of packages per purchase order. Place first derivative equal to zero and solve.)

12–21. Approximately 400 complicated castings are used per year of 200 days. The setup to machine the castings costs $200 and the rent on storage space per year is $4. The variable outlay per casting is $80, and 4 can be machined per day. The minimum attractive rate of return is 20%.

Determine the economic lot size for this casting by both the formula and the tabular method illustrated in Table 12–7.

12–22. Determine the economic size of a manufacturing lot under the following conditions: Preparation cost is $50; variable outlay per piece is 20 cents; annual rental of storage space per piece is 2 cents; minimum attractive rate of return is 15%; annual demand (250 working days per year) is 10,000 pieces; machine output per working day is 400 pieces.

How would a change in the use rate to 20,000 pieces per year affect the economic lot size?

12–23. Ten proposals have been made for cost reduction in a certain manufacturing plant. All have lives of 10 years and zero salvage values. The required investment and the estimated after-tax reduction in annual disbursements are given for each proposal. Prospective rates of return are also shown for each proposal; these were computed by interpolation using the appropriate capital recovery factors. Proposals J1, J2, J3, and J4 are mutually exclusive because they are alternate ways of changing operation J. Similarly K1, K2, and K3 are mutually exclusive; also L1 and L2 are mutually exclusive.

(a) Which proposals would you accept if it is stated that the minimum attractive rate of return is 10% after taxes and if there is no limitation on available funds? Show any additional calculations needed to support your answer.

(b) Which proposals would you accept if the available funds are limited to $80,000 and the minimum attractive after-tax rate of return is 10%? Explain your answer.

Proposal	Required Investment	After-tax Reduction in Annual Disbursements	Approximate Rate of Return
J1	$20,000	$ 5,600	25%
J2	30,000	6,900	19%
J3	40,000	8,180	16%
J4	50,000	10,070	15%
K1	10,000	1,360	6%
K2	20,000	3,840	14%
K3	30,000	5,200	12%
L1	20,000	5,440	24%
L2	40,000	8,700	17%
M	20,000	3,540	12%

13

Dealing with Uncertainties
in Forecasts

This chapter has several purposes. One is to illustrate and comment on a number of types of economy studies. Another is to introduce the concepts of sensitivity and the break-even point as useful aids in making decisions in the face of certain kinds of uncertainty. Still another purpose is to give some simple examples of the use of the mathematics of probability as a guide to decision making in the face of certain other kinds of uncertainty.

Uncertainties in Forecasts in Relation to Decision Making. The examples and problems in the preceding chapters have involved choosing among alternatives with a single set of forecasts given. Presumably in each case the stated forecasts represent someone's best judgment on the way in which future receipts and disbursements and other matters will be influenced by the choice among the stated alternatives.

There is always uncertainty about the future; it will rarely if ever turn out that events occur exactly as forecast. This uncertainty in itself is not a reason why we should not make the best forecasts that we can and then be governed by our analysis of these forecasts. Nevertheless, a decision among alternatives often can be made more sensibly if we can see whether the conclusion of our economy study is sensitive to moderate changes in certain forecasts.

The Concept of Sensitivity. All of the examples and problems of the previous chapters have involved estimates of such cost elements as fuel, power, labor, taxes, repairs, maintenance, and insurance, and some have involved estimates of revenue, salvage value, life, and other factors affecting the economic analysis of the particular proposal. Recommendations for or against a proposal were the result of the economy studies making use of those estimates or forecasts, and possibly some irreducible factors. It is obvious that if the estimates in some of the examples had been different, the decisions would also have been different. In some examples, however, it would have been possible to alter one of the elements quite radically without changing the decision resulting from the economy study.

Sensitivity refers to the relative magnitude of the change in one or more elements of an engineering economy problem that will reverse a decision among alternatives. Thus, if one particular element can be varied over a wide range of values without affecting the decision, the decision under consideration is said not to be sensitive to uncertainties regarding that particular element. On the other hand, if a small change in the estimate of one element will alter the decision, the decision is said to be very sensitive to changes in the estimates of that element.

Since all estimates are subject to some amount of uncertainty, the sensitivity approach may be very helpful in analyzing a proposal or set of proposals. The application of the sensitivity concept becomes an intermediate step between the numerical analysis based on the best estimates for the various elements and the final decision. Each element can be tested to see how sensitive the decision is to variations from the best estimate, and the results used in the final decision-making process. Several examples will be given in this chapter to illustrate how the sensitivity concept can be applied.

The Concept of the Break-Even Point. Often we have a choice between two alternatives where one of them may be more economical under one set of conditions and the other may be more economical under another set of conditions. By altering the value of some one of the variables in the situation, holding all of the other points of difference between the two alternatives constant, it is possible to find a value for the variable that makes the two alternatives equally economical. This value may be described as the break-even point.

It frequently happens that a knowledge of the approximate value of the break-even point for some variable of design in the comparison of two alternatives is a considerable help in preliminary engineering studies and designs.

The term "break-even point" is also used in management literature to describe the percentage of capacity operation of a manufacturing plant at which income will just cover expenses.

The literature of engineering economy contains many formulas to determine break-even points, although such formulas are not necessarily described by this name.

Break-even-point formulas deal with such matters as the investment justified by a prospective cost saving, annual hours of operation necessary before a proposed extra investment is profitable, the period of time in which a proposed investment will "pay for itself" (i.e., the life to break even). In general, although such formulas may appear to be complicated, the only mathematics involved in their preparation is elementary algebra. The formulas are merely expressions of cost situations in symbols rather than in figures; the apparent complexity is the result of a large number of symbols.

Break-even formulas do not really save much time as compared to direct calculations for the break-even point. Moreover, the mistake is often made of using such formulas as substitutes for direct comparisons of the costs of specific alternatives under specific circumstances. When they are so used—a choice between alternatives being based on the relation between a calculated break-even point and the hours per year (or life or investment or whatever the break-even point has been calculated for) actually expected—the estimator is less apt to give intelligent weight to irreducibles than if he had made a direct comparison of alternative costs. Just as in the minimum-cost-point situations described in Chapter 12, the use of the formulas as a time saver is at the sacrifice of desirable information. Where a choice is to be made between specific alternatives, a direct comparison of the expected costs for each is likely to be more illuminating than any break-even-point calculation. However, several examples employing the break-even-point concept will be given in this chapter.

The break-even-point calculation may be particularly useful in the situation where a decision is very sensitive to a certain variable. If the break-even point for that variable can be calculated, it may be possible to estimate on which side of the break-even point the operations may fall even though there may be considerable uncertainty regarding the exact value of the variable. Even in this use, however, it is desirable to investigate the range of values of the variable that would permit that alternative to be attractive, and to estimate the consequences of its occurring outside that range.

The Influence on Economy of the Amount of Utilization of Fixed Assets. Subject to certain exceptions,[1] the annual cost of capital recovery with a return is independent of the amount of

---

[1] In some cases accelerated use of machinery—for example, on three shifts rather than on one—will increase maintenance costs to the point where replacements will be economical sooner than would otherwise be the case. Thus economic life will be shortened by increased utilization. But the important economic factors causing most retirements (such as improved alternatives and changes in service requirements) are likely to be independent of the amount of utilization of machines and structures. Therefore it is reasonable in most instances to consider the capital recovery period to be independent of the amount of operation—at least within a fairly wide range.

utilization of fixed assets. So also are the other investment charges of taxes and insurance. Many other current disbursements may be practically independent of the amount of utilization. Examples are space charges and attendance costs on some machines and maintenance costs on some structures. Moreover, machinery is often considerably less efficient operating at fractional load than at full load; energy costs per unit of output will therefore be less at full load than at partial load.

Hence, in the majority of cases, the greater the utilization of fixed assets, the less the unit costs of product or service. As a result, the attractiveness of many proposed investments in machines and structures depends on the prospective amount of utilization. The variation of the unit costs with the amount of utilization is illustrated in Example 13–1. This example, with Figure 13–1, also illustrates the use of the break-even concept in analyzing the prospective differences among several alternatives.

EXAMPLE 13–1. EFFECTS OF HOURS OF OPERATION ON THE CHOICE OF A LIGHTING SYSTEM

Statement of Alternatives. A company is planning the construction of service and repair shops of a standardized design to be constructed at a number of different locations. The following estimates are made for three types of electric lighting systems any one of which will provide the desired level of illumination:

	Incandescent	Fluorescent Type I	Fluorescent Type II
First cost installed (including lamps)	$150	$1,200	$1,400
Number of fixtures required	25	40	15
Number of lamps per fixture	1	2	4
Cost per lamp	$1.25	$1.75	$3.50
Rated life of lamps in hours	1,000	4,000	5,000
Watts per fixture	500	90	200

The investment in wiring is determined by other considerations and in this case will be independent of the type of fixture selected. The unit cost of labor for each lamp replacement is estimated as 20 cents, regardless of the type. Electric energy is estimated to cost 2.6 cents per kw-hr. Capital recovery on the original investment is desired in 10 years with a minimum attractive rate of return before income taxes of 15%. Insurance and property taxes are estimated at 2.5% of the first cost.

Differences in the climatic conditions of the several locations indicate that lighting needs will vary considerably in daylight hours, and also the volume of business will vary with the locations. Some locations may consistently require two or three-shift operation while some may require only one shift. The amount of utilization of the lighting system will obviously affect the annual cost of providing the required illumination.

Table 13–1 compares the equivalent annual cost of the three systems at 1,000 and at 4,000 hours per year. The annual investment costs are independent of the amount of utilization of the systems. These costs are fixed by the decision to se-

TABLE 13–1

COMPARISON OF ANNUAL COSTS FOR THREE LIGHTING SYSTEMS

	1,000 Hours per Year			4,000 Hours per Year		
	Incand.	Fluor. Type I	Fluor. Type II	Incand.	Fluor. Type I	Fluor. Type II
Annual investment charges	$ 33.26	$266.10	$310.45	$ 33.26	$266.10	$310.45
Lamp replacement	36.25	39.00	44.40	145.00	156.00	177.60
Annual power cost	325.00	93.60	78.00	1,300.00	374.40	312.00
Equivalent annual cost	$394.51	$398.70	$432.85	$1,478.26	$796.50	$800.05

lect one of the systems. On the other hand, both the lamp replacement costs and the power costs vary directly with the amount of utilization. Figure 13–1 shows graphically the comparison of the equivalent annual costs of the three systems as the number of hours of utilization increases. The cost curves for the incandescent and the Type I fluorescent systems intersect at approximately 1,000 hours. This is the break-even point betweeen the two systems. If the prospect is that the average utilization will be more than 1,000 hours per year, the Type I fluorescent

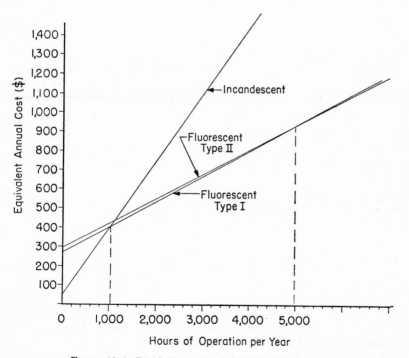

FIGURE 13–1. Break-Even Chart for Lighting Systems

system should be chosen over the incandescent system. The break-even point between the two types of fluorescent systems occurs at approximately 5,000 hours. Similarly, if the prospect is that the average annual utilization will be greater than 5,000 hours, the Type II fluorescent system should be chosen over Type I. It should be noted that difference in equivalent annual cost of the two fluorescent systems is very small, and irreducibles might easily alter the decision.

Comments on Example 13–1. This example provides a good illustration of several important points. The first point to be emphasized is that the estimate of the amount of utilization is the key factor in making the decision. It is assumed that the other factors (such as installed cost, lamp costs, and power costs) can be estimated with considerable confidence that the estimates will be reasonably accurate. The amount of utilization, however, will vary with the number of cloudy days, weather, and the amount of business for the service and repair shops. Variations in the economic conditions in the various localities are more likely to affect the volume of business than to affect the price of power or lamps.

The break-even charts in Figure 13–1 show that between 1,000 and 5,000 hours of operation the Type I fluorescent system is more economical than either of the others. They also show that there is a large difference between the incandescent lights and the Type I fluorescent at all levels of utilization, while there is a relatively small difference between the two types of fluorescent systems. This information makes it somewhat easier to make a decision because the probable minimum utilization can be estimated with reasonable confidence. For example, if a shop is expected to work on a single shift basis during daylight hours and the average number of cloudy days per year (obtained from weather bureau records) is 125, then 1,000 hours per year (8×125) can be expected. The prospect of increasing business to the point of adding overtime work or a second shift would tend to indicate that the Type I is preferable to the incandescent system.

Similarly, if the shop were to operate 5 days a week on a three-shift basis, there would be about 250 working days per year (excluding holidays). Lights could be assumed necessary on the second and third shifts and on the 125 cloudy days for day shifts. The maximum number of hours per year would probably not exceed $250(8)(2) + 125(8) = 5,000$. Thus the chance of needing more than 5,000 hours per year is rather small. The possible range of utilization has now been reasonably well established as between 1,000 and 5,000 hours, and the decision is obvious. Type I fluorescent lighting should be selected.

This design problem might also be used to illustrate the sensitivity of a decision to several aspects of the original estimates. For instance, how sensitive is the decision to changes in such matters as price of lamps or price of energy?

EXAMPLE 13–2. SENSITIVITY OF DECISION IN EXAMPLE 13–1 TO CHANGES IN PRICE OF ELECTRIC ENERGY

Facts of the Case. The present electric power rates are such that it is believed that 2.6 cents per kw-hr is a fair price to use in making the decision as to which lighting system to select for the standardized service and repair shops. However, it is believed that there is some possibility of changes in rate structures so that the price in a few years will be reduced. How sensitive is the problem to changes in the cost of energy per kw-hr? One way to determine the sensitivity is to compute the break-even points between the Type I fluorescent system and the incandescent system at various rates.

The break-even points can be computed directly. Let x equal the number of hours of utilization per year at which the equivalent annual cost of the incandescent will equal the equivalent annual cost of the fluorescent system. At 2.6 cents per kw-hr, the equation is:

$$\$150[(\text{crf–}15\%\text{–}10) + 0.025] + \frac{(\$0.026)(500)(25)x}{1,000} + \frac{(\$1.45)(25)x}{1,000}$$

$$= \$1,200[(\text{crf–}15\%\text{–}10) + 0.025] + \frac{(\$0.026)(90)(40)x}{1,000} + \frac{(\$1.95)(80)x}{4,000}$$

Substituting the value of the capital recovery factor into the equation and solving for x, we find that the break-even point is 1,018 hours per year. This corresponds with the value found in Figure 13–1. Repeating this operation for successively smaller prices for electric energy gives the break-even points shown in Table 13–2. It will be noted that the decision is not very sensitive to the price of energy in this case.

TABLE 13–2

BREAK-EVEN POINTS FOR INCANDESCENT AND TYPE I FLUORESCENT LIGHTING SYSTEMS AT DIFFERENT PRICES OF ENERGY

	Price of Energy (Cents per Kw-Hr)				
	2.6	2.4	2.2	2.0	1.8
Break-even points (hours of utilization per year)	1,018	1,084	1,206	1,328	1,479

If the same comparison is made between the two types of fluorescent systems, only one calculation is necessary to find that the break-even point increases and that we are not interested in considering a choice between Types I and II if a prospective reduction in the price of energy will make it more difficult to justify the selection of Type II. The break-even point at 1.8 cents per kw-hr is 8,212 hours per year.

Long-Lived vs. Short-Lived Alternatives. Chapter 6 discussed certain aspects of the comparison of the economy of alternatives having different estimated lives. Some further discussion of this subject seems appropriate here. Certain points to keep in mind regarding monetary comparisons of this type are as follows:

1. The fact that money has a time value tends to reduce the attractiveness of distant future services to be received from an asset. For example, with interest at any figure above 0%, it will never pay to double the investment merely to double the prospective length of life.

2. The greater the interest rate or minimum attractive rate of return, the less favorable is the competitive position of the longer-lived alternative.

3. The recognition of mortality dispersion results in a greater annual cost of capital recovery than if it is assumed that all units survive for exactly the same life. Nevertheless, for most economy studies it is not necessary to consider prospective mortality dispersion.

The first two of these points are illustrated in Example 13–3. The third point is illustrated in Example 13–4.

EXAMPLE 13–3. SENSITIVITY TO INTEREST RATE OF DECISIONS BETWEEN ALTERNATIVES HAVING DIFFERENT LIVES

Comparison of a More Durable and a Less Durable Structure. Assume that a $10,000 structure having an estimated life of 10 years is to be compared with a $20,000 structure having an estimated life of 40 years. Assume that except for the difference in lives the two structures will provide exactly the same service, and that the total annual disbursements for operation, maintenance, taxes, and insurance will be equal. Hence the only difference in annual cost is in the annual cost of capital recovery.

If the minimum attractive return is 5%, the comparison is as follows:

$$\$10,000(0.12950) = \$1,295$$
$$\$20,000(0.05828) = \$1,166$$

Under these circumstances the $20,000 structure is somewhat more economical. However, its annual cost of capital recovery is only 10% less than that of the $10,000 structure even though its life is four times as long and its first cost is only twice as great.

If the minimum attractive return is 8%, the capital recovery costs are:

$$\$10,000(0.14903) = \$1,490$$
$$\$20,000(0.08386) = \$1,677$$

With this higher interest rate, the shorter-lived alternative has the lower annual cost. Even if the $20,000 structure were expected to last forever, it would not prove as economical as a $10,000 structure with a 10-year life, provided interest was at 8%.

EXAMPLE 13–4. INFLUENCE OF MORTALITY DISPERSION ON ESTIMATED ANNUAL COSTS

Comparison of the Economy of Treated and Untreated Railway Ties. Assume the first cost of an untreated Douglas fir cross tie, in place in a railway roadbed, to be $3.85. The average life of such a tie will be about 7 years. Assume

TABLE 13–3

DETERMINATION OF AVERAGE CAPITAL RECOVERY FACTORS BASED ON
EXPECTED MORTALITY CHARACTERISTICS OF GROUPS OF CROSS TIES

Life Years (1)	6% Capital Recovery Factor (2)	Untreated Tie Av. Life 7 Years		ZnCl₂ Treated Tie Av. Life 12 Years		Creosote Treated Tie Av. Life 20 Years	
		Per Cent of Ties (3)	(2) × (3) (4)	Per Cent of Ties (5)	(2) × (5) (6)	Per Cent of Ties (7)	(2) × (7) (8)
3	0.374	2	0.748				
4	0.289	4	1.156				
5	0.237	12	2.844	1	0.237		
6	0.203	20	4.060	2	0.406		
7	0.179	24	4.296	4	0.716		
8	0.160	20	3.200	6	0.960		
9	0.147	12	1.764	8	1.176	1	0.147
10	0.136	4	0.544	10	1.360	1	0.136
11	0.127	2	0.254	12	1.514	2	0.254
12	0.119			14	1.666	2	0.238
13	0.113			12	1.356	3	0.339
14	0.108			10	1.080	3	0.324
15	0.103			8	0.824	4	0.412
16	0.099			6	0.594	5	0.495
17	0.095			4	0.380	7	0.665
18	0.092			2	0.184	8	0.736
19	0.090			1	0.090	9	0.810
20	0.087					10	0.870
21	0.085					9	0.765
22	0.083					8	0.664
23	0.081					7	0.567
24	0.080					5	0.400
25	0.078					4	0.312
26	0.077					3	0.231
27	0.076					3	0.228
28	0.075					2	0.150
29	0.074					2	0.148
30	0.073					1	0.073
31	0.072					1	0.072
			18.866		12.543		9.036
Average Capital Recovery Factor		0.1887		0.1254		0.0904	

that zinc chloride treatment will increase the cost by 50 cents and will increase the average life to 12 years. Assume that pressure treatment with creosote will increase the cost by $1.15 and will increase the expected life to 20 years. These three types of tie are to be compared, assuming that maintenance cost, taxes, and all disbursements other than for tie renewals are unaffected by the choice. Interest is to be assumed at 6%.

Capital recovery costs based on average life are as follows:

Untreated tie	$3.85(0.17914) = $0.690
ZnCl₂ tie	$4.35(0.11928) = $0.519
Creosoted tie	$5.00(0.08718) = $0.436

Cross ties may be expected to have a mortality distribution. If the average life of treated ties is 20 years, some will be retired short of that date and others will last longer. If the appropriate capital recovery factor is applied to each asset, and the capital recovery factors for the entire mortality distribution are averaged, the resulting average will be somewhat greater than the capital recovery factor based on the average life. This is illustrated in Table 13–3 in which average capital recovery factors are computed for assumed life tables for the three classes of tie. Annual capital recovery costs based on the average capital recovery factor may be compared with costs based on average life, as follows:

	Average Annual Capital Recovery Cost Using Mortality Curve	Annual Capital Recovery Cost Using Average Life
Untreated tie	$0.726	$0.690
ZnCl₂ tie	0.545	0.519
Creosoted tie	0.452	0.436

The recognition of a mortality distribution is necessary in certain economic problems, such as the determination of a selling price sufficient to cover cost, in certain problems of valuation of fixed assets, and in the use of the sinking-fund method of depreciation accounting. But it is seldom necessary to complicate matters by introducing the expected mortality distribution into economy studies. Many economy studies involve the use of a capital recovery period shorter than full service life. Even in cases such as the cross-tie example where it is appropriate to use full service life in the economy study, the recognition of a mortality distribution will seldom influence the result of the study, since the costs for all alternatives tend to be increased by a small amount. Hence in these cases it is generally good enough for practical purposes to base capital recovery cost on estimated average life.

Importance of Forecast of the Situation After the Expiration of the Life of the Shorter-Lived Alternative.
It should be recognized that a mere comparison of the annual costs of two alternatives, one with a short estimated life and the other with a long one, does not necessarily measure the relative economy of the two alternatives over the prospective life of the longer-lived one. It is always pertinent to consider what is likely to happen after the shorter-lived one is retired.

The prospect of improved alternatives or changes in service requirements during the life of the shorter-lived alternative is favorable to the selection of that alternative. This point is developed further in Chapter 16 and Appendix D in connection with the discussion of economy studies for replacement. The prospect of a decreased replacement cost for the shorter-lived alternative is also favorable to its selection.

The prospect of increased replacement cost of the shorter-lived alternative is favorable to the longer-lived alternative. This may sometimes be anticipated due to expected price rises. Replacement costs may also be higher than initial costs due to the expense of removing the old unit and putting in the new one. The greater the difficulty and expense of replacement—as in the case of timbers in the substructure of a building or utility mains laid under pavement —the greater the economy of making an extra investment to secure a longer life.

If specific forecasts in money terms are made on the preceding matters, they may be incorporated into the monetary comparison. More frequently, it seems reasonable to make such forecasts as probable general trends or tendencies, and to consider them as irreducible data in choosing among the alternatives. Such irreducibles may properly control decisions in borderline cases.

A special irreducible that sometimes exists, which is favorable to the longer-lived alternative, is the possibility that replacements for the shorter-lived alternative may not be available when needed. This lack of availability of replacement assets was a common experience during World War II and the immediate postwar period of shortages.

Effects of Anticipated Growth of Demand on the Choice Between an Immediate and a Deferred Investment. An engineer is often concerned with trying to get something done that must be completed tomorrow at two o'clock or that has some similar urgency concerned with it. In such circumstances it is sometimes better to make a second-rate decision immediately than to make a first-rate one at some later time. Nevertheless, decisions made only with a view to meeting immediate emergencies are likely to prove costly in the long run.

Piecemeal construction, in which each piece of apparatus is installed to meet a present emergency without regard to its adequacy under prospective future conditions, will ordinarily be less economical than development of a long-range planned expansion. Where planning is neglected, mistakes are likely to be made that will cost a great deal more to correct than they would have cost to avoid. A forecast of growth is an essential part of engineering designs.

In a program of planned development the installation of extra capacity as part of the original construction is likely to require less money outlay than will be required to add this capacity when needed in the future. This saving in money outlay may be due to the inherently lower costs per unit of capacity that are often associated with larger units. It may be due to the fact that future changes involve expenses that are avoidable when excess capacity is provided initially. As an example, each addition to the capacity of any underground conduit in a city's streets requires a ditch that must be refilled and repaved.

This necessity of providing excess capacity against an expected growth of demand exists whenever that growth is reasonably certain to occur and where its rate may be predicted with some degree of confidence in the forecast. This is usually the situation in the engineering of most public utility equipment. Examples 13–5 and 13–6 deal with the financial calculations that are appropriate once forecasts of growth have been made.

EXAMPLE 13–5. COMPARING AN IMMEDIATE WITH A DEFERRED
INVESTMENT

A Preliminary Solution Considering Investments Only. Cost comparisons to determine whether a proposed investment in capacity that is in excess of present needs is economically justifiable are usually made on a present worth basis. The degree of complexity of the calculations will depend on the assumptions made by the estimator. An example of an economy study in which these assumptions are very simple is as follows:

In the design of an aqueduct for municipal water supply, a tunnel is necessary. It is estimated that a tunnel built to half the ultimate capacity of the aqueduct will be adequate for 20 years. However, because of certain fixed elements in the cost of tunnel construction, it is estimated that a full-capacity tunnel can be built now for $300,000 as compared with $200,000 for a half-capacity tunnel. The problem is whether to build the full-capacity tunnel now, or to build a half-capacity tunnel now—supplementing it by a parallel half-capacity tunnel when needed.

At first glance it appears as if the disbursements to be compared are as follows:

Full Capacity Now	*Half Capacity Now*
$300,000 now	$200,000 now
	$200,000 20 years hence

Since the $200,000 present investment necessary in either case can be canceled out as irrelevant, this appears to be the question of whether it is better to spend $100,000 now or $200,000 in 20 years. If interest is taken at 5%, the present worth of $200,000 20 years hence is $200,000(0.3769) = $75,400. This indicates an advantage of $24,600 in present worth for the half-capacity plan.

An alternative solution is to calculate the prospective rate of return on the extra investment in the full-capacity plan. This is approximately 3½%, the interest rate which makes $200,000 in 20 years equivalent to $100,000 now.

These solutions to the problem imply "all other things being equal." Two matters that might not be equal are the expected service lives with the two plans, and their respective operation and maintenance costs.

A Solution Considering Capitalized Operation and Maintenance Costs. In these circumstances it might be reasonable to assume the expected service lives as perpetual for both plans; if this assumption is made, the two plans do not differ in expected service life. However, there does appear to be a prospective difference in operation and maintenance costs. (In studies of this character there is sometimes a tendency to neglect the possibility of such differences; this tendency should be resisted by an examination of the circumstances to see if differences are likely to occur.)

Let us assume that in this situation the estimator notes that the two half-capacity tunnels will involve a larger area of tunnel lining with correspondingly greater periodic costs of lining repairs. Lining repair costs for the full-capacity tunnel is estimated as $10,000 every 10 years; for each half-capacity tunnel it is estimated as $8,000 every 10 years. The estimator also notes that friction losses will be somewhat greater in the half-capacity tunnel; it is estimated that this will increase pumping costs in the aqueduct line by $1,000 a year so long as a single tunnel is in use, and by $2,000 a year after the second tunnel has come into use. It now appears as if the disbursements to be compared for perpetual service with the two plans are as follows:

Full Capacity Now	Half Capacity Now
$300,000 now	$200,000 now
10,000 10 years hence and every 10th year thereafter	8,000 10 years hence and every 10th year thereafter
	1,000 a year forever
	200,000 in 20 years
	8,000 30 years hence and every 10th year thereafter
	1,000 a year, starting 20 years hence

With interest at 5%, a capitalized cost comparison of these alternatives is as follows:

Full Capacity Now

Investment	$300,000
Lining repairs $10,000 $\left(\dfrac{0.07950}{0.05}\right)$..	15,900
Total capitalized cost	$315,900

Half Capacity Now

First tunnel:

Investment	$200,000
Lining repairs $8,000 $\left(\dfrac{0.07950}{0.05}\right)$....................................	12,720
Extra pumping costs $\left(\dfrac{\$1,000}{0.05}\right)$....................................	20,000

Second tunnel:

Investment $200,000(0.3769)$	$ 75,380
Lining repairs $12,720(0.3769)$	4,790
Extra pumping costs $20,000(0.3769)$	7,540
	$320,430

The recognition of the higher operation and maintenance costs associated with the half-capacity plan therefore shifts the advantage to the full-capacity plan. The rate of return on the extra $100,000 investment is evidently slightly greater than the 5% interest rate assumed in this calculation; that is, a slightly higher interest rate would result in the two plans having the same capitalized cost.

Why Use Present Worth Comparisons for Deferred Investment Studies?

Most of the illustrations of economy studies in this book use equivalent annual cost as a basis of comparison. The reasons why such studies are easier to interpret than present worth studies have already been pointed out. Moreover, when annual disbursements are substantial in proportion to investment, it seems reasonable to make comparisons on an annual cost basis.

On the other hand, when present investments are large in proportion to other disbursements, it seems natural to make comparisons on a present worth basis. This is generally true in comparisons of immediate and deferred investments. In addition, because of the irregular expenditure series involved in these problems, the calculations for present worth comparisons are likely to be somewhat simpler than for annual cost comparisons. Moreover, equivalent annual costs for an alternative that involves investments in two or more steps are difficult to interpret. For these reasons such studies usually involve comparisons of present worths.

One warning given in Chapter 7 regarding the interpretation of economy studies made on a present worth basis should be repeated here. This is that a small change in interest rate may result in a large difference in present worth. Whenever the interest rate used is the average cost of capital and is thus lower than the rate of return required to justify an investment, the study is biased in favor of the alternative with the higher present investment. If this bias is not recognized in the interpretation of the results of such studies, many investments of doubtful economy may result.

EXAMPLE 13-6. RECOGNIZING THE ADVANTAGE OF A LONGER PERIOD OF SERVICE OBTAINABLE FROM A DEFERRED INVESTMENT

Statement of Alternatives. Suppose that in the design of an aqueduct, wood pipe is to be used in one section. A pipe to carry half the ultimate capacity will cost $4,000; it is estimated that this will be adequate for 15 years. A full-capacity pipe will cost $5,500. The life of a wood pipe in this location is estimated as 25 years. Assuming interest at 6% and assuming that operation and maintenance costs will be the same in either case, is it more economical to install the full-capacity pipe now or to install the half-capacity pipe now and add a parallel half-capacity pipe when needed?

If it seems reasonable to assume that the period of service obtainable from each structure under consideration is a fixed number of years from the date of its installation, the alternative involving the deferred investment has an advantage of longer life expectancy. This advantage may be recognized by comparing the present worths of the annual charges for a study period equal to the expected life of the immediate investment.

The differences between the alternatives as stated will be made clearer if we assume a definite installation date, let us say, 1960:

Alternative A	*Alternative B*
Spend $5,500 now to satisfy all service needs from 1960 to 1985	Spend $4,000 now to satisfy all service needs from 1960 to 1975 and half the service needs from 1975 to 1985
	Spend $4,000 in 1975 to satisfy half the service needs from 1975 to 2000

The present worths of the annual charges for 25 years for the present installations are obviously the present investments, $5,500 and $4,000. The annual charges on the second half-capacity pipe will be $4,000(0.07823) = $313. The present worth of these charges during the years 1975–85 is $313(7.360)(0.4173) = $961. The comparison of present worths for the 25-year study period thus becomes:

Alternative A	*Alternative B*
$5,500	$4,000
	961
$5,500	$4,961

This comparison indicates an advantage for Alternative B, the plan which calls for a half-capacity installation. It should be emphasized that the "study period" technique here applied was necessary for the recognition of that advantage. A mere comparison of the present worths of the investments would have favored Alternative A; this incorrect conclusion would have resulted because a straight present worth comparison would have related to a shorter period of service with Alternative A than with Alternative B.

Solving for Period of Deferment as a Break-Even Point. Forecasts of a definite date when a given increment of capacity will be needed are, at best, very uncertain. A choice between alternatives may often be helped by finding such a date as a break-even point. If the given demand should develop before this break-even-point date, immediate investment is economical; otherwise deferred investment is economical. The estimator may then simply forecast whether or not the required capacity will be needed before or after this calculated date as a basis for his choice between the two alternatives. The method of making such calculations may be illustrated by using the data of Examples 13–5 and 13–6.

In the case of the first solution of Example 13–5 in which operation and maintenance costs were neglected, the question is merely how long it will take $100,000 now to amount to $200,000 with interest at 5%. Inspection of a 5% interest table indicates this period as between 14 and 15 years.

With the complicating factors of operation and maintenance costs introduced into Example 13–5, it is necessary to make an algebraic solution. Let x be the present worth factor (at 5% interest) corresponding to the period of deferment of the construction of the second half-capacity tunnel which just makes the costs break even for the two plans. Then:

$$\$315,900 = \$232,720 + \$232,720x$$

$$x = 0.358$$

This corresponds to a period of deferment of 21 years.

For the two alternatives in Example 13–6 to break even, the present worth of the annual charges on the second pipe during the 25-year study period should equal $5,500 − $4,000 = $1,500. If this present worth is calculated for various periods of deferment, the break-even point may be determined by cut and try, as follows:

Period of Deferment	P. W. Annual Charges During Study Period
10 years	$313(9.712)(0.5584) = $1,700
11 years	$313(9.295)(0.5268) = $1,530
12 years	$313(8.853)(0.4970) = $1,380

It appears, therefore, as if it is economical to choose Alternative B, the half-capacity pipe now, if it is probable that its capacity will be adequate for more than 11 years.

Using a Growth Forecast To Justify an Apparently Uneconomical Present Investment. Examples 13–5 and 13–6 related to determining whether or not to provide excess capacity above present needs, rather than to the question of whether to undertake some new activity. Growth forecasts are often relevant in answering the latter question as well.

In this latter type of study, if an investment does not seem likely to be profitable on the basis of an immediate demand for a service but does appear to be profitable if expected growth in demand takes place, care should be taken to examine critically the basis of the forecast of growth. If this forecast is not dependent on the existence of the plant supplying the service, there is generally an alternative of waiting until the growth has taken place before undertaking the investment.

For instance, a city that owned its electric distribution system bought electric energy at a wholesale rate from a power company. A study made to determine whether it would pay the city to construct its own generating station reached the conclusion that this would be profitable. However, this conclusion was dependent on a forecast of an 80% growth of load in a 15-year period; if the load should not grow at all, it would not pay to put in the generating station. Since the forecast of load growth was based on forecasts of population growth and of growth in per capita use of electricity that were in no way related to the source of electric energy, an obvious alternative was to defer the construction of the generating station until the load had reached a point where it would prove immediately economical.

In contrast, a forecast of growth of demand for a given service may be dependent on the creation of facilities to supply that service. For example, an air transport company, contemplating the starting of service over a new route, may recognize that considerable time will elapse before the public will make full use of the service provided; many people will not use it until it has "proved itself" by having provided reliable service over a considerable period. In this case the alternative of waiting to see if the demand grows of its own accord is not available. An economy study for such an enterprise should include, as part of the investment, the expected losses in the early years; for the project to be attractive, the prospective ultimate earnings should be sufficient to show a fair return on an investment figure so calculated.

Interpreting the Results of Economy Studies Comparing Immediate and Deferred Investments. Calculations of the type illustrated in Examples 13–5 and 13–6 may sometimes seem highly theoretical. Nevertheless, they are likely to be better guides to sound decisions than an unaided hunch. Their primary purpose should be to determine whether there is a clear-cut advantage for one or another of the alternative plans of development proposed. In borderline cases the irreducible factors should govern the choice.

Generally speaking, in any borderline case the irreducible factors are favorable to the alternative that involves a deferred investment rather than to an immediate investment with considerable excess capacity. This is particularly true if the interest rate used in the study has been the average cost of capital to an enterprise, without any increase to allow for a margin of safety. Unless the prospective rate of return is sufficiently higher than the cost of capital to justify a risk, that risk should not be undertaken.

One irreducible factor favorable to the deferred investment is the possibility that the forecast growth may never materialize, and thus the excess capacity may never be needed. Another such factor in many situations may be the difficulty of securing investment funds with the resulting pressure to keep all investments to a minimum. Still another factor in some cases may be the possibility that anything installed in the future may be superior, or somehow better adapted to the needs of the service, than excess capacity installed at present in advance of such need.

On the other hand, there is a nuisance aspect to many deferred investment plans that is favorable to immediate construction with considerable excess capacity. This is particularly true with regard to public utility services that must be placed underground in paved streets so that any addition to them requires cutting through the pavement and repaving.

A motive for a plan of development with considerable excess capacity in some public works projects that must be financed by bond issues is the possible difficulty of getting voters to approve bonds for increasing capacity within a few years after they have voted bonds for the original investment. It is also true in public works that the uncritical public is likely to censure an engineer much more for having built with capacity that soon proves inadequate than for having built with excess capacity that is never required.

In situations in which the excess capacity under consideration consists of real estate to be acquired for purposes of permitting future expansion, the possibility that this property simply will not be available for purchase at some future date when it may be needed is a motive toward immediate investment. The prospect of rising price levels—if not already considered in cost estimates—is also favorable to providing excess capacity now.

Before making a decision as to which of several alternative plans to select, all such relevant irreducible factors should be noted; they may then be given weight in the final choice.

The Significance of Price Changes in Economy Studies. All economy studies relate to decisions for the future. Hence, past changes in prices and price levels are of interest in economy studies only to the extent that a study of them may help in forecasting the future changes.

To the extent that specific price changes or general price-level changes are anticipated, this anticipation should properly enter into economy studies. It is often true that the selection of one alternative will be appropriate if it is expected that prices will not change, but that a different alternative should be selected if, for example, it is believed that a sharp rise in certain prices is likely to take place.

It is not the intention here to enter into a discussion of the numerous factors influencing price changes and price-level changes. An adequate discussion of this subject would doubtless require several volumes. One conclusion from any study of the subject would be that it is extremely difficult to make satisfactory forecasts of the behavior of prices. Nevertheless, it is sometimes true that general influences and trends, both with respect to certain specific prices and with respect to general price levels, may be evident even to the amateur in the field of price forecasting. Many situations do exist where it seems more reasonable for an economy study to reflect the prospect of a price change than to assume that no change will occur.

How Price Changes May Affect Economy Studies. The sensitivity of a set of alternative proposals to changes in price should be investigated whenever there is reason to believe that prices or price levels will change in the future. The usual method of applying this principle is to solve the problem with two or more different sets of assumptions regarding the prices of the various factors in the problem. One solution may be carried out with optimistic estimates of the prices, another may be carried out with less optimistic estimates, and a third may be carried out with pessimistic estimates. Examination of the solutions under the different conditions will indicate the sensitivity of a decision to possible changes in future prices.

Generally speaking, the prospect of a price increase tends to favor the higher of two alternative investments. This may be the result of several different types of situations. In one case the prospect of an increase in the price of a service that you are rendering may make an alternative attractive that would be unattractive at present prices. Similarly, the prospect of an increase in the disbursements for materials, labor, or a service may justify a present investment to avoid such disbursements that could not be justified at present price levels. The prospect of a price increase may justify a present investment over a deferred investment, or the investment in a long-lived item as opposed to a series of short-lived items. The foregoing matters are illustrated by several of the problems at the end of this chapter.

Some Comments on Price-Level Changes and Cost Indexes. Figures 13–2 and 13–3, applicable particularly to certain construction costs, illustrate several interesting points. One point is the general upward trend of costs during the years 1940 to 1959. Another point is that special-purpose indexes may do a better job of reflecting particular price changes than can possibly be done by a general-purpose index. Still another point is that different classes of costs often vary in quite different ways; the pattern of variation of different elements of cost is influenced by technological change as well as by changes in wage rates and material costs.

Figure 13–2, taken from *California Highways and Public Works*,[2] shows one general-purpose index of construction costs, the well-

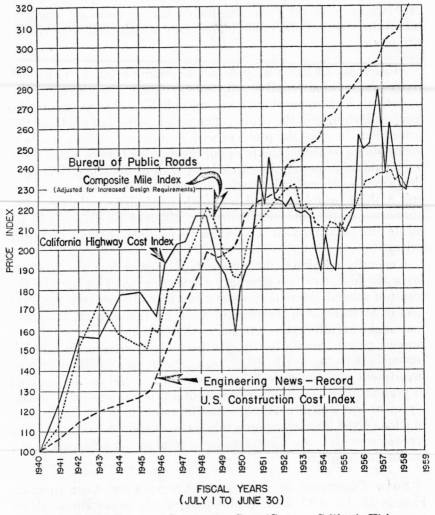

FIGURE 13–2. Price Indexes of Construction Costs (Courtesy California Highways and Public Works)

known index of *Engineering News-Record*. This is a synthetic index, based on a combination of certain material prices and certain hourly wage rates for labor. The other two indexes shown in this

[2] XXXVIII, Nos. 3–4 (March–April, 1959), 20.

figure are derived from an analysis of actual bid prices on highway construction. The composite mile index of the U. S. Bureau of Public Roads is based on nationwide prices; the California highway cost index reflects prices within a single state.

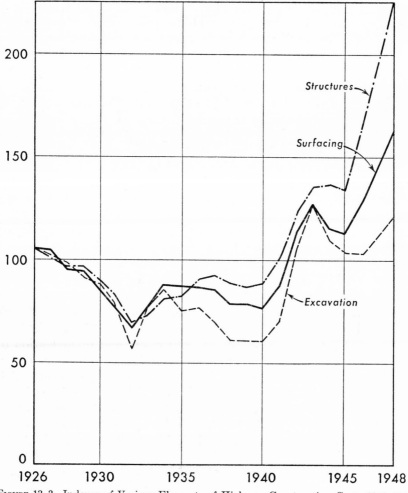

FIGURE 13–3. Indexes of Various Elements of Highway Construction Costs 1926–1949 (U. S. Bureau of Public Roads)

Figure 13–3 shows indexes of three different elements of highway construction cost over a 22-year period as prepared by the U. S. Bureau of Public Roads. It will be noted that, although the three elements tended to rise or fall at the same time, there were considerable differences in the rates of increase or decrease. The changes in the price index for excavation are particularly striking; the great improvements in earth-moving machinery that started in the early 1930's are reflected in the fact that excavation costs increased much less than the cost of other components of a highway.

Will It Pay To Make an Investment To Reduce a Risk? Although it may be difficult to place a money value on a risk, it is desirable to do this whenever possible, particularly when an expenditure of money is proposed to reduce or eliminate the risk. To see the way in which such a valuation may be used, let us consider first an artificially simple question that avoids many of the complications present in actual situations:

A certain individual is forced to throw two dice once a year. If they come double sixes, he is required to pay $1,000; otherwise, he pays nothing. How much could he afford to pay now to be relieved of the risk for 10 years, if interest is at 6%?

In the long run, double sixes would be thrown in 1/36 of the trials. If a very large number of individuals were subjected to this hazard, the number making the payment each year would be in the neighborhood of 1/36 of the total, although it might be somewhat greater or less than this in any particular year. If the individuals subject to this hazard should join together to eliminate the hazard of severe loss to any one member of the group, and each should pay into a common pool $27.77 (i.e., 1/36 of $1,000) each year, this would—in the long run—be sufficient to meet the losses incurred by the unfortunate ones who threw the double sixes. Of course if such a mutual insurance company were actually formed, it would have expenses of selling, administration, collection, and investigation of claims, and its charges to its members would have to be sufficient to provide the necessary benefit payments in those years in which losses were greater than average; thus its annual premium charge would doubtless be considerably more than $27.77. Nevertheless, the figure of $27.77 might be thought of as the bare "cost of the risk"; in gambling parlance, the individual who paid it would be getting a fair bet.

To determine how much the individual could afford to pay now to be relieved of the risk for 10 years requires the use of the 6% desired rate of return on investment. The answer is the present worth of $27.77 per year for 10 years. This is $27.77(7.360) = $204.[3]

If the question had been, "How much could a corporation with perpetual life pay to be relieved of this hazard forever?" the answer would have been $27.77/0.06 = $463.

[3] This calculation implies the certainty of survival of the individual for the 10-year period.

EXAMPLE 13–7. A PROPOSED INVESTMENT TO REDUCE A FIRE RISK

Facts of the Case. Fire insurance companies attempt to measure the effect of various structural changes and of changes in the fire protection devices installed in industrial buildings, and to reflect the differences in fire hazard in corresponding differences in the insurance rates. This may be illustrated by the following problem:

A city contemplating the construction of a municipal warehouse is in doubt whether to install an automatic sprinkler system for fire protection. Fire insurance for $25,000 on warehouse and contents will cost $110 a year without the system, and $60 a year if it is installed. (The insurance company's rate presumably depends on its estimate of the chance of fires of various degrees of destructiveness, as it agrees to pay damages for small fires as well as big ones; thus it relates to a more complex situation than that in the dice-throwing example.) The sprinkler system will cost $1,300 and have an estimated life of 20 years. Interest is at 6%. Should the system be installed?

The city engineer estimates that the losses that would occur if a warehouse fire took place would include various items (such as provision of temporary warehouse space, extra costs of municipal operations carried on under unusual conditions) that would not be covered by insurance; he believes the total losses of one sort or another resulting from a fire would be double the insurance collectible. From this he reasons that the saving in annual insurance cost of $50 (i.e., $110 − $60) from the sprinkler system will be half of the true saving therefrom in the cost of assuming the fire risk. (This accepts the insurance company's estimate of the "probability" of fire under the alternative conditions as superior to any independent estimate which might be made by the city engineer.)

This total estimated saving in the "cost of the risk" of $100 a year must be measured against the $1,300 first cost of the sprinkler system. This first cost is equivalent to an annual capital recovery cost of $1,300(0.08718) = $113. This cost comparison seems to indicate a small margin against the sprinkler system installation.

However, as in all situations where the reduction of risk of catastrophe is involved, the irreducible factors are on the side of reducing the risk. In this case, because the cost comparison seemed so close, it was decided to build the warehouse with the sprinkler system.

EXAMPLE 13–8. A PROPOSED INVESTMENT TO REDUCE THE RISK OF FLOOD DAMAGE

Determination of the Economic Capacity of a Spillway. The following illustration was suggested by one prepared by the late Allen Hazen: [4]

A large public utility company has acquired a recently constructed small hydroelectric plant in connection with the purchase of a small utility property. It seemed probable to the engineers of the large company that the spillway capacity of 1,500 cu. ft. per sec. provided by the dam at the plant was inadequate; if a flow occurred that exceeded the capacity of the spillway, the stream was likely to cut a channel around the power plant. A rough estimate of the cost of the necessary repairs if this should occur was $200,000.

---

[4] Allen Hazen, *Flood Flows* (New York: John Wiley & Sons, 1930).

In order to determine what, if any, increase in spillway capacity was justified, the engineers estimated the costs of increasing the spillway capacity by various amounts. They also estimated from the available records of stream flow the probabilities of floods of various magnitudes.

Flood Flow in Cu. Ft. per Sec.	Probability [5] of Greater Flood Occurring in Any One Year	Cost of Enlarging Spillway Capacity To Provide for This Flood
1,500	0.10	No cost
1,700	0.05	$ 24,000
1,900	0.02	34,000
2,100	0.01	46,000
2,300	0.005	62,000
2,500	0.002	81,000
2,700	0.001	104,000
3,100	0.0005	130,000

Investment charges on the spillway enlargement were assumed at 9% (capital recovery in 50 years with interest at $7\% = 7.25\%$; taxes at 1.75%). The annual "cost of the risk" is considered to be an annual amount that would be a fair charge for flood insurance if there were any such type of insurance. This is determined in the same way that the $27.77 figure was found in the artificial example of dice throwing—that is, by multiplying the expected damage ($200,000) by the probability of its occurrence. The total annual cost variable with spillway size is the sum of the investment charges on the spillway enlargement and the "cost of the risk." The tabulation of these costs for the various spillway sizes is as follows:

Spillway Capacity	Annual Investment Charges	Annual "Cost of Flood Risk"	Sum of Annual Costs
1,500	$ 0	$20,000	$20,000
1,700	2,160	10,000	12,160
1,900	3,060	4,000	7,060
2,100	4,140	2,000	6,140
2,300	5,580	1,000	6,580
2,500	7,290	400	7,690
2,700	9,360	200	9,560
3,100	11,700	100	11,800

These calculations appear to indicate that it will pay to design the spillway with sufficient capacity to take care of any flood such as would be expected on the average, 1 year in 100 (the probability for the 2,100 sec. ft. flood), but not to provide against more extreme floods than this. However, with a lower interest rate it would pay to design against a more extreme flood. For example, with 3% interest and no taxes (a common assumption in public flood control projects), it would clearly pay to design against the flood expected 1 year in 200 and costs

[5] The statistical or frequency definition of probability may be stated as follows: Assume that if a large number of trials of an event are made under the same essential conditions, the ratio of the total number of trials in which a certain event happens, to the total number of trials made, will approach a limit as the latter number is increased indefinitely; then the limit thus described is defined as the probability that the event shall happen under these conditions.

would be increased only very slightly by designing against the flood expected 1 year in 500.

The Concept of Average Annual Damages in the Long Run. In Example 13–8, the remaining life of the power plant and spillway was estimated to be 50 years. Nevertheless, we concluded that it was economical to design against a flood that would be expected on the average only once in 100 years. It is logical for our analysis to give weight to the hazard of events that are so extreme that they may not happen at all during the life of our structure. In effect, our calculations recognize that the flood that is expected on the average only once in 100 years is as likely to occur next year (or in any other specified year) as to occur 100 years from now.

In solving Example 13–8, we computed the annual "cost of flood risk" for each capacity of spillway by multiplying the $200,000 estimated damage that would be caused by a flood greater than the spillway capacity by the estimated probability of occurrence of such a flood. This "cost of the risk" was explained as an annual amount that would be a fair charge for flood insurance if such insurance were available. It is evident that this "cost" could also be described as expected average damages in the long run. For example, if damages of $200,000 are expected to occur once in 100 years, the average damage per year is $2,000, 1/100 of $200,000.

In the language of the mathematics of probability, the figure for expected average annual damages in the long run is described as the *mathematical expectation* of annual damages.

Computing Average Annual Damages When Different Expected Damages Are Associated with Different Probabilities of Extreme Events.[6] In Example 13–8, the damage from a flood exceeding the spillway capacity was estimated to be $200,000 regardless of whether the flood was slightly more than capacity or a great deal more. Under this simple assumption, the average annual damage was the product of the $200,000 and the probability that the spillway capacity would be exceeded in any year.

Frequently, the amount of the estimated damage from an extreme event depends on the magnitude of the extreme event. For example, in analyzing most flood control projects, it is necessary to recognize that, generally speaking, the larger the flood, the greater the prospective damage.

We may illustrate the procedures for computing expected average annual damages under such circumstances by a slight modification of the data of Example 13–8. Assume that it is estimated the

[6] This discussion was suggested by an unpublished paper by Professor Joseph B. Franzini of Stanford University.

damage will be $0 for any flood less than the spillway capacity, $200,000 if the flood exceeds the spillway capacity by not more than 200 sec. ft., $300,000 if the flood exceeds capacity by from 200 to 400 sec. ft., and $400,000 if the flood exceeds capacity by more than 400 sec. ft. The average annual damages with a capacity of 2,100 sec. ft. may be computed as follows:

Damages D	Probability of Stated Damage p	Dp
$400,000	$0.002 - 0.000 = 0.002$	$ 800
300,000	$0.005 - 0.002 = 0.003$	900
200,000	$0.01 - 0.005 = 0.005$	1,000
0	$1.00 - 0.01 = 0.99$	0
	Average annual damage $= \Sigma Dp$.....	$2,700

Similar calculations for spillway capacities of 1,900 and 2,300 sec. ft. will yield figures for average annual damages of $5,500 and $1,300 respectively.

A more general case is one in which the expected damage D varies continuously with the magnitude of the flood flow. In such a case, D can be plotted on rectangular coordinate paper as a function of p; the area under the curve will give the average annual damages. In cases where it is possible to describe the relationship between D and p by a mathematical function, the average annual damages may be determined by integration.

Certain Limitations of Decision Making Based on the Type of Analysis Illustrated in Example 13–8. The decision rule implied by our analysis in Example 13–8 is that it is justifiable to incur an increment of annual cost intended to reduce a risk of loss from some extreme event only if this increment of cost is less than the reduction in the "cost of the risk" of the extreme event. For example, an increase in spillway capacity from 2,100 to 2,300 sec. ft. was deemed uneconomical since it caused an increase in annual investment charges of $1,440 (i.e., $5,580 - $4,140), whereas it caused a decrease in the annual cost of the flood risk of only $1,000 (i.e., $2,000 - $1,000).

It should be recognized that this decision rule merely aims to give us a good gamble in dealing with a special class of uncertain events, namely, events that can be characterized by a probability distribution. Even where we have made correct estimates of probabilities and expected damages, the rule does not guarantee that, viewed in retrospect, decisions based on this rule will seem to have been good ones. For instance, assume that this rule is applied in Example 13–8 and our spillway is designed for a capacity of 2,100 sec. ft., the flood expected on the average 1 year in 100. If a flood of 2,300 sec. ft., expected on the average only once in 200 years, occurs in the near future, we shall be sorry we did not build the spillway with enough capacity to provide for this larger flood. On the other hand, if no flood greater than 1,900 sec. ft., expected on the average once in 50 years, occurs during the 50-year life of the spillway, no damages will have been prevented by the increment of annual investment charges caused by the last 200 sec. ft. of capacity.

Except where risks of extreme events are widely diversified, it usually is sound policy to carry a design somewhat beyond the point indicated by the decision rule implied in Example 13–8. If damage from an extreme event occurs, its adverse consequences may be disastrous to an individual or business enterprise—much more serious than the adverse consequences of extra outlays to reduce the risk of damage.

In a somewhat different setting from that of engineering design, the viewpoint stated in the preceding paragraph is implied by the actions of persons and business enterprises that take fire or casualty insurance. The premiums charged by insurance companies must necessarily be higher than the mathematical expectation of the loss insured against; premium rates must be high enough to cover administrative and selling costs as well as to pay damage claims. Thus, although large geographically diversified enterprises may find it economical to act as self-insurers, individuals and small business enterprises are well advised to carry fire and casualty insurance even though premiums are higher than would seem justified by the decision rule illustrated in Example 13–8.

General Comments on Economic Aspects of Engineering Design to Reduce Risk of Some Undesired Event. Examples 13–7 and 13–8 are representative of a type of problem occurring in practically every field of engineering. The selection of a safety factor in structural design implies the balancing of the greater risk of structural failure with a lower safety factor against the larger investment required by a higher safety factor; the design of a sewer that carries storm water implies balancing the damages that will occur if sewer capacities are inadequate in severe storms against the extra cost of building sewers with larger diameters; a similar problem exists in the selection of the waterway area for any highway or railway drainage structure. Similarly, a program of acceptance inspection of manufactured product may require the balancing of the costs associated with the risk of passing defective parts or defective final product against increased inspection costs if more product is inspected; the allotment of public funds to grade-crossing-elimination projects implies balancing the prospective accidents at any crossing against the cost of eliminating that crossing; the design of an electric generating station and distribution system implies weighing the prospective damages from service outages against the cost of reducing the chance of such outages. Illustrations of this sort might be multiplied indefinitely.

If such problems are to be solved quantitatively rather than by someone's guess, estimates must be made of:

1. The expected frequencies of the undesired events under various alternative plans of design and operation
2. The expected consequences if the undesired events occur, expressed in money terms in so far as is practicable
3. The money outlays (both immediate investment and subsequent disbursements) to make various degrees of reduction in the risk
4. Any other future differences—either measurable in money terms or otherwise—associated with alternative designs or operating policies to be compared

The practical difficulty lies in evaluating these items, particularly the first two. It is generally easy to recognize cases in which it clearly pays to reduce a risk because the cost of reducing the risk is small, and the risk itself and the prospective damages if the undesired event occurs are large. Similarly, it is easy to recognize cases at the other extreme where the cost of reducing the risk is high, and the risk of the undesired event occurring is very slight.

But often it is not possible to make a quantitative approach to those many troublesome cases in which the answer is not obvious, simply because of the absence of any reliable information as to the frequencies of the events against which it is desired to protect, and as to the amount of the damages that will occur if the events take place. Often this information does not exist merely because of the absence of any systematic effort to get it. In some cases, however, even after such systematic effort is started, the securing of useful data may require the passage of a considerable period of time.

For instance, in the flood spillway illustration, flood probabilities were estimated as low as 0.0005, that is, one year in 2,000. On most of the streams in the United States, the available records on which such estimates must be based vary from none at all to records extending for approximately 60 years. Even with a 60-year record, extrapolation from fitted curves is required to estimate the probabilities (such as 1 year in 100) that are likely to be significant in economic design, and different extrapolators may get different results from the same data.

Even though records are available as to the frequencies of undesired events and as to the kinds of damages that have occurred from them, it may be difficult or impossible to place a money valuation on all of the damages. This is particularly true in estimates relative to those types of catastrophe that involve human suffering. Thus irreducibles may play an important part in economy studies of this type, even though the necessary facts are available to take decisions out of the "hunch" class.

Some Comments on the Relationship Between the Mathematics of Probability and Decision Making in the Face of Uncertainty. Some years ago, Dr. Walter Shewhart, the distinguished father of modern statistical quality control, wrote as follows: [7]

> What can we say about the future behavior of a phenomenon acting under the influence of unknown or chance causes? I doubt, that, in general, we can say anything. For example, let me ask: "What will be the price of your favorite stock thirty years from today?" Are you willing to gamble much on your powers of prediction in such a case? Probably not. However, if I ask: "Suppose you were to toss a penny one hundred times, thirty years from today, what proportion of heads would you expect to find?," your willingness to gamble on your powers of prediction would be of an entirely different order than in the previous case.

Dr. Shewhart's statement makes the point clearly that there are different kinds of uncertainties. Some types of uncertainty obviously can be treated to best advantage using the mathematics of probability; others cannot be so treated.

An exposition of the subject of the mathematics of probability in relation to the making of decisions is beyond the scope of this book; an entire book longer than this one would be needed for an adequate treatment of this complex topic. We have limited our examples of the use of probability to cases of design against the risk of an extreme event where data are available to estimate the relative frequency of occurrence of the event in the long run if successive trials of the event are made "under the same essential conditions." Where no such data are available and where uncertainties are troublesome to a decision maker, we have suggested using analyses based on the concept of sensitivity.[8]

---

[7] W. S. Shewhart, *Economic Control of Quality of Manufactured Product* (Princeton, N.J.: D. Van Nostrand Co., Inc., 1931), p. 8.

[8] Many modern writers on statistical decision theory and operations research advocate the use of probabilities obtained through intuition in cases where no data are available to estimate relative frequencies in the long run. For a clear exposition of the case for the use of such "personal" probabilities in decision making, see Robert Schlaifer, *Probability and Statistics for Business Decisions* (New York: McGraw-Hill Book Co., Inc., 1959).

Summary. Some common types of economy studies discussed in this chapter are:

1. Studies in which the relative economy of different alternatives depends on the prospective amount of utilization
2. Studies comparing long-lived and short-lived alternatives
3. Studies of proposals to design with excess capacity to provide for expected future growth
4. Studies involving forecasts of price changes
5. Studies involving proposed investments to reduce or eliminate the adverse consequences of certain extreme events

These types of economy studies have been used to illustrate the concepts of sensitivity and the break-even point. The use of the mathematics of probability in decision making was illustrated by the examples dealing with extreme events.

Problems

13-1. A commercial rental property is offered for sale for $58,000. The property consists of a two-story building in the business district of a small, but rapidly growing, city. The building is currently leased for $7,000 a year, and the lease has 3 years to run.

A prospective purchaser estimates that if he buys it he will hold it for about 10 years. At present the average annual disbursements for all purposes in connection with its ownership and operation (maintenance, repairs, janitor service, utilities, taxes, insurance, etc.) are about $2,700. He believes that the building can be sold 10 years from now for at least $40,000, and he wants to earn 10%, before income taxes, on his investment.

(a) Should he buy the building?

(b) After reviewing the history of property values and rents for several years he decides that he has been too conservative in his estimates. He now estimates that he can obtain an average annual gross income of $9,000 after the present lease expires. He also estimates that the average annual disbursements will go up to $3,400 at the same time. What prospective minimum resale value must the building have 10 years hence to make it return him 10% interest on his investment?

13-2. A small utility company is considering the purchase of a power-driven post hole auger mounted on a truck, to dig holes for poles used in the extension of its electric distribution system. This machine will cost $8,000 new, including the truck. Its life is estimated as 8 years with $1,000 salvage value. Annual cost of storage, maintenance, painting, insurance, and taxes is estimated at 15% of first cost regardless of the amount the equipment is used. Costs incident to its operation are:

Operators—2 men at $15 per day each
Fuel and lubricants—$10 per day

Observation of similar machines indicates that it can dig 25 post holes 6 feet deep per day. At present, holes are being dug by hand labor. An average laborer requires 1½ days to dig a hole. Labor costs $11.20 per day.

How many holes must be dug per year to make this machine an economical investment? Assume the minimum attractive rate of return to be 8%. (*Ans.* = 164 holes per year.)

13–3. The private branch exchange telephone switchboard of a certain company is so designed that all interoffice calls must be handled by manual switching. It is proposed that the necessary changes in the company's telephone system be made to permit direct dialing on all interoffice calls. This will require an immediate investment of $6,000 by the company and will increase the monthly telephone bill by $110. At present two operators are required. Each receives $320 per month (including salary extras). It is thought that when manual switching on interoffice calls is eliminated, equally good service on incoming and outgoing calls can be provided with a single operator plus one-fourth time of another employee who receives the same salary as part-time relief operator and part-time typist. It is believed there will be a time saving on the completion of interoffice calls. If no money value is placed on this time saving, how many years are required for this $6,000 investment to pay off? Assume a minimum attractive rate of return before taxes of 12%. How many years if the time saving is valued at $50 per month? (*Ans.* = (a) 5.5 years; (b) 3.8 years.)

13–4. In the construction of an aqueduct to serve a large city with water, a tunnel is necessary. In order to determine whether it will pay to build this tunnel to the ultimate capacity of the aqueduct, the engineers have forecast the growth of the demand for water in terms of tunnel capacity as follows:

A one-third capacity tunnel will be adequate for 10 years.
A one-half capacity tunnel will be adequate for 20 years.
A two-thirds capacity tunnel will be adequate for 35 years.

Estimated construction costs are as follows:

One-third capacity	$2,000,000
One-half capacity	2,400,000
Two-thirds capacity	2,700,000
Full capacity	3,400,000

Extra pumping costs for the smaller size tunnels above costs for the full capacity tunnel are estimated as follows:

One-third capacity tunnel, running full, $11,000 a year. Thus for an ultimate development of 3 such tunnels the extra pumping costs would be $33,000 a year.

One-half capacity tunnel, running full, $10,000 a year. Thus for an ultimate development of 2 such tunnels the extra pumping costs would be $20,000 a year.

Two-thirds capacity tunnel, running full, $8,000 a year. Thus for an ultimate development of 1 two-thirds and 1 one-third capacity the extra pumping costs would be $19,000 a year.

Set up the four plans of development suggested by these estimates. Compare them on the basis of the capitalized cost of perpetual service, using interest at 5% and assuming the continuance of present price levels. In calculating excess pumping costs, assume that the differences in costs given apply from the date a tunnel is put in service. What size tunnel would you recommend for present construction? (*Ans.* = two-thirds capacity now; capitalized cost is $3,263,000.)

13–5. In a factory with fire insurance based on a value of $360,000, an engineer suggests the installation of an automatic sprinkler system costing $22,000.

This will reduce the annual fire insurance cost from 1.32% to 0.54%. The management estimates that the total losses from a destructive fire will be at least 2½ times the losses on which recovery can be made from the insurance company. The annual cost of operation and maintenance of the sprinkler system is estimated as $120.

Assuming the capital recovery period for the sprinkler system as 15 years, and using a minimum attractive rate of return of 15% before income taxes, determine whether it will pay to install the sprinkler system.

13-6. There is 1 chance in 20 that a certain event will occur in any given year; if it occurs it will require an expenditure of $30,000. With interest at 8%, what is the justifiable present expenditure to eliminate this risk for 20 years? What is the justifiable present expenditure to reduce the risk from 1 in 20 to 1 in 50, for the same 20 years? (*Ans.* = (a) $14,730; (b) $8,840.)

13-7. A full program of development of a portion of a certain water supply project is to be compared with a stepped program of development. The full program calls for a $700,000 investment now. The stepped program requires $400,000 now, $300,000 in 10 years, and $300,000 in 20 years. Estimated annual disbursements under the full program will be $10,000 during the first 10 years, equal during the second 10 years, and $5,000 less thereafter. Compare capitalized costs of the two programs, using 3½% interest. For purposes of this economy study, assume the investments are in permanent construction and that the service is perpetual. (*Ans.* = full program now, $783,200; stepped program, $835,250.)

13-8. Make the same comparison as in Problem 13-7, assuming interest at 7%. By examining the results with 3½% and 7% interest, what general conclusions can you draw about the importance of the interest rate in economy studies comparing immediate with deferred investments? At what interest rate do these break even?

13-9. In Problems 13-7 and 13-8 assume that substantial rises in price levels are forecast. Assume that a 30% rise in 10 years will increase the cost of the second step to $390,000, and that the third step 20 years hence will cost $500,000. Assume that the extra annual disbursements for the full program will still be $10,000 for the first 10 years but that the estimated extra disbursements starting 20 years hence for the stepped program are now increased to $8,000. State in general terms how this forecast would influence the choice with interest at 3½% as in Problem 13-7. Make a specific comparison of capitalized costs at 7% interest, modifying the figures obtained in the solution of Problem 13-8 to fit these new forecasts. In general, what conclusions are apparent about the interrelationships between interest rates and forecasts of price changes in this type of economy study?

13-10. The owner of an orange grove in a relatively frost-free area is considering the question whether or not to purchase and operate smudge pots as a protection against frost. An investigation of the weather records in this area shows that during the past 50 years there have been 4 years with freezes sufficiently bad to injure the fruit. It is estimated that on the average this will reduce the value of the crop by about 75%. Average annual gross receipts from this grove during a year without frost are estimated as $6,000.

The initial investment in smudge pots required to protect this grove is $1,500. The life of the pots is estimated as 20 years. Annual labor cost for setting out pots in the autumn, removing in the spring, and cleaning is $150. Average annual fuel cost is $50. If it is assumed that this will give complete protection against loss due to frost, will it be desirable to purchase and operate the pots? Assume interest at 5%. (*Ans.* = annual cost of smudge pots, $320.40; cost of risk, $360.)

13–11. In the purchase of land for the construction of a manufacturing plant, the question arises regarding the desirability of purchasing certain adjoining unimproved land for possible use for future plant expansion. At present this land is available at a price of $30,000. On the assumption that the land will not be needed for 15 years and that average taxes will be 2%, what must be the prospective price of the land 15 years hence to make it pay to purchase the land now? Assume interest at 7%. What are some of the irreducible data that should enter into a decision on such a matter?

13–12. In the design of a 2-story municipal office building, the question arises whether provision should be made for the addition of 2 more stories at a later date. The architect makes two designs; the one that provides for this possible expansion involves an estimated first cost of $69,500; the one without this provision involves an estimated first cost of $63,000.

If the former plan is adopted, it is estimated that the subsequent addition of 2 stories will cost $42,000. Without the additional strength of columns and footings provided by this plan, it is likely that if it were ever decided to add the 2 stories, the necessary reconstruction and strengthening of the lower stories would cost at least $15,000 in addition to the cost of the 2 new stories.

Assume the life of the building as 50 years from now, either with or without the additions. How soon must the additional stories be needed in order to justify the selection of the $69,500 design? Assume interest at 3½%. Building upkeep will be the same with either design. Since this is a government building, there will be no taxes.

13–13. A warehouse building is to be erected that will be insured against fire for $200,000. Two sites under consideration differ only in the first cost and in fire protection. On the more costly site, the annual insurance rate will be 0.65%; on the less costly site it will be 0.90%. It is estimated that these rates fairly reflect the difference in fire risk and that the full losses from any fire would be approximately double the losses on which recovery could be made from the insurance company. With interest at 8% and assuming no change in land values over the years, how much extra could be paid for the more costly site?

13–14. A man who holds a license to give flying lessons is considering the purchase of a light airplane for personal use. He plans to give instruction to student pilots in order to pay the costs of owning and operating the plane. He can buy a secondhand light plane for $3,600 and estimates that it will depreciate at the constant rate of $600 a year regardless of the amount of flying that he does in it. Insurance will cost $220 a year, hangar rental will be $250 per year, and repair and maintenance will amount to approximately $1.25 per flying hour. Fuel and lubrication costs will amount to about $1.50 per flying hour. He can charge $10 an hour for flight instruction.

Prepare a table showing the annual cost of operating the airplane at different numbers of total flying hours per year, beginning at 100 hours and going up by 100 hours in each column. Show the number of hours of instruction that he must give to cover the cost of owning and operating the plane at each different number of total hours. At what number of hours will his income just equal the cost of owning and operating the plane? For simplicity, assume 0% interest rate and disregard any possible income taxes.

13-15. Two 10-HP motors are under consideration for a certain application. Motor A costs $340 and has a guaranteed full-load efficiency of 85.2%. The motor B costs $290 and has a full-load efficiency of 82.1%. Electric energy is purchased at 2.3 cents per kw-hr. (1 HP = 0.746 kw.) The minimum attractive rate of return is 12% before income taxes, and annual property taxes and insurance amount to about 2.5% of the first cost. Whenever the motors will be operated, they will be run at full load. Plot a break-even chart to show the number of hours of operation per year at which the two motors will be equally economical.

13-16. The lining of a plating tank must be replaced every three years at a cost of approximately $1,800. A new lining material has been developed that is more resistant to the corrosive effects of the plating liquid. This new lining will cost approximately $3,100. If the minimum attractive rate of return is 15% and annual taxes and insurance amount to about 3% of the first cost, how long must the new lining last to be more economical than the present lining?

13-17. A mining company operates its own narrow gage railroad from the ore pits to the processing plant. A timber trestle bridge over a small stream needs to be replaced. A new timber trestle can be installed for $16,000 and is expected to have a life of 15 years. A steel bridge can be built for $20,000 and will last for 45 years. The annual maintenance on the steel bridge will be about $1,000 a year greater than for the timber bridge. Which type of bridge should be selected if the interest rate is 12%? How sensitive is the decision to changes in the prospective cost of replacing the timber bridge with a similar one in the future? (Consider that the timber bridge might cost 25% more 15 years hence and 50% more 30 years hence.)

13-18. A manufacturing company needs to expand its production facilities and needs to add about 15,000 sq. ft. of space. The company can build an addition to its present plant at a total cost of $100,000. This addition will be particularly advantageous because it can be specifically designed to meet the company's needs.

The owner of an adjacent building has offered to sell it to the company. Preliminary estimates indicate that remodeling of the old building would require the expenditure of about $15,000 and that annual operating expenses would be about $3,000 (for increased materials handling costs) more than for the proposed new addition.

The prospective life of the addition is estimated to be 30 years while the prospective life of the old building is only 20 years. If the minimum attractive rate of return is 12% and taxes and insurance will amount to about 2.25% per year, how much can the company afford to pay for the old building? What irreducibles can you think of that might affect the decision?

13-19. In the selection of the spillway capacity of a reservoir, estimates were made of the spillway cost to provide for various flows, and of the probabilities of the flows being exceeded, as follows:

Flow in Cu. Ft. per Sec.	Probability of Greater Flow in Any One Year	Cost of Spillway To Provide for This Flow
8,400	0.08	$200,000
9,900	0.05	225,000
12,200	0.02	260,000
14,000	0.01	300,000
17,000	0.005	330,000
19,000	0.002	360,000

Investment charges on the spillway are to be calculated on the basis of a 100-year life, 5% interest, and no taxes (as this is a public works project). Operation and maintenance will be unaffected by the spillway capacity chosen. The expected damages if the flow is substantially in excess of the spillway capacity are estimated at approximately $300,000.

What spillway capacity makes the sum of the annual cost of the spillway and the "cost of the risk" a minimum?

13–20. An $8,000 investment is proposed. It is expected that this investment will eliminate a certain manual operation that now costs $1,000 per year. It is estimated that the life of the investment is 10 years and the company requires a minimum attractive rate of return of 12% before income taxes on any proposed investments.

(a) If the price of labor remains the same throughout the next 10 years, should this investment be made?

(b) The person who proposed this investment points out that the base labor rate has gone up about 5% per year. If it can be assumed that the labor cost for this task will be $1,000 the first year, $1,050 the second, $1,100 the third, and increase by $50 each year thereafter, is the proposed investment justified?

13–21. A small city is considering the development of its water supply system. A stepped program requiring $200,000 now, $300,000 10 years hence, and $300,000 20 years hence has been proposed. A local engineer proposes that the entire project be built now. He estimates that the whole project now would cost only $600,000. It is further estimated that the annual operating costs for the full program will be $15,000 a year more than for the first stage of the stepped program, equal to the costs for the stepped program during the second period of 10 years, and $8,000 less than the annual operating costs for the stepped program thereafter. Compare the capitalized cost of the two programs, assuming interest at 3½%. Assume that the investments are in permanent construction and that the service is perpetual.

13–22. Determine how sensitive the decision in Problem 13–21 is to changes in the price of the second and third steps in the stepped program. Should the decision be different if the prices are estimated to increase to $360,000 and $400,000 for the second and third steps in the stepped program?

13–23. A man is contemplating the purchase of a home for $25,000. However, he believes that it is a highly inflated price, and that the property will not have a favorable resale value 5 years from now. He estimates that the taxes will be about $500 a year and the insurance about $125 on the proposed house. He estimates annual repair and maintenance at about $300. His other alternative is to rent a house of about the same size and desirability for $250 a month. He considers 6% to be a minimum attractive rate of return on his investment in the house. What must the resale value be 5 years hence to justify buying the house?

13–24. In the construction of a hydroelectric power plant, it is planned to install only 4 turbo-generators at the start, although the ultimate design calls for 10. The question arises in the design whether to provide foundations, draft tubes, and other necessary facilities to permit the installation of the additional turbo-generators when needed merely by the purchase and installation of the machines, or to defer the investment in these facilities until the turbo-generators are about to be installed.

The extra cost now to provide these facilities for all 6 future turbines will be $100,000. It is contemplated that 2 more turbo-generators will be needed in 6 years, 2 in 11 years, and the final 2 in 15 years. The installation of these facilities at the time they are required is estimated to cost $90,000 per pair of turbines.

With interest at 10% and annual taxes at 1.8% of investment, compare the present worth of the disbursements for 15 years under the plan calling for the present investment and the plan calling for the deferred investment. Which has the lower cost? What implied money advantage of the present investment plan is omitted from this comparison?

13–25. Tanks to hold a certain chemical are now being made of Material A. The first cost of a tank is $30,000 and the life is 8 years. When a tank is 4 years old it must be relined at a cost of $10,000. It has been suggested that it might be preferable to make the tanks from Material B. Accelerated tests give the estimate that the life using Material B will be 20 years and that no relining will be needed. The first cost of the tanks using Material B is not yet known. If the minimum attractive rate of return is 12% before income taxes, what is the greatest amount that it would be justifiable to spend for a tank constructed of Material B? Assume zero salvage value for tanks made of either material.

13–26. A manufacturing company guarantees its product against defects in workmanship and materials for a certain period of time. Whenever a customer finds a defective unit within the warranty period, he returns it to the factory for free repair. Current records show that approximately 15% of the company's output is returned once and another 5% is returned twice, due to defects in manufacture. The total cost to repair a unit amounts to about $100.

The company's quality control director thinks the percentage of returned items can be reduced by an intensive quality control program. He estimates that the expenditure of $85,000 a year for labor and salary expense and $100,000 for improved inspection and quality control equipment will reduce the number of returned items to 8% of the output and that none will be returned a second time.

(a) Determine the annual production rate that would be required to justify the quality control director's proposal. Assume that the minimum attractive rate of return is 15% before income taxes and that the quality control equipment will have a life of 10 years with no salvage value.

(b) Assuming interest at 15%, 10-year life for equipment with no salvage value, and an annual production rate of 10,000 units, determine the maximum percentage of the products that the company could afford to have returned one time and still justify the quality control director's proposal.

13–27. Two structures are under consideration for a certain purpose. The annual disbursements will be the same for both structures, but Structure A will cost $20,000 and has a prospective life of 15 years, while Structure B will cost only $8,500 and have a 5-year life. A minimum attractive rate of return of 10% is required on such investments.

(a) Which structure should be chosen, assuming that there will be need for its service for 15 years? Assume a cost of $8,500 for renewals of Structure B.

(b) Which structure should be chosen if it is estimated that Structure B will cost $11,000 5 years from now and $12,500 10 years from now?

14

Increment Costs and Sunk Costs

Chapters 2 and 11 emphasized that it is always prospective *differences* between alternatives that are significant in making a choice. In a going concern all past receipts and disbursements and many future ones will be unaffected by a particular choice. It often happens that average costs per unit (sometimes called "unit costs") are misleading guides to making decisions.

A critical examination of the influence on cost of a particular decision often is required. Examples 14–1, 14–2, and 14–3 illustrate this point in relatively simple cases. These examples serve the incidental purpose of illustrating some common types of public utility rates.

EXAMPLE 14–1. INCREMENT COST OF ELECTRICITY FOR HOUSEHOLD PURPOSES

Facts of the Case. Consider the purchase of electric energy under the following domestic monthly rate:

Service charge of 50 cents
First 30 kw-hr at 5 cents per kw-hr
Next 70 kw-hr at 3 cents per kw-hr
All over 100 kw-hr at 1.5 cents per kw-hr

A householder's monthly consumption of electricity is about 120 kw-hr, resulting in a monthly bill of $4.40. This is a "unit cost" of 3⅔ cents per kw-hr.

He is anxious to economize, and considers various ways to reduce the monthly electricity bill by eliminating or reducing the use of certain lights or electric appliances. Considering each possibility in turn, it is clear that unless the resulting reduction in monthly consumption is more than 20 kw-hr, the unit saving will be only 1½ cents per kw-hr; this is less than half of the above "unit cost" of 3⅔ cents. This reasoning may be applied to the lights in the living room, to the electric toaster, to the radio, or to any other device using electricity. Thus the average cost or so-called "unit cost" is not relevant to a decision regarding the elimination or reduction of any individual item of use.[1] Similarly, it is irrelevant in the consideration of any proposed addition of load.

---

[1] It should be emphasized that this reasoning applies to all the uses of electricity included in the 120 kw-hr. Up to 20 kw-hr, the 1½-cent unit saving may be applied to the elimination or the reduction of each on the assumption that no other elimination or reduction will be made. But the addition of the separate savings figured at the 1½-cent rate is meaningless. This is a simple example of what is called by J. B. Canning, the problem of "non-additive economic valuations."

EXAMPLE 14–2. INCREMENT COST OF ELECTRICITY FOR INDUSTRIAL PURPOSES

Facts of the Case. A manufacturer purchases electricity under the following rate:

First 50 kw-hr per HP of maximum demand @ 3.0 cents per kw-hr
Next 50 kw-hr per HP of maximum demand @ 2.0 cents per kw-hr
Next 100 kw-hr per HP of maximum demand @ 0.7 cents per kw-hr
All over 200 kw-hr per HP of maximum demand @ 0.6 cents per kw-hr

In a representative month in which he uses 50,000 kw-hr with a maximum demand of 200 HP(149.2 kw.), his bill is computed as follows:

$$
\begin{array}{rcl}
10,000 \text{ kw-hr } @ \quad 3 \text{ cents} & = & \$300 \\
10,000 \text{ kw-hr } @ \quad 2 \text{ cents} & = & 200 \\
20,000 \text{ kw-hr } @ \quad 0.7 \text{ cents} & = & 140 \\
10,000 \text{ kw-hr } @ \quad 0.6 \text{ cents} & = & \underline{\quad 60} \\
\text{Total bill} & & \$700
\end{array}
$$

His average cost per kw-hr is therefore $700 ÷ 50,000 = 1.4 cents.

The manufacturer contemplates installing certain equipment that will reduce labor costs on certain special jobs. This equipment will add 100 HP(74.6 kw.) to the maximum demand. As its average use will be about 10 hours per month, it will add only 750 kw-hr of energy per month. For a study to determine the economy of installing this new equipment, a figure is needed for the "cost" of this extra 750 kw-hr.

Solution. Unlike Example 14–1, the extra costs of extra kilowatt-hours cannot be found merely by examining the rates per kw-hr in the incremental blocks on the rate schedule. Because the size of each block in this rate depends on the maximum demand and because it is planned to change the maximum demand, it is necessary to compute the monthly bill with and without the new load. With the proposed load added to the representative month, the monthly bill is computed as follows:

$$
\begin{array}{rcl}
15,000 \text{ kw-hr } @ \quad 3 \text{ cents} & = & \$450.00 \\
15,000 \text{ kw-hr } @ \quad 2 \text{ cents} & = & 300.00 \\
20,750 \text{ kw-hr } @ \quad 0.7 \text{ cents} & = & \underline{145.25} \\
\text{Total bill} & & \$895.25
\end{array}
$$

This addition of $195.25 to the original $700 monthly bill results from the increase in the proportion of the total energy that is purchased at the higher blocks of the rate. It is of interest to note that the average cost per extra kw-hr is $195.25 ÷ 750 = 26 cents. This is in striking contrast to the previous average cost of 1.4 cents per kw-hr. It is evident that this is a situation in which it would be decidedly misleading to make the assumption (one very commonly made in industrial economy studies) that additional kilowatt-hours can be purchased at the average unit cost of the energy already being purchased.

However, it would also be misleading to think of the 26 cent figure as an increment cost per unit. A more accurate view is that the additional 100 HP of maximum demand will add $190 to the monthly bill. With this extra demand added, each extra kw-hr of energy will add 0.7 cent to the bill. Thus 750 extra kw-hr add $5.25, making the total addition to the bill $190 + $5.25 = $195.25.

EXAMPLE 14–3. INCREMENT COST OF WHOLESALE GAS

Facts of the Case. A city buys gas for distribution and resale at the following monthly wholesale rate:

A "demand" charge of $3.30 times the maximum number of MCF (thousand cubic feet) used during any 24-hour period during the preceding 12 months, plus

A "commodity" charge of $0.18 times the number of MCF used during the current month

The city's current annual purchase of gas is 280,000 MCF. On the maximum day of the year, 1,600 MCF is used. From these two figures, the city's annual bill may be computed as follows:

Demand charge:	$3.30(12)(1,600)	= $ 63,360
Commodity charge:	$0.18(280,000)	= 50,400
Total annual bill		= $113,760

This is an average cost of $113,760 ÷ 280,000 = $0.4063 per MCF.

The distribution system includes a number of old mains from which there is a moderate amount of leakage. Because the pressure in the mains is approximately constant throughout the year and because the leakage depends on pressure rather than on gas consumption, the leakage per day from any main will be approximately constant. In order to make economy studies regarding gas main replacement, it is desired to compute a unit figure per MCF to apply to the estimated gas losses that would be eliminated by the replacement of any particular main.

Solution. The key point here is that, unlike the gas consumption, the gas loss is uniform throughout the year. The loss on the maximum day of a 365-day year will be 1/365 of the annual loss. The amount added to the city's annual gas bill by each MCF of loss may be computed as follows:

Demand charge:	$3.30(12)(1/365)	= $0.1085
Commodity charge		= 0.18
Increment cost of a MCF lost		= $0.2885

This is nearly 30% less than the average cost per MCF purchased. The economy studies for gas main replacement would have given incorrect conclusions if the average cost of gas had been used rather than its incremental cost.

Load Factor and Capacity Factor. Two useful phrases originating in the generation of electricity are *load factor* and *capacity factor*. Load factor is defined as the ratio of average load to maximum load. Average and maximum loads may be taken for any desired period of time. Thus a power company will have a daily load factor each day that is the ratio of the average load for that day to the day's maximum load, and it will have an annual load factor that is the ratio of the average load for the year to the maximum load occurring during the year. A company with a typical daily load factor of 60% might conceivably have an annual load factor of 40% because of seasonal fluctuations in load.

Capacity factor is defined as the ratio of average load to maximum capacity. In comparing entire power systems it is more common to use load factor than capacity factor. This is chiefly because of the difficulty of securing a satisfactory uniform measure of power system capacity. It is appropriate, however, to speak of the capacity factor of an individual generating unit or of a generating station.

Although the terms "load factor" and "capacity factor" have a definite quantitative meaning in the electric power field, they are often used loosely in a qualitative sense in other fields of production. Thus one might say that a factory with a seasonal demand for its product might improve its load factor by taking on another product to be produced in the off season.

Some Aspects of Public Utility Rate Structures. In so far as practicable, the rate structures of regulated utilities are designed to reflect the behavior of the utility's costs. In many cases a large fraction of a utility's costs are caused by the utility's readiness to serve rather than by the number of service units supplied. For example, a considerable part of the cost of serving natural gas to the city in Example 14–3 depended on the capacity of the pipe line. It was necessary to have sufficient pipe line capacity to supply the demand on the maximum day of the year. (Because of the use of gas for space heating, this was usually the coldest day of the year.) In a similar manner an electric utility's costs are related to the maximum generating and transmission capacity that must be provided. An urban transportation utility's costs depend on the peak loads of traffic when people go to work and return home.

Example 14–3 illustrated a gas rate in which one element was a charge for readiness to serve, based on the measured maximum demand during the year. Such a two-part rate, containing both a demand charge and a commodity charge, is referred to as a *Hopkinson* type of rate. In such a rate, it is obvious that the unit cost decreases as a customer's load factor increases.

Customers may object to direct charges that depend on maximum demand or connected load. The same result is obtained, with less objection because the relation of the maximum demand to the rate is not superficially obvious, by the *Wright* type of demand rate. This is a block rate in which the size of the respective blocks depends on the maximum demand. Example 14–2 illustrated such a rate.

A thorough discussion of the interesting subject of utility rate structures is beyond the scope of this book. The problems at the end of this chapter give a few instances of more complex rates than those illustrated in Examples 14–1 to 14–3. Problem 14–2 illustrates a wholesale electric rate that combines the Hopkinson and

Wright types of rate. Problem 14–3 illustrates an electric rate under which off-peak demand (i.e., demand not occurring close to the system peak) is priced at a lower figure than on-peak demand.

Our examples and problems here are from the viewpoint of economy studies made for the purchasers of utility products or service rather than from the viewpoint of a utility company attempting to develop an equitable rate structure. We have used utility rates to emphasize the point that the uncritical use of average costs can lead to an unsound analysis and incorrect conclusions. Because a utility rate provides such a definite basis for predicting how a particular cost will be influenced by a proposed decision, examples involving utility rates provide clear illustrations of why economy studies need to be based on prospective *differences* between alternatives. Presumably such illustrations should be noncontroversial.

Nevertheless, even where utility rates are involved, many persons are inclined to use average costs as a basis for making decisions. For instance, in the case described in Example 14–3, in the initial phases of the replacement studies, the 40-cent average cost of purchased gas was adopted as the "obvious" figure for the unit cost of gas lost.

Relation of Economy Studies to the Accounts of an Enterprise. The tendency to use "unit cost" figures that are readily available, rather than to take a critical look at differences, seems to be even greater when data for economy studies are drawn from the accounts of an enterprise. Many economy studies will combine information obtained from the accounting system with information obtained from other sources, such as time studies or other types of performance tests. The usefulness of accounting information will depend upon the detail of the classification of accounts, the skill with which it has been drawn, and the care with which actual expenditures have been charged to the appropriate accounts.

However, even the best accounting systems may give misleading conclusions if the figures shown by the books of account are uncritically used. As pointed out in Chapter 2, the point of view of an estimator for an economy study is necessarily different from the point of view of the accountant. The economy study is concerned with prospective differences between future alternatives. The accounts of the enterprise are a record of past receipts and disbursements. They generally involve apportionments of past costs against future periods of time, and apportionment of joint costs among various services or products; such apportionments are sometimes misleading to estimators who are making economy studies.

Illustrations of Incorrect Inferences from Accounting Apportionments. The following three cases relate to the experience of a city that owned its electrical distribution system, retailing electric energy. Although most of its power was purchased at wholesale rates from a large power system, a small part was generated at peak load periods by its diesel engines (of relatively small capacity) in its own generating plant. In the accounts of this city the expenses of the electric utility were carefully distinguished from the cost of carrying on governmental functions and from the cost of running the municipally owned water utility. The expenses of joint departments were prorated between the city government and the electric and water utilities on an equitable basis; the governmental departments and the water utility were charged by the electric utility for electricity used at rates such as might reasonably have been charged by a privately owned corporation. Three situations arose in which this well-organized plan of accounting served to block an understanding of the true differences between the alternatives which it was desired to compare.

In the first situation some of the councilmen examined the municipal report, which showed the cost of purchased energy at about 1 cent per kw-hr and the cost of generated energy at about 2.5 cents. They concluded from these costs that a substantial saving would result if the diesel plant were shut down and all power were purchased.

It turned out that no such conclusion as this was justified by the facts. Many of the charges included in the 2.5-cent unit cost were allocated charges which would not have been reduced if the generating station were shut down; they would simply have been allotted to some other account than "Power Generation." The crew that operated the diesel engines also operated the substation and the pumping plant for the water department; the labor cost was, therefore, divided uniformly among those three activities. But as it still would have been necessary to run the substation and waterworks, no reduction in labor cost could have been made by discontinuing the operation of the diesels. Another charge allotted against the "Power Generation" account was the depreciation of the diesel engines. This, however, was simply a time allotment against the current year of an expenditure that had been made many years before; no part of that past expenditure could be eliminated or recovered by shutting down the diesels.

Thus the generating costs that were really relevant to the question "Shall we continue to operate the diesels, or shut them down and purchase all power?" appeared to be merely fuel, lubricants, and maintenance; these totaled about 0.8 cents per kw-hr. As power purchased was on a rate that included a substantial charge for maximum demand, the diesels had been operated only at periods of peak load in order to reduce the demand charge. If the diesels were shut down, the extra cost of purchasing the peak load energy would be considerably greater than the 1-cent average cost for the base load energy. When the councilmen finally recognized this as a problem in determining differences between alternatives, they were able to see that it was clearly economical to continue to generate peak load energy, despite the apparent showing of the accounts that generated energy cost much more than purchased energy.

In the second situation the question arose as to what savings were possible by a proposed temporary reduction of street lighting as a measure of economy. The city-owned electric utility charged the general city government for street-lighting energy at 2.5 cents per kw-hr, a fair rate, all things considered. In estimating the saving from this proposed temporary street-lighting reduction, the engineer making the estimate multiplied the expected reduction in energy consumption of 80,000 kw-hr per year by the 2.5-cent rate and concluded that the saving would be $2,000 a year. Here the engineer used the average cost that he found used in the accounting system and failed to recognize that most of the items that went into the 2.5-cent rate were not variable downward with a small reduction of street lighting.

When the increment cost situation was later recognized, it was apparent that almost the only cost that would be decreased was the cost of energy purchased at wholesale. Because of the structure of the wholesale rate, the last increment of energy cost considerably less than the average of purchased energy; in fact, less than one-third of the 2.5-cent figure previously estimated. When this real net saving to the city of about $600 in the power bill for the year was balanced against several hundred dollars of extra cost for wiring to make the change possible, it was clear that there was little or no real economy possible from the proposed temporary change and the city might as well have the benefit of the existing street lights.

In the third situation the question arose regarding the economy of the city's building its own generating station rather than continuing to purchase power. Here, in estimating the expense of the proposed generating station, the engineer's report included merely direct generating station costs and made no allowances for increased costs in other departments. In justification of this he argued that overhead costs were apportioned in the accounting system in proportion to direct costs and that as direct costs would not be increased with the proposed plant there would, therefore, be no increase in indirect costs as a result of the plant.

A more realistic examination of this situation indicated that his reasoning was in the same class with assuming that the increment cost of extra miles on your automobile was merely the out-of-pocket expense for gasoline; that is, this reasoning took a too short-run viewpoint. It seemed reasonable to believe that doubling the investment in the electric utility, as this would do, would increase the responsibility of the manager of that utility, and in the long run he would be better paid and would require an assistant sooner with the generating station than without it. It also seemed reasonable to believe that the operation of a generating station would involve more of such services as engineering, accounting, purchasing, and storekeeping than would the paying of a single power bill once a month. These conclusions were reinforced by an examination of the experience of other cities, which seemed to indicate quite definitely that expenses of these service departments always tended to move upward with any increase in activity. From such a study, it was possible to make a judgment as to what this long-run increase in expense in indirect departments would be. This item of cost had considerable weight in throwing the final decision against the generating plant which, on the basis of preliminary study, had appeared as if it might be economical.

The "With or Without" Viewpoint and the Concept of Cash Flow as Aids in Decision Making. The three cases just described had one characteristic in common with one another and with Examples 14–1 to 14–3. In each instance one alternative was to make some proposed change from the existing way of doing things and the other alternative was to continue this existing way. A search for the differences between such alternatives calls for a prediction of what will happen *with* the proposed change and *without* it. The phrase "with or without" will sometimes help to clarify the issues in such cases.

Throughout this book we have emphasized that, wherever practicable, the prospective physical differences between alternatives should be converted into prospective differences in cash flow. Although our concentration of attention on cash flow has been aimed particularly at the securing of data permitting the calculation of rates of return on proposed investments, the cash flow viewpoint is also helpful in avoiding the types of estimating errors that are discussed in the present chapter. Once an analyst adopts the cash flow viewpoint, he is likely to take a critical look at all figures based on allocations.

Treatment of Unused Capacity in Economy Studies. In any organization it is likely that various kinds of unused facilities will exist from time to time. Extra space may exist in office or warehouse or factory; extra capacity may exist for various service facilities (such as water, steam, or compressed air). Under such circumstances, a proposal for a new activity needing such facilities (e.g., expanded output, a new product, the production of items previously purchased) may not require any immediate investment to secure the facilities.

A similar, but slightly different, condition exists when it is possible to carry out the proposed new activities using existing facilities at some kind of a cost penalty until the time comes that the need for still further capacity makes it practicable to install a new unit of economic size. For example, the storage of additional material in an existing warehouse, already crowded to its economic capacity, might cause a disproportionately large increase in materials handling costs.

In an expanding organization most unused capacity that now exists is likely to be only temporary. For this reason it usually is incorrect for economy studies to assume that proposed new activities that will use existing unused facilities will never be responsible for investments in new facilities of the types in question. On the other hand, because an immediate investment in such facilities will not be required, it obviously is incorrect to make the economy studies assuming an investment before it will need to be made. Frequently, it should be recognized that the question at issue is the *timing* of an investment that will be required eventually. Ray I. Reul has made the following practical suggestion on this topic: [2]

> The solution recommended for this problem is to specify that where facilities are to be provided from surpluses or where acquisition of facilities is to be postponed, the full cost of these acquisitions shall be included in the evaluation as a future requirement but not charged until the time the actual expenditure of these funds is anticipated. To guard against accidental or deliberate overoptimism in postponement, it is further suggested that permissible assumption of deferment be limited to five years or one-third of the life of the project, whichever is the lesser. In this way, such expenditures are included in the total investment specified, but their impact on profitability is lessened.

Figures 19-1 to 19-3 in Chapter 19 include an example of future investment requirements treated in the manner suggested by Reul.

Burden Rates Are Seldom Adapted for Use in Economy Studies. Cost accounting in the manufacturing industries classifies production expense into direct labor, direct material, and indirect manu-

[2] R. I. Reul, "Profitability Index for Investments," *Harvard Business Review*, XXXV, No. 4 (July–August, 1957), 122.

facturing expense. This latter class may include a wide variety of items (such as salaries and wages of foremen, inspectors, clerical employees, crane operators, and storekeepers; operating supplies; packing and unpacking; shop losses due to defective material or workmanship; purchasing; receiving; shipping; heat, light, and power; plant maintenance; taxes, insurance, and rentals; and depreciation).

Indirect manufacturing expense is called by various shorter names, the most common of which are "burden," "overhead," and "expense." Although there is great variation in cost accounting systems, in many of them each item included in burden is allotted among the various departments (or production centers) on some basis that appears reasonable. Then the total burden allotted against a department is charged against the product of that department in proportion to some "burden vehicle." This burden vehicle will be something that is readily measurable regarding the product (such as its direct labor cost, its total direct cost, its labor hours, or its machine hours). More often than not the burden rate is "predetermined"; that is, it is based on the allotment of estimated indirect manufacturing expenses and on estimated direct labor cost (or other burden vehicle) reflecting estimated production.

In a department in which the vehicle is direct labor cost and the burden rate is 130%, each product is charged with $1.30 for every dollar of direct labor cost. Such burden allocation in cost accounting serves many useful purposes.

It does not follow, however, that a change in production methods that reduces direct labor cost by $100 will reduce indirect manufacturing expense by $130. Or, that if one of two alternative new machines involves $500 less direct labor cost than the other it will also involve $650 less indirect manufacturing expense. The only way to judge the relative effect of two alternatives on burden is to consider their probable effect on each of the individual items of indirect manufacturing expense that have been combined together in the burden rates.

Although the error of assuming that any saving in direct cost will be accompanied by a proportionate saving in indirect cost should be obvious, it appears that this error (which has appeared in several published formulas for determining economy) is often made in industry.

Allocations in Accounting and in Economy Studies. Thus it is necessary that the engineer look beneath the surface of an accounting figure before he uses it in his economy study.

For instance, an engineer for a railway company was called upon to compare the cost of increasing the generating capacity of the power plant serving one of the railway company's shops with the cost of purchasing power. In making the comparison, he found it necessary to recognize that the accounting charges to shop power that the railway made under its accounting routines did not reflect all of the costs that were pertinent to his comparison. For instance, one of the major savings that would result from purchased power was in the cost of coal, and a considerable portion of the coal cost was the cost of its transportation from the mine. But this transportation cost was not allocated to the account showing shop power expense; the railway accounts considered it merely as part of the cost of conducting transportation. Another major advantage of purchasing power as compared with increasing generating capacity was in the lower investment involved, with corresponding lower investment costs of interest, depreciation, and taxes. But none of these investment costs were allocated against shop power expense in the railway's accounts.

Treatment in Economy Studies of an Investment-Type Disbursement Charged as a Current Expense in the Accounts. In tabulating the effect of a decision on cash flow before income taxes, a disbursement is negative cash flow regardless of whether it is capitalized on the books of account or treated as a current expense. It often happens that certain nonrecurrent disbursements that will be "expensed" in the accounts are associated with the acquisition or replacement of physical assets. For example, in considering the replacement of a railway bridge, the cost of handling traffic during the replacement period may be different beween alternative replacement structures. This cost of handling traffic will be considered as an operating expense in the railway accounts. Nevertheless, its effect on cash flow before income taxes is just the same as if it were capitalized in the accounts.

However, in any analysis to determine cash flow after income taxes, it is essential to differentiate between disbursements that are to be capitalized and those that are to be expensed. This point is developed in Chapter 15.

Cost Information That Accounting Records Will Not Give. Where the economy of some new process or machine is involved, estimates of operating costs must be obtained by experimental studies rather than from accounting records. Time studies or laboratory studies regarding the characteristics of new machinery may be combined with known wage rates and material costs and with an analysis of indirect costs in order to arrive at cost figures.

Frequently, an economy study requires the consideration of some cost that, by its very nature, cannot be isolated by accounting charges. For instance, in considering the economy of automatic block signal systems for railway trains, an important saving will be in the elimination of train stops. But what is the cost of stopping a train? The railway accounts cannot isolate this cost. It must be determined on the basis of fuel saved from an analysis of locomotive performance curves, and on the basis of the economies resulting from time saved.

In designing any cost accounting system, the question always arises as to the detail to which accounting records ought to be carried. To what extent may approximations be used in allocating costs in place of more precise methods of cost allocation that are more expensive? There is always the conflict between the expense of getting better accounting records and the value of the information obtainable from such records. No cost accounting system is justified that will not pay its way by giving information that is worth more than the cost of getting it. Where cost systems are planned with the idea of simplifying determinations of economy, the question is likely to arise whether it will be more economical to maintain regular continuous records or to make an occasional analysis when a particular sort of cost information is required. There will be, in many organizations, cost information useful to engineers, that must be obtained by analysis, rather than from the accounting records, simply because it does not pay to keep accounting records in such detail as would be required to furnish this information.

Allocation of a Previously Incurred Loss. It is not practicable for accountants to go back into past records and revise past figures when an error is discovered.

Once an industrial engineer made some suggestions of methods aimed to reduce the operating cost of the power plant in a factory. In the course of his investigations he also discovered that the amount of coal in the coal pile was much less than the amount shown by the inventory figure in the books of account.

He was greatly surprised some months later when the factory superintendent told him that the power plant operating costs had gone up rather than down. On investigation he discovered that the accountant had decided to spread the cost of the fuel shortage uniformly over the next 6 months after it was discovered, in order not to make it seem as if expenses had been very high in the month in which the shortage was discovered. This avoided distorting the comparative operating cost statements for various months. But the fuel shortage cost charged subsequent to its discovery more than neutralized the economies resulting from the engineer's suggestions! On superficial examination the situation appeared as if the fuel costs had not been reduced by his suggestions.

Increment Cost. The phrase *increment cost* has been used in this chapter to refer to a prospective difference in cost in certain "with or without" situations. This is not a phrase that can be given a precise definition in general terms; it is a phrase that is useful chiefly in reference to specific alternatives. Other phrases sometimes used in the same meaning are *incremental cost* and *differential cost*.

These phrases are also used in economic literature in connection with discussions of determination of pricing policies. The topic of pricing policy is a complex one that is beyond the scope of this book.

Difficulty in Estimating Increment Costs. A common type of difficulty was illustrated by the simple example in Chapter 2 that dealt with the increment cost of extra mileage for an automobile. The out-of-pocket expense for gasoline for a short trip, estimated as 2.2 cents per mile, was a cost that could be measured by keeping records for such a trip. Similarly, the average cost per mile over the total life of a car, estimated as 13.5 cents per mile for certain stipulated conditions, may be measured if the necessary records are kept over the life of an automobile. But the long-run increment cost of extra mileage, estimated as 5.9 cents per mile, depends on estimates of long-run differences that it is not possible to check by cost and performance records on a single car. If Tom Smith actually makes the contemplated extra 600-mile trip, he will be unable to tell, either at the end of the trip or at the end of his period of ownership, exactly what disbursements were caused by the trip. Nevertheless, neither the 2.2 cents per mile figure nor the 13.5 cents per mile figure was appropriate to the decision whether or not to drive the extra mileage; if this decision was to be based on "cost," a realistic approach required an estimate of long-run differences of the type that produced the 5.9 cents per mile figure.

Similarly, even though increment costs are not precisely determinable in industry, they need to be estimated wherever decisions are to be based on cost. As has been pointed out, questions of relative economy of technical alternatives are often complicated by the difference between the short-run and long-run viewpoints. This difference is even more troublesome in cases of increment cost pricing.

Cost Allocations in Accounting in Relation to Economy Studies. Illustrations have been given in situations in which accounting allocations of cost seemed to block a clear recognition of differences between alternatives. This suggests an important problem arising in the management of every business organization having more than one department, that is, "What should be the basis of joint cost allocations and interdepartmental charges?"

Of course, this question cannot be answered in general terms. Interdepartmental charges, for instance, may be established on an average cost basis or on an increment cost basis. (Either permits considerable room for controversy; in fact, the question of interdepartmental charges may be a source of bitter argument between department heads within an organization.) The point to be emphasized here is that no matter what basis is used, there will be some types of decisions in which it will be misleading to use the interdepartmental charges and joint cost allocations as established by the accounting system; no one answer can serve all purposes. No scheme is satisfactory without managerial understanding of its limitations.

The Concept of a Sunk Cost. Once the principle is recognized that it is the *difference* between alternatives that is relevant in their comparison, it follows that the only possible differences between alternatives for the future are differences in the future. The consequences of any decision regarding a course of action for the future cannot start before the moment of decision. Whatever has happened up to date has already happened and cannot be changed by any choice among alternatives for the future. This applies to past receipts and disbursements as well as to other matters in the past.

From the viewpoint of an economy study, a past cost should be thought of as a *sunk cost*, irrelevant in the study except as its magnitude may somehow influence future receipts or disbursements or other future matters. Although this principle that a decision made now necessarily deals with the future seems simple enough, many people have difficulty in accepting the logical implications of the principle when they make decisions between alternatives. This seems particularly true when sunk costs are involved. Although some of the failures to recognize the irrelevance of sunk costs involve a misuse of accounting figures, these mental obstacles to clear reasoning are by no means restricted to people who have had contact with the principles and methods of accounting.

This concept of the irrelevance of past costs is illustrated in a simple way in Examples 14–4 and 14–5.

EXAMPLE 14-4. IRRELEVANCE OF A PAST OUTLAY

Facts of the Case. Four years ago, Green contracted to buy a lot in a new subdivision in a large city with the intention of ultimately building a home on it. The purchase price was $3,000. He made a $300 down payment and has been paying $250 a year plus interest of 6% on the unpaid balance. He has also paid the taxes of $34 a year. He now owes $1,700 on the lot.

Under the terms of his contract, he has not yet secured legal title to the lot. In the event of a default on any payment due, his contract stipulates that he loses all of his past payments; however, he cannot be held for any additional payments through the operation of a deficiency judgment. His contract also permits him to pay off the unpaid balance in a lump sum at any time and thus to secure clear title to the property.

On returning to this city after an absence of two years or so, Green is ready to build his house. He has the funds in hand to pay $1,700 and take title to this lot. He discovers that prices of unimproved property in this city are now greatly depressed, particularly in this subdivision, but this does not alter Green's decision to build his home there. However, before Green has paid his $1,700, Brown, who owns a lot in the same block, offers to sell his lot to Green for $1,200. Brown's lot is the same size as the one on which Green has been making his payments, and, as far as Green can see, it is equally desirable in all respects. Green must therefore decide between (a) rejecting Brown's offer and paying the remaining $1,700 on his contract, and (b) defaulting on his contract and buying Brown's lot for $1,200.

The difference between these alternatives is clear enough. In (a) Green pays $1,700 and acquires title to a lot; in (b) he pays $1,200 and acquires title to an equally good lot. Alternative (b) saves $500 immediately and, as far as can be seen, there are no other differences between the alternatives. It is evident that it is better to buy Brown's lot and default on the original contract.

The type of mental obstacle that so often interferes with correct decisions is also evident. Green has paid out over the past 4 years a total of $1,986 (including interest and taxes) on his original lot. He appears to "lose" this amount if he defaults on his contract. Moreover, this default seems to admit a past error of judgment that would not be admitted if he pays the $1,700 to complete the purchase of the original lot.

The realistic view regarding this past outlay of $1,986 is, of course, that the money has been spent regardless of which alternative is selected for the future. As the past outlay is the same regardless of the alternative selected, it should not influence the choice between the alternatives.

EXAMPLE 14-5. NEED TO CONSIDER PROSPECTIVE RECEIPTS AND DISBURSEMENTS AFFECTED BY THE DECISION ON DISPOSAL IN JUDGING A PROPOSAL TO DISPOSE OF A FIXED ASSET

Facts of the Case. The hobby of a businessman, who for purposes of this example will be called Richard Roe, was the design of houses. Over a period of a number of years, he would design a new house every year or two, contract for its construction, and move his family into it when completed. Because of the original ideas incorporated into his designs, he was always able to sell the previous home at a moderate profit.

During 1941 he completed a new home that, including the land, cost him about $9,500. Early in 1942, a few months after the entrance of the United States into World War II, he was offered $11,000 for this house. He accepted the offer.

While Roe was considering this offer, he discussed the matter with some friends. In the discussion it was pointed out that because of wartime restrictions he would probably not be able to build another house for some time. It also seemed likely that when he did so, it would be at a considerably higher cost; one of the inevitable results of a war seems to be a higher price level. But Roe dismissed these objections with the comment, "You can never go wrong taking a profit!"

As matters turned out, Roe would have been much better off to have rejected the $11,000 offer and to have kept his house for several years. Throughout the succeeding years he and his family had less satisfactory accommodations than they would have had if he had kept the house. When he finally built another house, construction costs had more than doubled. If he had kept the house, he could have sold it several years later at a price that would have been much higher than $11,000.

Just as Green's past outlay of $1,986 in Example 14–4 should not have influenced his decision between the two lots, Roe's $9,500 cost of his house should not have influenced his decision regarding the acceptance of the $11,000 offer. He should rather have asked himself: "What future receipts and disbursements are likely to be affected by this decision? And what matters not reducible to money terms will probably be influenced by the decision?"

The difficulty with Roe was that he thought primarily of the "profit" he was making on the sale. His habit of thought was to look backward at past costs rather than to look forward at prospective future differences between alternatives. It was not that Roe did not recognize the likelihood of the events that later occurred (such as higher construction costs and increased restrictions on private building), but rather that he did not recognize that these were the relevant matters for consideration in his decision. He failed to realize that in choosing between alternatives for the future, the important question is not, "Where have we been?" but rather, "Where do we go from here?"

Retirements and Replacements.

A decision on a *retirement* is a decision whether or not to continue to own some fixed asset, for example, some machine or structure. In some cases an asset retired may be scrapped, with no salvage value (or even with a negative salvage value if the cost of removal and disposal exceeds any receipts from disposal). In other cases there may be substantial net resale values, even (as in Example 14–5) higher than the original cost.

An asset retired may or may not be replaced. In modern industry, with its frequent improvements in design and changes in service requirements, it is common for the replacement machine or structure to differ in various ways from the machine or structure being retired. Often the new machine or structure may serve other functions in addition to providing the same services given by the machine or structure retired.

In some cases a new asset may be acquired to replace the services of an old asset, but the old asset will not be retired. Sometimes the old asset may be used for another purpose, as when an old main-line railroad locomotive is relegated to branch-line service. In other instances the old asset may be continued in the same general type of service but used less frequently than before; for example, an old steam power plant originally used to carry base load might be used only a few hours a year for peak load purposes.

Thus a retirement may be made either with or without a replacement. And the services of an existing old asset may be replaced by the services of a new one either with or without the retirement of the old asset.

The Question of the Cost of Extending the Service of an Asset Already Owned. In any economy study involving a prospective retirement, it is necessary to consider the money difference between disposing of the old asset at once and disposing of it at some future date. In determining this figure, the past investment in the asset is irrelevant. The current book value is a result of the past investment and the past depreciation charges made in the accounts; this also is irrelevant. So also are the future depreciation charges to be made in the books if the asset is continued in service.

The relevant estimates include the prospective net receipts, if any, from disposal of the asset (1) on the assumption that it is retired immediately, and (2) on the assumption that it is continued in service for the immediate future and retired at some specified later date. Under assumption (2) it is necessary to consider all prospective receipts and disbursements that will take place if ownership is continued but will not take place if the asset is retired immediately. In many economy studies regarding retirements, it may be desirable to consider several different specified future dates on which the asset might be retired if continued in service for the time being. For example, it may be appropriate to consider the costs of keeping the old asset in service for 1 year, for 2 years, for 3 years, etc.

Example 14–6 illustrates the estimates and calculations that are needed relative to the capital recovery costs of extending the service of an asset. This example provides essential background for the discussion in Chapter 16 of practical problems of judging the economy of proposed retirements and replacements. The reader should therefore examine Example 14–6 carefully before starting Chapter 16.

EXAMPLE 14–6. COMPUTING CAPITAL RECOVERY COSTS OF
EXTENDING THE SERVICE OF AN ASSET FOR VARIOUS PERIODS

(a) Capital Recovery Cost of Extending a Service for One Year. A 2-year-old piece of construction machinery had a first cost of $2,000 and has been depreciated on the books of its owner by the straight-line method at 20% a year.

Its present book value is therefore $1,200. Its present net resale value in a second-hand market is $750. It is estimated this resale value will decrease to $500 if the machine is held for another year, to $300 if it is held for 2 years more, and to $200 if held for 3 years more. Interest (minimum attractive return) is at 8%. The question arises whether to dispose of this machine immediately for $750 and to rent a similar machine if one should be needed, or to continue it in service for another year or more.

As a first step in finding the money difference between disposing of the machine at once and disposing of it at some later date, it should be noted that at the present moment it is possible to have either the $750 or the machine but not both. As far as immediate money receipts and disbursements are concerned, the difference is as follows:

Keep Machine   *Dispose of Machine*

No receipts or disbursements   Receive $750

The immediate money difference is just the same as if the question at issue were the purchase of a secondhand machine for $750. In this case the immediate receipts and disbursements would be:

Buy Machine   *Do Not Buy Machine*

Disburse $750   No receipts or disbursements

Whether it is a question of keeping a machine that can be sold for $750 or acquiring one that can be purchased for $750, in either case we have $750 more without the machine than with it. If all future estimates (i.e., annual receipts and disbursements, future salvage values, and irreducible data) are the same,[3] an economy study comparing the alternatives of (a) continuing an asset in service and (b) disposing of the asset at once is identical with an economy study comparing the alternatives of (a) acquiring the same asset at a price equal to its present net realizable value if disposed of and (b) not acquiring it. This general principle may be applied in all economy studies regarding proposed retirements.

In all such economy studies the capital recovery costs on any asset already owned should be based on its present net realizable value if disposed of (i.e., on the amount of capital that could be recovered from its disposition). With interest at 8%, the capital recovery cost of extending for one more year the service of the 2-year-old asset in Example 14–6 is:

$$CR = (\$750 - \$500)(\text{crf-}8\%\text{--}1) + \$500(0.08)$$
$$= (\$750 - \$500)(1.08) + \$500(0.08) = \$310$$

Another way to express the capital recovery cost of extending the service for one year is as follows:

Depreciation $= \$750 - \$500 = \$250$
Interest $= \$750(0.08)$ $=$ 60
Total capital recovery cost $= \overline{\$310}$

[3] In most cases there would be some differences between the cost estimates that would seem appropriate for a used asset already owned and an apparently identical used asset to be acquired. For example, the net realizable salvage value of a machine already installed in the plant is the secondhand price *minus* the cost of removing it, transporting it to the market, and selling it. In contrast, the installed cost of a purchased second-hand machine is the secondhand price *plus* the costs of buying it, transporting it to the plant, and installing it. Moreover, the appropriate estimates of future repair costs might differ. There might well be a great deal more known about the maintenance history of a used machine already owned than about that of an apparently identical used machine purchased in the secondhand market. Hence the factor of uncertainty might well lead to a higher estimate of repair costs for a purchased machine. The point made in Example 14–6 does not bear on these matters but is simply that a decision to continue an asset in service is, in principle, identical with a decision to acquire the same asset at an outlay equal to the present net realizable value.

This is of course mathematically identical with the preceding calculation. The depreciation figure used here is depreciation in the popular sense of decrease in value; the value figures are market values. In effect this calculation says that by extending the service of the asset 1 year more, we receive $250 less for the asset, and we lose the services of $750 in cash for a 1-year period. With interest at 8%, these latter services are valued at $60. The total is $310, as of a date 1 year hence.

(b) Equivalent Annual Capital Recovery Cost of Extending a Service for Two or More Years. Now consider the question of the capital recovery cost of extending the service of the asset for 3 years more. The net realizable value 3 years hence is $200.

$$CR = (\$750 - \$200)(\text{crf-8\%-3}) + \$200(0.08)$$
$$= \$550(0.38803) + \$200(0.08) = \$229.40$$

It is of interest to relate this equivalent uniform annual cost of 3 years to the separate capital recovery costs of extending the service for each of the next 3 years.

$$CR \text{ cost next year } = (\$750 - \$500) + \$750(0.08)$$
$$= \$250 + \$60 = \$310$$
$$CR \text{ cost 2nd year } = (\$500 - \$300) + \$500(0.08)$$
$$= \$200 + \$40 = \$240$$
$$CR \text{ cost 3rd year } = (\$300 - \$200) + \$300(0.08)$$
$$= \$100 + \$24 = \$124$$

These separate costs of extending service year by year may be converted into an equivalent annual cost for 3 years by finding their present worths and multiplying the sum of the present worths by the capital recovery factor, as follows:

PW of $310 = $310(0.9259) = $287.00
PW of $240 = $240(0.8573) = 205.80
PW of $124 = $124(0.7938) =   98.40

Sum of present worths   = $591.20

CR = $591.20(0.38803)   = $229.40

This of course agrees with the $229.40 figure previously obtained by considering only the $750 present realizable value and the $200 realizable value 3 years hence. The year-by-year capital recovery costs of extending the service of an asset may always be converted into an equivalent annual cost that is equal to the capital recovery cost of extending the service for the entire period of years under study. This is mathematically true regardless of the pattern of year-by-year decline in salvage values.

(c) Year-by-Year Capital Recovery Costs Throughout the Life of an Asset. Assume that the asset in Example 14–6 had a net realizable value of $1,100 at the end of its first year of life, and prospective net realizable value at the end of each year from the 6th to the 10th as shown in Table 14–1. The resulting capital recovery costs of extending service for each year of life are then given in column E of Table 14–1. The first year's cost, $1,060, the sum of $900 depreciation and $160 interest, is the capital recovery cost of one year's service to a *prospective purchaser* of the machine for $2,000 on the assumption that the machine is disposed of for $1,100 at the end of its first year of life. The succeeding figures in column E are of course the capital recovery costs of each successive year's extension of service to a *present owner* of the machine in question. Once the net realizable value has fallen to zero, as it has after 8 years, the capital recovery costs of extending the service are also zero.

TABLE 14-1

YEAR-BY-YEAR CAPITAL RECOVERY COSTS OF EXTENDING SERVICE OF A $2,000 MACHINE, AND EQUIVALENT ANNUAL COSTS IF HELD FOR n YEARS, WITH INTEREST AT 8%

(A) Year n	(B) Net Realizable Value at Year-End	(C) Decrease in Realizable Value During nth Year	(D) Interest on Realizable Value at Start of Year	(E) Capital Recovery Cost of Extending Service Through nth Year	(F) Present Worth of Capital Recovery Cost for nth Year	(G) Present Worth of Capital Recovery Costs for n Years	(H) Equivalent Uniform Annual Capital Recovery Cost if Retired After n Years
1	$1,100	$900	$160	$1,060	$981.50	$ 981.50	$1,060
2	750	350	88	438	375.50	1,357.00	761
3	500	250	60	310	246.10	1,603.10	622
4	300	200	40	240	176.40	1,779.50	537
5	200	100	24	124	84.40	1,863.90	467
6	100	100	16	116	73.10	1,937.00	419
7	50	50	8	58	33.80	1,970.80	379
8	0	50	4	54	29.20	2,000.00	348
9	0	0	0	0	0.00	2,000.00	320
10	0	0	0	0	0.00	2,000.00	298

Column F gives the present worth at zero date of each year's capital recovery cost of extending service. Column G gives the sum of the present worths of these costs for n years. It will be noted that as soon as the net realizable value has fallen to zero, the sum of these present worths is necessarily equal to the first cost, in this case $2,000. Column H shows the annual cost of capital recovery for n years' service computed by multiplying the figure from column G by the appropriate capital recovery factor. (Present worth factors and crfs are taken from the 8% table, Table E-15.) The main purpose of including this calculation is to demonstrate the identity of the capital recovery cost computed in this way with the capital recovery cost computed in the conventional way from first cost and the salvage value at the end of the life.

For example, if the machine is retired at the end of 3 years with a $500 salvage value, the conventional calculation is:

$$CR = (\$2,000 - \$500)(crf-8\%-3) + \$500(0.08)$$
$$= (\$2,000 - \$500)(0.38803) + \$40 = \$622$$

Or if retired after 6 years with $100 salvage value, it is:

$$CR = (\$2,000 - \$100)(crf-8\%-6) + \$100(0.08)$$
$$= (\$2,000 - \$500)(0.21632) + \$8 = \$419$$

Or if retired after 10 years with a zero salvage value, it is:

$$CR = \$2,000(crf-8\%-10)$$
$$= \$2,000(0.14903) = \$298$$

Irrelevance of Book Value and Current Depreciation Accounting Charges in a Before-Tax Analysis To Guide a Decision on a Proposed Retirement. In Example 14–6(a) it was stated that the 2-year-old asset in question had been depreciated by the straight-line method at 20% ($400) a year and had a current book value of $1,200. However, these figures were given no weight in the preceding calculation of the cost of extending the service of this asset one or more years. This neglect of the book value and the current annual depreciation charge was entirely proper for this particular purpose.

The original $2,000 purchase price of this asset was spent 2 years ago. This money has already been paid out regardless of whether it is decided to retire the asset at once or to continue it in service. No future decision regarding the disposal or retention of the asset can alter the fact of this past $2,000 disbursement.

As brought out in Chapter 10, the depreciation charges in the accounts are simply a time allotment of this past disbursement, which, when made, was considered in the accounts to be a prepaid expense of service for a number of years. The book value of an asset or group of assets is simply that portion of the cost that has not yet been written off in the accounts as depreciation expense. Regardless of the date of the retirement and regardless of the method of depreciation accounting in use, the first cost less salvage value will all eventually be written off in the books. But, as explained in Chapter 10, the entry made on the books to record a retirement under the single-asset (item) method of depreciation accounting differs from that under multiple-asset methods (group, classified, or composite).

The straight-line item method of depreciation accounting was in common use in the United States prior to 1934, particularly in the manufacturing industries. The accounting entries to record retirements under the item method led to great confusion of thought on the part of many engineers and industrialists regarding the economic aspects of proposed replacements of machinery and other assets.

A Common Error in Reasoning in Economy Studies Involving Prospective Replacements. If the 2-year-old asset in Example 14–6 has been depreciated by the straight-line item method at $400 a year, $800 of the original $2,000 investment has been written off and the current book value (unamortized cost) is $1,200. If the asset is now disposed of for a net $750, the item method requires that $450. the difference between the book value and the net salvage value, be written off at once. This $450 might be charged to an account with some such title as "Loss on Disposal of Fixed Assets."

This "loss on disposal" type of entry, common in the United States up to 1934, proved to be an obstacle to clear thinking on matters of replacement economy. Much of the literature of this subject in the 1920's and 1930's involved formulas or other methods of analysis in which the excess of book value over net salvage value of the old asset was considered as an addition to the first cost of the proposed new asset. For example, if an economy study were to be made to determine whether to replace the 2-year-old asset in Example 14–6 with a new asset costing $2,500, these writers on replacement economy would consider the first cost of the new asset to be $2,950, the sum of the $2,500 purchase price and the $450 "loss on disposal."

The preceding discussion of sunk costs and of Example 14–6 has shown the fallacy of this idea. In further consideration of the unsoundness of this view, it should be pointed out that the loss on disposal entry related only to the timing of the write-off of a prepaid expense. The money spent for an asset already owned was already spent, regardless of the decision on retirement; this fact was not altered by the timing of an accounting write-off. Under straight-line item accounting the need for a loss on disposal entry resulted from the past use of a depreciation rate that turned out to be insufficient to write off the difference between first cost and actual salvage value during the actual realized life.

Need To Consider Book Value and Current Depreciation Accounting Charges in Estimating the Influence of a Proposed Retirement on Cash Flow for Income Taxes. In the 1920's and 1930's, income tax rates in the United States were low enough for most economy studies to be made without examining the income tax consequences of proposed decisions. Like other literature of that period, the incorrect formulas we have mentioned did not consider income taxes.

Because the concept of taxable income corresponds in most respects to the concept of accounting income, matters that affect the accounts usually influence income tax payments. Thus the retirement of an asset under circumstances where the accounts show a "gain" or "loss" will generally have a tax consequence. If the retirement of an asset eliminates a depreciation charge that would continue if the asset were not retired, this also will affect cash flow for income taxes. Since the subject of income taxation is to be developed in Chapter 15, a discussion of the foregoing aspects of economy studies for retirements is deferred until our general consideration of replacement economy in Chapter 16.

Some Suggested Readings on Topics Introduced in This Chapter. Clark's classic work on overhead costs, published in 1923, is desirable background reading for the subject matter of this chapter. Modern writings by Dean and Goetz are excellent. Norton's writings on engineering economy contain helpful examples along these lines. One of the authors of the present book, in collaboration with Norton, has discussed at length the relationship between depreciation accounting and the viewpoint expressed in the present chapter.[4]

The "With or Without" Viewpoint with Reference to Prospective Rates of Return on Investments in Competitive Industry. The president of a large manufacturing company in a highly competitive industry was discussing various matters with the engineer responsible for review and analysis of investment proposals. The president made comments along the following line:

> In our company, we approve many proposals for investments aimed at cost reduction. Generally speaking, the proposals approved show prospective rates of return of 16% or more after income taxes. When we post-audit the results of these investments, we conclude that the cost reductions realized have been, on the average, somewhat greater than we forecast in computing the prospective rates of return. Nevertheless, our average overall rate of return on investment is only about 8% after taxes and does not seem to be improved by these numerous cost reduction investments that individually seem to be so successful.

The president was, in fact, describing a condition that reasonably may be expected to be the normal state of affairs in competitive industry. The difference between *making* the investments in cost reduction equipment and *not making* these investments was measured by the 16% rate of return. However, under the stress of competition, the favorable consequences of these good investments were shared among the owners of the enterprise, its employees, and its customers. Wage and salary rates to the company's employees were increased from year to year; prices of the industry's product were reduced (if measured in monetary units of constant purchasing power) and the quality of the product was improved.

---

[4] Detailed references to the writings cited are as follows: J. M. Clark, *Studies in the Economics of Overhead Costs* (Chicago: University of Chicago Press, 1923). Joel Dean, *Managerial Economics* (Englewood Cliffs, N.J.: Prentice-Hall, Inc., 1951). B. E. Goetz, *Management Planning and Control* (New York: McGraw-Hill Book Co., Inc., 1949). E. L. Grant and P. T. Norton, Jr., *Depreciation* (New York: The Ronald Press Co., 1955), particularly chap. xv. W. G. Ireson and E. L. Grant (eds.), *Handbook of Industrial Engineering and Management* (Englewood Cliffs, N.J.: Prentice-Hall, Inc., 1955), see particularly the section by Joel Dean on "Managerial Economics" and the section by P. T. Norton, Jr., on "Engineering Economy."

In spite of the fact that the owners of the enterprise did not keep all the return yielded by the cost reduction equipment, the 16% rate was a valid measure of the productivity of this equipment from their point of view. If their company had *not* installed the modern equipment but its competitors had done so, competition would still have made it necessary to reduce prices and improve product quality; it would also have been necessary to raise wage and salary rates because such rates are responsive to industry-wide conditions, not merely to conditions in one particular company. Under conditions of competition the over-all rate of return of 8% could not have been maintained unless there had been cost reductions that, considered on a "with or without" basis, yielded rates of return of much more than 8%.

Increment Cost Aspects of the Estimation of Working Capital Requirements for an Investment Proposal.[5] Most of the discussion in this book deals with the economic analysis of proposals involving the flow of business funds for so-called fixed assets (land, buildings and structures, machinery, transportation equipment, furniture and fixtures, and so forth). Many proposals for fixed assets also influence cash flow associated with such matters as accounts receivable and payable and inventories of raw materials, work in process, and finished goods. It is as important for an analyst to recognize the cash flow associated with working capital, wherever relevant, as to recognize the cash flow associated with proposed investments in physical plant.

It was pointed out in Chapter 10 that economy studies usually treat proposed investments in working capital as if they will have 100% salvage values at the end of the life of a project (or possibly at the end of an assumed study period). Because working capital investments are not depreciated for accounting or income tax purposes, such treatment is consistent with the books of account. Nevertheless, the analyst making an economy study that involves working capital requirements will not find adequate guidance in the standard accounting definition of net working capital as the excess of current assets (chiefly cash, receivables, and inventories) over current liabilities (usually obligations payable within one year). It is essential to apply the "with or without" viewpoint to the influ-

[5] Our exposition of this topic is largely influenced by a paper by J. B. Weaver, Director, Development Appraisal Department of Atlas Powder Company, given at a conference sponsored by the Engineering Economy Division of the American Society for Engineering Education at Pittsburgh, Pa., in June, 1959. For a more complete presentation of Weaver's viewpoint on this topic, the reader is referred to his articles in the June and August, 1959, issues of *Industrial and Engineering Chemistry*.

ence of a proposal on prospective cash flow in order to make a rational estimate of working capital requirements.

For example, consider the prospective cash flow involved in the financing of additional accounts receivable in a manufacturing business. A company's books will always show accounts receivable at the full selling price. However, the commitment of cash necessary to finance, say, 30 days' accounts receivable is considerably less than the selling price of the product sold in 30 days. The accounts will "value" accounts receivable at the selling price. But this price normally includes such items as allowances for profit and depreciation that have not involved current cash outlays by the manufacturer. Similarly, book values for inventories of finished goods and work in process include depreciation and possibly other noncash items that should be excluded in the estimation of working capital requirements for purposes of an economy study.

The kinds of proposals that obviously call for the estimates of working capital requirements are proposals for a new product or for expanded production of an existing product. But the common use of simple rules of thumb to apply to *all* such proposals in a business organization (e.g., 30 days' accounts receivable; 60 days' inventory) is likely to disregard important differences between different products and between different material sources. For instance, although natural gas and fuel oil are interchangeable for many purposes, they may involve quite different working capital requirements. A user of natural gas generally receives it via a pipe line and therefore carries no inventory; in fact, there may be a negative element in the working capital requirement because of the time lag between the use of gas and the payment for it. In contrast, in many cases the economical way to purchase oil is in tankers or barges, and it may be necessary to carry a considerable inventory at all times to ensure against running out.

Summary. The following points brought out in this chapter may be restated for emphasis as follows:

Average costs per unit, whether generated from accounting records or elsewhere, should not be used uncritically as guides to decision making. It should always be remembered that it is prospective *differences* between alternatives that are relevant to their comparison.

It is particularly important to keep in mind that all economy studies start from the moment of decision. The only possible differences between alternatives for the future are future differences.

Past receipts and disbursements and other past events are irrelevant in economy studies except as they may influence future receipts or disbursements or other future events.

For purposes of an economy study to decide whether or not to dispose of assets already owned, capital recovery costs on these assets should be based on the present net realizable value if disposed of rather than on original cost.

Problems

14–1. A portion of the general power service schedule of a certain utility company is as follows:

Monthly Block Rate in Cents per Kw-hr

HP of Measured Maximum Demand	First 50 Kw-hr per HP of Maximum Demand	Next 50 Kw-hr per HP of Maximum Demand	Next 100 Kw-hr per HP of Maximum Demand	All over 200 Kw-hr per HP of Maximum Demand
25 to 49............. ...	2.8	1.8	0.95	0.80
50 to 99..............	2.4	1.6	0.90	0.75
100 to 249..............	2.2	1.5	0.85	0.70
250 to 499..............	2.1	1.4	0.80	0.65

A customer under this rate has a monthly maximum demand of 60 kw. (1 HP = 0.746 kw.) and a monthly energy consumption of 11,000 kw-hr.

(a) What is his monthly bill? What is his average cost per kw-hr? (*Ans.* = $187.48; 1.704¢.)

(b) How much will be added to the monthly bill if a load is added which increases the maximum demand by 10 kw. and increases the monthly energy consumption by 300 kw-hr? What is the average cost per kw-hr of this additional load? (*Ans.* = $17.44; 5.81¢.)

(c) How much will be added to the monthly bill if a load is added which increases the maximum demand by 40 kw. and requires the use of this 40 kw. for 600 hours per month? What is the average cost per kw-hr of this additional load? (*Ans.* = $231.77; 0.966¢.)

14–2. A city which distributes its own electric energy buys the bulk of its power at the following rate:

A monthly demand charge based on measured maximum demand of:

  A flat charge of $90 per month for 50 kw. or less
  $1.50 per kw. for the next 150 kw.
  $1.00 per kw. for the next 300 kw.
  $0.75 per kw. for the next 500 kw.
  $0.60 per kw. for all over 1,000 kw.

Plus an energy charge which is calculated monthly as follows:

  $0.008 per kw-hr for the first block of kw-hr equal to 150 times the month's maximum demand (i.e., the equivalent in a 30-day month of 5 hours per day use of the maximum demand)

$0.006 per kw-hr for the next block of kw-hr equal to 250 times the month's
maximum demand

$0.0055 per kw-hr for all additional energy

(a) What will be the monthly bill and average cost per kw-hr in a typical
month in which the maximum demand is 2,500 kw. and the energy purchased is
1,000,000 kw-hr? (*Ans.* = $8,640; 0.864¢.)

(b) By generating about 40,000 kw-hr per month in its own small diesel plant
which is operated only at peak load hours, the city is able to reduce the peak demand for purchased power by about 800 kw. In other words, without this peak
load diesel operation, the maximum demand in the typical month cited in (a)
would have been 3,300 kw. and the energy purchased would have been 1,040,000
kw-hr. The increment cost of this peak load operation of the diesels is about $650
a month. Does it appear to pay to operate them, or would the city save money
to shut them down and purchase all its energy requirements? What would be
the increment cost per kw-hr of purchasing the peak load energy which is now
being generated? (*Ans.* = It pays to operate diesels; 2.4¢.)

(c) As a matter of accounting between different departments of the city government, the city charges itself 3 cents per kw-hr for all energy used for street
lighting. However, in considering a proposed program of improved street lighting,
it is desired to know the increment cost of additional energy for street lights.
Assume that an increased street-lighting program will use an extra 200 kw. from
5 P.M. till 11 P.M. every night (which includes the peak load period on the electric system), and 100 kw. from 11 P.M. till 5 A.M., all of which will be purchased
rather than generated. In a 30-day month such as was described under (a), what
would be the increment cost per kw-hr of this street-lighting energy? (*Ans.*
= 0.933¢.)

14-3. An electric light and power company offers the following two-part rate
for primary (23,000 volt) industrial power, part of which is to be "off-peak" use.
There is to be a monthly maximum demand charge of $2 per kw. for the first
200 kw., and $1.50 per kw. for all additional unlimited or "on-peak" service. The
on-peak period is defined as the hours between 4 P.M. and 7 P.M. from Monday
to Friday, inclusive, during the months from October to March, inclusive. During the other 6 months the unlimited service charge is at its minimum figure,
which is 75% of the maximum on-peak demand recorded in the previous 6-month
period. For each kilowatt of additional maximum demand (the difference between the off-peak maximum and on-peak maximum) the customer pays a
monthly charge of 75 cents. In addition to the monthly maximum demand charge
the customer pays a monthly energy charge, as follows:

1.25 cents per kw-hr for the first   25,000 kw-hr
1.10 cents per kw-hr for the next   25,000 kw-hr
1.00 cent per kw-hr for the next   50,000 kw-hr
0.90 cent per kw-hr for the next   50,000 kw-hr
0.80 cent per kw-hr for the next   50,000 kw-hr
0.70 cent per kw-hr for the next   100,000 kw-hr
0.65 cent per kw-hr for the next   700,000 kw-hr
0.60 cent per kw-hr for all energy in excess of 1,000,000 kw-hr

The maximum demand charge assumes a power factor of 80%. Where the
maximum demand is higher or lower, the billed demand equals the measured
demand multiplied by 0.80 and divided by the monthly average power factor.

A manufacturing company has an annual load about as follows:

Month	On-Peak Maximum Kw.	Monthly Maximum Kw.	Energy Consumed Kw-hr
January	480	1,600	462,000
February	460	1,400	429,000
March	400	1,400	418,000
April		1,200	372,000
May		1,200	358,000
June		1,000	320,000
July		900	291,000
August		1,100	310,000
September		1,700	465,000
October	440	2,000	562,000
November	440	2,100	567,000
December	480	1,900	540,000

(a) What will be the annual bill assuming an 80% power factor? What is the average cost per kw-hr? (*Ans.* = $59,326; 1.165¢.)

(b) What will be the increment cost per kw-hr of an extra uniform 24-hr. load of 500 kw. to run through June, July, August, and September? (*Ans.* = 0.753¢.)

(c) What will be the increment cost per kw-hr of an extra 500-kw. load used on the average of 4 hours per day including the on-peak hours? (*Ans.* = 1.806¢.)

(d) By installing synchronous condensers, the manufacturing company may raise its power factor to 90% and at the same time reduce the energy losses in its own system by 4,000 kw-hr per month. What will be the annual saving in the power bill? (*Ans.* = $2,177.)

14–4. A manufacturing concern estimates monthly expenses at various percentages of "normal" plant capacity as follows:

	120%	100%	80%	60%	0% (temporary)
Office, sales, etc.	$ 4,020	$ 3,380	$ 3,290	$ 3,250	$1,800
Repairs, maintenance	1,000	640	640	590	280
Indirect costs of operation	4,200	3,580	3,380	3,220	380
Direct costs of operation	13,600	10,280	8,540	6,800	1,200
Overhead charges	4,850	4,800	4,750	4,700	4,680
	$27,670	$22,680	$20,600	$18,560	$8,340

If 100% output represents 100 machines per month, what is the unit cost per machine at each output? What is the increment cost per machine of the first 60 machines? What is the increment cost per machine of each additional 20 machines?

If the selling price is $275 per machine, how many machines must be sold before any profit is made? (*Ans.* = $231, $227, $258, $309; $170; $102, $104, $250; 72 machines.)

14–5. A large chemical company has recently acquired two plants that manufacture a certain chemical. These plants use different production processes, although their products are identical. During the first 6 months of operation neither plant is operated at capacity.

The Los Trancos plant has produced 100 tons per month of output at an average cost of $40 per ton. Of the total monthly costs it is estimated that $2,000 will remain fixed regardless of substantial variations in output either upward or downward, and that the remainder of costs will vary in direct proportion to output. The San Francisquito plant has produced 80 tons per month at an average cost of $38 per ton. Of the total monthly costs it is estimated that $1,200 will remain fixed regardless of substantial variations in output either upward or downward and that the remainder of the costs will vary in direct proportion to output.

(a) If the total amount produced at the two plants is to continue at the present figure of 180 tons per month, does there appear to be any advantage in increasing the production at one of the plants and making an equal decrease at the other? If so, at which plant would you increase production? (*Ans.* = $3 per ton will be saved by increasing production at Los Trancos and reducing it at San Francisquito.)

(b) Assume that for reasons of policy it is not desired to make the production shift indicated in (a). The total required production increases from 180 to 200 tons per month. At which plant would it be more economical to produce the extra 20 tons? (*Ans.* = produce at L.T. since increment cost is $400 compared to $460 at S.F.)

14–6. A certain type of machine has a first cost of $1,000. End-of-year salvage values are as follows:

Year	Salvage Values
1	$530
2	290
3	210
4	160
5	120
6	90

Assuming interest at 10%, what is the capital recovery cost of extending service for each year of life? (*Ans.* = (1) $570; (2) $293; (3) $109; (4) $71; (5) $56; (6) $42.)

14–7. (a) Using only the first cost of $1,000 and salvage value of $90, find the equivalent uniform annual cost of capital recovery for an asset in Problem 14–6 purchased new and disposed of at the end of 6 years. Use interest at 10%. Also find the uniform series for 6 years equivalent to the irregular series of year-by-year capital recovery costs of extending service obtained in the solution to Problem 14–6. These two figures should be the same. (*Ans.* = $217.94.)

(b) A 1-year-old asset is acquired for $530. It is disposed of for $120 when it is 5 years old. Compute the uniform annual cost of capital recovery with interest at 10%. Also find the uniform series for 4 years equivalent to the year-by-year capital recovery costs of extending service for the 2nd, 3rd, 4th, and 5th years obtained in the solution to Problem 14–6. These two figures should be the same. (*Ans.* = $141.34.)

14–8. A 9-hole golf course in the outskirts of a large city is operated on a commercial basis. The proposal has been made that this golf course be illuminated and operated at night. Early last year the owner purchased this course for $47,000 at forced sale to satisfy the creditors of the previous owners, a private club. His receipts from operations during the 28-week season of operation were $23,000; his total disbursements for the year for all purposes were $11,800.

The required investment in lighting this course is estimated as $17,200. There will be required 150 lamps of 1,000 watts each; electric energy costs 3.3 cents per kw-hr. The expected number of average hours of operation per night is 5. Because of occasional bad weather and because of probable curtailment of night operation at the beginning and end of the season, it is estimated that there will be only about 130 nights of operation per year. Labor cost of keeping the course open at night will be $15 per night. Lamp renewals are estimated at $300 per year; other annual upkeep and repairs on the lighting system at 5% of its first cost. Taxes will be about 2% of first cost. It is estimated that the average revenues per night of operation will be $60. Considering the probability of competition from the illumination of other golf courses if his illumination is successful in securing a good night trade, the owner of the course decides that he will not make the investment unless there is the prospect of capital recovery in 5 years or less plus a 15% return.

(a) On this basis will it pay to install the lighting system?

(b) If the system is installed, the question will arise whether night operation at the beginning and end of the season—particularly on midweek nights—is justified. In these circumstances what should be the prospective revenue per night to justify operation? What irreducibles would necessarily enter into this decision and how should they affect managerial policy in making it?

14-9. In a period of rising prices a merchant attempted to maintain his stock of goods at a constant physical volume. He had purchased his stock of one item sometime ago at $3 per unit. He sold these items at $5 per unit (applying his usual markup) and immediately replaced them by identical ones purchased at the new wholesale price of a $6 per unit. What do you think of the profitableness of this transaction?

14-10. A student, arrested for speeding, was given his choice between a $10 fine and a day in jail. He elected the latter. On emerging from jail, he wrote a story about his experience there, which he sold to a newspaper for $15. Commenting on this incident, one of his friends remarked, "Steve made $5 by going to jail, the $15 from the newspaper minus the $10 fine." "No," said another, "he made $15 by the decision to go to jail as he didn't pay the fine." How about it?

14-11. A machine has a first cost of $1,500 and net realizable salvage values at the end of each of the first 7 years of its life as follows: 1—$900; 2—$660; 3—$500; 4—$400; 5—$300; 6—$240; 7—$200. With interest at 5%, show that the capital recovery costs of extending service each year are as follows: 1—$675; 2—$285; 3—$193; 4—$125; 5—$120; 6—$75; 7—$52. Show that the uniform annual series equivalent at 5% interest to this year-by-year series of capital recovery costs is equal to 5% interest on first cost plus the annual deposit in a 5% sinking fund that would amount to the difference between the $1,500 first cost and the $200 salvage value at the end of 7 years.

14-12. A paperboard manufacturing company has two plants, one in Washington and one in California, producing equivalent grades of "cardboard." The Washington plant has been operating at 75% capacity, producing 2,700 tons per month at a total cost per ton of $77⅓. The California plant has been operating at 60% capacity, producing 3,600 tons per month at a total cost per ton of $85.

Included in the total cost per ton is the cost of waste paper, the major raw material. For each 100 tons of product, 80 tons of waste paper are required. At the Washington plant the local waste paper costs $18.75 per ton (of waste paper), but the supply is limited to 1,440 tons per month. At the California plant, local waste paper costs $20 per ton and is limited to 4,000 tons per month. Additional waste paper must be purchased through brokers at $27.50 per ton (delivered at either plant).

Of the total monthly costs at the Washington plant, $59,400 is estimated to be fixed regardless of production level. The remainder of the costs, with the exception of the cost of waste paper, are expected to vary in proportion to output. The comparable figure for the California plant is $108,000 per month.

(a) If the total production of both is to be continued at the present rate of 6,300 tons per month, would there be any apparent advantage to shifting part of the scheduled production from one of the plants to the other? If so, which plant's production should be increased and by how much? Why?

(b) If production requirements increased to 9,100 tons per month, how much would you recommend be produced at each plant? What would be the total cost per month for each plant in this case?

14–13. Jones and Smith are engineers from the United States employed in a foreign country. Both expect to stay on this assignment for another year or more. Each has just converted $1,000 (U. S.) to the currency of this country at the existing rate of 8 to 1, thus receiving 8,000 currency units in exchange. Suddenly, to the surprise of Jones and Smith, the exchange rate changes to 10 to 1. Now 8,000 currency units changed back into U. S. dollars will bring only $800. A few days later Jones and Smith learn that they are to be transferred back to the United States in two weeks. Each is confronted with the question of what purchases, if any, he will make of various products of the country to take back to the United States. The two men take different attitudes toward this. Jones says that he can get so few dollars for his currency units that he is going to spend them all before going back to the United States. In contrast to this, Smith says that each of his currency units cost him 12½ cents and that he will not spend one unless he believes he is getting 12½ cents worth of goods for it; otherwise he will convert his currency units back into dollars.

Which of these views seems reasonable to you? Or is there some other point of view, not expressed by either Jones or Smith, that seems more sensible than either? If so, what is it? Explain your reasoning.

14–14. A public surveyor owns two transits that he purchased from the Surveyor's Service Co. a year ago for $450 each. He is currently renting a third one from this company at $10 per month. One of his transits becomes damaged in a way not covered by insurance. The S. S. Co. representative estimates the repair cost to be $120. He suggests that the surveyor sell him the two transits "as is" for $540 and rent two more transits at $10 a month. He reasons that his company can rent a transit for less than it costs the surveyor to own one "because we get them wholesale and have our own setup for repairing and adjusting them." He presents the following cost comparison to the surveyor:

Cost of Continuing To Own Two Transits		Cost of Renting Two Transits	
Depreciation = $900/10	= $ 90	Rental cost = 12($20)	= $240
Taxes and insurance = 3% of $900 =	27	Less	
Repair cost	= 120	Depreciation saved by sale of	
Cleaning and adjustment	= 40	transits = $540/9	60
Net cost	= $277	Net cost	= $180

Criticize the salesman's analysis.

14–15. A power user buys electricity under the following monthly rate:

$1.80 per kw. for each kw. of maximum demand up to 100 kw.
$1.10 per kw. for all maximum demand above 100 kw.

plus

$0.0075 per kw-hr for all energy used

His maximum demand is 120 kw. and his monthly energy consumption is 10,000 kw-hr.

(a) What is his average cost per kw-hr?

(b) What will be the increment cost per month of an additional load that adds 10 kw. to the maximum demand and 2,000 kw-hr to the monthly energy consumption? What is the average cost per kw-hr of this extra load?

14–16. (a) A customer under the power rate given in Problem 14–1 uses 28,800 kw-hr in a 30-day month with a load factor of 20%. What is his monthly bill and his average cost per kw-hr?

(b) Make a similar calculation for a customer who uses 28,800 kw-hr with a load factor of 80%.

14–17. The electric rate described in Problem 14–1 and referred to in Problem 14–16 contains a power factor clause. Under this clause ¼ of 1% is added to the monthly bill for each per cent the customer's average power factor falls below 80% and ¼ of 1% is subtracted for each per cent above 80%.

The customer in Problem 14–16(b) is considering an $1,800 investment in static condensers to raise his present 75% power factor to 90%. His minimum attractive rate of return before income taxes is 15%. Annual disbursements in connection with the ownership of the condensers (e.g., property taxes, insurance) will be 3% of first cost. Should this investment be made if the estimated life of the condensers is 20 years with zero salvage value?

14–18. Electric power is sold under the following rate:

First 40 kw-hr per kw. of maximum demand at 3¢ per kw-hr
Next 40 kw-hr per kw. of maximum demand at 2¢ per kw-hr
Next 120 kw-hr per kw. of maximum demand at 1¢ per kw-hr
All over 200 kw-hr per kw. of maximum demand at 0.75¢ per kw-hr

What will be the bill in a 30-day month of a customer who uses 216,000 kw-hr with a load factor of 50%?

14–19. The owner of an office building in a city in southern United States is considering the installation of an air-conditioning system. His 6-story building has a total rentable area of 120,000 sq. ft. The estimated cost of a complete plant for summer cooling and winter ventilation is $240,000.

It is estimated that summer cooling operation will be required for about 2,100 hr. per year. Variable costs (power and water) for summer operation will average $8 per hour; for winter operation they will average $2 per hour. Upkeep and attendance will cost about $6,000 per year. Property taxes will be 1.2% and insurance 0.3% of first cost. Estimated life is 15 years with zero salvage value. Winter operation will be 1,500 hr. per year.

(a) Recently the building has had an average occupancy of 90% with an average annual rental price of $3.00 per sq. ft. It is believed that if the air conditioning is installed the average occupancy can be increased to 95% and the average rental price to $3.25 per sq. ft. If the recent rental price and percentage of occupancy should be maintained without the air-conditioning system, what would be the prospective rate of return before income taxes on the $240,000 investment?

(b) Because the owners of competing office buildings are installing air conditioning, it is believed that unless air conditioning is installed in this building the average occupancy will drop to 75% and the average rental price will have to be dropped to $2.50. Considering the expected differences with and without the air conditioning, what is the prospective rate of return on investment before in-income taxes?

(c) Discuss the relevance of the rates of return computed in (a) and (b) with reference to the owner's decision whether or not to install the air conditioning.

14–20. Burden rates in a certain factory are on a machine-hour basis. They are established by first apportioning all of the various expected indirect manufacturing expenses of the factory at normal output among all of the machines in the factory; the total estimated indirect manufacturing expense apportioned to any given machine is then divided by the expected normal hours of operation of this machine in order to arrive at a rate per machine-hour. Thus if the estimated indirect manufacturing expense apportioned to a certain milling machine is $1,620, and its expected normal hours of operation are 1,800 per year, the burden rate per hour of operation is 90 cents.

Most of the product of this factory is manufactured to buyers' specifications on contract jobs. In planning many of the operations carried on in this production, the question arises whether they shall be done on general purpose machines or special purpose machines. This involves a comparison of the cost of machine setups and the direct labor and material costs for each given operation on alternative machines. In such comparisons the problem arises as to what use, if any, should be made of the machine burden rates.

Discuss this problem, considering as separate cases (a) the factory operating at about the expected normal hours of operation, (b) the factory operating at greatly curtailed output (such as 30% of normal in a period of business depression), and (c) the factory operating at more than normal output with a large volume of unfilled orders.

14–21. A writer on management subjects discussed the topic of the use of rate of return as a criterion for investment decisions somewhat as follows:

"Prospective rate of return is of limited usefulness as a guide to decision making. For instance, this criterion would be of no use in the following case:

"At the end of his freshman year at the XYZ College, John Doe is offered the campus concession for a certain soft drink. He must pay $900 for the concession and certain equipment. He estimates that the concession will bring him $450 a year for the next 3 years in addition to a reasonable payment for his labor, and that the concession and equipment will be salable for $900 at the end of the 3-year period. He therefore expects a 50% rate of return on his investment.

"However, Richard Roe, who for many years has been concessionaire for a competing soft drink, would prefer less energetic competition than he expects to receive from Doe. Roe therefore offers Doe an outright immediate payment of $100 if Doe will refrain from purchasing this concession. Because Doe will make no investment at all if he accepts Roe's offer, it is evident that his rate of return will be infinite.

"Doe's problem of decision making between the purchase of the concession and the acceptance of Roe's offer illustrates the weakness of the rate-of-return technique. Doe appears to have the choice between a 50% rate of return and an infinite rate of return. But this would also appear to be his choice if Roe had offered him only \$1 or if Roe had offered him \$1,000. Thus the rate of return technique does not permit Doe to give any weight whatsoever to the size of Roe's offer. No matter how small Roe's offer is, it appears to have a better rate of return than the 50% expected from the purchase of the concession."

Do you agree with the writer that the rate-of-return technique cannot be used by Doe to help him choose between these two alternatives? Or do you see any way to apply the rate-of-return technique to this particular case? Explain your answers fully.

15

Some Income Tax Considerations
in Decision Making

Wherever net income is taxed at a substantial rate, many decisions are influenced by their probable income tax consequences. The higher the tax rate, the more important it is to examine the income tax aspects of any proposal. It seems probable that for a long time to come income tax rates in many countries, including the United States, will continue to be so high that many economy studies will require consideration of income taxes.

It is not the purpose of this chapter to give detailed up-to-date information on income tax laws and regulations in the United States or elsewhere. Detailed information would require much more space than is available.[1] Up-to-date information would call for annual revision. The objective of this chapter is to present general principles underlying the relationship of income taxes to the making of certain types of decisions. These general principles do not change and may be applied wherever and whenever a tax is levied on net income.

In illustrating these principles, it is helpful to refer to some particular set of income tax laws and regulations. Some of the examples in this and following chapters are based on the federal tax laws and regulations applicable to 1958 income in the United States. The reader who wishes to apply the principles to his own problems must secure up-to-date information about the income tax laws, regulations, and administrative practices that pertain to his specific case.

A General Principle—Income Taxes Are Disbursements. Economy studies deal with prospective receipts and disbursements. Prospective income taxes merely constitute another disbursement to add to those for operation, maintenance, property taxes, insurance, etc. In the examples of economy studies for competitive industry given

[1] The *Federal Regulations on Income Tax* in the United States contain more than three times as many words as this entire book.

thus far in this book, the prospective outlays for income taxes have been omitted and minimum attractive rates of return have been stated as rates before income taxes rather than after income taxes.

It follows that once the disbursements for income taxes have been estimated, their treatment in an economy study is exactly like the treatment of any other prospective money outlay. The principles that have been developed for economy studies omitting consideration of income taxes are just as applicable to economy studies that include this additional prospective disbursement. Of course the minimum attractive rate of return after income taxes should differ considerably from that before taxes.

A complicating factor is that the persons competent to make the ordinary estimates in engineering economy studies may be so unfamiliar with income tax matters that they are unable to estimate the extent to which income taxes will be affected by a particular decision. The difficulty of forecasting income taxes is greatest where the tax is a graduated one levied on net income with complex laws and regulations defining net income for tax purposes, and with tax rates and tax laws subject to change every year.

Distinction Between Taxes on Net Income and Taxes on Gross Income. Where a flat tax is levied on gross receipts (so-called gross income), the estimates of receipts and future tax rates supply an estimate of future tax payments. However, taxes on gross income are subject to a number of serious objections. Hence income taxes are most commonly levied on net income.

The concept of the net income of a business enterprise for tax purposes is similar to the accounting concept of profit. But there are a number of points of difference between the two concepts because legislative bodies are free to define net income in any way they see fit. The determination of taxable net income may sometimes involve a number of technicalities. The income tax discussion in this chapter relates entirely to taxes on net income.

A General Principle—The Relationship Between Rates of Return Before and After Income Taxes Depends on the Rules Governing Write-Off for Tax Purposes. To illustrate the foregoing important principle, let us assume four $42,000 proposed immediate disbursements, each expected to reduce future disbursements (other than those for income taxes) by $10,000 a year for the next 10 years. At 20% interest, the present worth of $10,000 a year for 10 years is $41,920; the prospective return before income taxes is therefore approximately 20%.

These four investments yielding 20% before income taxes are examined in Examples 15–1 to 15–4. Their returns after income taxes vary all the way from 7.2% to 20%. The examples differ only in the manner in which the $42,000 investment is permitted to be written off for income tax purposes.

The higher the tax rate, the greater the importance of the rules governing the write-off of an outlay for tax purposes. In Examples 15–1 to 15–4 we shall assume that a 55% tax rate is applicable throughout the entire period of each study. It is explained later in this chapter that 55% was a common rate used in economy studies for many corporations in the United States during the late 1950's, considering both federal and state income taxes.

EXAMPLE 15–1. RATE OF RETURN AFTER INCOME TAXES
ASSUMING THAT THE INITIAL OUTLAY IS WRITTEN OFF
UNIFORMLY DURING THE PERIOD OF ITS EFFECTIVENESS

Facts of the Case. An outlay of $42,000 for materials handling equipment is proposed. It is estimated that this equipment will reduce disbursements for labor and labor extras by $14,000 a year for 10 years and will be responsible for annual

TABLE 15–1

ESTIMATION OF CASH FLOW AFTER INCOME TAXES, EXAMPLE 15–1

Year	A Cash Flow Before Income Taxes	B Write-Off of Initial Outlay for Tax Purposes	C Effect of Outlay on Taxable Income (A + B) for years 1 to 10	D Effect of Outlay on Cash Flow for Income Taxes −0.55C	E Cash Flow After Income Taxes (A + D)
0	−$42,000				−$42,000
1	+10,000	−$ 4,200	+$ 5,800	−$ 3,190	+6,810
2	+10,000	−4,200	+5,800	−3,190	+6,810
3	+10,000	−4,200	+5,800	−3,190	+6,810
4	+10,000	−4,200	+5,800	−3,190	+6,810
5	+10,000	−4,200	+5,800	−3,190	+6,810
6	+10,000	−4,200	+5,800	−3,190	+6,810
7	+10,000	−4,200	+5,800	−3,190	+6,810
8	+10,000	−4,200	+5,800	−3,190	+6,810
9	+10,000	−4,200	+5,800	−3,190	+6,810
10	+10,000	−4,200	+5,800	−3,190	+6,810
Totals	+$58,000	−$42,000	+$58,000	−$31,900	+$26,100

disbursements of $4,000 for maintenance, power, property taxes, and insurance. The estimated life of the equipment is 10 years with zero salvage value; this estimate is acceptable to the taxing authorities. The taxpayer elects to use the straight-line method in his depreciation accounting and in reporting depreciation for tax purposes.

Calculation of Rate of Return After Income Taxes. Table 15–1 shows the calculation of the prospective effect of the investment on cash flow after income taxes, assuming a 55% tax rate throughout the entire 10-year period. Under the simple assumptions in this example of uniform annual savings, straight-line depreciation, and a constant tax rate, it is evident that the immediate disbursement of $42,000 will increase cash receipts after taxes by $6,810 a year for 10 years. The rate of return after taxes may be determined by computing present worth of cash flow after taxes using rates of 8% and 10%.

$$\text{PW at } 8\% = -\$42{,}000 + \$6{,}810(\text{pwf--}8\%\text{--}10)$$
$$= -\$42{,}000 + \$6{,}810(6.710) = +\$3{,}700$$
$$\text{PW at } 10\% = -\$42{,}000 + \$6{,}810(\text{pwf--}10\%\text{--}10)$$
$$= -\$42{,}000 + \$6{,}810(6.144) = -\$160$$

Interpolation indicates a return of about 9.9% after income taxes. The 55% tax rate has cut the return before taxes approximately in half.

EXAMPLE 15–2. RATE OF RETURN AFTER INCOME TAXES ASSUMING THAT THE INITIAL OUTLAY IS WRITTEN OFF OVER A CONSIDERABLY LONGER TIME THAN ITS PERIOD OF MAJOR PRODUCTIVITY

Facts of the Case. An outlay of $42,000 for certain machine tools is proposed. It is anticipated that the period of primary service of these tools will be 10 years. During these years it is estimated that these tools will reduce annual disbursements for labor and labor extras by $16,000 a year and will be responsible for annual disbursements of $6,000 for maintenance, power, property taxes, and insurance. No additional influence on annual disbursements is anticipated after the expiration of this 10-year primary service life.

Because machine tools of this type have an industry-wide average life of 25 years, and because there is no evidence that the average lives of such tools have been less than 25 years in the service of this particular taxpayer, the taxing authorities insist that the write-off for tax purposes be based on a 25-year life. An estimated zero salvage value at the end of this life will be permitted. It is expected that the taxpayer's ownership of these tools will actually continue for 25 years, with the tools used for standby purposes during the final 15 years of their lives. The policy of this taxpayer is to use the straight-line method in his depreciation accounting and in reporting depreciation for tax purposes.

Calculation of Rate of Return After Income Taxes. Table 15–2 shows the calculation of the prospective effect of the investment on cash flow after income taxes, assuming a 55% tax rate throughout the next 25 years. Although the algebraic sum of the prospective income tax payments resulting from this $42,000 investment will be $31,900, just as in Example 15–1, the timing of the tax consequences of the investment will be considerably different because of the slower write-off permitted. Table 15–2 has been shortened by showing only one line for the uniform cash flow of years 1 to 10 and another line for the uniform cash flow of years 11 to 25. The totals for this table are, of course, the same as if a separate line had been shown for each year.

The rate of return after taxes may be determined by computing present worth of cash flow after taxes using rates of 7% and 8%.

TABLE 15–2

ESTIMATION OF CASH FLOW AFTER INCOME TAXES, EXAMPLE 15–2

Years	A Cash Flow Before Income Taxes	B Write-Off of Initial Outlay for Tax Purposes	C Effect of Outlay on Taxable Income (A + B) for years 1 to 25	D Effect of Outlay on Cash Flow for Income Taxes −0.55C	E Cash Flow After Income Taxes (A + D)
0	−$42,000				−$42,000
1 to 10	+10,000	−$ 1,680	+$ 8,320	−$ 4,576	+5,424 per year
11 to 25	0	−1,680	−1,680	+924	+924 per year
Totals	+$58,000	−$42,000	+$58,000	−$31,900	+$26,100

PW at 7% = −$42,000 + $5,424(pwf-7%-10) + $924(pwf-7%-25 minus pwf-7%-10)
$$= -\$42,000 + \$5,424(7.024) + \$924(11.654 - 7.024) = +\$380$$
PW at 8% = −$42,000 + $5,424(6.710) + $924(10.675 − 6.710)
$$= -\$1,940$$

Interpolation indicates a return of about 7.2% after income taxes. This is considerably less than the 9.9% return obtained in Example 15–1 and only a little more than one-third of the 20% return before income taxes.

EXAMPLE 15–3. RATE OF RETURN AFTER INCOME TAXES ASSUMING THAT THE INITIAL OUTLAY IS WRITTEN OFF OVER A CONSIDERABLY SHORTER PERIOD THAN ITS PERIOD OF MAJOR PRODUCTIVITY

Facts of the Case. The facts and estimates are identical with those in Example 15–2 with one exception. This exception is that, because the product to be made by these proposed machine tools is deemed to be important to the national defense, the cost of the tools may be written off at a uniform rate over a 5-year period under the terms of a "certificate of necessity" issued by the appropriate government agency.

Calculation of Rate of Return After Income Taxes. Table 15–3 shows the calculation of the prospective effect of the investment on cash flow after income taxes, assuming a 55% tax rate for the next 10 years. The rate of return after taxes may be determined by computing present worth of cash flow after taxes, using rates of 12% and 15%.

TABLE 15–3

ESTIMATION OF CASH FLOW AFTER INCOME TAXES, EXAMPLE 15–3

Years	A Cash Flow Before Income Taxes	B Write-Off of Initial Outlay for Tax Purposes	C Effect of Outlay on Taxable Income $(A + B)$ for years 1 to 10	D Effect of Outlay on Cash Flow for Income Taxes $-0.55C$	E Cash Flow After Income Taxes $(A + D)$
0	−$42,000				−$42,000
1 to 5	+10,000	−$ 8,400	+$ 1,600	−$ 880	+9,120 per year
6 to 10	+10,000	0	+10,000	−5,500	+4,500 per year
Totals	+$58,000	−$42,000	+$58,000	−$31,900	+$26,100

PW at 12% = −$42,000 + $9,120(3.605) + $4,500(5.650 − 3.605) = +$80
PW at 15% = −$42,000 + $9,120(3.352) + $4,500(5.019 − 3.352) = −$3,930

Interpolation indicates a return of about 12.1% after taxes.

EXAMPLE 15–4. RATE OF RETURN AFTER INCOME TAXES ASSUMING THAT THE INITIAL OUTLAY IS WRITTEN OFF AGAINST CURRENT INCOME

Facts of the Case. The company's industrial engineering department has devised an improved plant layout for existing production equipment in an existing building. An immediate outlay of $42,000 will be required to rearrange the machinery. It is estimated that the new layout will reduce annual disbursements for materials handling by $10,000 a year for the next 10 years. Because the $42,000

TABLE 15–4

ESTIMATION OF CASH FLOW AFTER INCOME TAXES, EXAMPLE 15–4

Years	A Cash Flow Before Income Taxes	B Write-Off of Initial Outlay for Tax Purposes	C Effect of Outlay on Taxable Income $(A + B)$ for years 0 to 10	D Effect of Outlay on Cash Flow for Income Taxes $-0.55C$	E Cash Flow After Income Taxes $(A + D)$
0	−$42,000	−$42,000	−$42,000	+$23,100	−$18,900
1 to 10	+10,000		+10,000	−5,500	+4,500 per year
Totals	+$58,000	−$42,000	+$58,000	−$31,900	+$26,100

outlay does not involve the acquisition of new assets or the extension of the lives of old ones, the entire amount will be treated as a current expense for accounting and income tax purposes in the year in which it is made (zero year on our time scale).

Calculation of Rate of Return After Income Taxes. Table 15–4 shows the calculation of the prospective effect of the $42,000 outlay on cash flow after income taxes, assuming a 55% tax rate from years 0 to 10. It will be noted that in zero year, the increased disbursement of $42,000 for machine rearrangement is partially offset by a decrease in the required disbursements to the tax collector amounting to $23,100. On the other hand, there is no subsequent depreciation deduction that results from the $42,000 outlay, and the tax collector will therefore take $5,500 each year out of the $10,000 saving in materials handling costs.

The following present worth calculation at 20% shows that the prospective rate of return after taxes is approximately 20%, the same as the prospective rate of return before income taxes.

$$\text{PW at } 20\% = -\$18,900 + \$4,500(4.192) = -\$40$$

A General Approach to the Introduction of Income Tax Considerations into Economy Studies. Examples 15–1 to 15–4 illustrate the procedure that is necessary if alternatives in competitive industry are to be compared after income taxes rather than before income taxes. Given two alternatives to be compared, the required steps in the analysis are as follows:

1. The year-by-year prospective differences between the alternatives in cash flow before income taxes must be estimated. (This is an essential step whether alternatives are to be compared before income taxes or after income taxes.) It should be noted that in each of our four examples one alternative is a continuation of a present condition and the other alternative is to make an immediate $42,000 outlay to effect a future cost reduction.
2. The year-by-year differences between the alternatives in prospective taxable income must be computed. These differences should be consistent with the estimated differences in cash flow. In Examples 15–1 to 15–4, this computation was a comparatively simple matter of applying the appropriate depreciation charge to the initial cash flow figures. Often the calculation of prospective differences in taxable income is a considerably more complicated matter, requiring a sophisticated understanding of income tax laws and regulations.
3. The applicable income tax rates must be estimated and applied to the estimated differences in taxable income to compute the differences between the alternatives in prospective cash flow for income taxes.
4. The year-by-year figures for differences in cash flow before income taxes should be combined with the year-by-year differences in cash flow for income taxes to obtain the estimated differences in cash flow after income taxes.

5. The cash flow after income taxes may then be analyzed with relation to the selected criterion for decision making. The analysis in Examples 15–1 to 15–4 implied that the criterion in these examples was rate of return after income taxes.

Comment on Certain Simplifying Assumptions in Examples 15–1 to 15–4. In these examples it was assumed that the cost reductions caused by the $42,000 initial outlay would continue at a uniform rate for a stated period of years and then abruptly cease. It was assumed that the depreciation write-off in the first three examples would be at a uniform annual figure. It was assumed that, except for the write-off of the initial outlay in the first three examples, all cash outlays affected taxable income in the years in which they were made. The tax payments for each year's taxable income were assumed to be concurrent with the other cash disbursements for the year. The end-of-year convention was assumed in all four examples. It was assumed that all taxable income throughout the period of the study would be taxed at the same rate, 55%. All of these assumptions were intended to simplify the computations and to permit concentration of attention on the two main points at issue, namely, the general approach to comparisons made after income taxes and the importance of the rate of write-off in influencing the ratio between return after taxes and return before taxes.

The general method illustrated in the examples can, of course, be applied equally well when the appropriate assumptions are much more complex. Although many economy studies made after income taxes naturally have more complications than Examples 15–1 to 15–4, each example represents a simplified version of a type of case that occurs frequently in modern industry. Perhaps Example 15–1 represents the most common case, in which the investment is to be written off throughout the period of its expected favorable consequences. But the case illustrated in Example 15–2 is almost equally common in the United States; write-off periods for tax purposes are often extended well beyond the date when proposed new assets are expected to have their chief economic usefulness. And many billions of dollars' worth of long-lived assets in the United States have been written off for tax purposes in 5 years under "certificates of necessity," just as was illustrated in Example 15–3. And industry has numerous opportunities for productive outlays that, like the one in Example 15–4, can properly be charged off immediately for income tax purposes.

The Partnership of the Government in Productive Business Outlays. It is illuminating to examine the totals of the five columns in Tables 15–1 to 15–4 and to note that these totals are identical. In all four examples it is proposed to spend $42,000 at once to avoid spending $100,000 in the future; the prospective total addition to profits before income taxes is $58,000. The government will finally take 55% of this $58,000, leaving $26,100 for the owners of the business enterprise.

Although in all four cases the government's share of the ultimate profits is $31,900, the time at which the government collects its share differs greatly in the various examples. In Example 15–1 the government collects its $31,900 at the rate of $3,190 a year for 10 years. In Example 15–2 it collects $4,576 a year for 10 years, a total of $45,760, and—in effect—refunds $13,860 of this by means of collecting $924 a year less taxes for the years 11 to 25 than would have been collected if the initial $42,000 outlay had not been made. In Example 15–3, the government collects $880 a year for the first 5 years and $5,500 a year for the second 5 years. In Example 15–4 the government reduces its tax collections by $23,100 in the zero year on our time scale and then collects a total of $55,000 at $5,500 a year for the next 10 years. It is the difference in the timing of the collection of the $31,900 of taxes that makes the difference between the returns to the taxpayer of 9.9%, 7.2%, 12.1%, and 20% after taxes from investments that all have a 20% return before taxes.

Only in the type of case illustrated in Example 15–4 is the taxpayer's rate of return undiminished by the government's partnership in the profits of the decision to make the $42,000 outlay. The effect of the tax treatment of the $42,000 outlay in Example 15–4 is as if the taxpayer had made an investment of $18,900 from which he receives $4,500 a year for 10 years, a return of 20%, and the government had made an investment of $23,100 from which it receives $5,500 a year for 10 years, also a return of 20%.

Some Other Advantages of a Rapid Write-Off for Tax Purposes. Examples 15–1 to 15–4 illustrated the point that the more rapid the write-off for tax purposes, the greater the rate of return after income taxes. A rapid write-off for tax purposes has certain other advantages that were not brought out by the calculation of rates of return in these four examples. These advantages are:

1. Generally speaking, if matters turn out badly, they will not turn out so badly with a rapid write-off as they will with a slow write-off.
2. In the common case where enterprise funds are limited, more cash is made available for productive use at an early date by a rapid write-off than by a slow one.

These advantages are elaborated in the next few pages.

The Partnership of the Government in Unproductive Business Disbursements. The government may be a partner in unproductive business outlays as well as in productive ones. For instance, if the new plant layout in Example 15–4 should fail to reduce future disbursements, the government will be a partner in the unproductive $42,000 outlay to the extent of $23,100. (That is, because of the outlay the government will forego taxes of $23,100 that it otherwise would collect.) Or assume that the $42,000 investment in Example 15–1 turns out to be unproductive. If so, the taxpayer will have a $4,200 depreciation deduction for the next 10 years; this deduction will reduce taxable income and will reduce income taxes to be paid during the 10-year period; the government may be viewed as participating in the original investment to the extent of the present worth of future income taxes foregone.

Any partnership of the government in unproductive outlays depends on the taxpayer having taxable income from some other source. Otherwise there is no tax liability that can be reduced by the unproductive outlay. A future depreciation write-off (such as the $4,200 a year for 10 years in Example 15–1) will have value to the taxpayer only if he continues to have taxable income.

In case an outlay turns out to be unproductive (or less productive than was forecast), the more rapid write-off has two advantages over the slower write-off for tax purposes. One advantage is that the tax saving comes sooner and therefore has a greater present worth. The other advantage is that a possible tax saving in the near future is more certain to be realized than a possible tax saving in the distant future.

Influence of Rate of Write-Off on Available Cash. When enterprise funds are limited and have to be rationed among competing proposals, it is helpful to examine the immediate net cash requirements of various proposals and also to look at their net cash requirements in the near future. The cash requirements of proposals are greatly influenced by the rate of write-off. For instance, the proposal to spend $42,000 in Example 15–4 has an immediate net cash requirement of only $18,900,[2] whereas the proposals in the other three examples all have immediate requirements of $42,000.

It is pointed out in Chapter 19 that under certain circumstances it is helpful to compute a figure for crude "payback" after income taxes as a numerical index of the short-term cash aspects of various proposals. This payback is defined as the number of years required for net cash flow to equal zero (without consideration of interest)

---

[2] For a qualification of this statement, see the discussion later in this chapter of the timing of income tax payments in relation to the timing of taxable income.

in a tabulation such as Tables 15–1 to 15–4. Other matters being equal, the more rapid the write-off for tax purposes, the shorter the payback period. This point is illustrated by the following comparison of payback periods in our four examples:

Example	Write-Off Period	Payback Period
15–4	at once	4.2 years
15–3	5 years	4.6 years
15–1	10 years	6.2 years
15–2	25 years	7.7 years

Effect of the Method of Depreciation Accounting Used for Tax Purposes on the Rate of Return After Income Taxes.

In Chapter 10 it was pointed out that the double-rate declining-balance method and the sum-of-the-years-digits method, both authorized for federal income tax purposes in the United States in 1954, permit cost to be written off more rapidly than is possible with the straight-line method. Given any particular estimated life and salvage value acceptable to the taxing authorities, either of these 1954 methods will result in a slightly higher return after income taxes than will be obtained with the use of the straight-line method. The differences in return among the different depreciation accounting methods are not nearly as large as the differences in returns illustrated in Examples 15–1 to 15-4 where there were great differences in write-off periods.

Example 15–5 illustrates the calculation of return after taxes with two different depreciation accounting methods in a case where estimated cash receipts differ from year to year and where a prospective salvage value is present.

EXAMPLE 15–5. RATES OF RETURN AFTER INCOME TAXES WITH TWO METHODS OF DEPRECIATION ACCOUNTING

Facts of the Case. In Example 8–2 (pages 116 to 117) we considered a proposed investment of $12,000 in rental machinery. This machinery had an estimated life of 8 years in the service of its first owner and an estimated salvage value of $1,200. On the basis of year-by-year estimates of cash flow before income taxes we found that the prospective rate of return before income taxes was 12%. It is now desired to find the prospective rate of return after income taxes assuming a tax rate of 30%. Two alternate methods of depreciation accounting are to be considered, the straight-line method and the sum-of-the-years-digits method.

Calculation of Rates of Return After Income Taxes. Tables 15–5 and 15–6 show the year-by-year calculations to determine prospective taxable income, income tax payments, and cash flow after taxes using the two depreciation accounting methods. The tables also show the year-by-year present worths of cash flow after taxes with interest rates at 8% and 10%. Interpolation shows that the prospective rate of return after taxes is 8.1% using straight-line depreciation accounting, and 8.6% using sum-of-the-years-digits depreciation accounting.

TABLE 15–5

CALCULATIONS TO DETERMINE RATE OF RETURN AFTER INCOME TAXES,
EXAMPLE 8–2, USING STRAIGHT-LINE DEPRECIATION ACCOUNTING

Year	Cash Flow Before Taxes	Depre- ciation	Taxable Income	Cash Flow for Taxes	Cash Flow After Taxes	PW at 8%	PW at 10%
0	−$12,000				−$12,000	−$12,000	−$12,000
1	+3,700	−$ 1,350	+$2,350	−$ 705	+2,995	+2,773	+2,723
2	+3,000	−1,350	+1,650	−495	+2,505	+2,148	+2,070
3	+2,400	−1,350	+1,050	−315	+2,085	+1,655	+1,566
4	+2,100	−1,350	+750	−225	+1,875	+1,378	+1,281
5	+1,700	−1,350	+350	−105	+1,595	+1,086	+990
6	+1,500	−1,350	+150	−45	+1,455	+917	+821
7	+1,300	−1,350	−50	+15	+1,315	+767	+675
8	+1,150	−1,350	−200	+60	+1,210	+654	+564
8*	+1,200				+1,200	+648	+560
Totals	+$ 6,050	−$10,800	+$6,050	−$1,815	+$ 4,235	+$ 26	−$ 750

* Salvage value.

TABLE 15–6

CALCULATIONS TO DETERMINE RATE OF RETURN AFTER INCOME TAXES,
EXAMPLE 8–2, USING SUM-OF-THE-YEARS-DIGITS DEPRECIATION ACCOUNTING

Year	Cash Flow Before Taxes	Depre- ciation	Taxable Income	Cash Flow for Taxes	Cash Flow After Taxes	PW at 8%	PW at 10%
0	−$12,000				−$12,000	−$12,000	−$12,000
1	+3,700	−$2,400	+$1,300	−$ 390	+3,310	+3,065	+3,009
2	+3,000	−2,100	+900	−270	+2,730	+2,340	+2,256
3	+2,400	−1,800	+600	−180	+2,220	+1,762	+1,668
4	+2,100	−1,500	+600	−180	+1,920	+1,411	+1,311
5	+1,700	−1,200	+500	−150	+1,550	+1,055	+962
6	+1,500	−900	+600	−180	+1,320	+832	+745
7	+1,300	−600	+700	−210	+1,090	+636	+559
8	+1,150	−300	+850	−255	+895	+484	+418
8*	+1,200				+1,200	+648	+560
Totals	+$ 6,050	−$10,800	+$6,050	−$1,815	+$ 4,235	+$ 233	−$ 512

* Salvage value.

Use of Gradient Tables To Simplify Compound Interest Calculations with Sum-of-the-Years-Digits Depreciation Accounting.

In sum-of-the-years-digits depreciation accounting, the annual depreciation charge decreases by a uniform amount each year. This annual decrease is the product of the so-called depreciable value (first cost minus estimated salvage value) and a fraction having a numerator of one and a denominator equal to the sum of the digits in the estimated life. If it is assumed that the tax rate will not change, the tax effect of the depreciation charge will follow a uniform gradient. Where economy studies are made after income taxes and sum-of-the-years-digits depreciation accounting is to be used, it often is helpful to use the gradient tables, Tables E–23 and E–24, for compound interest conversions. These tables are particularly useful where cash flow before income taxes is assumed to be uniform or to follow a uniform gradient. The use of these tables is illustrated in Examples 15–6 and 15–7.

EXAMPLE 15–6. USE OF GRADIENT TABLES IN COMPUTING RATE OF RETURN AFTER INCOME TAXES

Facts of the Case. Assume the facts of Example 15–1 with the sum-of-the-years-digits method substituted for the straight-line method of depreciation accounting.

Calculation of Rate of Return After Income Taxes. The sum of the digits from 1 to 10 is 55. In the first year the depreciation write-off is 10/55 of $42,000 or $7,636.36. This write-off will decrease by $763.64 a year, 1/55 of $42,000. The taxable income in the first year will be $10,000 − $7,636.36 = $2,363.64. The income tax disbursement for the first year will be 55% of $2,363.64 = $1,300. Each year the income tax disbursement will increase by $420 (i.e., by 55% of the $763.64 increase in taxable income).

If a table similar to Table 15–1 should be prepared, the figures in column E (cash flow after income taxes) for years 1, 2, and 3 would be +$8,700, +$8,280, and +$7,860. Each year cash flow would decrease by $420 down to $4,920 in the 10th year. Of course the sum of the figures in column E would be $26,100 just as in Table 15–1.

In the following calculations Table E–24, for present worth of a gradient, has been used in connection with the 10% and 12% interest tables.

$$PW \text{ at } 10\% = -\$42,000 + \$8,700(\text{pwf-10\%-10}) - \$420(\text{gpwf-10\%-10})$$
$$= -\$42,000 + \$8,700(6.145) - \$420(22.891) = +\$1,847$$
$$PW \text{ at } 12\% = -\$42,000 + \$8,700(\text{pwf-12\%-10}) - \$420(\text{gpwf-12\%-10})$$
$$= -\$42,000 + \$8,700(5.650) - \$420(20.254) = -\$1,352$$

Interpolation indicates a rate of return of about 11.2%. This contrasts with 9.9% computed using the straight-line method in Example 15–1.

Consideration of Differences in Income Tax Disbursements in Comparing Alternatives by Annual Cost or Present Worth. Our

examples in this chapter up to this point have assumed that rate of return after income taxes is to be calculated for each proposal. In many cases, however, it is desired to compare alternatives by equivalent uniform annual cost or by present worth, using a stipulated minimum attractive rate of return after income taxes as the interest rate for all compound interest conversions.

If only two alternatives are to be compared, a year-by-year listing of their differences in taxable income should be made and the appropriate tax rates applied to find the year-by-year differences in prospective income tax payments. This series of differences in income tax disbursements is then converted into an equivalent uniform annual figure or into present worth, as the case may be, and added to the costs of the alternative requiring the higher income taxes.

If three or more alternatives are to be compared, the alternative having the lowest prospective income tax payments should be selected as a base. The income taxes in excess of this base should be computed for each of the other alternatives. These should be converted to annual cost or present worth, whichever is required, and added to the cost totals for the respective alternatives. The foregoing procedure is illustrated in the annual cost comparison in Example 15–7.

In general, when specific estimates of differences in income taxes are to be introduced into comparisons using annual cost or present worth, there should be two points of difference from the annual cost and present worth studies for competitive industry illustrated in Chapters 6 and 7:

1. A lower interest rate should be used, the minimum attractive rate of return after income taxes rather than the minimum rate before taxes.

2. An additional item for extra income taxes should be added to the annual costs or present worths of all but one of the alternatives.

EXAMPLE 15–7. ANNUAL COST COMPARISON CONSIDERING DIFFERENCES IN DISBURSEMENTS FOR INCOME TAXES

Facts of the Case. This is the familiar comparison first introduced in Examples 6–1 and 6–2 (pages 78 to 83) that has been examined from various viewpoints in intervening chapters. It will be recalled that Plan A involves annual disbursements of $8,200 for 10 years. Plan B requires assets with a first cost of $15,000, an estimated life of 10 years, and no salvage value; annual disbursements will be reduced to $5,100. Plan C calls for assets with a first cost of $25,000, a 10-year life, and a $5,000 salvage value; annual disbursements will be $4,300.

It is desired to compare the annual costs of these alternatives using a minimum attractive return after taxes of 6%. A tax rate of 40% of taxable income is to be assumed. (It will be recalled that our previous comparisons of these alternatives have been based on a minimum attractive return of 10% before income taxes.)

It will be assumed that the estimates of life and salvage value in Plans B and C will be accepted by the taxing authorities. Two sets of comparisons are to be made, one assuming straight-line depreciation and the other assuming years-digits depreciation for tax purposes.

Comparison of Annual Costs. This solution differs from the one in Chapter 6 only because of the use of a 6% interest rate instead of 10% and because of the addition of income taxes to the annual costs of Plans B and C.

If straight-line depreciation accounting is to be used, the annual income tax payments will be uniform. In Plan A the deductible expense in computing taxable income is $8,200. In Plan B this figure is $5,100 plus $1,500 annual depreciation. In Plan C it is $4,300 plus $2,000 annual depreciation. Plan B will have

$1,600 more taxable income ($8,200 − $6,600) than Plan A; with a 40% tax rate it will have $640 more annual income taxes. Similarly, Plan C will have $1,900 more taxable income than Plan A and $760 more income taxes. The comparative annual costs after income taxes, assuming straight-line depreciation, are as follows:

Plan A

Labor and labor extras...	$8,200

Plan B

CR at 6% = $15,000(0.13587)...	$2,038
Labor, power, maintenance, etc..	5,100
Extra income taxes above Plan A.......................................	640
Total for comparison with Plans A and C.........	$7,778

Plan C

CR at 6% = $20,000(0.13587) + $5,000(0.06)..............................	$3,017
Labor, power, maintenance, etc..	4,300
Extra income taxes above Plan A..	760
Total for comparison with Plans A and B...............................	$8,077

If years-digits depreciation accounting is used, the equivalent uniform annual extra income taxes for Plans B and C are $589 and $690 respectively. The comparative annual costs for Plans A, B, and C are $8,200, $7,727, and $8,007 respectively. The following calculation illustrates how Table E–23, the table of gradient factors, is used in computing the $589 figure.

The first year's depreciation charge in Plan B will be 10/55 of $15,000 = $2,727.27. The depreciation write-off will decrease by $272.73 a year (1/55 of $15,000). In the first year the extra taxable income over Plan A will be $8,200 − $5,100 − $2,727.27 = $372.73, and the extra income tax will be 0.40($372.73) = $149.09. The income tax will increase each year by 0.40($272.73) = $109.09. The extra income tax payment with Plan B as compared to Plan A therefore is a series: $149.09, $258.18, $367.27, etc. As this series contains a gradient of $109.09, it may be converted into an equivalent uniform annual series as follows:

$$\text{Equivalent annual cost of extra income taxes}$$
$$= \$149.09 + \$109.09(\text{gf-}6\%\text{-}10)$$
$$= \$149.09 + \$109.09(4.022) = \$589$$

Economy Studies Where Declining-Balance Depreciation Accounting Is To Be Used.

Rates of return after income taxes with double-rate declining-balance depreciation accounting will be very close to those with years-digits depreciation accounting. For example, Table 15–6, which applied the years-digits method to the data of Example 8–2, showed a present worth of cash flow after taxes of +$233 at 8% and −$512 at 10%; interpolation between these figures gave a rate of return of about 8.6%. The corresponding figures using the declining-balance method are +$277, −$458, and 8.8%.

Prospective rates of return after taxes with declining-balance depreciation accounting may be slightly more or slightly less than with years-digits depreciation accounting depending on a number of matters, the most important of which are salvage value ratios and the choice among item, group, classified, or composite depreciation accounting. Nevertheless, the differences in rate of return between the two methods will rarely, if ever, be enough to influence the conclusions of an economy study.

It was pointed out in Chapter 10 that the declining-balance method is a simpler method of depreciation accounting than the years-digits method. However, because of the availability of gradient tables (Tables E–23 and E–24) and because the depreciation charge in the years-digits method changes by a constant amount each year, it is easier to make compound interest conversions for economy studies with the years-digits method.

Where declining-balance depreciation accounting will actually be used and where income tax disbursements are to be introduced into economy studies, a possible simplification is to make the economy study assuming years-digits accounting. This simplification may save considerable arithmetic and will usually make a negligible change in the conclusions of the economy study.

Further Comment on the Selection of a Method of Depreciation Accounting in the United States. For depreciable business assets acquired new after 1954 in the United States, the decision on a method of depreciation accounting may reasonably be made in two steps. First the decision must be made whether it is desired to have a more rapid write-off in the early years than is possible with the straight-line method based on full service life. If the rapid write-off is wanted, it is necessary to choose among the various permissible methods of securing this write-off. Usually the choice is between the declining-balance method and the years-digits method.

The authors of this book believe that in competitive industry the straight-line method based on full service life will rarely give a write-off that is rapid enough for business purposes entirely apart from income tax considerations. Most retirements are made for economic reasons; the same factors that ultimately cause retirements also cause a rapid decline in the competitive value of fixed assets in the early years of their economic lives. Moreover, full service lives are typically much longer than economic lives. Most business decisions influenced by the depreciation accounts will be better made if the depreciation write-off is more rapid in the early years of service life.[3]

---

[3] For a more complete presentation of this viewpoint, see E. L. Grant and P. T. Norton, Jr., *Depreciation* (rev. prtg.; New York: The Ronald Press Co., 1955), chap. xvi.

The higher the income tax rates, the greater the financial advantage of writing off cost as rapidly as possible. This point has been brought out by the examples and comments so far in this chapter. The only condition where income tax considerations favor a slow write-off is one where the prospective tax rate in the more distant future is considerably greater than the rate in the near future.

Once the decision is made to adopt some depreciation accounting method giving a rapid write-off in the early years, the choice among the different permissible methods may properly be influenced by the convenience, simplicity, and accounting costs associated with the various methods. Particularly for group accounts, and for classified accounts (such as Machinery or Furniture and Fixtures), these considerations favor the declining-balance method.[4] For assets recorded in item accounts and having low estimated salvage values, the advantage of the slightly more rapid write-off may justify the choice of the years-digits method in spite of its somewhat greater accounting complexity and expense.

A study of the depreciation tax practices of a number of industrial companies in the United States made in 1957 indicated that about one-third of the companies studied continued to use the straight-line method for new assets, about one-third used declining-balance, and about one-third used years-digits.

Selection of a Tax Rate for Use in Economy Studies. In our examples in this chapter up to this point we have assumed tax rates of 55%, 30%, and 40% without any explanation of how these rates were determined. It is apparent that the tax rates used will have an important influence on the conclusions of economy studies. In order to examine the question of how to select a tax rate or rates for use in economy studies, it is helpful to consider some specific set of tax laws. The corporate and individual income taxes in effect in the United States in 1958 are therefore described briefly in the next few pages. No attempt is made to explain all the numerous ramifications of the tax laws that need to be understood for the actual preparation of income tax returns.[5]

Tax Rates on Corporate Income. The federal income tax on corporations was in two parts, a normal tax of 30% of taxable income and surtax of 22% of all taxable income in excess of $25,000. Certain items, usually of minor importance, were subject to surtax

[4] See Grant and Norton, *op. cit.*, chap. xix.
[5] Two helpful and inexpensive pamphlets that may be obtained from the Superintendent of Documents, U. S. Government Printing Office, Washington 25, D.C., are: Internal Revenue Service Publication No. 17, *Your Federal Income Tax—for Individuals;* Internal Revenue Service Publication No. 334, *Tax Guide for Small Business.*

but not to normal tax. For the purposes of our discussion here, it is accurate enough to say that small corporations—those with taxable incomes of less than $25,000—were taxed at 30%; all corporations large enough or successful enough to have incomes over $25,000 were taxed at 52% on all income in excess of $25,000.

Many of the states of the United States also had corporation income taxes. The rates varied considerably from one state to another.

Tax Rates on Individual Income. There were three federal tax rate schedules applicable to individual income, namely: Schedule I —for single taxpayers not qualifying for rates in Schedules II and III and for married persons filing separate returns; Schedule II—

TABLE 15–7

1958 FEDERAL TAX RATES ON INDIVIDUAL INCOME—SCHEDULE I

Taxable Income	Amount of Tax
Not over $2,000	20% of taxable income
Over $2,000 but not over $4.000	$400 + 22% of excess over $2,000
Over $4,000 but not over $6.000	$840 + 26% of excess over $4,000
Over $6,000 but not over $8.000	$1.360 + 30% of excess over $6,000
Over $8,000 but not over $10,000	$1.960 + 34% of excess over $8.000
Over $10,000 but not over $12,000	$2,640 + 38% of excess over $10,000
Over $12,000 but not over $14,000	$3,400 + 43% of excess over $12,000
Over $14,000 but not over $16.000	$4.260 + 47% of excess over $14,000
Over $16,000 but not over $18,000	$5,200 + 50% of excess over $16,000
Over $18,000 but not over $20,000	$6,200 + 53% of excess over $18,000
Over $20,000 but not over $22,000	$7.260 + 56% of excess over $20,000
Over $22,000 but not over $26,000	$8,380 + 59% of excess over $22,000
Over $26,000 but not over $32,000	$10,740 + 62% of excess over $26,000
Over $32,000 but not over $38.000	$14,460 + 65% of excess over $32,000
Over $38,000 but not over $44,000	$18,360 + 69% of excess over $38,000
Over $44,000 but not over $50.000	$22,500 + 72% of excess over $44,000
Over $50,000 but not over $60,000	$26.820 + 75% of excess over $50,000
Over $60,000 but not over $70,000	$34.320 + 78% of excess over $60,000
Over $70,000 but not over $80,000	$42,120 + 81% of excess over $70.000
Over $80.000 but not over $90,000	$50,220 + 84% of excess over $80,000
Over $90,000 but not over $100,000	$58,620 + 87% of excess over $90,000
Over $100,000 but not over $150,000	$67,320 + 89% of excess over $100,000
Over $150,000 but not over $200,000	$111,820 + 90% of excess over $150,000
Over $200,000	$156,820 + 91% of excess over $200,000

for married taxpayers filing joint returns and for certain widows and widowers; and Schedule III—for unmarried (or legally separated) taxpayers qualifying as "head of household." Table 15–7 reproduces Schedule I, the basic schedule In Schedule II all dollar figures were double those in Schedule I; for example, the first four lines were:

Not over $4,000................................20% of taxable income
Over $4,000 but not over $8,000................$800 + 22% of excess over $4,000
Over $8,000 but not over $12,000...............$1,680 + 26% of excess over $8,000
Over $12,000 but not over $16,000..............$2,720 + 30% of excess over $12,000

Schedule III for head of household was intermediate between Schedules I and II. For example, the 30% incremental rate, applicable to the bracket of taxable income $6,000–$8,000 in Schedule I and to the bracket $12,000–$16,000 in Schedule II, applied to the bracket $8,000–$10,000 in Schedule III.

Any business income included in personal taxable income was *net* business income; the expenses of the business (including depreciation) were deductible. Taxpayers could also deduct certain "nonbusiness deductions" including certain contributions, interest payments, tax payments, and other specified items. In lieu of itemizing the nonbusiness deductions, taxpayers could elect to take a "standard deduction"; this was 10% of the income before nonbusiness deductions (described as *adjusted gross income*) but could not exceed $1,000.

The taxable income was the adjusted gross income minus nonbusiness deductions (either itemized or standard) minus one or more exemptions of $600 each. Every taxpayer was entitled to a $600 exemption for himself or herself and for any other person classified as a "dependent" under the law. Extra exemptions of $600 each were allowable if the taxpayer or his wife were over 65 or blind. As an example of calculation of exemptions, a married couple (both under 65 and neither blind) having two dependent children was entitled to an exemption of $2,400.

A simplified tax table, assuming the standard 10% nonbusiness deduction, was available for taxpayers with incomes under $5,000 who did not elect to itemize their deductions. This simplified table gave the actual tax as a function of taxable income, taxpayer's status (e.g., single person, head of household, married couple filing jointly), and number of exemptions. The tax determined from the simplified table was approximately the same as the tax that would have been computed from Schedules I, II, or III, whichever was applicable, if the standard deduction had been taken.

The majority of the states of the United States also levied taxes on personal income. Although the tax rate schedules differed greatly from state to state, all used a format similar to the federal schedules in which successive increments of income were taxed at progressively higher rates.

A General Principle—Where a Graduated Income Tax Is in Effect, the Increment Cost Viewpoint Is Necessary. The domestic electric rate quoted at the start of Chapter 14 illustrated the block principle. It was pointed out that for any buyer of electricity under this rate, a determination of the money difference between purchasing more or less electricity involved only those extreme blocks of the rate that would be affected by the difference in consumption.

Graduated income taxes, such as the one illustrated in Table 15–7, employ the block principle in the same manner as electric rates. The major point of difference between block electric rates and a graduated income tax is that the unit price of electricity decreases with increased consumption, whereas the unit tax rate goes up as income increases. The increment cost viewpoint is essential in economy studies involving income taxes just as in studies involving electric rates. The prospective difference in income taxes between a greater and a smaller taxable income depends only on the particular extreme blocks of the tax rate schedule that are affected by the prospective difference in income.

Relationship Between Corporate and Individual Income Taxes in the United States. One subject that has received much discussion by students of taxation is the double taxation of corporate income. If corporations are taxed on their profits, and if that part of the profits remaining after income taxation is subject to a second income tax when received as dividends by the stockholders, this is clearly double taxation.

Originally the income tax laws of the United States did not involve full double taxation. In 1936, dividends received by individuals were made subject to the full individual income tax. In 1954 and thereafter this rule was slightly modified; the first $50 of dividends received by an individual was excluded from gross income; in computing an individual's tax, a "dividends received credit" was also allowed, amounting to 4% of the dividends received in excess of those excluded from gross income but not to exceed 4% of the taxable income.

Although corporate income in the United States is taxed as of the year in which it is earned, its second taxation as individual income does not take place until the dividends are received by the stockholders. The tax rates in the upper brackets on the individual income tax are much higher than the maximum corporate rate. This leads to the following paradox.

In general, the owners of a business that is incorporated will, in the long run, pay a higher percentage of their profits as income taxes than they would pay if the same business were unincorporated. Nevertheless, under certain circumstances, the corporate form of organization has the possibility of being used as a device to reduce the immediate taxes on business profits. Assume that a corporation is controlled by stockholders whose incomes place them in the upper brackets. If, without penalty, these stockholders could elect to leave all the profits of this corporation in the business, the immediate income tax on these profits would be limited to the corporation tax. If the same profits could be taxed at the rates in the highest brackets of the individual income tax, the government would collect more taxes immediately.

To discourage the use of the corporate form of organization as a means of reducing the immediate payment of income taxes, Sections 531 to 537 of the Internal Revenue Code have imposed an additional tax on "corporations improperly accumulating surplus." A corporation was permitted to accumulate a total of $100,000 of surplus before this additional tax applied. In each year the tax was $27\frac{1}{2}\%$ of the first $100,000 accumulated beyond the "reasonably anticipated needs" of the business and $38\frac{1}{2}\%$ on all in excess of $100,000. This particular provision of the tax law was aimed particularly at corporations where a relatively few persons owned a large part of the stock. It exerted strong pressure on many such corporations to distribute a substantial part of their current earnings as dividends each year.

Ordinarily, all the business income of partnerships and sole proprietorships was subject to the individual income tax in the year earned regardless of whether or not any business profits were withdrawn by the owners. However, under certain stipulations, some businesses organized as partnerships or sole proprietorships could elect to be taxed as corporations. Also, under certain restrictions, corporations having 10 or less stockholders could elect to be taxed as partnerships.

What Viewpoint Toward Individual Income Taxes Should Be Taken in Economy Studies for Corporations? In any decision between alternatives made from the viewpoint of the owners of a business enterprise, all receipts and disbursements affecting the owners and influenced by the decision should properly be considered. For this reason the income tax aspects of an economy study for a corporation really involve both the corporation taxes and the individual income taxes to be paid by the stockholders on their dividends.

As a practical matter, prospective income taxes paid by the stockholders are likely to be disregarded in some corporations and considered in others, somewhat as follows:

1. In corporations with many stockholders, in which most policy decisions are made by executives whose personal stock ownership is relatively small, the tendency is to consider only the corporate income tax. Most large corporations fall into this class. Where there are many stockholders whose personal incomes are unknown to the management, it is hardly practicable to consider stockholders' income taxes. Moreover, the performance of hired managers is judged by the profit showing on the corporate books.

2. In corporations with few stockholders, with those stockholders taking an active part in policy decisions, individual income taxes are much more likely to be considered. In such corporations, Sections 531 to 537 often force distribution of most of current earnings as dividends. Stockholders taking an active part in management are likely to be very conscious of the income taxes they pay on these dividends. Although corporations in this class are generally smaller, they are more numerous.

The Timing of Income Tax Payments in Relation to the Timing of Taxable Income. The payment of federal income taxes by individuals in the United States is so organized that individuals pay their tax throughout the year in which the income is received. Employers are required to withhold income taxes from payments of wages and salaries. Individuals having other sources of income are required to make declarations of estimated income taxes and to make quarterly payments based on these declarations.

The timing of federal income taxes on corporations is a somewhat more complex subject. Corporations with income taxes of less than $100,000 pay taxes in two equal installments during the first half of the year following the one in which the income was earned. Corporations with estimated taxes above $100,000 are required to file declarations of estimated tax and to pay a portion of the estimated tax during the last half of the year in which the income is earned and to pay the remainder of the year's tax in the first half of the next year. During the late 1950's the percentages to be paid in the current year were being increased from year to year; on 1959 income and thereafter it was anticipated that 50% of the tax in excess of $100,000 was to be paid in the year the income was earned.

State income taxes generally were payable in the year following the one in which income was earned.

The exact time lag between the cash receipts and disbursements affecting current taxable income and the payment of the various income taxes based on this taxable income is an extremely important matter in the preparation of cash budgets. Where business enterprises must plan their week-by-week cash positions in order to be sure to meet payrolls, pay for needed supplies and materials, pay taxes when due, etc., the exact timing of cash payments for all purposes must be considered.

In contrast, in economy studies in which the minimum time unit is one year, it is common to disregard any possible time lag between taxable income and the payment of income taxes. We have done so in Examples 15–1 to 15–6. The column showing cash flow after income taxes in Tables 15–1 to 15–6 was based on the assumption that tax payments would take place in the same year as the current cash flow influencing the year's taxable income.

This simplifying assumption will continue to be made in the examples and problems throughout the remainder of this book. The assumption is fairly close to the truth in most cases. The average time lag between taxable income and tax payments is only a month or two for individuals and usually not much over 6 months or so for corporations.

It is not intended here to suggest that this time lag should automatically be disregarded in all economy studies in industry. Let us take an extreme example in which it might properly be considered. Assume that the economy study in Example 15–4 is being made for a corporation using the calendar year as the fiscal year. Assume that the $42,000 disbursement for the rearrangement of machinery is proposed for January of 1959. This disbursement, entirely deductible from 1959 income, affects tax payments during the second half of 1959 and the first half of 1960. The $23,100 tax saving resulting from the outlay therefore centers at a time approximately one year after the date of the outlay. If this saving is assigned to year 1 rather than year zero on the time scale of Table 15–4, a recalculation gives a rate of return of about 15.7%. However, if the $42,000 disbursement should take place in December, 1959, the assumptions in Example 15–4 are very nearly correct and the 20% figure for prospective rate of return is the appropriate one.

The Concept of an Effective Tax Rate for Use in Economy Studies. Even though income may be subject to two or more taxes with slightly different timing, it usually is good enough for practical purposes in an economy study to combine the taxes into a single rate. Frequently no better assumption can be made than the simple one that this same tax rate will continue throughout the period of the economy study. It is hard to get any great precision into estimates of incremental tax rates for many years into the future because of the possibility of changes in the particular taxpayer's income and changes in the tax law. As long as precision is not possible, matters may as well be simplified by the use of a single rate.

The phrase *effective tax rate* used in examples and problems throughout the remainder of this book refers to a single incremental tax rate to be used in the particular economy study in question. Each specified effective tax rate is assumed to have been determined after consideration of all income taxes believed to be relevant, both individual and corporate and both federal and state, and after consideration of the interrelationships of these taxes and of the appropriate incremental brackets.

Sometimes pertinent matters may be concealed by the simplification of using a single income tax rate throughout an economy study. The possibility of this should be examined before deciding to use an effective tax rate. The use of such a rate in many examples and problems in this book is not intended to imply that a single tax rate should be used in all instances.

Consideration of a Prospective Large Change in the Incremental Tax Rate. Sometimes there is good reason to forecast an abrupt sharp change in the tax rate applicable to the highest increment of a particular taxpayer's income. For example, it may be expected that a certain corporation in the 30% bracket will soon increase its income so that it will be taxed in the 52% bracket. Or an 82% "excess profits" tax applicable to the final increment of a corporation's income may be scheduled to expire at a definite future date with the effect of dropping the corporation's incremental tax rate from 82% to 52%. Or an individual may anticipate considerably higher or lower income with a corresponding change in incremental rates. The same techniques of analysis that have been illustrated for a single effective tax rate can be applied equally well if it is forecast that there will be two or more different tax rates applicable to different years of a study period.

Examples 15–1 to 15–4 illustrated the influence of the speed at which certain outlays are written off on the rate of return after taxes, assuming a uniform tax rate throughout the period of the economy study. The advantage of the rapid write-off is increased when it is expected that tax rates in the near future will be greater than in the more distant future. (For example, if the rate applicable to zero year is 82% in Example 15–4 and the rate applicable to years 1 to 10 is 55%, the return is increased from 20% to 59%.) Conversely, the advantage of a rapid write-off is decreased or eliminated when tax rates in the near future are expected to be less than in the distant future.

Combining Income Tax Rates for Different Governmental Units. It often happens that the same income is subject to taxation by two or more governmental bodies. Sometimes income may be taxed by two countries, particularly where an enterprise incorporated in one country does business in another country. In the United States it is common for the same income to be taxed by federal and state governments; many states have both corporation income taxes and individual income taxes. Some cities also have individual income taxes.

Economy studies are simplified where a single effective tax rate can be used to combine the incremental tax rates from the various governmental units that tax the same income. The appropriate rules for combining tax rates depend on the way in which the tax payments to each governmental unit influence the taxable income reported to the other governmental units.

In the United States, state income taxes imposed on corporations are deductible in computing the income to be taxed by the federal government. Individuals who do not take the standard nonbusiness deduction may include income taxes paid to a state among their itemized nonbusiness deductions on their federal tax returns.

A simple formula for combining state and federal incremental tax rates may be given for the common case where the state tax is deductible on the federal tax return but the federal tax is not deductible on the state return, as follows:

Let s represent the incremental state tax rate expressed as a decimal.
Let f represent the incremental federal tax rate expressed as a decimal.

$$\text{Combined incremental rate} = s + (1 - s)f$$

For example, assume that a \$1,000 increment of income is subject to a 4% state tax rate and a 30% federal rate. The state tax on this increment of income will be \$40. As the federal tax will apply only to the difference between the \$1,000 income before taxes and the \$40 state tax, it will be \$288, 30% of \$960. The total tax on the \$1,000 increment of income will therefore be \$40 + \$288 = \$328, or 32.8% of the income. Of course this same combined rate may be obtained from the foregoing formula as $0.04 + (1 - 0.04)(0.30) = 0.328$.

Where there are two or more taxes to be paid that are independent of one another, the tax rates may be combined by simple addition. For example, consider an individual in the United States who takes the standard deduction rather than itemizing nonbusiness deductions. If his incremental rate on his state tax is 4% and his incremental rate on his federal tax is 30%, a combined rate of 34% will apply to the highest increment of his income.

The most difficult problems of combining tax rates arise where the tax due to each of the taxing units cannot be computed without somehow recognizing the past tax payments or current tax liabilities to the other taxing units. The laws and regulations under which such recognitions occur vary so greatly that no simple rules for combination of tax rates can be given here. But it can be said that, given the specific laws and regulations, it usually is possible to compute an approximate combined incremental rate on an increment of income at any level.

Sometimes the various governmental units taxing the same income have substantially different rules for determining taxable income. In such cases it may not be advisable to simplify economy studies by the use of a single effective tax rate.

Selecting Tax Rates for Use in Economy Studies for Corporations. The 55% effective tax rate used in Examples 15–1 to 15–4 was an appropriate one for use by many large and moderate-sized corporations in the United States in the late 1950's. This rate considered only corporate taxes. It exceeded the 52% federal rate on all corporate income above $25,000 because of state income taxes and, where appropriate, because of the extra federal tax on consolidated returns.

Corporations often have one or more subsidiary corporations. For tax and other reasons, it may be advantageous for such corporations to make one consolidated tax return covering both the parent company and its subsidiaries.[6] A consolidated return was permissible if the subsidiary corporations were wholly owned or sufficiently nearly so to meet the conditions laid down in the tax law. An extra tax of 2% was levied on all income reported in such consolidated returns except when the consolidation applied to regulated public utility companies.

A number of corporations used a 50% tax rate in economy studies. Apparently this rate was chosen partly for ease of calculation and partly because it was believed that a moderate reduction in federal tax rates could be expected over a period of years.

In many small corporations where it was expected that taxable income would continue to be below $25,000, effective tax rates of 30% to 35% were appropriate considering both federal and state

---

[6] In computing the taxable income of corporations, an 85% credit was allowed on dividends received from other corporations. Thus a corporation paying a 52% tax on other income would, in effect, be paying 7.8% on dividends received from subsidiaries unless a consolidated return was submitted. Moreover, in a consolidated return it was possible to offset the losses of one subsidiary against the profits of others.

taxes and disregarding personal income taxes on dividends received by stockholders.

In closely held corporations where consideration is given to all taxes on corporate income, both corporate taxes and personal taxes, the appropriate effective tax rates may sometimes be extremely high. For example, assume corporate taxes of 55% and stock-holders' incremental tax rates on personal income of 50%. If the income remaining after corporate taxes is distributed as dividends each year, each extra dollar of corporate income before taxes will lead to the payment of 55 cents in corporate taxes and 22.5 cents in personal taxes; this is an effective tax rate of 77.5%.

Selecting a Tax Rate in Economy Studies for Individuals. Because of the numerous brackets in both federal and state tax schedules in the United States, the selection of a single effective tax rate is somewhat less appropriate for individuals than for corporations. In many decisions made by individuals where there are prospective differences in taxable income, the best thing to do may be to compute a total taxable income and a total income tax for each alternative under consideration.

Nevertheless, in many economy studies for individuals it is close enough for purposes of decision making to simplify matters by selecting a single rate applicable to the expected highest bracket of the individual's income. In the frequent case where the exact bracket is uncertain, a rate averaging two or more brackets may be used. For example, consider a single person who is sole proprietor of a business and who is subject to the federal tax rate schedule shown in Table 15–7.   Assume that he expects his annual taxable income to be between $10,000 and $16,000. In decision making related to income taxes, he might use the 43% rate applicable to the bracket $12,000–$14,000. Or if state taxes raised the final increment of his combined tax by about 2% of income, he could make economy studies with an effective rate of 45%.

Need for Consideration in Economy Studies of Laws and Regulations Regarding the Determination of Taxable Income. Every governmental unit that levies income taxes has its own laws and regulations that govern the way in which taxable income is computed. These rules vary considerably from one government to another and change from time to time in any given government. Generally speaking, legislative bodies are free to define taxable income in any way they see fit. Although the concept of taxable income corresponds in a general way to the concept of accounting income, there are likely to be some significant points of difference.

As already mentioned, the discussion in this book is intended to stress the general principles of introducing income tax considerations into economy studies. These principles are not limited to any particular set of tax laws and regulations. The steps outlined in the discussion that followed Example 15–4 are appropriate regardless of the laws and regulations that exist at the time and place of a particular economy study.

Converting Cash Flow Before Income Taxes into Taxable Income. Among these steps, the most critical one in any analysis is likely to be the conversion of an estimated difference in cash flow between two alternatives into an estimated difference in taxable income. In many cases this is a problem for the tax specialist. Fortunately, however, there are a number of common types of cases in which this conversion is reasonably simple and straightforward. Our examples in this chapter up to this point have dealt with only one aspect of this subject, as they have concentrated attention on the way in which the depreciation method used for tax purposes enters into this conversion. Some other aspects of this conversion are discussed in the next few pages.

It is convenient to examine the conversion of cash flow into taxable income in two steps, namely, (1) the relationship between cash flow and accounting income and (2) some possible points of difference between accounting income and taxable income. In the second of these steps our illustrations are based on the federal income tax laws and regulations of the United States (particularly those in effect in 1958).

A Guide for Nonaccountants in Judging the Influence of Certain Transactions on Accounting Income.[7] A common method of presenting the elements of accounting is by means of the so-called balance sheet approach. This approach starts with the following rule for obtaining the valuation placed by the books of account on the owners' equity in a business enterprise:

Owners' equity = valuation placed by the accounts on what the enterprise owns minus what it owes

or, expressed more briefly,

Owners' equity = assets minus liabilities

---

[7] If persons responsible for the conduct or supervision of economy studies have not studied accounting at some time in their careers, it is recommended that they read a text on elementary accounting. Many good standard works on this subject are available. A short presentation by one of the authors of this book, aimed particularly at non-accountants, is: E. L. Grant, *Basic Accounting and Cost Accounting* (New York: McGraw-Hill Book Co., Inc., 1956).

The preceding equation is, in effect, simply a definition of owners' equity. It is important to recognize that owners' equity in the sense used here is a derived figure. It is the valuation that the accounts place on the assets and liabilities that determines the valuation that they place on owners' equity. The equation may be rewritten in the conventional balance sheet form as follows:

$$\text{Assets} = \text{liabilities} + \text{ownership}$$

As pointed out in Chapter 10, two major statements that always may be derived from the accounts of a business enterprise are the balance sheet and the profit and loss statement (also called the income statement). The balance sheet always applies to a particular date, stating book valuations for the various assets, liabilities, and for the owners' equity as of the stated date. The profit and loss statement applies to a stated period of time (such as a particular year); it serves to summarize the business transactions that have increased or decreased owners' equity during the period (usually excluding certain transactions between the enterprise and its owners—such as the withdrawal of ownership funds or the investment of new funds by the owners).

In converting estimated cash flow into its estimated influence on profit, it is essential to recognize that there are many cash transactions that have no immediate effect on the accounting figure for profit. Thus if the asset, cash, is decreased in a transaction to acquire some other asset given an equal value on the balance sheet, owners' equity is unchanged and the immediate effect on profit is nil. (Examples are the purchase of land for cash, and the purchase of a depreciable asset—such as a building or machine.) Or if cash is increased and some other asset is decreased by an equal amount, there has been no change in owners' equity. (Examples are the sale of land for its original cost and the sale of an old building at exactly its depreciated book value.) Or if cash is increased and there is an equal increase in a liability, owners' equity is unchanged. (An example is the borrowing of money.) Neither is owners' equity changed when cash is decreased and there is an equal decrease in a liability. (An example is the repayment of a loan.)

The student of accounting will recognize that the foregoing simple statements about cash transactions that *do not* make immediate changes in owners' equity cannot be matched by equally simple statements identifying cash transactions that *do* make such changes. Nevertheless, many cash transactions are clearly identifiable as changing owners' equity in the year in which they occur. Fortunately, the use of the year as the time unit in a cash flow analysis for economy studies makes it possible to disregard certain matters that are important in day-by-day accounting. It should be recognized that many incomes (increases in owners' equity) are partially offset by associated expenses (decreases in owners' equity). For example, receipts from the sale of a product or service are offset by the costs of supplying the product or service.

The Difference in the Income Tax Status of Owners' Capital and Borrowed Capital. For accounting purposes, interest paid on a loan is a current expense that reduces the accounting figure for profit (or increases the figure for loss). In contrast, a desired minimum attractive return on money furnished by the owners of an enterprise is not deducted as an expense in the orthodox accounting determination of profit.

In this respect, as in so many others, the income tax concept of taxable income corresponds to the accounting view of profit. Hence, when an enterprise is financed entirely by ownership funds, the entire return on the investment is subject to income taxation. When part of the financing is by borrowed money, the taxable income is reduced by the interest paid. This is illustrated in Example 15-8.

EXAMPLE 15-8. RATE OF RETURN AFTER INCOME TAXES WITH PART OF THE FINANCING BY BORROWED MONEY

Facts of the Case. In Examples 8-2 and 15-5 we considered a proposed $12,000 investment in rental machinery. In Example 8-2 the prospective rate of return before income taxes was found to be 12.0%. In Example 15-5 a 30% income tax rate was assumed and the prospective rate of return after income taxes was found to be 8.1% using straight-line depreciation and 8.6% using years-digits depreciation. In computing cash flow for income taxes, equity financing was assumed.

Now we vary the conditions of the example by assuming that half of the initial financing of the $12,000 machine will come from the borrowing of $6,000. This loan is to be repaid over 8 years at $750 a year with interest each year at 8% of the unpaid balance.

Calculation of Rate of Return After Income Taxes. Table 15-8 shows calculations to find cash flow after income taxes assuming years-digits depreciation and the same 30% effective tax rate used in Example 15-5. A separate calculation, not shown in the table, gives +$33 as the present worth of this cash flow with interest at 12% and −$413 as the present worth with interest at 15%. Interpolation indicates a return of 12.2% after income taxes on the equity capital invested.

The student of engineering economy may note certain aspects of the difference between 100% equity financing and partial financing by borrowing by comparing Table 15-8 with Table 15-6 (in which 100% equity financing was assumed for

TABLE 15-8

CALCULATIONS TO DETERMINE CASH FLOW AFTER INCOME TAXES, EXAMPLE 8-2, ASSUMING HALF OF INITIAL FINANCING BY A $6,000 8% LOAN

Year	A Cash Flow Before Debt Service and Taxes	B Cash Flow for Debt Repayment	C Cash Flow for Interest on Debt	D Cash Flow After Debt Service	E Depreciation	F Taxable Income	G Cash Flow for Taxes	H Cash Flow After Taxes
0	−$12,000 +6,000			−$6,000				−$6,000
1	+3,700	−$750	−$480	+2,470	−$2,400	+$820	−$246	+2,224
2	+3,000	−750	−420	+1,830	−2,100	+480	−144	+1,686
3	+2,400	−750	−360	+1,290	−1,800	+240	−72	+1,218
4	+2,100	−750	−300	+1,050	−1,500	+300	−90	+960
5	+1,700	−750	−240	+710	−1,200	+260	−78	+632
6	+1,500	−750	−180	+570	−900	+420	−126	+444
7	+1,300	−750	−120	+430	−600	+580	−174	+256
8	+1,150	−750	−60	+340	−300	+790	−237	+103
8*	+1,200			+1,200				+1,200
	+$12,050	−$6,000	−$2,160	+$3,890	−$10,800	+$3,890	−$1,167	+$2,723

* Salvage value.

the same project). Although, as pointed out in earlier chapters, column totals in such tables are not a reliable guide to decision making, certain aspects of the differences between the two methods of financing can be brought out to good advantage merely by comparing column totals.

The figures for years 1 to 8 in column A of Table 15–8 are the same as those in column A of Table 15–6. For year 0, however, Table 15–8 shows separate figures indicating the disbursement of $12,000 for the machine and the receipt of $6,000 from the lender.

The two segments of the annual payments to the lender are shown separately in columns B and C of Table 15–8 because the debt repayment of $750 a year does not affect taxable income, whereas the interest payment is a deduction from taxable income.

Column A of Table 15–6 showed that the total positive cash flow before taxes was $6,050; this was also the total taxable income (column C). The totals of columns D and F in Table 15–8 show this figure to be $3,890; cash flow before taxes and taxable income have been reduced by the total interest payment of $2,160 (shown as the total of column C of Table 15–8).

The depreciation deduction from taxable income in column E of Table 15–8 is unchanged from column B of Table 15–6; the depreciation charged on the books of account and on the tax return is not affected by the fact that part of the financing is by borrowed money.

Each year's taxable income in column F of Table 15–8 is less than the same year's taxable income in column C of Table 15–6 by the amount of the year's interest payment. With our assumed tax rate of 30%, each year's cash flow for taxes in column G of Table 15–8 is less than the corresponding figure in column D of Table 15–6 by 30% of the interest. Where with 100% equity financing, the total income taxes were $1,815, in Table 15–8 they are only $1,167; the difference is $648, 30% of the $2,160 total interest payment.

The total positive cash flow after taxes is $2,723 in Table 15–8 and $4,235 in Table 15–6; the borrowing has diminished this favorable cash flow by $1,512, 70% of the $2,160 interest. But the rate of return to equity capital is greater in Table 15–8 (12.2% as compared to 8.6% in Table 15–6) because only $6,000 of equity capital has been invested in Table 15–8 in contrast to the $12,000 invested in Table 15–6.

The Influence of Income Taxes on the Net Cost of Borrowed Money. Our investor in Example 15–8 proposed to borrow money at an interest rate of 8%. However, he anticipated that every payment of a dollar of interest would reduce his required income tax payments by 30 cents. Although his before-tax cost of borrowed money is 8%, his net cost after taxes is only 5.6% (i.e., 70% of 8%).

Generally speaking, income taxes have the effect of reducing the cost of borrowed money to business enterprises because the payment of interest reduces taxable income; the higher the effective tax rate, the greater is the percentage reduction in the cost of money. It should be recognized, however, that there is no reduction in the cost of money unless there is some taxable income to be reduced. If our investor in Example 15–8 has, in fact, made estimates of income that are unrealistically high and if it turns out that he has no taxable income at all, his net cost of borrowed money will be 8%, not 5.6%.

Relationship of Decision Making on Proposed Physical Plant to Certain Income Tax Aspects of Business Finance. It was pointed out in Chapters 11 and 14 that a general principle of decision making is that decisions that are separable from one another ought to be made separately. To the extent that decisions regarding the acquisition of physical plant are separable from decisions regarding the financing of this plant, these decisions should be subject to a separate analysis.

Chapter 17 expands the foregoing general statement, not only with reference to the case of John Smith, our proposed investor in Examples 8–2, 15–5, and 15–8, but also with reference to a number of other cases. Where alternative plans of financing are available, it often happens that different financing plans will have quite different income tax consequences. This topic is explored in Chapter 17 with reference to financing by leasing as well as by borrowing and by equity capital.

Nevertheless, most of the subsequent examples and problems in this book will consider income taxes on the basis of 100% equity financing. It will be assumed that decisions on methods of financing in competitive industry can and should be made separately from decisions on the selection of physical plant. This usually is a valid assumption.

In regulated public utilities, on the other hand, it usually is desirable to introduce income tax considerations into economy studies on the assumption that a stipulated fraction of the cost of any new physical plant will be financed by long-term borrowing. This topic is discussed later in the present chapter.

Accounting Treatment of "Gains" and "Losses" on the Disposal of Certain Assets. It is a convention of accounting that certain business assets are carried on the books at their original cost regardless of changes in market value; some examples are land and certain securities (such as corporate stocks). It was explained in Chapter 10 that the cost of certain other assets is written off "in a systematic and rational manner." This systematic write-off applies not only to depreciable physical assets but also to certain intangible assets (such as patents).

Whenever an asset is disposed of for more or less than its book value, an increase or decrease occurs in the owners' equity as shown by the books of account. It is the convention of accounting to assign this so-called "gain" or "loss" on disposal entirely to the year in which the disposal takes place. For example, if land acquired for $10,000 in 1930 is sold for $100,000 in 1960, the $90,000 excess over the original cost serves to increase the profit for 1960. Or if stock purchased for $50,000 in 1956 is sold for $30,000 in 1961, the $20,000 shortage below the original cost serves to reduce the profit for 1961.

Chapter 14 pointed out that in an economy study dealing with the influence on future cash flow of a choice between alternatives, past outlays are irrelevant except as they are expected to influence future cash flow. From the viewpoint of economy studies, the chief importance of a prospective "gain" or "loss" on disposal consists in the effect of this accounting entry on cash flow for income taxes.

Income Tax Treatment of Such "Gains" and "Losses" in the United States. At one time in the United States such gains were included in taxable income and such losses were fully deductible from taxable income in the year in which the disposal of the assets occurred. In the 1930's the law was changed in a way that subjected long-term gains to a lower tax rate than ordinary income and severely limited the extent to which capital losses could be deducted from taxable income except to offset similar gains. The exact rules on this matter have changed many times and have always been full of technicalities. The following simplified statement regarding the 1958 law is intended to give the reader a clear enough idea of the subject so that he can understand the examples and work the problems in this book. The statement is not sufficiently detailed to be a reliable guide for actual economy studies or for the preparation of tax returns.

The law affecting the individual income tax was somewhat different from that affecting the corporation income tax. For both individuals and corporations, gains and losses on assets held for more than 6 months were designated as *long term;* for assets held a shorter period, the gains and losses were *short term.* A distinction was made between gains and losses on so-called *capital assets* and certain other similar assets including *depreciable property used in the trade or business.* Capital assets included securities (with a few exceptions) and real estate not used in the trade or business.

The general effect of a rather complex set of rules was to apply a tax rate of 25% or less to long-term capital gains and to long-term gains on certain other assets (such as depreciable property used in the trade or business). The rate was 25% to corporations; individuals could also use the 25% rate whenever it was to their advantage to do so. Individuals had the option of including half the long-term gain in ordinary income. It was generally advantageous for individuals in the lower income brackets to use this option; for example, a small long-term capital gain made by an individual in the 20% bracket would, in effect, be taxed at 10%.

Short-term capital gains were handled in the same way as ordinary income, except that they could be used to offset long-term and short-term capital losses. Losses, whether short or long term, on the sale or exchange of capital assets were not treated the same as ordinary losses. Corporations could not use such losses to reduce taxable income at all except to offset capital gains; individuals were limited to $1,000 a year of such losses in computing taxable income except as the losses were used to offset capital gains.

Losses on the sale of depreciable assets used in the trade or business or real estate used in the trade or business were not subject to these restrictions, either for individuals or corporations. Under certain limitations such losses were fully deductible from taxable income in the years in which they occurred. An important limitation was that such losses must first be offset against certain related gains.

There were certain nontaxable exchanges that, in effect, postponed the tax consequences of the gain or loss until the disposal of the property received in the exchange. A common example of such an exchange was the trade-in of an old machine as part payment on a new machine of like kind.

Economy Studies in Relation to Income Tax Treatment of Gains and Losses on Disposal of Certain Assets. Engineering economy studies are more likely to deal with the acquisition and retirement of "real estate or depreciable assets used in the trade or business" than with so-called "capital assets." The determination of the appropriate tax rate to use in predicting the income tax consequences of a gain or loss is complicated by the rules governing the offsetting of such gains and losses.

For example, consider a corporation that is in the 52% tax bracket on ordinary income. If, in a given year, the corporation has a $10,000 loss on the sale of real estate used in the business and has no offsetting gains, this loss will be fully deductible and will decrease the income tax by $5,200. If, in the next year, the corporation has a gain on the sale of depreciable property used in the business of $10,000 and has no offsetting losses, the gain will be taxable at 25% and will increase the income tax by $2,500. But if the $10,000 loss and the $10,000 gain occur in the same year, they will offset one another and the income tax will be the same as if neither had occurred.

Now imagine that the loss has already occurred in the current year and that a decision must be made whether during the same year to make the transaction involving the gain. In effect, the tax rate on the gain will be 52% because the offsetting effect of the transaction will increase the year's tax by $5,200. Or imagine that the gain has already occurred and that the transaction involving the loss is under consideration. In effect, the rate of 25% is applicable to the loss because the offsetting effect of the loss will be to reduce taxes by $2,500.

The tax consequences of prospective gains and losses may enter into economy studies both in connection with the proposal for immediate disposal of assets already owned and in connection with the forecast that assets will be sold in some later year at more or less than their book values. Generally speaking, it is only in connection with immediate disposal that it is practicable to consider the effect of offsetting gains and losses in the same year. A reasonable procedure in most economy studies is to disregard possible offsetting of gains and losses in future years. Thus the corporation in our example might use 25% as the tax rate assumed for predicted future gains on disposal and 52% as the rate applicable to predicted future losses on disposal of real estate or depreciable assets used in the trade or business.[8]

Exemption of Certain Interest Income from Income Taxation. Interest received on bonds or other obligations of a state, territory, or the District of Columbia has been completely exempt from federal income taxes in the United States. As a result, states, counties, cities, and the many different types of local improvement districts can borrow at lower rates than would be possible without this tax exemption.

Chapter 9 pointed out that one element in deciding on a minimum attractive rate of return on a proposed investment is to consider the rate of return foregone on other opportunities to invest the same funds. The return available from tax-exempt bonds tends to establish a lower limit on the before-tax minimum attractive rate of return for many individuals and corporations in the United States. For example, if a taxpayer's effective tax rate is 60% and the yield on tax-exempt bonds is 3.5%, an investment subject to taxation must earn at least 8.75% before taxes to have the same after-tax return as the bonds.

---

[8] For the historical reasons for different treatment of gains and losses on disposal of depreciable assets used in the trade or business, see Grant and Norton, *op. cit.*, pp. 234–36

Special Income Tax Treatment of Certain Natural Resources.
For accounting purposes, the cost of an exhaustible natural resource
(such as a mineral deposit) is written off over the estimated life of
the resource. This write-off, usually on a unit-of-production basis,
is described as *depletion* rather than as depreciation.

For income tax purposes, the laws of the United States have allowed taxpayers the option of making depletion charges for tax
purposes by a method that may permit the total depletion deduction over the life of a resource to exceed its cost. Under the law in
1958, taxpayers could make depletion deductions for certain exhaustible resources equal to a specified percentage of the gross income from the property during the year. Some of the depletion
percentages were 27½ for oil and gas wells; 23 or 15 for many
metals and minerals, depending on the type of metal or mineral and
on whether or not the deposit was in the United States; 10 for coal;
and 5 for gravel, sand, and brick and tile clay. The depletion under
this percentage method in any year was not permitted to exceed
50% of the net income of the taxpayer from the property in that
year computed without the allowance for depletion.

In economy studies relative to the acquisition or disposal of such
natural resources, special consideration needs to be given to the
income tax treatment of depletion.

**Carry-Back and Carry-Forward Provisions of United States
Income Tax Laws.**[9] It was pointed out in Chapters 8 and 10 that
the profitableness of an enterprise cannot be measured exactly until
the enterprise has terminated, and that accounting figures for profit
or loss should properly be thought of as tentative judgments that
may later turn out to have been either too favorable or not favorable
enough. This viewpoint, in spite of its obvious soundness, is not a
practicable one to adopt in the administration of income taxes. The
laws, regulations, and practices governing income taxes are necessarily based on the fiction that there is some determinable correct
figure for profit or loss for each year of the existence of an enterprise.

Adherence to this fiction is unfair to business enterprises that are
of the feast-or-famine type unless the losses reported in tax returns
for some years can be offset against profits reported for other years.
Otherwise, two enterprises that have equal net profits over a period
of years may have had quite different taxable incomes. For example, Corporation A, producing certain consumers' goods for which

---

[9] Although the Internal Revenue Code uses the designations "carry-back" and "carry-
over," the popular designations "carry-back" and "carry-forward" are used here.
Otherwise, when used by itself, "carry-over" might be misunderstood to mean the
carrying of a loss either forward or back.

there is a fairly stable demand, may be contrasted with Corporation B, producing certain capital goods for which there are great fluctuations in demand. Over a 20-year period, each corporation has total net profits before income taxes of $2,000,000. The profits of Corporation A have never fallen below $50,000 or risen above $150,000. In contrast, Corporation B has had total profits of $3,800,000 for 12 profitable years and total losses of $1,800,000 for 8 unprofitable years.

Despite the fact that their respective accounts show Corporations A and B to be equally profitable over the 20-year period, Corporation B has had nearly twice as much taxable income as Corporation A. In the absence of any provision for using the loss years to offset the profit years in the determination of income tax liability, income taxation places an inequitably large burden on Corporation B.

The income tax laws of the United States have changed from time to time with respect to the use of loss years to offset profit years. Under the law in 1958, net operating losses could be carried back to the 3 preceding years or forward to the 5 succeeding years. The rule was that a net operating loss of any year might first be carried back to the third preceding year, and then, if it exceeded the net income of that year, to the second year, and finally to the year immediately preceding the taxable year. If there still remained a portion of the net operating loss, it could be used to decrease the taxable income of the next succeeding year, and, if necessary, to each of the 4 years thereafter.

Neither a carry-forward nor a carry-back was allowed from 1933 to 1939. The business losses of the depression years of the early 1930's were therefore never used to offset the profits of earlier or later years in income tax returns. A provision for a 2-year carry-forward was added in 1940. A 2-year carry-back was added in 1942. The carry-forward period was increased to 5 years in 1954. The carry-back period was increased to 3 years in 1958.

In contrast to the recent United States laws, income tax laws of many of the states of the United States have not permitted either carry-back or carry-forward of business losses.

Special Aspects of Treatment of Income Taxes in Economy Studies for Regulated Public Utilities in the United States. Chapter 9 contained a brief discussion of the appropriate criteria for decision making between alternative types of physical plant in regulated public utility companies. For reasons that were there explained, it was suggested that economy studies for a regulated utility be made in a way that aims to minimize the utility's revenue requirements and thus results in the lowest total charge to the customers of the utility's product or service. Under common rules of regulation in many parts of the United States, a utility's revenue requirements are made up of current operating disbursements (not including interest on debt), an allowance for depreciation, income taxes, and a "fair return" on depreciated book value. It is appropriate to use this "fair return" rate, which reflects the utility's over-all cost of capital, as the interest rate or minimum attractive rate of return in the utility's economy studies.

Given the rules under which utility rates are to be regulated, it usually is possible to express the income tax element in the revenue requirement as percentage of the first cost of plant. The appropriate formulas for this percentage will depend on the expected rules of rate regulation.

Examples of Formulas for the Ratio of Income Tax Requirements to First Cost of Plant for Regulated Utilities. The following formulas assume that straight-line depreciation is used in the determination of regulated rates and also in the calculation of taxable income. They assume that each year the "fair return" is allowed on the depreciated book value. They assume that the "fair return" is used as the interest rate to convert a diminishing series of income tax requirements into an equivalent uniform annual series. They assume that the borrowed money applicable to any particular physical assets may be considered to be a stated fraction of the depreciated book value of the assets, and that this fraction will remain constant throughout the life of the assets. They assume that the "fair return" and the interest rate on borrowed money will remain constant throughout the life of any assets.

The presentation of the formulas is simplified by using the mnemonic representation of the gradient factor rather than the algebraic symbols for this factor.

Let a = rate of return ("fair return") on depreciated investment
　　b = interest rate paid on borrowed funds
　　c = fraction of plant investment financed by borrowing
　　e = effective income tax rate
　　n = life of plant
　　s = ratio of terminal salvage value to first cost of plant
　　t = ratio of equivalent annual income taxes to first cost of plant
　　　　(with equivalence calculated at rate a)

The general formula for t is

$$t = \frac{e}{1-e}(a - bc)\left[s + (1-s)\left(1 - \frac{(\text{gf-}a\%\text{-}n)}{n}\right)\right] \tag{1}$$

For the special case where the salvage value is zero, the formula becomes

$$t = \frac{e}{1-e}(a - bc)\left(1 - \frac{(gf-a\%-n)}{n}\right) \tag{2}$$

For the special case of 100% salvage value, the formula becomes

$$t = \frac{e}{1-e}(a - bc) \tag{3}$$

For the special case of 100% salvage value and 100% equity financing, it is

$$t = \frac{e}{1-e}a \tag{4}$$

Explanation of the Basis of the Foregoing Formulas. In explaining the assumptions on which these formulas are based, it is helpful to use several numerical examples and to start with the simplest case, gradually adding various complicating factors to the examples. In all of the following examples, the effective income tax rate e is 0.55 (i.e., 55%), and the permitted rate of return a is 0.07 (i.e., 7%).

First assume $1,000 of investment in an asset assumed to have 100% salvage value (such as land) and assume that the utility is financed entirely from equity funds. The utility will be permitted to earn $70 after income taxes on this investment, i.e., 7% of $1,000. The before-tax earnings, subject to 55% income tax, must be high enough to cover the tax and leave $70 remaining after taxes. Let T represent the income tax. Then

$$T = 0.55(\$70 + T)$$

$$T - 0.55T = 0.55(\$70)$$

$$T = \frac{0.55}{0.45}(\$70) = \$85.55 \text{ or } 8.56\% \text{ of the investment}$$

The foregoing reasoning is the basis of Formula (4), which we may apply as follows:

$$t = \frac{e}{1-e}a = \frac{0.55}{1-0.55}(0.07) = 0.0856$$

Now change the conditions of the example by assuming that this $1,000 asset is financed half by equity funds and half by money borrowed at 4% interest. In the terminology of our formulas, $b = 0.04$ and $c = 0.50$. The permitted earnings, before interest but after income taxes, will still be $70. However, $20 of this will go for interest on debt (4% of the $500 borrowed), and this $20 will be a deduction from taxable income. Thus

$$T = 0.55(\$70 + T - \$20)$$

$$T - 0.55T = 0.55(\$70 - \$20)$$

$$T = \$61.11 \text{ or } 6.11\% \text{ of the investment}$$

The foregoing reasoning is the basis of formula (3), which we may apply as follows:

$$t = \frac{e}{1-e}(a - bc) = \frac{0.55}{0.45}[0.07 - 0.04(0.5)] = 0.0611$$

Now make a further change in the conditions of the example by assuming that the $1,000 asset has an estimated life of 10 years with zero salvage value. In the first year of life of the asset, the 7% earnings permitted will apply to the full $1,000 of investment, and the tax deduction for interest will apply to 4% of $500, just as in the previous example; it follows that the income tax will be $61.11, just as before. But in the second year, the 7% will apply to the depreciated book value of $900, and the 4% interest is applicable to a debt of $450. And so on. Year-by-year figures are shown in Table 15–9.

TABLE 15–9

YEAR-BY-YEAR INCOME TAX PAYMENTS CAUSED BY $1,000 INVESTMENT IN UTILITY PLANT HAVING 10-YEAR LIFE AND ZERO SALVAGE VALUE

(Effective tax rate assumed as 55%. "Fair return" on depreciated book value assumed as 7%. Straight-line depreciation assumed for both rate regulation and income tax purposes. Half of utility financing by debt with interest at 4%.)

Year	Required Earnings To Cover Depreciation, "Fair Return," and Income Taxes	Depreciation Deduction from Taxable Income	Interest Deduction from Taxable Income	Taxable Income	Income Tax
1	$170 + T_1$	$100	$20	$50 + T_1$	$T_1 = \$61.11$
2	$163 + T_2$	100	18	$45 + T_2$	$T_2 = 55.00$
3	$156 + T_3$	100	16	$40 + T_3$	$T_3 = 48.89$
4	$149 + T_4$	100	14	$35 + T_4$	$T_4 = 42.78$
5	$142 + T_5$	100	12	$30 + T_5$	$T_5 = 36.67$
6	$135 + T_6$	100	10	$25 + T_6$	$T_6 = 30.56$
7	$128 + T_7$	100	8	$20 + T_7$	$T_7 = 24.44$
8	$121 + T_8$	100	6	$15 + T_8$	$T_8 = 18.33$
9	$114 + T_9$	100	4	$10 + T_9$	$T_9 = 12.22$
10	$107 + T_{10}$	100	2	$5 + T_{10}$	$T_{10} = 6.11$

The income tax made necessary by the $1,000 investment starts at $61.11 in the first year and reduces each year by $6.11. At 7% interest, the equivalent uniform annual figure is $61.11 − $6.11-(gf–7%–10) = $61.11 − $6.11(3.95) = $36.97 or 3.70% of the investment.

The foregoing reasoning is the basis of formula (2), which we may apply as follows:

$$t = \frac{e}{1-e}(a-bc)\left(1 - \frac{(\text{gf}-a\%-n)}{n}\right)$$

$$= \frac{0.55}{0.45}[0.07 - 0.04(0.5)]\left(1 - \frac{3.95}{10}\right) = 0.0370$$

Now make a still further change in the conditions of the example by assuming that the $1,000 asset has a 10-year life with a prospective 50% salvage value at the end of the life. This may be thought of as a $500 asset with 100% salvage value, responsible for a tax of half of $61.11 or $30.56, and another $500 asset with a zero salvage value, responsible for a tax of half of $36.97 or $18.48. The total tax will be the sum of these two figures, $49.04, midway between the figure for zero and 100% salvage values. In general, the income tax percentage for any salvage value above zero and less than 100% can be found by a linear interpolation between the figures for salvage percentages of 0 and 100. Formula (1), our general formula, may be viewed as giving a linear interpolation between the results computed from formulas (2) and (3).

TABLE 15–10

PUBLIC UTILITY REVENUE REQUIREMENTS FOR INCOME TAXES EXPRESSED AS A PERCENTAGE OF FIRST COST OF PLANT

(Effective tax rate assumed as 55%. "Fair return" on depreciated book value assumed as 7%. Straight-line depreciation assumed in rate regulation and income taxation. Half of utility financing by debt with interest at 4%. Equivalent uniform annual taxes computed assuming 7% interest.)

Life of Plant in Years	Ratio of Salvage Value to First Cost of Plant				
	0%	10%	20%	50%	100%
5	3.84	4.07	4.29	4.97	6.11
10	3.70	3.94	4.18	4.90	6.11
15	3.76	4.00	4.23	4.94	6.11
20	3.87	4.10	4.32	4.99	6.11
30	4.13	4.32	4.52	5.12	6.11
40	4.37	4.54	4.72	5.24	6.11
50	4.58	4.73	4.89	5.35	6.11
100	5.25	5.33	5.42	5.68	6.11

The influence of life n and salvage percentage s on income taxes is shown in Table 15–10. This table is based on the values of a, b, c, and e that we have used in the foregoing examples.

Contrast Between Regulated Public Utilities and Competitive Industry with Respect to Economy Studies and Income Taxes. Our discussion in Chapter 9 and in the present chapter has assumed that, in a regulated utility, income taxes will be allowed by the regulatory authority as one of the components of the price of the utility's product or service, and that economy studies comparing alternative types of plant should—in effect—be made from the viewpoint of the utility's customers. In contrast, our discussion has implied that the price of a competitive product or service will be established by market conditions unrelated to an individual producer's decision on alternative types of plant and that economy studies for a competitive enterprise should be made from the viewpoint of the owners of the enterprise.

Some important aspects of this difference in viewpoint may be clearer if we examine a specific numerical example. Let us consider Example 15–1 in which an outlay of $42,000 for materials handling equipment having a 10-year life was expected to decrease annual operating disbursements by $10,000. If this equipment were to be installed by a manufacturer in competitive industry, the price of the manufactured product presumably would be unaffected by the method of materials handling used by this one manufacturer. The influence of the investment on the manufacturer's income taxes would arise as a result of the change in taxable income caused by the $10,000 annual saving in operating disbursements, partially offset by the $4,200 annual increase in his depreciation charge. If the annual saving in operating disbursements should be $15,000 instead of $10,000, taxable income would be increased by $5,000 and annual income taxes would be increased by $2,750, 55% of $5,000.

In contrast, if the materials handling equipment had been proposed for a regulated public utility, an additional saving of $5,000 in annual operating disbursements would have no influence on taxable income because this saving would be accompanied by an equal decrease in revenues from the sale of the utility's product or service. The influence of the investment on income taxes would depend on the size of the investment itself and on the company's over-all cost of money, reflected in its permitted rate of "fair return." The higher the after-tax return permitted on the $42,000, the greater the before-tax return must be and the greater the element in income taxes caused by this $42,000 investment.

A Further Comment on Income Tax Considerations in Economy Studies for Regulated Utilities. The formulas given in this chapter for ratio of equivalent annual income taxes to first cost of plant in a regulated utility were based on certain stated assumptions about the rules of regulation and the method of depreciation used in computing taxable income. They have been presented here to illustrate how formulas may be developed to fit a particular set of assumptions on these matters. It is not intended to suggest that these are the only such formulas that are appropriate. In many public utilities other assumptions regarding the rules of rate regulation and methods of tax depreciation may be closer to the facts. Various other formulas have been published based on a number of different assumptions.[10] Even though the different formulas naturally give somewhat different results from one another as well as from the formulas in this chapter, the ratios of income tax to first cost for given tax rates and rates of return on investment all seem to be of the same general order of magnitude.

A Further Comment on the Question of How To Introduce Consideration of Income Taxes into Economy Studies in Competitive Industry. There is no room for debate on the point *that* income taxes need to be considered in choosing between alternatives in competitive industry; the only issue is *how* tax considerations can best be introduced into decision-making procedures. Two methods of considering income taxes in economy studies, both frequently used in industry, have been presented in this book:

1. The first method, used in our examples from Chapters 7 to 14, is to compare alternatives *before* income taxes. In this method, comparisons must be made using a minimum attractive rate of return before taxes that is high enough to yield a desired after-tax rate. Often a stipulated rate of return after taxes is divided by one minus the effective tax rate to find the minimum attractive rate before taxes. For example, if the minimum attractive rate after taxes were 8% and the tax rate were 55%, the before-tax rate would be 8% ÷ (1 − 0.55) = 17.8%.
2. The second method, illustrated in the examples in the present chapter, is to compare alternatives *after* income taxes. The year-by-year differences in disbursements for taxes are estimated, and the analysis is made using a minimum attractive rate of return after taxes.

The first method has two major advantages. It is simpler in the sense of involving less calculation, and it can be applied by persons

---

[10] American Telephone and Telegraph Co., *Engineering Economy* (New York: A. T. & T. Co., 1952), see particularly chap. v and appendix B.

who are not familiar with the technicalities of income taxation. Nevertheless, the second method clearly is the one that is correct in principle. The first method is appropriate only where it is reasonable to expect that it will lead to the same *decisions* among alternatives that would be reached by applying the second method.

A rough generalization, subject to exceptions, is that the first method often is good enough for practical purposes at the level of decisions on design alternatives but that it will rarely be satisfactory in comparing alternative projects on the level of capital budgeting.

In principle the interest rate used in the first method (the minimum attractive rate of return before income taxes) has the defect of discounting the future too greatly. Therefore the first method places insufficient weight on the more distant consequences of alternatives.

If it is desired to be sure to array investment proposals in their correct order, some circumstances requiring the use of the second method are as follows:

1. Whenever there are substantial differences in the rates of write-off for different alternatives. (This was illustrated in Examples 15–1 to 15–4.)
2. Whenever a substantial change in the applicable tax rate is expected during the period of the study
3. In the United States, for all investment proposals in the mining and petroleum industries. (This is because of the percentage depletion method permitted for tax purposes. After-tax analyses generally need to be made for all proposals, not merely for those involving percentage depletion, because proposals without this tax advantage must compete for limited funds against proposals that have this advantage.)
4. In the United States, whenever one or more alternatives involve a prospective capital gain or loss or a gain or loss on disposal of real estate or depreciable assets used in the trade or business
5. Whenever a crude payout period after taxes is to be used as a supplementary criterion for investment decisions

Consideration of Income Taxes in Personal Decisions. In our modern age of high personal income tax rates, many choices between personal alternatives appear in a somewhat different light when the income tax consequences of the different alternatives are examined. Some representative cases of this type are illustrated at the end of this chapter (Problems 15–9 to 15–15) and at the end of Chapter 17 (Problems 17–5 and 17–6). Answers are given to all of these problems. Rules on tax matters used in these problems are based on the tax laws and regulations of the United States in 1958.

An important point in a number of these problems is the decision by the individual whether to itemize nonbusiness deductions or to take the standard deduction. Presumably this decision will always be made in the way that results in the minimum tax. However, the tax consequences of a number of types of choice between personal alternatives are greatly influenced by this particular decision.

The Impact of Income Taxation on Capital Formation and Technological Progress. A high standard of living depends on the use of capital goods. Generally speaking, it is technological progress that makes it possible for the standard of living to be improved. Obstacles to capital formation and to technological progress are obstacles to improvements in the standard of living. They may also be obstacles to effective national defense.

Examples 15–1 to 15–6 brought out the point that the tax deterrent to capital investment is greatest when high income tax rates are combined with the requirement that depreciation be written off over a long period of years. Moreover, high income tax rates combined with low depreciation rates often create obstacles in the way of financing capital goods. It is of great social importance that income tax laws be so drawn that this undesirable effect of income taxation be kept at a minimum.

Summary. This chapter has illustrated a rational approach to the introduction of income tax considerations into the making of decisions between alternative investments. In general, this approach has been based on an analysis of alternatives in terms of prospective differences in cash flow and a recognition of income tax payments as a disbursement that should be included in any cash flow analysis.

The reader should recognize that it has been possible to discuss tax matters only in broad general terms. Any brief explanation of such complex matters must necessarily oversimplify certain subjects and omit many details that would be important in the actual preparation of income tax returns.

Problems

In the following problems, assume 100% equity funds unless otherwise stated. Assume the end-of-year convention. Unless otherwise stated, assume that the cash flow for income taxes that results from each year's taxable income occurs at the end of the respective tax year.

15–1. A $60,000 investment in machinery is proposed. It is anticipated that this investment will cause a reduction in annual operating disbursements of $10,000 a year for 15 years. The investment will be depreciated for income tax purposes by the straight-line method assuming a 15-year life and zero salvage value. The forecast of zero salvage value is also to be used in the economy study. The effective income tax rate is 50%. What are the prospective rates of return before and after income taxes? (*Ans.* = 14.5%; 8.0%.)

15–2. Compute the after-tax rate of return in Problem 15–1 assuming years-digits depreciation for tax purposes. (*Ans.* = 8.9%.)

15–3. Compute the after-tax rate of return in Problem 15–1 assuming that the investment is to be written off for tax purposes at $12,000 a year during the first 5 years. (*Ans.* = 10.3%.)

15–4. Compute the after-tax rate of return in Problem 15–1 assuming that the investment must be written off for tax purposes by the straight-line method assuming a 30-year life and zero salvage value, even though the expected operating saving will occur only during the first 15 years of life. (*Ans.* = 6.5%.)

15–5. The solution to Problem 15–4 assumed a positive cash flow during years 16 to 30 due to the depreciation deduction that was assumed to continue through that period. If, for some reason, it is believed that this tax credit in years 16 to 30 will not be realized, what is the prospective rate of return after taxes? (*Ans.* = 5.6%.)

15–6. Change the conditions of Problem 15–4 to assume that the machine will be retired at zero salvage value at the end of 15 years and that the $30,000 "loss on disposal" will be fully deductible from taxable income for the 15th year. (*Ans.* = 7.0%.)

15–7. If the $60,000 disbursement at zero date in Problem 15–1 could be treated as a current expense for tax purposes, and if the tax consequence of this treatment should take place at zero date on our time scale (just as was assumed in Example 15–4), what is the after-tax rate of return? (*Ans.* = 14.5%.)

15–8. If the $60,000 disbursement at zero date in Problem 15–1 could be treated as a current expense for tax purposes but the tax consequence of this treatment should take place at date 1 on our time scale, what is the after-tax rate of return? (*Ans.* = 12.5%.)

15–9. Harry Roe receives a salary of $9,000 a year. This is the entire family income. He and his wife Grace have one dependent child. In their joint federal income tax return they take the standard deduction rather than itemizing non-business deductions. Grace is offered a job at $250 a month. Her acceptance of the job will cause her to spend $75 a month for a baby sitter and $25 a month for a cleaning woman. She will have to pay 2½% social security taxes for each of these employees. Her salary will be subject to a 2½% social security tax and a 2% state income tax and will, of course, increase the federal income taxes that must be paid by the Roes. How much will Grace's $3,000-per-year employment add to the annual cash resources of the Roe family? Assume 1958 federal tax rates are applicable. (Note that if Grace does not work, the Roes' standard nonbusiness deduction will be $900, 10% of the family income. However, this standard deduction cannot exceed $1,000 regardless of the size of the family income.) (*Ans.* = $949.)

15–10. Solve Problem 15–9 assuming Harry Roe's salary to be $18,000 rather than $9,000. (*Ans.* = $647.)

15–11. Wilma Doe lives in a rented apartment for which she pays $100 a month. She owns a small house that she purchased 2 years ago to give her a rental income. Her total income consists of her $6,500 a year salary and the $125 a month that she receives as rental income. The purchase price of her income property was $12,000. She paid $3,000 down and assumed a mortgage loan of $9,000 bearing 5% interest. Her annual repayment on this loan is $500; she now owes $8,000 on the mortgage. Annual upkeep on the house is about $150 a year. She pays local property taxes on the house of $200 a year. On her federal income tax returns she has assigned $2,000 of the $12,000 purchase price of her property as land value; she has depreciated the $10,000 investment in the house by the straight-line method, using a 2.5% rate. She itemizes her nonbusiness deductions on her federal return; these (chiefly charitable contributions, sales taxes, auto license fees) have been about $900 a year. Wilma is single and has no dependents.

She would prefer to live in her house but has continued her present arrangement because her receipts from rentals are $300 a year more than she pays for her apartment. Considering only receipts and disbursements in connection with the house, with federal income taxes, and with apartment rental, what will it cost her next year to give up the apartment and move into her house? (When she rents her house, interest, property taxes, depreciation, and upkeep are deductions from her gross rental income; if she lives in her house and itemizes nonbusiness deductions, interest and property taxes will be allowable nonbusiness deductions.) (*Ans.* = $14.)

15-12. Mr. Y has just sold his personal residence for a net $30,000 with a capital gain for tax purposes of $5,000. His tax bracket is sufficiently high so that, if taxed at all, the gain will be taxed at a 25% rate. The tax on the gain will be deferred if within one year after the sale he buys another personal residence costing at least $30,000. Under certain circumstances the deferred tax will never be paid; one of these circumstances will occur if Mr. Y continues to own and live in the newly purchased residence for the rest of his life. He does in fact intend to do this.

His choice for his new residence is between two houses, A and B. House A costs $25,000; if he purchases A, his capital gains tax will be fully payable at once. House B costs $30,000; if he purchases B his capital gains tax will be deferred, and he believes it will never have to be paid. House B contains a number of desirable features not present in A, including an extra room and a better location. Under the stated circumstances, what extra money outlay must be made by Mr. Y to secure the desirable additional features in house B? (*Ans.* = $3,750.)

15-13. An unmarried taxpayer with no dependents has a taxable income that falls in the bracket $22,000 to $26,000 in Table 15-7. He can invest in tax-free municipal bonds yielding 3.50%. If he should lend money at interest to a private individual, what interest rate is necessary to yield him the same after-tax rate of return as the municipal bonds? (*Ans.* = 8.54%.)

15-14. The taxpayer in Problem 15-13 is considering a $1,000 gift to a scholarship fund at his university. As his nonbusiness deductions have always exceeded the standard deduction, they have always been itemized on his federal tax returns. The gift will be an additional nonbusiness deduction. How much will he be out of pocket by reason of making this gift? (*Ans.* = $410.)

15-15. Wilson is married, with two dependent children. His annual salary is $7,500; in addition, he has $500 taxable income from investments. He takes the standard nonbusiness deduction on his federal return. He is anxious to have certain improvements made to his home during the coming year. If he contracts for these improvements, the labor will cost him $1,000. He has the chance of a part-time job on week ends that will enable him to finance this labor expense. Alternately, he might do the improvement work himself. His part-time work will be subject to a 2% state tax. What must be his before-tax earnings from the part-time employment for him to break even after taxes with making his improvements as a "do-it-yourself" project? Assume 1958 federal tax rates are applicable. (*Ans.* = \$1,279.)

15–16. Assume an investment of \$1,500 in utility plant having an estimated life of 5 years with zero salvage value. Years-digits depreciation will be used in determining utility rates and in computing taxable income. Prepare an analysis along the same general lines as the one shown in Table 15–9. Assume the "fair return" on depreciated book value to be 7%. Assume half of utility financing by debt with interest at 4%; assume that the interest applicable to this plant declines in proportion to the decline in book value. Assume an income tax rate of 55%. Compute the equivalent uniform annual income tax in dollars, using an interest rate of 7% in equivalence calculations. Express this tax as a percentage of first cost of plant. How does this percentage compare with the one given in Table 15–10 where straight-line depreciation was used with the same life and salvage value? (*Ans.* = \$45.68; 3.04%; 21% lower than with straight-line depreciation.)

15–17. Using the method of analysis developed for public utility income taxes in this chapter, compute the ratio of income tax to first cost of plant under the following assumptions: "fair return" is 6%; half of financing is by equity funds and half by borrowing at 3% interest; life is 20 years; salvage value is 10% of first cost; income tax rate is 55%; straight-line depreciation is used in rate regulation and income taxation. (*Ans.* = 3.62%.)

15–18. The proposal is made that a manufacturer produce a new product. An economy study is to be made on the assumption that the sales of the product will commence at zero date and terminate after 12 years. An effective income tax rate of 50% is to be used in the study. Compute the prospective rate of return after income taxes that is indicated by the following estimates.

An investment in machinery and equipment of \$90,000 is required. An estimated life of 12 years with \$12,000 terminal salvage value will be used in the economy study and for income tax purposes. Years-digits depreciation will be used for tax purposes.

The total of a group of nonrecurrent outlays at zero date is \$20,000. All of these are appropriately chargeable as current expenses for tax purposes.

At zero date, an addition of \$30,000 to working capital is required. It is assumed that this will be fully recoverable at the end of the 12 years.

Estimated receipts from sale of product are \$60,000 in year 1, \$90,000 in year 2, and \$120,000 a year from years 3 to 12. Estimated operating disbursements are \$48,000 in year 1, \$65,000 in year 2, and \$80,000 a year from years 3 to 12. These disbursement figures include materials, labor, current payments of indirect manufacturing expenses including rental of factory space, incremental costs of general administration, and marketing expenses. (*Ans.* = 13.5%.)

15–19. Example 6–3 (page 85) compared the annual costs of Plans D and E assuming a before-tax minimum attractive rate of return of 8%. Compare these annual costs after income taxes assuming a tax rate of 30%, straight-line depreciation, and an after-tax minimum attractive rate of return of 5½%. (In this comparison, add the difference in annual income taxes to the computed annual cost of the plan involving the higher taxes.) (*Ans.* = D, \$12,897; E, \$14,082.)

15–20. Change the conditions of Example 15–4 so that a 75% effective tax rate is applicable to year zero. Assume that this is an "excess-profits" tax rate that is scheduled to expire at the end of the current year and that a 55% rate is forecast for years 1 to 10. Under these assumptions, what is the prospective after-tax rate of return? (*Ans.* = 41.5%.)

15–21. In Problem 8–3 (page 132), assume that straight-line depreciation will be used for tax purposes with the stated life and salvage value. Assuming an effective tax rate of 30%, what is the prospective after-tax rate of return? (*Ans.* = 5.8%.)

15–22. In Problem 15–21, assume that $75,000 will be borrowed at 5% interest and that $3,000 of the principal of the debt will be repaid each year for 25 years. What is the prospective after-tax rate of return on the equity investment? (*Ans.* = 8.2%.)

15–23. Five years ago an investor purchased a commercial rental property for $30,000. His annual depreciation charge on this property for income tax purposes has been $600. This has been based on a $6,000 valuation of the land, a $24,000 valuation of the building, straight-line depreciation, and an estimated remaining life of 40 years at time of purchase.

He has now received an offer of $40,000 for the property, net to him before income tax on the capital gain. If he refuses this offer, he estimates that he will keep the property for another 10 years. Annual rent receipts for this 10 years are estimated as $4,500, and annual disbursements for operation, maintenance, property taxes, and insurance are estimated as $1,800.

The investor's effective tax rate is 60% on ordinary income and will be 25% on any long-term capital gain. If he sells this property now, he will invest the net proceeds ($40,000 minus the income tax on the capital gain) in tax-exempt municipal bonds yielding 3.5% interest.

It is estimated that the property could be sold for $50,000 10 years hence. Compute an after-tax rate of return on continued ownership to compare with the return obtainable on the tax-exempt bonds. (*Ans.* = 5.2%.)

15–24. In Problem 15–23, what net price for the property (before capital gains tax) 10 years hence would break even after taxes with the 3.5% return obtainable from tax-exempt bonds?

15–25. On page 323, it is stated that if Table 15–6 is modified to substitute the double-rate declining-balance method for the years-digits method, the prospective rate of return is 8.8%. Make the necessary calculations to check this figure.

15–26. A $39,000 investment in machinery is proposed. It is anticipated that this investment will cause a reduction in annual operating disbursements of $10,500 a year for 12 years. The investment will be depreciated for income tax purposes by the straight-line method assuming a 12-year life and zero salvage value. The forecast of zero salvage value is also to be used in the economy study. The effective income tax rate is 55%. What are the prospective rates of return before and after income taxes?

15–27. Compute the after-tax rate of return in Problem 15–26 assuming years-digits depreciation for tax purposes.

15–28. Compute the after-tax rate of return in Problem 15–26 assuming that the investment is to be written off for tax purposes at $7,800 a year during the first 5 years.

15–29. Compute the after-tax rate of return in Problem 15–26 assuming that the investment must be written off for tax purposes by the straight-line method assuming a 25-year life and zero salvage value, even though the expected operating saving will occur only during the first 12 years of life.

15-30. Change the conditions of Problem 15-29 to assume that the machine will be retired at zero salvage value at the end of 12 years and that the $20,280 "loss on disposal" will be fully deductible from taxable income for the 12th year.

15-31. If the $39,000 disbursement at zero date in Problem 15-26 could be treated as a current expense for tax purposes, and if the tax consequence of this treatment should take place at zero date on our time scale (just as was assumed in Example 15-4), what is the after-tax rate of return?

15-32. If the $39,000 disbursement at zero date in Problem 15-26 could be treated as a current expense for tax purposes but the tax consequence of this treatment should take place at date 1 on our time scale, what is the after-tax rate of return?

15-33. A utility company is considering the following two plans to provide a certain service required by present demand and the prospective growth of demand for the coming 18 years:

Plan R requires an immediate investment of $500,000 in property that has an estimated life of 18 years with 20% terminal salvage value. Annual disbursements for operation and maintenance will be $50,000. Annual property taxes will be 2% of first cost.

Plan S requires an immediate investment of $300,000 in property that has an estimated life of 18 years with 20% terminal salvage value. Annual disbursements for its operation and maintenance during the first 6 years will be $40,000. After 6 years, an additional investment of $400,000 will be required in property having an estimated life of 12 years with 40% terminal salvage value. After this additional property is installed, annual disbursements (for years 7 to 18) for operation and maintenance of the combined properties will be $60,000. Annual property taxes will be 2% of the first cost of property in service at any time.

Make your recommendation for a choice between the two plans on the basis of minimum equivalent annual revenue requirements for the coming 18 years. The regulatory commission is allowing a 7% "fair return" on depreciated book value to cover the cost of money to the utility. Assume that this rate of return will continue throughout the 18 years. The utility company's effective income tax rate is 52%. Straight-line depreciation is to be used for both rate regulation and income tax purposes. Half of the utility's financing is by debt with interest at 3½%.

15-34. Two proposals for additional machinery for a certain manufacturing operation are under consideration. The continuation of the present method is designated as Plan A; the two alternate plans for change are designated as Plans B and C. Estimates are as follows:

	Plan A	Plan B	Plan C
First cost	none	$20,000	$60,000
Life		10 years	20 years
Annual disbursements for labor and labor extras	$40,000	$33,000	$25,000
Annual disbursements for property taxes, insurance, and maintenance	$ 4,000	$ 6,000	$10,000

Which plan should be selected if the minimum attractive rate of return is 8% after income taxes? Assume an income tax rate of 45% throughout the entire study period. Assume straight-line depreciation for tax purposes with zero salvage values and with the foregoing estimated lives. Assume that at the end of 10 years, Plan B will be replaced with machinery having the same first cost, life, salvage value, and annual disbursements.

15–35. Make an after-tax comparison of the equivalent annual costs of the new and secondhand centerless grinders in Problem 6–12 (page 94). Use an effective tax rate of 50% and a 6% minimum attractive rate of return after taxes. Assume straight-line depreciation for tax purposes for the secondhand machine and years-digits depreciation for the new machine. For both machines assume that the lives and salvage values used in the economy study will also be used in computing depreciation for tax purposes.

15–36. For the data of Problem 6–17 (page 95), tabulate the year-by-year differences between Machines J and K in cash flow after income taxes. Assume an effective tax rate of 50%. Assume straight-line depreciation for tax purposes for both machines, with the same estimated lives and salvage values used in the economy study. Assume that the $10,000 overhaul cost for Machine J can be treated for tax purposes as a current expense of the 6th year. Compute the after-tax rate of return on the extra investment in Machine J.

15–37. Compute the after-tax rates of return in Problem 8–5 (page 133). Assume straight-line depreciation and an effective tax rate of 50% throughout the 20-year period.

15–38. Compute the after-tax rate of return in Problem 8–12 (page 133). Assume years-digits depreciation and effective tax rate of 30% throughout the 15-year period.

15–39. Compute the after-tax rate of return in Problem 8–13 (page 133). Assume straight-line depreciation for tax purposes based on $30,000 valuation of land, a $60,000 valuation of the building, and an estimated remaining life of 30 years for the building. Assume an effective tax rate of 50% on ordinary income and 25% on long-term capital gains.

15–40. Compute the after-tax rate of return in Problem 8–15 (page 134). Assume a tax rate of 40% on ordinary income and 20% on long-term capital gains.

15–41. Make an after-tax solution of Problem 8–24 (page 135). Assume straight-line depreciation, a 50% effective tax rate, and a 5% minimum attractive rate of return after taxes.

15–42. Compute the after-tax rate of return in Problem 8–33 (page 136). Assume straight-line depreciation of $2,000 a year and an effective tax rate of 30%. Assume that the $2,000 overhaul cost can be treated for tax purposes as a current expense of the 5th year.

15–43. Make an after-tax solution of Problem 9–4 (page 158). Assume an effective tax rate of 50%. Where it is necessary to compute depreciation for tax purposes, use the straight-line method and assume the same lives and salvage values for tax purposes that are used in the economy study.

15–44. On pages 175 to 180 of Chapter 10, two competing investment proposals for an oil company were discussed. Before-tax rates of return were computed as about 19% for a vacuum still and about 12% for a product terminal. Compute the after-tax rates of return for these two proposed investments assuming years-digits depreciation and a 50% effective tax rate.

15–45. Four years ago Green, who is unmarried and has no dependents, purchased the patents on a specialty item for $5,000. He subsequently licensed Corporation X to manufacture the item under an agreement specifying royalties at 10% of gross sales. The patents and license agreement expire 6 years hence. Green is now interested in selling his patents for cash. Calculate the minimum price that he can afford to take for these patents and the maximum price that Corporation X can afford to pay for them. Assume that 1958 U. S. income tax rates will apply throughout the next 6 years. Neglect state income taxes and neglect federal individual income taxes on the incomes of the stockholders in Corporation X. Green has written off straight-line depreciation on the patents based on their 10-year remaining life at the time he purchased them. If sold for a price above their depreciated book value, the profit on the sale of the patents will be treated for tax purposes as if it were a capital gain. Make the following assumptions:

Average annual gross sales of the item by Corporation X will be $18,000 for the next 6 years.

	Green	Corporation X
Net taxable income from other sources each year..........	$27,000	$100,000
Expected annual disbursements connected with patent ownership	$ 100	none
Required rate of return on investment after taxes........	3%	6%

15–46. An unmarried individual without dependents anticipates an adjusted gross income of $48,000 in a given year. His nonbusiness deductions are expected to be $2,400. Answer the following questions assuming 1958 U. S. federal income tax rates to be applicable:

(a) What will be his federal income tax?

(b) He is considering an additional activity expected to increase his adjusted gross income. If this increase should be $6,000 and there should be no change in nonbusiness deductions or exemptions, what will be his federal income tax?

(c) How much of his extra $6,000 of income in (b) will remain after he has paid the additional federal income tax for which it is responsible?

15–47. Answer the questions in Problem 15–46 assuming that the individual is married and has 2 dependent children. Assume the stated income to include the wife's income as well as the husband's.

15–48. In 1958, as an aid to small business, the U. S. Congress passed a law allowing "additional first year depreciation" on certain assets for income tax purposes. This law permitted the deduction of 20% of the cost of qualifying property (determined without regard to salvage value) in addition to regular depreciation. The cost of property on which the additional allowance could be taken was limited to $10,000 on a separate return and $20,000 on a joint return. The allowance was applicable to equipment purchased secondhand as well as to new equipment.

Consider a sole proprietor in the construction industry, married, and submitting a joint return. In his depreciation accounting he used an averaging convention under which assets acquired during the first half of the year had a full year's depreciation in the year of acquisition. His fiscal year was the calendar year.

At the start of January, 1959, he had a chance to purchase a used power shovel for $20,000. The estimated remaining useful life of this shovel was 10 years, with a $2,000 terminal salvage value. If he bought this shovel, he could charge $5,400 of depreciation on it in his tax return for 1959. This $5,400 was a combination of $4,000 of "additional" depreciation (20% of the $20,000 first cost) and $1,400 of regular depreciation. This $1,400 was 1/10 of $14,000 (the first cost of $20,000 diminished by the $4,000 additional depreciation and the $2,000 salvage value). The total write-off during the 10-year life would, of course, be $18,000, the difference between first cost and salvage value, just as in any other method.

In the past this contractor had rented a power shovel whenever one was needed for a job. He estimated that owning this shovel would reduce his equipment rental disbursements by $7,000 a year for the next 10 years. This saving would be partially offset by extra disbursements of $2,200 a year for maintenance, storage, property taxes, and insurance.

His taxable income had fluctuated a bit from year to year. However, his highest tax bracket generally fell between 30% and 50%. For purposes of the following questions, assume an effective tax rate of 40% each year for the 10 years starting with 1959.

(a) Compute the prospective rate of return on the proposed investment before income taxes.

(b) Compute the prospective rate of return after income taxes assuming that his right to use 20% additional first-year depreciation would be applied to this power shovel.

(c) Compute the prospective rate of return after income taxes assuming that ordinary straight-line depreciation based on a 10-year life and 10% salvage would be applied to the shovel.

(d) Assuming that money was worth 8% to him after income taxes, what was the present worth (on January 1, 1959) of this right to use additional first-year depreciation rather than ordinary straight-line depreciation throughout the 10 years?

15–49. Consider that two $20,000 assets have been purchased, one with a 10-year estimated life and the other with a 20-year estimated life, both with zero salvage values. Would it be advantageous for a taxpayer to select the shorter-lived or the longer-lived asset for the additional first-year depreciation described in Problem 15–48, or would the length of life be a matter of indifference? Show calculations to support your answer, assuming a tax rate of 40%.

15–50. Consider that two $20,000 used assets have been purchased, both with 10-year estimated lives, one with an estimated zero salvage value and the other with an estimated 30% salvage value. Which would it be advantageous for a taxpayer to select for the additional first-year depreciation described in Problem 15–48, or would the salvage value be a matter of indifference? Show calculations to support your answer, assuming a tax rate of 40%. (Assume that the straight-line method will be used for regular depreciation charges on both assets, because the years-digits and double-rate declining-balance methods are not applicable to used assets.)

15–51. Consider two $20,000 assets, one used and one new, both with 15-year estimated lives and with 10% estimated salvage values. Assume that regular depreciation for the new asset will be by the years-digits method and that regular depreciation for the used asset will be by the straight-line method. Which would it be advantageous for a taxpayer to select for the additional first-year depreciation described in Problem 15–48, or would it be a matter of indifference whether the asset was purchased new or secondhand? Show calculations to support your answer, assuming a tax rate of 40%.

15–52. It is proposed to invest $75,000 in certain materials handling machinery that has an estimated life of 10 years and an estimated terminal salvage value of $20,000. It is believed that the machinery will cause a net reduction in disbursements for other than income taxes of $15,000 a year for the 10-year period. The machine will be depreciated for tax purposes by the years-digits method. An effective tax rate of 52% throughout the 10-year period is to be assumed. What is the prospective rate of return after income taxes?

15–53. An investment of $150,000 in a certain income property is under consideration. For accounting and income tax purposes, this investment is divided into $90,000 for land (not subject to a depreciation charge) and $60,000 for a building that has an estimated remaining life of 15 years. It is estimated that annual receipts from the rental of the land and building will be $20,000. Annual disbursements for other than income taxes will be $6,000. Although the building will be valueless at the end of 15 years, it is estimated that the land can be sold for $170,000.

Compute the prospective rate of return after income taxes. Assume that the building will be depreciated for tax purposes by the straight-line method, assuming a 15-year life and zero salvage value. Assume a 50% effective tax rate on ordinary income throughout the entire period. Assume that when the land is sold at a profit after 15 years, the gain realized from the increase in land value will be taxable at a capital gains rate of 25%.

16

Economy Studies for Retirement
and Replacement

Chapter 10 listed various types of causes of property retirement, namely: (1) improved alternatives, (2) changes in service requirements, (3) changes in the old assets themselves, (4) changes in public requirements, and (5) casualties. It was pointed out that these causes are not mutually exclusive; for instance, an asset may be retired partly because of obsolescence (cause 1), partly because of inadequacy (an example of cause 2), and partly because of increasing annual disbursements for repairs and maintenance (an example of cause 3).

In modern industry the usual experience is that assets are retired when they are still physically capable of continuing to render service. Someone must make a *decision* to make such retirements. Generally speaking, such decisions should be made on grounds of economy. This chapter discusses the kinds of analysis needed to guide such economic decisions.

Distinction Between Retirement and Replacement. The disposal of an asset by its owner is referred to as a retirement. Not all retirements involve the actual scrapping of the asset retired; many assets, retired by their present owners, may be used by one or more other owners before reaching the scrap heap.

If an asset (or group of assets) is retired, and another asset (or group of assets) is acquired to perform the same service, this is a replacement.

It frequently happens that new assets are acquired to perform the services of existing assets, with the existing assets not retired but merely transferred to some other use—frequently an "inferior use" (such as stand-by service). In such cases, the acquisition of the new assets sometimes is also described as a replacement.

Two Words That Are Useful in Discussing Replacement Economy. In his book, *Dynamic Equipment Policy*,[1] George Terborgh coined two terms that simplify explanations of the principles governing replacement decisions. An existing old asset, considered as a possible candidate for replacement, is called the *defender*. The proposed new replacement asset is called the *challenger*. These useful terms are employed throughout the present chapter.

Some Characteristics of Economy Studies for Retirements and Replacements. This chapter concentrates attention on certain special aspects of studies for retirement and replacement, as follows:

1. Capital recovery costs for extending the services of assets already owned (e.g., defenders in replacement economy studies) are computed differently from capital recovery costs for assets yet to be acquired (e.g., all proposed assets in economy studies discussed in previous chapters, and challengers in replacement economy studies). The reasons for this difference were explained in Chapter 14. Various aspects of this topic are illustrated in all of the examples in the present chapter.
2. There are special difficulties in estimating the effect of a decision regarding retirement or replacement on cash flow for income taxes. Some aspects of this topic are illustrated in Examples 16–1 to 16–3.
3. In many replacement studies the appropriate assumption regarding the defender is that, if retained in service at all, it will be kept for a relatively short time, often only one year. In contrast, the appropriate assumption regarding the challenger may be that, if acquired, it will be kept for its full economic life. Although we have already given some consideration (particularly in Chapters 6, 7, and 13) to the interpretation of economy studies in which the alternatives have different service lives, there are special aspects to this problem in replacement economy. Some of these aspects are discussed in connection with Examples 16–4 to 16–6; others are discussed in Appendix D.

In order to start our discussion by concentrating attention solely on points (1) and (2), Examples 16–1 to 16–3 deal with cases where the expected remaining service life of the defender is the same as the expected full service life of the challenger.

Each of these examples will first be analyzed by an annual cost comparison before income taxes. The effect on prospective disbursements for income taxes of the decision on retirement or replacement will then be computed and an annual cost comparison

[1] George Terborgh, *Dynamic Equipment Policy* (New York: McGraw-Hill Book Co., Inc., 1949).

will then be made after income taxes. Finally, prospective rates of
return before and after income taxes will be calculated.

EXAMPLE 16–1. ANALYSIS OF A PROPOSED RETIREMENT

Facts of the Case. A manufacturing company owns a warehouse in a city
some distance from its main plant. The warehouse is used by the branch sales
office in the area to make deliveries of certain products from stock. An equal
amount of storage space is available in a new commercial warehouse. As a favorable offer for the old warehouse has been received, consideration is given to its
sale and the rental of the needed space.

The property was purchased 10 years ago for $50,000. For accounting and
tax purposes, this was divided into $40,000 for the warehouse building and $10,000
for land. Straight-line item depreciation on the building has been used for accounting and tax purposes, assuming a 40-year life and zero salvage value. The
warehouse can be sold now for a net $60,000 after payment of selling expenses.

In recent years annual warehouse expenses have averaged $3,220 for opera-
tion and maintenance, $1,120 for property taxes on the land and building, $210
for fire insurance on the building, and $700 for fire insurance on the stock. It is
believed that costs will continue at approximately these figures if the warehouse
is not sold.

A 10-year contract can be secured for equal space in the commercial warehouse
at $9,300 a year. Estimated additional annual disbursements for operation and
upkeep of this space are $1,200. Fire insurance on the stock will be reduced to
$450 a year.

If the decision is made to keep the old warehouse, it is believed it will be kept
for another 10 years. The estimated net selling price of the property 10 years
hence is $45,000.

In before-tax studies in this company, a minimum attractive rate of return of
12% is used; in after-tax studies, 6%. An effective tax rate of 50% on ordinary
income is assumed in all economy studies. Long-term capital gains and gains on
sale of real estate and depreciable assets used in the trade or business will be
taxed at 25%.

Before-Tax Comparison of Annual Costs. Using the stipulated 12% minimum attractive rate of return before taxes, the comparative annual costs for a
10-year study period are as follows:

Comparative Annual Cost—Continued Ownership of Warehouse

CR = ($60,000 − $45,000)(crf–12%–10) + $45,000(0.12)	$ 8,055
Operation and maintenance...	3,220
Property taxes..	1,120
Fire insurance on building and stock...................................	910
Total	$13,305

Comparative Annual Cost—Rental of Equal Space

Rent	$ 9,300
Operation and upkeep...	1,200
Fire insurance on stock...	450
Total	$10,950

The foregoing comparison favors disposal of the warehouse and rental of
equal space.

After-Tax Comparison of Annual Costs. The decision to sell the warehouse at once will cause an immediate disbursement for the tax on the gain on disposal. As the property has been depreciated for tax purposes at $1,000 a year for the past 10 years, its present book value is $40,000, the difference between the $50,000 original cost and the $10,000 of depreciation charged against the warehouse up to date. There will be a taxable gain of $20,000, the difference between the $60,000 net selling price and the $40,000 book value.

Because this gain will be taxed at 25%, the tax will be $5,000. The effect of this tax will be to reduce the net amount received from the sale from $60,000 to $55,000. In effect, $55,000 is the net realizable salvage value after taxes.

A similar analysis will show that if the warehouse is sold for $45,000 in 10 years, the gain will be $15,000, the tax will be $3,750, and the net amount realized after taxes will be $41,250.

Annual taxes on ordinary income will also be influenced by the decision on retirement. If the warehouse is continued in service, annual deductions from taxable income will be the $1,000 annual depreciation plus current disbursements of $3,220, $1,120, and $910, a total of $6,250. If space is rented, annual deductions from taxable income will be $10,950. With continued ownership, annual taxable income will therefore be $4,700 (i.e., $10,950 − $6,250) higher than with rental. Using the effective tax rate of 50%, annual disbursements for income taxes will be $2,350 more with ownership than with rental.

Using the stipulated 6% minimum attractive rate of return after taxes, an after-tax comparison of equivalent annual costs is as follows:

Comparative Annual Cost—Continued Ownership of Warehouse

CR = ($55,000 − $41,250)(crf-6%-10) + $41,250(0.06)	$ 4,343
Operation and maintenance..	3,220
Property taxes..	1,120
Fire insurance on building and stock..................................	910
Additional income taxes above those under rental......................	2,350
Total	$11,943

Comparative Annual Cost—Rental of Equal Space

Rent	$ 9,300
Operation and upkeep...	1,200
Fire insurance on stock...	450
Total	$10,950

The margin favoring rental is considerably less in the after-tax analysis than in the before-tax analysis.

Calculation of Rates of Return. The prospective difference between cash flow under rental and under continued ownership may be tabulated as follows:

Year	Difference Before Taxes	Difference in Income Taxes	Difference After Taxes
0	+$60,000	−$ 5,000	+$55,000
1 to 10	−5,700 per year	+2,350 per year	−3,350 per year
10	−45,000	+3,750	−41,250
Totals	−$42,000	+$22,250	−$19,750

Trial-and-error calculations of the type that have been illustrated many times in the preceding chapters give the conclusion that the present worth of the before-tax series is zero with an interest rate of 7.8%, and the present worth of the after-tax series is zero with an interest rate of 4.0%.

Interpretation of Analysis in Example 16-1. Most of the economy studies discussed in previous chapters have dealt with proposals to make investments in fixed assets—to convert money into capital goods. In contrast, Example 16-1 might be described as a proposal for a disinvestment; the question at issue is whether it is desirable to convert capital goods into money.

The description of the facts of the example did not tell what would be done with the $55,000 (after taxes) realizable from the sale of the warehouse. However, the statement that the after-tax minimum attractive rate of return was 6% implied that this money could be invested in the business in a way that would provide an after-tax yield of at least 6%. Our analysis indicated that a decision to keep the warehouse would be—in effect—a decision to invest $55,000 at a yield of 4% after taxes. As 4% is less than the 6% or more obtainable from some unspecified investment elsewhere in the business, the analysis favors the sale of the warehouse.

Just as in our previous analyses by comparative annual costs and by rate of return, the two methods of comparison lead to the same decision between the alternatives as long as the minimum attractive rate of return is used as the interest rate in compound interest conversions in the annual cost method.

Comment on Economy Studies Where Retirements Involve Prospective Purchase of Product or Service of Asset Retired. The general type of situation illustrated in Example 16-1 is a common one. It often is necessary to consider the question "Can we buy this product or this service at a lower figure than our cost of continuing to produce it?" Many such economy studies require determination of increment costs and recognition of sunk costs. The book figure for present costs of production may contain certain allocated costs that would not be eliminated if production were stopped. And the depreciation charges in the books are, of course, based on the original cost, a figure that is irrelevant for purposes of the retirement economy study except for its influence on future income taxes.

The higher the present realizable value of the assets that are being considered for retirement, the more attractive is the proposal to dispose of the assets and purchase the goods or services that they have been producing. This point is generally recognized. If the warehouse in Example 16-1 had only a small resale price, the economy study would favor continued ownership.

Another important element in such comparisons, perhaps not so generally recognized as significant, is the estimated prospective future realizable value. The greater the future resale price, the more attractive is continued ownership, and vice versa. This may be illustrated in Example 16–1 by changing the $45,000 estimate of future net resale price before taxes to a substantially higher and to a substantially lower figure. Of course, the nearer the date of prospective future disposal, the greater the importance of the future resale price.

In many economy studies of this type a third alternative may be to purchase the goods or services in question from the outside source, but to keep the old assets for stand-by and emergency purposes. Conditions favorable to this third alternative are as follows: (1) a low present net realizable value; (2) relatively low annual disbursements required for continuing the ownership of the assets; and (3) the likelihood that continued ownership with its threat of resumption of production will strengthen bargaining power in the establishment of the price for the purchased goods or services.

EXAMPLE 16–2. REVIEWING AN ERROR IN JUDGMENT IN EQUIPMENT SELECTION

Facts of the Case. A year ago, an irrigator purchased a pump and motor which cost him $1,925 installed. He knew nothing of pump selection, and— making his choice on the recommendation of a clerk in a hardware store—selected a pump that was unsuited to the requirements of head and discharge under which it was to operate. As a result, his year's power bill for its operation was $900; this was much higher than if he had purchased a suitable pump.

Just at the start of the current irrigation season, a pump salesman offers him another pump and motor, suited to his requirements. This will cost $1,650 installed and is guaranteed to reduce power requirements to a point where the electric energy for pumping the same amount of water as before will cost only $500. He can sell the original pump and motor to a neighbor for $375.

For purposes of this economy study, we shall assume a 10-year study period with estimated zero salvage value for both pumps at the end of this period. It will be assumed that other expenditures (such as property taxes, insurance, and upkeep) will not be affected by the type of pump being used for this service. The irrigator's effective tax rate on ordinary income is 40%. A minimum attractive rate of return of 10% is to be used in the before-tax analysis and a rate of 6% is to be used in the after-tax analysis.

The irrigator has used years-digits item depreciation for tax purposes on the present pump, assuming a 10-year life and zero salvage value. If the new pump is substituted, the same depreciation method, life, and salvage value will be used.

Before-Tax Comparison of Annual Costs. Using the stipulated 10% minimum attractive rate of return before taxes, the comparative annual costs for a 10-year study period are as follows:

Comparative Annual Cost—Present Pump

CR = $375(crf–10%–10)	$ 61
Electric energy for pumping..	900
Total	$961

Comparative Annual Cost—Proposed New Pump

CR = $1,650(crf–10%–10) $269
Electric energy for pumping... 500

Total $769

The foregoing comparison favors the replacement.

After-Tax Comparison of Annual Costs. Under the years-digits method the past year's depreciation charge on the defender was 10/55 of $1,925 = $350. The defender's present book value is therefore $1,925 − $350 = $1,575. If the defender is sold for $375, the books will show a $1,200 "loss" on this sale.

On the assumption that this transaction occurs in the United States (and subject to certain limitations discussed later in this chapter), this $1,200 is viewed for tax purposes as a loss on disposal of depreciable property used in the trade or business. As such, the sale will reduce current taxable income by $1,200; with a 40% tax rate, it will reduce current taxes by $480. Considering the retirement separately from the acquisition of the replacement asset, a consequence of the retirement will be an immediate positive cash flow of $855, the sum of the $375 receipt from the buyer and the $480 reduction in disbursements to the tax collector. The after-tax net realizable salvage value of the defender is therefore $855.

If the defender is kept in service, the next-year deductions from taxable income that are relevant in our economy study will be the depreciation charge of $315 (9/55 of $1,925) and the $900 outlay for electric energy, a total of $1,215. Because years-digits depreciation is being used, this total will decrease by $35 a year to $900 in the 10th year. (For simplicity in this example, we are assuming that the defender can be kept in service for 10 years more, even though the depreciation charge on it will continue for only 9 years more.)

If the challenger is acquired, its relevant next-year tax deductions will be $300 depreciation (10/55 of $1,650) and $500 for electric energy, a total of $800. This total will decrease by $30 a year to $530 in the 10th year.

The next-year difference in taxable income between challenger and defender will therefore be $415 (i.e., $1,215 − $800). This difference will decrease by $5 a year to $370 in the 10th year.

With a tax rate of 40%, the next-year difference in disbursements for income taxes will be $166 (i.e., 40% of $415). This difference will decrease by $2 a year to $148 in the 10th year.

Using the stipulated 6% minimum attractive rate of return after taxes, an after-tax comparison of equivalent annual costs is as follows:

Comparative Annual Cost—Present Pump

CR = $855(crf–6%–10) .... $ 116
Electric energy for pumping... 900

Total $1,016

Comparative Annual Cost—Proposed New Pump

CR = $1,650(crf–6%–10) .... $ 224
Electric energy for pumping... 500
Extra income tax = $166 − $2(gf–6%–10)... 158

Total .... $ 882

This after-tax comparison also favors replacement.

Calculation of Rates of Return. The prospective differences in cash flow between defender and challenger may be tabulated as follows:

Year	Difference Before Taxes	Difference in Income Taxes	Difference After Taxes
0	−$1,275	+$ 480	−$ 795
1	+400	−166	+234
2	+400	−164	+236
3	+400	−162	+238
4	+400	−160	+240
5	+400	−158	+242
6	+400	−156	+244
7	+400	−154	+246
8	+400	−152	+248
9	+400	−150	+250
10	+400	−148	+252
Totals	+$2,725	−$1,090	+$1,635

Trial-and-error calculations indicate that the present worth of the before-tax series is zero with an interest rate of about 29% and the present worth of the after-tax series is zero with an interest rate of a little less than 28%.

The Relationship Between the Past Investment in a Defender and Decision Making About Its Proposed Retirement.

Examples 16–1 and 16–2 provide numerical illustrations of a point that was discussed in Chapters 2, 11, and 14. This point is that in choosing between alternatives, only the differences between the alternatives are relevant. No past occurrences can be changed by a decision between alternatives for the future. Nevertheless, past events may influence the future in different ways, depending on decisions that are made for the future.

In Example 16–1, the prospective difference in cash flow before income taxes between disposal and continued ownership was unaffected by the past investment in the warehouse. And in Example 16–2, the prospective difference in cash flow before income taxes between the defending pump and its challenger was unaffected by the past investment in the defender. In general, in economy studies for retirements and replacements, differences in cash flow *before* taxes will not be influenced by past investments in assets considered as candidates for retirement. Past investments should normally be viewed as irrelevant in before-tax studies.

(As explained in Chapter 14, there may be mental blocks to applying the foregoing rule in particular cases. Thus our irrigator in Example 16–2 might be reluctant to admit to himself his past mistake in judgment in equipment selection; he might reason that he "could not afford" to replace his present pump until he had "got his money out of it.")

In contrast, in economy studies involving proposed retirements, differences in cash flow for income taxes usually will be influenced by past investments. Example 16–1 illustrated prospective taxes on a gain on disposal of an asset. Example 16–2 illustrated how a disposal at less than book value could reduce immediate income taxes. Both the gain and the loss on disposal were influenced by the past investments and by the past method of making depreciation charges for tax purposes. In both examples, the depreciation deductions from taxable income if the existing asset were continued in service depended on the past investment in the asset. Generally speaking, past investments in defenders need to be considered in after-tax studies for retirements and replacements.

In fact, the rational consideration of the income tax aspects of retirements may lead to conclusions exactly opposite from the ones that many people would reach by intuition. Although intuition often favors disposal at an apparent profit, a taxable gain reduces the net cash realized from such a disposal. Although intuition often is opposed to disposal at an apparent loss, a loss deductible from taxable income increases the net cash realized from such a disposal.

Example 16–2 illustrated the tax advantage of such a deductible loss. The prospective rate of return before income taxes on the purchase of the challenger was 29%. Ordinarily, one would expect a 40% tax rate to make a nearly proportionate reduction in the rate of return. However, the after-tax rate of return was nearly 28%, a negligible reduction.

It should be noted that in Example 16–2, the entire $1,925 investment in the defender, less salvage value, was scheduled to be deducted from taxable income at some time regardless of whether the decision favored the challenger or the defender. The selection of the challenger merely changed the *timing* of the deduction in a way that favored the challenger.

Some Comments on Income Tax Aspects of Disposal of Fixed Assets in the United States. The tax aspects of proposed retirements often are more complex than the reader might assume from studying Examples 16–1 and 16–2. As related to retirements in the United States, an adequate discussion of this topic would not be possible without a fairly detailed consideration of various types of multiple-asset depreciation accounting and of income tax regulations. Such a discussion would require more space than would be appropriate in this book.[2]

---

[2] For a statement of the regulations themselves, see *Internal Revenue Service Publication 311—Regulations Relating to Depreciation—Treasury Decision 6182* (Washington, D.C.: Government Printing Office, 1956). For background reading to assist in understanding these regulations, see E. L. Grant and P. T. Norton, Jr., *Depreciation* (New York: The Ronald Press Co., 1955), particularly chaps. iv to viii, x, xi, and xix.

One question arising in an after-tax analysis of proposed retirements is the possible offsetting of capital gains and losses and gains and losses on disposal of real estate or depreciable assets used in the trade or business. This question bears on the appropriate tax rate applicable to a proposed gain or loss. Such offsetting may, in effect, increase the tax rate applicable to a proposed gain or decrease the tax rate applicable to a proposed loss.[3]

For instance, assume that the manufacturing company in Example 16–1 already had, during the current year, a loss of more than $20,000 on the disposal of some other real estate or depreciable asset used in the trade or business. If no offsetting gains should occur during the year, this previous loss would be fully deductible from ordinary income; in effect, it would reduce taxes by 50% of the loss. Under these circumstances, the $20,000 prospective gain on disposal in Example 16–1 would have to be offset against this loss; in effect, the gain would increase the current year's taxes by $10,000 rather than by the $5,000 that we assumed in our solution of Example 16–1.

Or assume that the irrigator in Example 16–2 already had a $1,200 long-term capital gain for the current year on the sale of certain stock, and that this gain would be taxable at 20%. If he disposes of his pump, his $1,200 loss must be offset against this previous gain; in effect, the disposal will reduce his taxes by $240 rather than by the $480 that we assumed in our solution of Example 16–2.

Another question arising in some after-tax analyses is whether certain retirements will cause a deductible "loss" at all. The reader will recall that the topic of mortality dispersion of physical property was introduced in Chapter 10. Figure 10–1 showed a representative survivor curve for a group of assets having an average service life of 20 years; this average resulted from retirements that occurred all the way from age 1 to age 45. In the usual case where it is reasonable to expect mortality dispersion, retirements short of the estimated average life are not "premature" in the sense that they are inconsistent with the estimated average; it is to be expected that there will also be assets that survive considerably longer than the estimated average life. The foregoing viewpoint is recognized in multiple-asset depreciation accounting by the continuation of depreciation charges after the expiration of the estimated average life and by the prohibition, under ordinary circumstances, of entries for loss on disposal when assets are retired before they have reached the

[3] This question is important because, as explained in Chapter 15, gains on disposal of real estate and depreciable assets used in the trade or business receive "capital gains" treatment—in effect, lower tax rates than ordinary income—whereas losses on disposal of such assets are deductible from ordinary income to the extent that there are no offsetting gains.

estimated average life. The policy of the U. S. Treasury Department has been, in effect, to apply the rules of multiple-asset accounting even when item accounting is used, wherever there are a number of assets of a similar type and it is reasonable to believe that the life estimate applies to the *average* life of the assets.[4] For this reason, a retirement at low salvage value short of the estimated life will not necessarily lead to a tax-deductible loss in the United States even when item accounting is used.

The $1,200 prospective loss on disposal of the defender in Example 16–2 illustrates the conventional treatment in item accounting. Where the taxpayer has only one asset of the type being retired, there is no question of the appropriateness of item accounting for tax purposes.

Still another question arising in an after-tax analysis of a proposed retirement is the effect of the retirement on future depreciation deductions from taxable income. This matter is closely related to the topic of entries for gain or loss on disposal. Examples 16–1 and 16–2 illustrated the required calculations under item accounting. In both examples, there were year-by-year depreciation deductions that would occur if the defender remained in service and would be eliminated by its retirement.

In multiple-asset accounting, the rules on this matter differ from those illustrated for item accounting. For example, in declining-balance group accounting using a so-called open end account, a retirement at zero salvage value will have no influence on future depreciation charges. Moreover, different types of multiple-asset accounting have different rules.

The examples in this book that deal with economy studies for retirements and replacements are based on the assumption of item accounting. The chief purpose in using this assumption is to avoid the necessity of devoting considerable space to an explanation of the technical aspects of a number of different types of multiple-asset depreciation accounting. Incidentally, the assumption provides uniformity in the examples and problems. It should go without saying that after-tax studies in industry should be based on the particular type of depreciation accounting that is being used for the assets that are candidates for retirement.

As pointed out in Chapter 15, the trade-in of certain assets on new ones leads to "nontaxable exchanges" that, in effect, transfer

---

[4] This general policy limiting the deductibility of so-called losses on disposal was adopted by the U. S. Treasury Department in 1934. See Grant and Norton, *Depreciation, op. cit.*, pp. 441–43, for an early statement of this policy in an official statement referred to as Mimeograph 4170. The policy was reaffirmed, with minor changes, in 1956 in Treasury Decision 6182, *op. cit.*

the remaining tax base of the old asset to the new one. Our examples in this book do not illustrate the tax effects of such exchanges.

EXAMPLE 16–3. PROPOSED REPLACEMENT DUE TO CHANGE IN SERVICE REQUIREMENTS

Facts of the Case. Ten years ago an industrial plant installed a process requiring the continuous use of 12 million gallons per day of water. A 30-in. diameter steel pipe line was put in to convey the water from the nearby river to the plant; its first cost was $12,000. Pumping costs to overcome the friction in the line have been $690 a year. Straight-line depreciation has been used for accounting and tax purposes assuming a 20-year life and zero salvage value.

Now a change is to be made in the production methods that will require a doubled use of water. This will greatly increase the friction losses in the present pipe line and thus increase pumping costs out of all proportion to the increased water requirements. To determine whether or not any change in the pipe line should be made, the company's engineers have set up four plans for comparison:

Plan A. Pump the total amount of water through the present 30-in. line. The estimated annual pumping cost to overcome pipe friction is $5,010. No new investment will be required.

Plan B. Install an additional 30-in. pipe line at a cost of $15,000. Each line would then carry half of the total flow and have pumping costs to overcome friction of $690 a year.

Plan C. Remove the existing pipe line; its net realizable value is estimated as $4,000. Replace it with a 42-in. pipe, the first cost of which will be $24,000. The annual cost to overcome pipe friction for the entire flow is estimated as $970.

Plan D. Remove the existing pipe line, replacing it with a 48-in. pipe, the first cost of which will be $30,000. The annual cost to overcome pipe friction is estimated as $510.

Because it is expected that the plant may be relocated in 10 years or so, the assumed study period is 10 years. However, a 5% straight-line depreciation rate must be used for tax purposes for the proposed new pipes in Plans B, C, and D; this is the same rate that has been used with the existing pipe. For purposes of the economy study, the present pipe will be assumed to have a zero salvage value 10 years hence and the new pipes will be assumed to have $33\frac{1}{3}$% salvage values at that time.

It is estimated that annual property taxes on all pipe lines—old and new—will be 1% of their respective first costs. It is not expected that the four plans will differ in required maintenance costs.

In before-tax studies in this company, a minimum attractive rate of return of 12% is used; in after-tax studies, 6%. An effective tax rate of 50% on ordinary income is used in all economy studies.

Before-Tax Comparison of Annual Costs. Using the stipulated 12% minimum attractive rate of return before taxes, the comparative annual costs for a 10-year study period are as follows:

Comparative Annual Cost—Plan A

CR(existing 30-in. pipe) = $4,000(crf–12%–10)	$ 708
Property tax = $12,000(0.01)	120
Pumping costs to overcome pipe friction	5,010
Total	$5,838

Comparative Annual Cost—Plan B

CR(existing 30-in. pipe) = $4,000(crf–12%–10)......... .... $ 708
CR(new 30-in. pipe) = ($15,000 − $5,000)(crf–12%–10) + $5,000(0.12).......   2,370
Property tax = ($12,000 + $15,000)(0.01).................................   270
Pumping costs to overcome pipe friction.................................   1,380

Total $4,728

Comparative Annual Cost—Plan C

CR(new 42-in. pipe) = ($24,000 − $8,000)(crf–12%–10) + $8,000(0.12)....... $3,792
Property tax = $24,000(0.01)...   240
Pumping costs to overcome pipe friction.................................   970

Total $5,002

Comparative Annual Cost—Plan D

CR(new 48-in. pipe) = ($30,000 − $10,000)(crf–12%–10) + $10,000(0.12)..... $4,740
Property tax = $30,000(0.01)...   300
Pumping costs to overcome pipe friction.................................   510

Total $5,550

The foregoing comparison favors Plan B.

After-Tax Comparison of Annual Costs. The relevant deductible expenses for tax purposes are depreciation, property taxes, and pumping costs. These may be tabulated for the four plans and the differences in taxes calculated as follows:

	Plan A	Plan B	Plan C	Plan D
Depreciation	$ 600	$1,350	$1,200	$1,500
Property taxes	120	270	240	300
Pumping costs	5,010	1,380	970	510
Total	$5,710	$3,000	$2,410	$2,310
Extra taxable income above Plan A		$2,710	$3,300	$3,400
Extra income tax above Plan A		$1,355	$1,650	$1,700

The book value of the present pipe line is $6,000. (Its first cost was $12,000, and it has been depreciated at $600 a year for the past 10 years.) As its salvage value is only $4,000 and as we are assuming item accounting, its disposal will cause a deductible expense of $2,000 for tax purposes. With a 50% tax rate this deduction will reduce current taxes by $1,000. For the purpose of the after-tax economy study, the realizable value of the present defender is $5,000, the sum of the $4,000 realizable from its disposal and the $1,000 decrease in tax disbursements caused by its disposal. A similar analysis for the proposed new 30-in., 42-in., and 48-in. pipe lines in Plans B, C, and D leads to after-tax salvage values 10 years hence of $6,250, $10,000, and $12,500 respectively. If the existing pipe line is not retired until the end of the study period 10 years hence, its retirement will have no tax effect as both book value and salvage value will be zero.

Using the stipulated 6% minimum attractive rate of return after taxes, an after-tax comparison of equivalent annual costs is as follows:

Comparative Annual Cost—Plan A

CR(existing 30-in. pipe) = $5,000(crf–6%–10)............................. $ 679
Property tax...   120
Pumping cost...   5,010

Total $5,809

Comparative Annual Cost—Plan B

CR(existing 30-in. pipe) = $5,000(crf–6%–10)..............................	$ 679
CR(new 30-in. pipe) = ($15,000 − $6,250)(crf–6%–10) + $6,250(0.06).........	1,564
Property tax...	270
Pumping cost...	1,380
Extra income tax above Plan A..	1,355
Total	$5,248

Comparative Annual Cost—Plan C

CR(new 42-in. pipe) = ($24,000 − $10,000)(crf–6%–10) + $10,000(0.06).......	$2,502
Property tax...	240
Pumping cost	970
Extra income tax above Plan A..	1,650
Total	$5,362

Comparative Annual Cost—Plan D

CR(new 48-in. pipe) = ($30,000 − $12,500)(crf–6%–10) + $12,500(0.06).......	$3,128
Property tax...	300
Pumping cost...	510
Extra income tax above Plan A..	1,700
Total	$5,638

The after-tax comparison also favors Plan B.

Calculation of Rates of Return. Consider the differences in cash flow between Plans B and A.

Year	Difference Before Taxes	Difference in Income Taxes	Difference After Taxes
0	−$15,000	$ 0	−$15,000
1 to 10	+3,480 per year	−1,355 per year	+2,125 per year
10	+5,000	+1,250	+6,250

Trial-and-error calculations will show that the before-tax rate of return on the extra investment in Plan B is approximately 20.8% and the after-tax rate is approximately 10.0%. As the stipulated minimum attractive rates of return are 12% and 6% respectively, each rate exceeds its standard. Either a before-tax or an after-tax analysis indicates the superiority of Plan B.

Consider the differences in cash flow between Plans C and B.

Year	Difference Before Taxes	Difference in Income taxes	Difference After Taxes
0	−$5,000	+$1,000	−$4,000
1 to 10	+440 per year	−295 per year	+145 per year
10	+3,000	+750	+3,750

Trial-and-error calculations will show that the before-tax rate of return on the extra investment in Plan C over Plan B is approximately 5.8% and the after-tax rate is approximately 3.1%. Both analyses indicate that the extra investment in Plan C is not justified.

A similar analysis comparing Plans D and B yields a before-tax rate of return of approximately 2.9% and an after-tax rate of approximately 1.5%.

Annual Cost vs. Rate of Return as a Method of Analysis in Replacement Economy. In Examples 16–1, 16–2, and 16–3, the

stipulated minimum attractive rate of return was used as the interest rate in the annual cost comparisons. Where this is done, the alternative favored by an annual cost analysis will be the same as the one favored by an analysis based on rate of return. In this respect economy studies for retirements and replacements are no different from other economy studies. In all studies the chief advantage of the rate of return technique is the better opportunity it affords to array a number of diverse investment proposals in order of merit. Just as in the examples of economy studies in previous chapters, the annual cost technique tends to be simpler to apply because so many studies based on rate of return require solutions by trial and error.

In Examples 16–1, 16–2, and 16–3, the assumed remaining service lives were the same for all alternatives. In this characteristic these examples are not typical of the majority of replacement studies. As already pointed out, we have introduced the subject with examples of this type in order to concentrate attention on certain aspects of replacement economy while avoiding the special complications often introduced by the difference between a relatively short assumed remaining service life for the defender and a relatively long one for the challenger.

Where two alternatives have the same service life, as in Examples 16–1, 16–2, and 16–3, an unknown rate of return can be computed by finding the interest rate that makes the present worth of the difference in cash flow equal to zero. (This is the so-called discounted cash flow technique.) Where the lives are different, this method cannot be used without making specific assumptions about differences in cash flow after the expiration of the life of the shorter-lived alternative.

In Examples 16–4 to 16–6 the assumed remaining service life of the defender is considerably shorter than the assumed service life of the challenger. In these examples our presentation will be simplified by making our comparisons solely on the basis of annual costs. This method of comparison will avoid the need for formal assumptions about cash flow differences after the expiration of the remaining service life of the defender. The use of mathematical models based on such formal assumptions is discussed in Appendix D.

Where To Introduce Present Defender Net Salvage Value in Annual Cost Comparisons. Chapter 14 presented the concept that in making decisions on whether or not to continue to own an asset, the capital costs of extending its service should be based on its present net salvage value and on its prospective future net salvage value at the end of a study period. (See Example 14–6.) This concept was applied in computing capital recovery costs of existing assets in the annual cost comparisons of Examples 16–1, 16–2, and 16–3.

An alternate method sometimes advocated for replacement economy studies is to assume zero capital costs for the defender and to subtract the present net defender salvage value from the challenger's first cost before computing capital costs of the challenger. In this method the capital recovery costs of the challenger are based on the new money required rather than on the total investment.

In a certain limited group of cases this alternate method gives a difference in annual costs identical with the difference obtained by the method illustrated in Examples 16–1, 16–2, and 16–3. For instance, consider the use of this alternate method for the after-tax comparison of annual costs in Example 16–2, as follows:

Comparative Annual Cost—Present Pump

Electric energy for pumping.. $900

Comparative Annual Cost—Proposed New Pump

CR = ($1,650 − $855)(crf-6%-10) $108
Electric energy for pumping.. 500
Extra income tax... 158

Total $766

The difference in annual costs favors the challenger by $134, just as in our solution in Example 16–2.

Nevertheless, this alternate method has certain weaknesses that lead the authors to recommend against its use in annual cost comparisons. The method clearly is not applicable where the defender has an estimated future salvage value. It is troublesome to interpret in multiple-alternative studies such as Example 16–3. And it can lead to misleading conclusions in the common case where the remaining life assumed for the defender differs from the assumed service life of the challenger.

An error that sometimes occurs in replacement studies is to base capital costs of the defender on present net salvage value and *also* to subtract this salvage from challenger first cost before computing the capital costs of the challenger. It should be evident that this procedure counts defender salvage value twice—as a basis for a plus item in defender annual costs and as a basis for a minus item in challenger annual costs. Such double counting has the effect of biasing the analysis in favor of the challenger. For instance, if this double counting of defender salvage value had been used in Example 16–3, Plan C would have appeared superior to Plan B.

The Need To Find the Best Challenger. In Example 16–3, the best alternative was Plan B. This alternative called for keeping the defender in service and supplementing it with a new pipe that would carry half the flow.

However, if only Plans A, C, and D had been considered, Plan C would have been selected, and the existing pipe would have been retired in favor of a new 42-in. one. The after-tax return on Plan C as compared to Plan A, is approximately 8.8%, considerably better than the stipulated 6%. If only Plans A and D had been considered, Plan D would have been selected as yielding an after-tax return of nearly 7%.

In replacement studies, just as in all other economy studies, it is essential that all promising alternatives be considered if the most economical choice is to be made.

EXAMPLE 16–4. REINFORCEMENT VS. REPLACEMENT

Facts of the Case. An old highway bridge must either be strengthened or replaced. The estimated outlay to strengthen the bridge is $8,000; a new bridge will cost $46,000. The old bridge has a present estimated net salvage value of $12,000. It is estimated that the reinforcement will be sufficient for 5 years, after which time the question of reinforcement versus replacement would again need to be considered. The net salvage value of the reinforced bridge is estimated as $14,000 at the end of 5 years; the salvage value of the new bridge is estimated as $22,000 after 30 years. The additional annual cost of maintenance and inspection on the old structure is $200.

The minimum attractive rate of return is to be assumed as 5%. Because this is a government project, there will be no disbursements for taxes.

Comparison of Annual Costs. From the viewpoint of a replacement economy study, an immediate nonrecurrent outlay required to keep a defender in service is properly viewed as an investment. The $8,000 outlay for reinforcement is of this type. (The treatment as an investment for economy study purposes has no relation to the decision whether the outlay will be capitalized or expensed in the books of account.)

Thus the capital recovery costs of the defender in this example should be based on $20,000, the sum of the $12,000 net salvage value and the $8,000 outlay needed for reinforcement. Keeping the defender in service involves an immediate disbursement of $8,000 and the foregoing of an immediate receipt of $12,000. Annual costs may be compared as follows:

Comparative Annual Cost—Reinforced Bridge

CR = ($20,000 − $14,000)(crf–5%–5) + $14,000(0.05) $2,086
Extra cost of maintenance and inspection........... 200

Total $2,286

Comparative Annual Cost—New Bridge

CR = ($46,000 − $22,000)(crf–5%–30) + $22,000(0.05) $2,661

It appears to be more economical to reinforce the old bridge.

EXAMPLE 16–5. ANALYSIS TO DETERMINE WHETHER CERTAIN GAS MAINS SHOULD BE REPLACED

Facts of the Case. A city is engaged in the distribution of natural gas, purchased at a flat rate of 30 cents per MCF (thousand cubic feet). As a result of corrosion, its gas mains eventually develop small leaks which increase as time goes on. The question arises of how much gas should be lost before it is economical to replace any given section of main.

Mains have no salvage value when retired. New mains cost about $8,000 per mile installed. Because of improved protective coatings and better methods of installation, it is believed that new mains will be tight for a longer period than was the case for the mains in the original distribution system. The engineer for the city's gas department estimates that under average conditions, a new main will lose no gas during its first 15 years of service; starting with the 16th year, gas losses will increase by about 200 MCF per mile of main per year. The only operation cost that is variable with the age or condition of the main is the cost of lost gas.

In this municipally owned utility, economy studies are made using an interest rate (minimum attractive rate of return) of 7%.

Calculation of Annual Cost of Challenger. In this comparison any section of main that is losing gas is a possible defender in a replacement economy study. In all cases the challenger is a new main that has an estimated first cost of $8,000, zero salvage value at all times, and operating costs that start at $60 in the 16th year and increase by $60 a year thereafter. Table 16–1 provides a basis for estimating challenger life and equivalent annual cost.

The actual compound interest calculations are not shown in the table. A sample calculation assuming retirement after 25 years is as follows:

$$\text{CR} = \$8,000(\text{crf-}7\%\text{-}25) = \$8,000(0.08581) \qquad = \$686$$

Equivalent annual cost of gas lost

$$= \$60(\text{gpwf-}7\%\text{-}11)(\text{pwf'-}7\%\text{-}14)(\text{crf-}7\%\text{-}14)$$
$$= \$60(32.47)(0.3878)(0.08581) \qquad = \underline{65}$$

Total equivalent annual cost = \$686 + \$65 \qquad = \$751

In this particular case, it is evident that the equivalent annual costs of the challenger are relatively insensitive to differences in assumptions regarding challenger service life over a considerable range of possible lives. Although the lowest equivalent annual cost, $749, is obtained at 27 years, this figure is changed by less than 3% within the range from 21 to 35 years.

Calculation of Annual Cost of Extending Service of Defenders. It has been stated that the gas mains in this example have zero salvage values at all times. Therefore there are no capital costs associated with extending the service of any defenders. It has also been stated that there is no difference in maintenance cost between old and new mains.

It follows that the costs of gas lost are the only defender costs that are relevant in comparison with challenger costs. For any particular section of main that is being considered for replacement, it is necessary to estimate the MCF of gas that will be lost next year, to express this quantity as a rate per mile of main, and to multiply the rate per mile by the unit price of 30 cents per MCF.

For instance, consider section X of main losing gas at 1,000 MCF per mile; this has a next-year cost of $300 per mile. Or consider section Y losing gas at 3,000 MCF per mile; its next-year cost is $900 per mile.

TABLE 16-1

EQUIVALENT ANNUAL COSTS FOR A MILE OF $8,000 GAS MAIN RETIRED AT
VARIOUS AGES, ASSUMING A MINIMUM ATTRACTIVE RATE OF RETURN OF 7%

Year n	Cost of Gas Lost During Year	Equivalent Uniform Annual Costs if Retired After n Years		
		Capital Recovery of $8,000	Equivalent Uniform Annual Cost of Gas Lost	Total Equivalent Uniform Annual Cost
A	B	C	D	E
3	$ 0	$3,048	$ 0	$3,048
6	0	1,678	0	1,678
9	0	1,228	0	1,228
12	0	1,007	0	1,007
15	0	878	0	878
16	60	847	2	849
17	120	819	6	825
18	180	795	11	806
19	240	774	17	791
20	300	755	24	779
21	360	738	32	770
22	420	723	40	763
23	480	710	48	758
24	540	698	56	754
25	600	686	65	751
26	660	676	74	750
27	720	667	82	749
28	780	659	91	750
29	840	652	99	751
30	900	645	108	753
31	960	638	116	754
32	1,020	633	124	757
33	1,080	627	132	759
34	1,140	623	140	763
35	1,200	618	148	766

Because gas losses tend to increase from year to year, it may be presumed that the annual costs in subsequent years for any section of main will be greater than those next year. Therefore, it merely is necessary to estimate next-year defender costs for purposes of comparison with challenger annual costs.

Comparison of Defender and Challenger. Consider the economy study relative to section X of main:

Comparative annual cost of defender = $300 per mile (for next year)

Comparative annual cost of challenger = at least $749 per mile (for 27 years, more or less)

It is evident that section X should be continued in service.

It is worth emphasizing that the use of next-year costs for the defender carries no implication that, if the decision favors the defender, it will be kept in service *only* one year more. It is merely that, for purposes of comparison, we are using the period most favorable to the defender. The challenger also has the benefit of the period most favorable to it, namely, approximately 27 years.

In contrast to the foregoing study, consider the comparison relative to section Y of main:

Comparative annual cost of defender = $900 per mile (for next year)

Comparative annual cost of challenger = at least $749 per mile (for 27 years, more or less)

This comparison seems to favor the challenger. However, in a case of this type, it is always pertinent to raise the question of what is expected to happen after the expiration of the one-year period assumed as the remaining life of the defender. This question is discussed later in the present chapter. (Because this type of question is a central one in a number of mathematical models developed for replacement economy, it also is discussed in Appendix D, which deals with these mathematical models.)

At the present stage of our discussion, we can say that if the next-year cost of extending the service of an existing main is not at least $750 per mile, it is doubtful whether replacement is justified. In other words, the sections of main where replacement should be considered are those expected to lose at least 2,500 MCF per mile per year (i.e., $750 per mile divided by the price of $0.30 per MCF).

EXAMPLE 16–6. ANALYSIS OF PROPOSED REPLACEMENT OF CERTAIN CONSTRUCTION EQUIPMENT

Facts of the Case. The first cost of a machine used to perform a certain service in construction is $2,000. It is expected that the secondhand value of this machine will be $1,100 after its first year, $750 after 2 years, $500 after 3 years, and will continue to decline as shown in Table 14–1, page 294. It is believed that the first-year disbursements in connection with ownership and operation of this machine will be $1,200, that second-year disbursements will be $1,350, and that disbursements will increase each year as shown in column C of Table 16–2.

The owner of a machine performing this service has a chance to sell it for a favorable price of $1,350. His machine cost $2,200 one year ago. However, the first costs of new machines have declined and the economy of performance has been slightly improved. A decision must be made between continuing this machine (defender) in service and replacing it with a new machine (challenger) that is expected to have costs for various lengths of life as shown in Table 16–2. All studies are made before income taxes with an interest rate of 8%.

The estimated future salvage values of the defender are $775 next year, $525 two years hence, and $275 three years hence. If the defender is continued in service, annual disbursements are estimated as $1,370 next year, $1,570 the following year, and $1,820 the year after that.

Calculation of Annual Cost of Challenger. It is evident from column G of Table 16–2 that there is a considerable range of possible challenger lives for which the equivalent uniform annual cost is very close to $2,000. However, as a 3-year

TABLE 16-2

EQUIVALENT ANNUAL COSTS OF $2,000 MACHINE OF TABLE 14-1 FOR ASSUMED
LIVES OF 1 TO 10 YEARS WITH INTEREST AT 8%

	COSTS OF EXTENDING SERVICE DURING nTH YEAR			EQUIVALENT UNIFORM ANNUAL COSTS IF RETIRED AFTER n YEARS		
Year n	Capital Recovery Cost (Column E of Table 14-1)	Disburse-ments During Year	Total Cost (B + C)	Equivalent Uniform Annual Capital Recovery Cost (Column H of Table 14-1)	Equivalent Uniform Annual Disburse-ments	Total Equiva-lent Uniform Annual Cost (E + F)
A	B	C	D	E	F	G
1	$1,060	$1,200	$2,260	$1,060	$1,200	$2,260
2	438	1,350	1,788	761	1,272	2,033
3	310	1,550	1,860	622	1,358	1,980
4	240	1,800	2,040	537	1,456	1,993
5	124	1,950	2,074	467	1,540	2,007
6	116	2,050	2,166	419	1,610	2,029
7	58	2,125	2,183	379	1,667	2,046
8	54	2,200	2,254	348	1,717	2,065
9	0	2,250	2,250	320	1,760	2,080
10	0	2,300	2,300	298	1,797	2,095

life yields slightly lower annual costs than any other life, this is the assumed life
that is most favorable to the challenger.

Comparative Annual Cost of Challenger (3-year life)

CR = ($2,000 − $500)(crf-8%-3) + $500(0.08) .... $ 622
Equivalent annual disbursements = [$1,200(pwf'-8%-1)
  + $1,350(pwf'-8%-2) + $1,550(pwf'-8%-3)](crf-8%-3) 1,358

Total $1,980

Calculation of Annual Cost of Defender. The first impulse of anyone
making this economy study might be to compare next year's costs for the defender
with the foregoing annual costs over the expected life of the challenger.

Comparative Annual Cost of Defender (1 year more)

CR = ($1,350 − $775)(crf-8%-1) + $775(0.08)
  = ($1,350 − $775)(1.08) + $775(0.08) .... $ 683
Operating disbursements.. 1,370

Total $2,053

It is evident that ($1,350 − $775)(1.08) + $775(0.08) may also be written
as ($1,350 − $775)(1.00) + $1,350(0.08). In general, where the assumed remain-
ing life of a defender is one year, it is convenient to think of the capital recovery
costs as made up of the prospective decline in salvage value (depreciation in the

popular sense) and interest on present salvage value. An alternate statement of next-year defender costs is therefore:

Decline in salvage value = $1,350 − $775	$ 575
Interest on salvage value = $1,350(0.08)	108
Operating disbursements	1,370
Total	$2,053

The challenger is favored by a comparison of this $2,053 next-year defender cost with the $1,980 annual cost for a 3-year challenger life. However, in this case the decline in defender salvage value forecast for next year ($575) is much greater than the decline forecast for the following year ($250). A comparison favorable to the defender by a slight margin will be obtained if defender costs are considered over the next 2 years.

Comparative Annual Cost of Defender (2 years more)

CR = ($1,350 − $525)(crf-8%-2) + $525(0.08)	$ 505
Equivalent annual disbursements = [$1,370(pwf'-8%-1)	
+ $1,570(pwf'-8%-2)](crf-8%-2)	1,466
Total	$1,971

A similar calculation assuming 3 years more for the defender yields an equivalent annual cost of $2,014.

One purpose of including this example has been to emphasize the point that in any declining salvage situation, it may be advisable to consider defender costs for several different assumed remaining lives. The practical conclusion of this particular study should be that the comparative cost figures are so close that the decision between challenger and defender ought to be made on so-called irreducibles—that is, on considerations that have not been reduced to money terms in the study.

The $2,200 original cost of the defender is, of course, irrelevant in any before-tax study.

Some Aspects of Tables Such as 16–1 and 16–2. The figures given in column E of Table 16–1 and column G of Table 16–2 are valid equivalent annual costs for the respective challengers, given the assumed interest rate and first cost, and the predictions of the patterns of salvage values and operating costs. Nevertheless, even though the various disbursements turn out exactly as predicted, the tables do not tell us that it will necessarily be economical to replace the challenger of Table 16–1 when it is 27 years old or the challenger of Table 16–2 when it is 3 years old. The economic replacement date may be sooner or later, depending on the costs and prospective performance of challengers that may be available in the future, and on other matters.

Calculations such as those illustrated in Tables 16–1 and 16–2 may be viewed as yielding "economic lives" only under very restrictive assumptions. All future challengers must have the same first cost as the present challenger, the same expected salvage values at each age, and the same expected operating costs for each year.

Moreover, it must be assumed that the need for the particular service continues indefinitely and that the minimum attractive rate of return remains unchanged.

In general, replacement decisions should not be based on such assumptions, which obviously are unrealistic in our modern world of changing technology and changing prices. The question in a replacement decision should not be "How old is the defender?" The issue should always be viewed as an economic choice between extending the service of the defender, regardless of its age, and its retirement in favor of the best available challenger. But a temporary view of Tables 16–1 and 16–2 as "economic life" calculations may be helpful as an aid to the exposition of certain theoretical aspects of replacement economy and as a basis for pointing out a useful check on the arithmetic and the analysis in any tables or formulas of this type.

For instance, consider Table 16–1 as applicable to future challengers as well as to the present one. As long as the cost of extending the service of the present challenger is less than $749, the annual cost of a future challenger, it will pay to keep the present challenger in service. Because salvage values are zero at all times, the only cost of extending service is the operating disbursement (cost of lost gas)

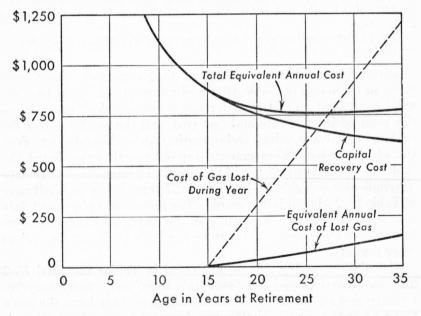

FIGURE 16–1. Equivalent Annual Cost of Gas Main as a Function of Age at Retirement—Data of Table 16–1

in column B. Consider the start of the 27th year; as the column B figure is $720, it will not pay to replace. Now consider the start of the 28th year; as the prospective cost of extending service another year is $780 and as $780 exceeds $749, replacement is justified after 27 years. The various elements in the analysis are shown graphically in Figure 16–1. The minimum point on the curve of total equivalent annual cost occurs where the curve is intersected by the dotted line for cost of lost gas during the year.

Figure 16–2 shows the same type of relationship for the more complicated facts of Table 16–2. Because salvage values are not zero and are declining, the cost of extending service in any year is the sum of operating disbursements, interest on salvage value at the start of the year, and decline in salvage during the year. But the same principle applies that the minimum annual cost is reached when the cost of extending service next year is greater than the equivalent annual cost up to date.

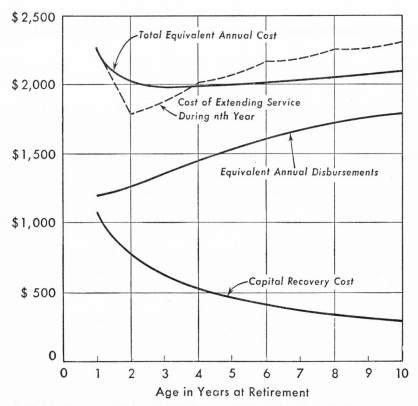

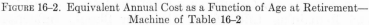

FIGURE 16–2. Equivalent Annual Cost as a Function of Age at Retirement—
Machine of Table 16–2

If the curves of total equivalent annual cost in Figures 16–1 and 16–2 should be interpreted as the basis for finding the economic life, they would suggest the conclusion that there is a wide range of possible lives of these assets that are almost equally economical. Although there are minimum cost points, these curves are relatively flat through a considerable range. Mathematical models developed in connection with replacement economy often indicate a substantial minimum cost range as well as a minimum cost point.

If one could imagine a static society in which prices and service requirements never changed and in which challengers always repeated the cost history of their defenders, the exact timing of replacements in such a society doubtless would be of little consequence. In our dynamic modern industrial society where challengers often differ greatly from their defenders, the timing of replacements is likely to be much more important than would be suggested by any mathematical model.

What Shall Be Assumed as Remaining Defender Service Life in a Replacement Economy Study? Examples 16–4, 16–5, and 16–6 are typical of many replacement studies in which the assumed remaining defender life is shorter than the assumed challenger life. In such studies, one problem is to select the defender remaining life that is most favorable to the defender.

When a major outlay for defender alteration or overhaul is needed, as in Example 16–4, the remaining defender life that will yield the least annual cost is likely to be the period that will elapse before the next major alteration or overhaul will be needed.

When there is no defender salvage value now or later (and no outlay for alteration or overhaul), and when defender operating disbursements are expected to increase annually, as in Example 16–5, the remaining life that will yield the least annual cost will be one year (or possibly less).

When salvage values are expected to decline from year to year, as in Example 16–6, it may be necessary to try several remaining service lives before selecting the one to be used in the comparison.

It should be emphasized that the selection of a remaining defender service life for use in a replacement study does not imply a commitment that if the decision favors the defender, it will be retired at the end of this period. The problem is merely to find the period that yields the lowest annual cost of continuing the service of the defender.

How Prospective Occurrences After the Expiration of the Assumed Remaining Life of the Defender Should Influence the

Choice Between Defender and Challenger. Consider the comparison of annual costs in Example 16–5 relative to section Y of main:

Defender—$900 per mile for next year

Present Challenger—$749 per mile for 27 years

Such a comparison appears to favor the present challenger. Nevertheless, it does not necessarily follow from such a comparison that a decision in favor of the present challenger will lead to maximum economy in the long run. If the replacement is put off for a while, a better challenger than the present one may be available. If the future challenger is enough better than the present one, a long-run comparison may favor continuing the defender in service for the time being in order to realize the advantages obtainable from the future challenger.

As a simple numerical illustration of this point, assume that it is expected that the first cost of new gas mains will decline a little during the coming year and that protective coatings will be somewhat improved. Let us assume that a monetary allowance for these changes leads to a figure of $720 a year as the annual cost per mile for 26 years of service from next year's challenger. Now our comparison is:

Defender and Next Year's Challenger—$900 next year followed by $720 a year for 26 years

Present Challenger—$749 a year for 27 years

The defender alternative may be converted (at 7%) to an equivalent uniform annual cost of $734 for 27 years. If our assumption about next year's challenger turns out to be correct, it is better to make our present decision in favor of the defender.

More often than not, an analyst is likely to feel that he has no basis for such a specific numerical estimate of the difference in annual cost between a known present challenger and an unknown future one. But coming events may cast their shadows before sufficiently well for the matter to be considered on a qualitative basis. In one instance it may be known that greatly improved designs of certain machines are in the development stage and that new commercial models may be expected in the near future. In another case new models containing drastic improvements may have recently appeared, and it may be thought unlikely that machines with further great improvements will be available soon. Sometimes there may be good reason to believe that future challengers will have higher first costs than the present one (perhaps because of their greater complexity or because of rising price levels); sometimes it may be expected that future challengers will be lower priced (perhaps because of economies realizable from their production in greater quantities).

Any forecast about differences between the present challenger and future challengers is relevant in decision making about a proposed replacement—particularly so in borderline cases. A forecast that future challengers will be superior to the present one or that they will have lower first costs is favorable to postponing replacement. A forecast that future challengers will be inferior [5] or that they will have higher first costs is favorable to immediate replacement. If an analyst desires to consider such forecasts quantitatively but is unwilling to make a single monetary estimate, he may test the sensitivity of the replacement decision to forecasts about future challengers by making an analysis of several different estimates.

Since 1949 in the United States there has been a considerable vogue for the use of mathematical models as a guide to decisions on replacements. A first step in the understanding of such models is an understanding of calculations of minimum annual cost such as the ones illustrated in Tables 16–1 and 16–2. A second step is an understanding of the problem of giving weight to the expectation that if replacement is deferred for a while a better challenger will be available. Several of the more popular models, discussed briefly in Appendix D, involve a formal monetary allowance (as a charge against the challenger) for the expectation that if replacement is deferred a better challenger will be available one year hence.

What Shall Be Assumed as Challenger Service Life in a Replacement Economy Study? In Examples 16–4, 16–5, and 16–6 we assumed the challenger life that would yield the lowest annual cost for the challenger. (We noted that in Examples 16–5 and 16–6, because of consideration of the prospective increase of annual disbursements with age, the challenger annual cost was not sensitive to a moderate change in assumed challenger life.)

In these examples we did not shorten the assumed life of the present challenger because of the expectation that better challengers would be available in the near future. However, decisions on replacements in industry sometimes are made by methods of analy-

---

[5] Of course the normal expectation in modern industry is that technological progress will cause future challengers to be superior. However, it sometimes happens that style change or technological change causes new machines to be less well adapted to certain services. Moreover, periods occur in history when it seems likely that the quality of new assets available in the future will be inferior to those presently available. For example, the period 1939–41 in the United States, prior to the entry of the country into World War II, was a time when an analyst making a replacement study might have forecast that challengers in the near future, if any, would be inferior to present ones.

sis that in effect make an excessive shortening of challenger service life for this reason.

The use of a very short payout period for a challenger that has a relatively long prospective life should not be regarded as "conservative." Using a one or two or three year payout period for such a challenger has the effect of continuing the service of defenders that are obsolete and uneconomical.[6]

Nevertheless, *some* shortening of assumed challenger service life may be appropriate in lieu of a formalized allowance for the prospect that if replacement is deferred, a superior challenger will be available. It is explained in Appendix D that the use of one of the common formulas containing such a formalized allowance has approximately the same effect on the analysis as cutting the estimated primary service life of the challenger in half before computing its capital recovery cost.

The Problem of Securing Adequate Cost Data for Certain Types of Replacement Economy Studies. It is a common condition for operation and repair costs of machinery and other assets to increase with age.[7] For adequate replacement studies, it is not enough to be aware of these matters in a qualitative way; specific quantitative information is needed applicable to each study.

In the frequent case where an organization operates many similar machines of different ages, there is an opportunity to secure such information. Usually the accounting system does not furnish data in the form needed by an analyst studying replacement policy. For example, the accounts may report the total repair costs for all machines of a given type but not give information on individual machines; an analyst may need to examine and classify individual repair work orders. The evaluation of some matters, such as the adverse consequences of breakdowns or other unsatisfactory performance, may require considerable information gathering and analysis that is entirely apart from the accounting system.

Limitation on Uses of "Comparative Annual Costs" Computed for Replacement Studies. It should be emphasized that "costs" such as have been calculated in the examples of replacement studies in this chapter are useful solely for the comparison of the

---

[6] George Terborgh has written forcefully on this point. See *Dynamic Equipment Policy, op. cit.*, chap. xii. See also his "fable," "The Profits of Procrastination," pp. 43 and 44 of his *Business Investment Policy*, discussed in Appendix D.

[7] See Terborgh, *Dynamic Equipment Policy, op. cit.*, pp. 70–71, for graphs showing the relation between age and repair cost per unit of service for certain metal working equipment, textile machinery, locomotives, farm implements, light trucks, passenger automobiles, intercity buses, and local buses. In all of these graphs repair costs per unit of service increase with age. In some instances the relationship is linear; in others the increase per year is less in the later years than in the earlier years.

specific alternatives under consideration. Such "comparative annual costs" are properly thought of merely as convenient measure of the differences between the proposed alternatives. Obviously no inferences should be drawn from them except inferences as to the relative merits of the alternatives being compared. This statement applies with particular force to the drawing of inferences about pricing policies.

Often the Source of a Product or Service Is Replaced Without a Retirement. The examples and problems in this chapter generally imply that if the challenger is acquired the defender will be retired. Often the circumstances of the case make it reasonable that the old asset be retired as soon as the new one is available. For instance, in Example 16–4 there would have been no point in having a spare highway bridge of insufficient strength adjoining the new bridge.

But frequently new assets are acquired for a given service in a way that displaces the old assets but does not involve their retirement. The old assets are simply relegated to a different use—one that might generally be described as an inferior use. Assignment for peak load or stand-by purposes is an example of this. Another familiar example is the assignment of a displaced main-line railroad locomotive to branch-line service. It may be many years before an asset displaced in this way is finally retired; in fact, there may be several successive different inferior uses before retirement.

In periods of expanding demand for a product or service (generally, but not necessarily, corresponding to periods of general business prosperity), the tendency is to acquire new assets of improved design but not to retire the older less economical assets. In periods when there is apparent overcapacity (generally, but not necessarily, in business depressions), the older assets are retired. Much replacement of industrial assets occurs with this type of time lag. Where this takes place, the economy studies in periods of expanding demand involve the displacement of the sources of a service and those in overcapacity periods involve retirements, but there are no replacement economy studies as such.

Common Errors in Replacement Studies. Observation of the practice of industrialists in such studies and of the published literature of the subject indicates four errors which it seems are often made in dealing with replacement economy:

1. Considering the excess of present book value over the net realizable value of the old asset as an addition to the investment in the new asset. This error increases the apparent cost associated with the

new asset, and thus tends to prevent replacements that are really economical.

2. Calculating depreciation and interest (i.e., capital recovery) on the old asset on the basis of its original cost rather than its present net realizable value. This usually increases the apparent costs associated with the old asset, and thus tends to favor replacements that are really uneconomical.

3. Where indirect costs (burden) are allotted in the cost accounting system in proportion to direct costs (usually in proportion to direct labor cost), assuming without investigation that a reduction of direct expenditures will effect a corresponding saving in indirect expenditures. This error usually makes the apparent saving from proposed replacements greater than the saving that is actually possible to realize, and thus tends to favor replacements that are really uneconomical.

4. In cases where the proposed new asset provides more capacity than the old asset, comparing calculated unit costs realizable only with full-capacity operation, rather than comparing the actual costs realizable with the expected output. Where such excess of capacity is not likely to be used, this unit cost comparison tends to favor the asset with the surplus capacity, and is therefore favorable to replacements that are really uneconomical.

The first two of these errors cited result from a failure to recognize the true nature of depreciation accounting as a time allotment against future dates of money already spent. The third results from a failure to understand clearly the nature of cost accounting allocations. The fourth is merely an unrealistic use of unit costs.

EXAMPLE 16–7. INFLUENCE OF BUDGETARY CONSIDERATIONS ON THE TIMING OF REPLACEMENT EXPENDITURES

Facts of the Case. As a result of a change from the purchase of manufactured gas to natural gas, a city that had its publicly owned gas distribution system was faced with a great increase in leakage of gas from its mains. (The moist manufactured gas contains bituminous compounds that tend to plug up any small holes caused by corrosion of the mains; the dry natural gas dries these plugs, with the result that the gas escapes through the holes.) An analysis of the cost of lost gas and the cost of main replacement indicated that it would pay to replace a number of the oldest mains and services. There were other old mains and services that had not quite reached the point where replacement was economically justified even though considerable gas was being lost from them.

If all of the gas mains that justified replacement were to be replaced at once, the only possible source of funds would have been a bond issue; this would have required an affirmative vote of two-thirds of the voters at a bond election. As gas main replacement was not considered well adapted to contract, a program of immediate replacement would have necessitated the hiring of a number of temporary employees for the gas department.

For a number of years this gas department had operated with a pay-as-you-go policy for financing capital improvements, with all capital expenditures budgeted out of current earnings from the sale of gas. If this policy were to be adopted for the replacement program, only enough funds could be budgeted annually to keep one crew busy on main replacement. As a result it would take several years to replace all of the mains requiring replacement.

After careful consideration, it was decided to continue this pay-as-you-go policy. It was believed to be desirable to avoid bond issues except for major expenditures for plant expansion. Moreover, it was felt that a single crew working full time on main and service replacement would become more efficient and, therefore, would operate at a lower cost than several temporary crews working a shorter period on the same type of work. Considerations of personnel policy were also against the hiring of temporary crews.

After several years, all of the mains that were losing enough gas to justify immediate replacement had been replaced. It was then decided to continue to budget funds for replacement for another year or two. These funds would be used to replace those mains that were losing considerable gas even though the losses had not quite reached the point where replacement was justified strictly on economic grounds. It was clearly possible to finance these replacements at once whereas the possibilities of financing at a later date were less certain.

Thus, because of budgetary considerations and other reasons, some mains were replaced a few years later than the date indicated by economy studies and others were replaced a few years sooner than the apparent economic date. Considerations such as these quite properly enter into decisions on the timing of expenditures for replacements.

Need for a System Viewpoint in Certain Types of Replacement Studies.

Ray I. Reul illustrates a common type of occurrence with the following example: [8]

Suppose we have a plant shutdown because of a burned-out transformer. This plant, when operating, produces an annual profit of $10,000. If a transformer is not immediately purchased and installed at a cost of $8,000, the $10,000 profit will no longer be received. Therefore, we can truthfully say that the investment of $8,000 will "save" $10,000 per year. This sounds like a magnificent return. So we buy and install the transformer.

One year later the steam boiler, which is also an integral part of the plant, breaks down and must be retubed with an investment of another $8,000. Again, we can truthfully state that expenditure of $8,000 will "save" $10,000 per year. (Theoretically, we could repeat the process of "saving" $10,000 per year over and over again with further expenditures.) The catch is that this is the *same* $10,000 per year we "saved" before. Actually, there is only *one* $10,000 per year to be "saved."

Reul classifies investment proposals into "profit-maintaining" and "profit-adding" as follows:

Profit-maintaining

1. Replacement of existing facilities which will no longer function.
2. Improvement of existing facilities to circumvent competition.
3. Provision of new facilities which were accidentally or intentionally omitted when the original facilities were installed but which have now become essential to the continuation of existing activities.

[8] R. I. Reul, "Profitability Index for Investments," *Harvard Business Review,* XXXV, No. 4 (July–August, 1957), 116–32.

Profit-adding

1. Provision of new facilities that will increase profit by providing new business or by expanding existing operations.
2. Provision of facilities that will improve product quality and permit higher prices and profit margins.
3. Provision of facilities that will reduce the cost of production and result in increased profit through larger profit margins or increased volume of sales.

He comments on the viewpoint that should be applied to profit-maintaining proposals, as follows:

To convert a profit-maintaining proposal to a profit-adding basis, we must investigate the future of the particular operations at stake. This investigation must cover the entire life of the proposed new facility. All income during this period must be predicted; all expenditures, including operating costs, replacements of other related facilities, revisions, additions, and so forth, must be anticipated. These data, viewed against the alternative of doing nothing and losing existing income, will permit the proposed investment to be evaluated as a true profit-adding proposal.

By way of illustration, let us return for a moment to the plant requiring replacement of the burned-out transformer. To evaluate this proposal properly we must include all other investments anticipated during the years for which continued profit is predicted. Thus, if savings are claimed in the second year, the investment required for boiler tubes must be included in the evaluation.

Summary. The following points brought out in this chapter may be restated for emphasis as follows:

1. It is helpful to use the word *defender* to apply to an existing asset being considered for replacement and to use the word *challenger* to apply to a proposed new replacement asset.
2. Capital recovery costs for extending the service of a defender should be based on its present net realizable value.
3. In evaluating the effect of a proposed replacement decision on cash flow for income taxes, it is necessary to consider the past investment in the defender as well as the depreciation accounting method that has been used for the defender in past tax returns.
4. As in all comparisons of alternatives, prospective receipts and disbursements that are unaffected by the choice may be omitted from a replacement study.
5. Generally speaking, the annual cost of extending the service of a defender should be based on the number of years of additional service that results in the lowest figure for this annual cost.
6. Where the remaining life assumed for the defender is shorter than the life expected for the challenger, it is appropriate to recognize that if replacement is deferred, a different challenger from the present one is likely to be available. This prospect may be given weight in the economy study in a number of different ways. Mathematical models that make a formalized allowance for better future challengers are discussed in Appendix D.

Problems

16–1. A corporation engaged in large-scale farming operates a fleet of tractors. Major overhauls generally have been needed when tractors are 4 and 8 years old. In the past most tractors have been retired after 8 years, just before the second major overhaul. However, a few tractors have been retired after 4 years, just before the first overhaul. Some others have been overhauled when 8 years old and kept in service until they were scrapped at the end of 12 years. In reviewing past replacement policy, an analyst estimates typical year-by-year annual disbursements that appear to have been influenced by the age of a tractor (chiefly routine maintenance, fuel, and lubricants) as follows:

Year	Disbursements	Year	Disbursements	Year	Disbursements
1	$4,000	5	$6,500	9	$8,000
2	5,000	6	7,000	10	8,000
3	6,000	7	7,500	11	8,000
4	7,000	8	8,000	12	8,000

The first cost of a tractor is $16,000. A typical salvage value before overhaul at the end of 4 years is $5,600. A typical cost of overhaul at the end of 4 years is $5,000. A typical salvage value before overhaul at the end of 8 years is $1,600. A typical cost of overhaul at the end of 8 years is $7,000. Salvage values at the end of 12 years are negligible.

Depreciation used in accounting and income tax returns has been based on the years-digits method assuming an 8-year life and 10% salvage value.

Assuming a minimum attractive rate of return (interest rate) of 12% before income taxes, compare the before-tax equivalent annual costs of service for lives of 4, 8, and 12 years, using the foregoing "typical" figures for the relevant costs. (*Ans.* = $9,460; $9,800; $10,000.)

16–2. In Problem 16–1, consider the decision whether a typical 4-year-old tractor should be overhauled and kept in service for 4 years more or replaced with a new tractor. Using 12% interest, make a before-tax comparison of equivalent annual costs of (a) extending the service of the old tractor for 4 years or (b) acquiring a new tractor to be retired after 4 years. (*Ans.* = (a) $10,340; (b) $9,460.)

16–3. Make an after-tax comparison of the alternatives in Problem 16–2 by the method of rate of return, assuming an effective tax rate of 50%. Assume that the entire $5,000 overhaul cost of the defender at the end of its 4th year of life may be treated as a current expense for tax purposes in that year (i.e., at zero date for this economy study). What is the prospective rate of return? If the minimum attractive rate of return is 6% after income taxes, does this comparison favor the defender or challenger? (*Ans.* = 11.2%; challenger.)

16–4. In the circumstances described in Problem 16–1, the question arises whether it would not be advantageous to retire tractors considerably earlier than the first overhaul date, say, at the end of 2 years. Obviously, an important element in comparing a policy of retirement after 2 years with retirement after 4 years is the salvage value after 2 years. How great must this salvage value be for the 2-year retirement to be as economical as the 4-year retirement for a typical tractor? Determine this figure by a before-tax analysis using a minimum attractive rate of return of 12%. (*Ans.* = $9,490.)

16–5. An individual owns a rental property in an industrial district of a city. This is rented to a single tenant at an annual rental of $10,000. The present lease is about to expire. The tenant is willing to renew the lease for a long term at the present figure but not at a higher one.

A manufacturing company adjoining the building site has made an offer of $120,000 for this property. Because of the particular needs of this manufacturer for an area to expand, the property owner believes that this is a better offer than can be secured from any other buyer. If the offer is not accepted at once, it is considered likely that the manufacturer will make other plans for plant expansion and that the offer will therefore not be renewed at a later date. A decision must therefore be made at once whether or not to accept this offer.

It is believed that if the property is not sold at once, ownership will be continued for a fairly long time. For purposes of the economy study to guide the decision, assume that ownership will continue for 20 years and that the net resale value before income taxes at the end of that period will be $50,000. The original cost of the property 5 years ago was $80,000, divided for accounting and tax purposes into $20,000 for land and $60,000 for the building. Since purchase, the building has been depreciated for accounting and tax purposes at $1,500 a year based on an estimated remaining life of 40 years from the purchase date and a terminal salvage value of zero.

If ownership is continued, it is estimated that receipts from rental will continue at $10,000 a year. Annual disbursements are estimated to be $1,500 for upkeep, $2,100 for property taxes, and $400 for insurance.

(a) Compute a rate of return before income taxes that provides a basis for comparison between the alternatives of continued ownership and immediate sale. (*Ans.* = 2.8%.)

(b) Compute a rate of return after income taxes that provides a basis for comparison between these two alternatives. Consider both the income taxes on any capital gain and on annual taxable income. Assume a 55% tax rate on ordinary income and a 25% tax rate on capital gains. (*Ans.* = 0.7%.)

16–6. A furniture manufacturer is considering the installation of an automatic machine for boring holes to replace two machines that now provide the same total capacity. The proposed machine will cost $10,000 ready to operate. If acquired, it will be depreciated for accounting and tax purposes by the straight-line item method assuming a 10-year life and zero salvage value. Annual disbursements for its operation are estimated as follows:

Direct labor will be one operator at $110 per week for the entire year.
Labor extras are 30% of direct labor cost.
Power will be 4,000 kw-hr per year at 3 cents per kw-hr.
Annual repairs and supplies are estimated as $240.
Property taxes and insurance total 2% of first cost.

The two present machines cost $2,250 each and are 5 years old. Straight-line item depreciation has been used for accounting and tax purposes assuming a 15-year life and zero terminal salvage value. Their present realizable value is $100 each. Annual expenditures are:

Direct labor is two operators at $90 per week each for the entire year.
Labor extras are 30% of direct labor cost.
Power is 2,500 kw-hr per machine per year at 3 cents.
Annual repairs and supplies are $150 per machine.
Property taxes and insurance total 2% of first cost.

(a) Assuming a 12% minimum attractive rate of return before income taxes, compute the before-tax annual cost of extending service of the defenders for 10 more years. Compare this with the annual cost of the challenger over a 10-year service life. Assume zero salvage values for both defender and challenger at the end of the 10 years. (*Ans.* = defender, \$12,749; challenger, \$9,766.)

(b) Make an after-tax comparison of annual costs assuming a 6% minimum attractive rate of return. Use a tax rate of 50%. Consider extra annual income taxes as an additional annual cost of the challenger. Assume that any "loss" on disposal of the defender will be fully deductible in the year of retirement; consider the resulting tax saving as an addition to the net salvage value of the defender. (*Ans.* = defender, \$12,931; challenger, \$11,364.)

(c) Compute the after-tax rate of return on the net investment needed to acquire the challenger, assuming a 10-year remaining life for both challenger and defender. (*Ans.* = 29.9%.)

(d) Disregarding any time value of money, find how long it will take for the difference in cash flow after income taxes to equal zero. (This may be viewed as the crude payout period after taxes.) (*Ans.* = 3.1 years.)

16–7. A 3-year-old machine has the following cost history:

	Disbursements for	
Year	Operation and Repairs	Delays Due to Breakdowns
1	\$ 700	\$ 0
2	900	200
3	1,100	400

If the machine is continued in service for the 4th year, it is estimated that the operation and repair costs will be \$1,300 and breakdowns will cost \$600. The corresponding estimates for the 5th year of service are \$1,500 and \$800. The machine has a present net realizable value of \$1,500; this will probably reduce to \$1,200 in another year and to \$1,000 in 2 years.

It is suggested that this be replaced by a new machine of improved design costing \$6,000. It is believed that this will completely eliminate any breakdowns and the resulting cost of delays, and that it will reduce operation and repair costs to \$200 a year less at each age than the corresponding costs with the old machine.

Make a before-tax comparison of annual costs using a minimum attractive rate of return of 12%. Base the annual cost of extending the service of the defender either on 1 or 2 years more of service, whichever gives the lower annual cost. Assume a 5-year life for the challenger with a \$1,000 terminal salvage value. (*Ans.* = defender, \$2,380; challenger, \$2,361.)

16–8. The question arises whether it is more economical to replace a certain motorboat engine with a new one, or to rebore the cylinders of the old engine and thoroughly recondition it. The original cost of the old engine 10 years ago was \$700; to rebore and recondition it now will extend its useful life for an estimated 5 years and will cost \$280. A new engine will have a first cost of \$620 and will have an estimated life of 10 years. It is expected that the annual cost of fuel and lubricants with the reconditioned engine will be about \$200 and that this cost will be 15% less with the new engine. It is also believed that repairs will be \$25 a year less with the new engine than with the reconditioned one. Assume that neither engine has any net realizable value when retired.

What irreducibles can you think of favorable to each plan? Compute comparative equivalent annual costs assuming interest at 6%. (*Ans.* = recondition, \$291; replace, \$254.)

16–9. The butt of a pole in a municipal electric distribution system has decayed to the point where it is necessary either to replace the pole or to "stub" it. A new pole will cost $58 installed and will have an estimated life of 21 years. The pole inspector estimates the remaining life in the upper portion of the present pole as 8 years; this may be realized if the pole is stubbed. Stubbing will cost $17. The stubbed pole will have zero salvage value after 8 years. The upper portion of the present pole has an estimated value for use elsewhere of $8. The terminal salvage value of a new pole after 21 years is estimated to be $12. Maintenance costs will be unaffected by the decision.

Compare equivalent annual costs of these alternatives using interest at 6%. (*Ans.* = stub, $4.03; new pole, $4.63.)

16–10. A flood that washed out a section of recently completed canal indicates the need for a larger drainage structure. Three possibilities are considered:

A. Leave the existing 48-in. corrugated metal culvert in place (it is undamaged) and install another of equal size alongside.
B. Remove the present 48-in. corrugated metal culvert and replace it with a single pipe 72 in. in diameter.
C. Remove the present metal culvert and replace it with a reinforced concrete box culvert of adequate cross section.

If the present 48-in. pipe is removed, it will have a salvage value of $400. Estimates regarding the new installations are as follows:

	48-in. Pipe	72-in. Pipe	Concrete Culvert
Cost of pipes, delivered	$1,000	$2,000	0
Installation cost	$500	$700	$2,800
Estimated life	25 years	25 years	50 years

With interest at 4%, which alternative would you recommend? Explain your analysis. (*Ans.* = Plan A.)

16–11. Black owns his home for which he paid $15,000 5 years ago. This property is free of debt. His employer has transferred him to another city where he has decided to rent an apartment. He has the opportunity to sell his house for $20,000; expenses of the sale would be a 5% broker's commission and $150 for title insurance. He also has the chance to rent the house on a 5-year lease to a desirable tenant for $200 a month. If he rents the property, he estimates his annual disbursements for property taxes, insurance, and upkeep as $600. He anticipates that if he rents the property now he will sell it at the end of the 5-year lease. He estimates the future selling price as $18,000, also subject to 5% broker's commission and $150 title insurance.

If he sells the property, he expects to invest the net proceeds in mortgages yielding 6%. His effective tax rate on ordinary income is 30% and on long-term capital gains is 15%.

If he sells the property now, he will be taxed on a long-term capital gain of $3,850, the difference between his selling price (net after deducting selling expenses) and his original cost. (No depreciation on the house has been allowed or allowable on tax returns during the years it has been his personal residence.) If he rents the house, he can deduct $300 a year depreciation in his tax return in addition to his disbursements each year for property taxes, insurance, and upkeep. (This figure is based on a division of his investment into $12,000 for house and $3,000 for land, and on the straight-line method assuming a 40-year life.)

Based on the foregoing estimates, will he have a greater after-tax yield from continued ownership of this property or from the proposed investment in mortgages? Explain your analysis, showing an after-tax rate of return on continued ownership.

Discuss the irreducibles that you think might reasonably enter into his decision. Discuss the sensitivity of the computed rate of return to the estimated selling price at the end of 5 years.

16–12. Two years ago a manufacturing company designed, built, and installed a gas-fired drying oven at a total cost of $24,000. A firm manufacturing drying ovens of a new and radically different design now offers a new oven for $26,000. The maker of the new oven guarantees a fuel saving of $6,000 per year compared to the present oven. Repairs and maintenance are estimated at $1,000 per year.

For accounting and income tax purposes, depreciation has been charged on the present oven at $2,000 a year, using the straight-line method with a 12-year life and zero salvage value. This depreciation rate will be continued if the oven is not retired. If the new oven is purchased, its depreciation charges will be based on a 10-year life, zero salvage value, and the straight-line method. Item depreciation accounting is used and is appropriate because only one oven is owned.

Repairs and maintenance costs on the present oven are about $600 a year and it is estimated they will continue at this figure. All other costs except fuel in connection with the drying operation will be unaffected by the type of oven used. Either oven, once installed, has value only as scrap if removed; the scrap value is about equal to the cost of dismantling and removal.

The company's effective tax rate on ordinary income is 50%. If the present oven is retired now, it is believed there will be no offsetting gains during the current year that will prevent securing the full advantage of the tax loss.

Assume that if continued in service the defender will be kept 10 years more, and that the challenger life is 10 years. If the company's minimum attractive rate of return is 12% after income taxes, which oven should be selected? Explain your answer.

Discuss the sensitivity of your conclusion to the assumed remaining defender service life.

16–13. Five years ago, at a cost of $9,600, a film processing concern designed and installed the necessary equipment to develop semiautomatically a certain size of film. A salesman now proposes that this equipment be discarded and that a new machine that his firm has just put on the market should be installed to do this work. His estimate of a $2,000 annual saving in the cost of labor and supplies seems to be reasonable. It is believed that there will be no other difference in annual disbursements between the old and new equipment. The price of the new machine is $12,000. The salesman has found a buyer willing to pay $1,000 for the old equipment.

The present equipment is fully depreciated on the books of account and for tax purposes, as the assumed life was 5 years with zero salvage value. Item accounting has been used. However, this equipment is still serviceable and could be used for several years more at approximately the present level of annual disbursements. Unless sold at once, it is expected to have zero salvage value. If acquired, the new machine will be depreciated by the years-digits method, assuming a 5-year life and zero salvage value; this estimated life and salvage value will also be used in the economy study to guide the decision on this suggested purchase.

The company's effective tax rate is 50% on ordinary income and 25% on capital gains. If the minimum attractive rate of return is 10% after income taxes, would you recommend purchase of the new equipment? Explain any assumptions that you make in your analysis.

16–14. An electrochemical company produces a portion of the electric energy required in its production processes in two hydroelectric power plants A and B. A consists of a dam and short wooden flume leading to a power house. B consists of a longer wooden flume leading from the tailwater of A to a second power house. The two plants use the same amount of water. The flumes are in such bad condition that their repair at once is imperative.

You are called in as engineer to make recommendations, and find the situation to be as follows:

The original investment in the two plants was $900,000. Of this, depreciation of $300,000 has been written off in the company's accounts so that the present book value is $600,000. Annual taxes on the two plants total $12,000.

The estimated cost of flume repair to maintain the power plants in service is $100,000. It is estimated that the repaired flume will have a life of 10 years after which another similar repair will be necessary. The life of the two plants as a whole is estimated to be 20 years. If the flume is repaired and plants A and B are maintained in service, their total operation and maintenance costs are estimated to be $15,000 a year.

However, investigation discloses that both plants are relatively inefficient compared to what is possible in modern hydroelectric design. Plant A is turning out 4,000 kw. at an over-all efficiency of 50%; plant B turns out 3,000 kw. at an over-all efficiency of 60%. (Efficiency is the ratio of energy output to energy input.)

Investigation further discloses that the existing power plants might be immediately scrapped, making use merely of a portion of the diversion dam at A. Repairs to the dam and a new intake would cost $50,000; a long tunnel costing $600,000 would be built leading to a new power house costing with machinery $350,000. The result would be a new modern plant operating at 80% over-all efficiency, with an expected life of 50 years. The net head would be the same as in A plus B, as the losses in the new tunnel equal the grade of the flumes. The same amount of water would be utilized. Plants A and B would become valueless, their scrap value being less than cost of dismantling. Operating costs of the new plant would be about $9,000 a year and taxes would be about $18,000 a year.

The increased power generated in the new plant would reduce the amount of power purchased by the electrochemical company from outside sources. This purchased power is costing $35 per kw. per year.

(a) Compute comparative annual costs before income taxes, assuming a minimum attractive rate of return of 15%.

(b) Compute comparative annual costs after income taxes, assuming a tax rate of 54% and a minimum attractive rate of return of 7%. Assume that the annual straight-line depreciation charge on the old plants has been $30,000 based on an estimated remaining life of 30 years when they were purchased 10 years ago. Assume that item depreciation has been used and that any write-off on the immediate scrapping of the old plants may be treated as a deduction from current taxable income. Assume that straight-line depreciation would be used for accounting and tax purposes if the new plant is built, using a 50-year life and zero salvage value.

16–15. A high-speed, special-purpose, automatic strip-feed punch press costing $15,000 has been proposed to replace 3 hand-fed presses now in use. The life of this automatic press has been estimated to be 5 years, with no salvage value at the end of that time. Expenditures for labor, maintenance, etc. have been estimated to be $3,000 per year.

The general-purpose, hand-fed punch presses cost $2,000 each 10 years ago and were estimated to have a life of 20 years, with a salvage value of $200 each at the end of that time. Their present net realizable value is $750 each. Operating expenditures for labor, etc. will be about $2,850 per year per machine. The net value is expected to decrease at the rate of about $100 per press per year.

It is expected that the required service will continue for only 5 years more and that the salvage value of the challenger will be $5,000 at the end of this period.

(a) Make an analysis before income taxes to provide a basis for the decision on whether or not to make this replacement. Assume a before-tax minimum attractive rate of return of 25%.

(b) Make a similar analysis after income taxes using a minimum attractive rate of return of 12%. Assume a tax rate of 52%. Although the expected service period of the challenger is only 5 years, it will be necessary to use a 15-year life (with zero salvage value) for depreciation used in tax returns; years-digits depreciation will be used. Straight-line depreciation has been used for the defenders. Assume that item depreciation is used in this company and that any "losses" on disposal will be fully deductible from taxable income in the year of disposal.

16–16. A municipal water department has as part of its system of delivery a flume that is 60 years old. Maintenance costs on this flume have averaged $4,200 a year during the last 10 years. Gagings made at both ends of the flume indicate an average loss of water in its length of about 15%.

This water department serves its customers in part with surface water brought in the aqueduct of which this flume is a part; the remainder of its water supply is pumped from wells located in the city. The loss of water in the flume thus requires additional pumping from wells. The average amount of water delivered at the inlet end of the flume is 10 millions of gallons per day. The increment cost of pumping from wells is $16.45 per million gallons.

It is estimated that a standard metal flume to replace the existing one would cost $112,000. It is believed that this would reduce the average loss of water in the flume to not more than 3%, and that the maintenance cost of such a flume would not exceed $1,000 a year. For the purposes of an economy study, the life of such a replacement flume is to be assumed as 20 years, although it would actually be much longer.

Irreducible factors favorable to the change are the lessened danger of breaks in the aqueduct line, and the reduced drain on the underground water supply.

Using interest at 5%, determine whether you would consider it economical to make the replacement.

16–17. A grain elevator requires additional capacity for the grinding of feed. Two plans for securing this capacity are to be compared.

Plan A. Replace the existing centrifugal bar mill with a patent feed grinding mill manufactured by the XYZ Company. This XYZ mill will provide 3 times the present capacity.

Plan B. Continue the present centrifugal bar mill in service and supplement it by another similar mill of like capacity. This will provide double the present capacity which appears to be adequate for all needs.

The existing centrifugal bar mill cost $1,400 5 years ago. Straight-line depreciation has been charged on the books against it based on an estimated life of 15 years. It has a present net realizable value of $400. A new similar mill will now cost $1,700. The XYZ mill has a first cost installed of $3,300.

It is estimated that the maintenance cost of the existing centrifugal bar mill will average at least $250 a year in the future. A new centrifugal bar mill with somewhat improved design can be maintained for about $175 a year, it is believed. The XYZ mill is expected to have an annual maintenance cost of $150.

Energy requirements for a centrifugal bar mill of this capacity are 23 kw-hr per hour of operation. It is expected that if two such mills are operated each will operate about 1,200 hours per year. Because of its greater capacity the XYZ mill will grind the same total amount of feed as the other two in 800 hours per year. Its energy requirements are 41 kw-hr per hour of operation. Energy is purchased for 3.6 cents per kw-hr. Labor cost and taxes will be practically unaffected by the choice of plan.

Make a before-tax comparison of equivalent annual costs for Plans A and B assuming a 10-year remaining life for the present mill and a 10-year life for both new mills with zero terminal salvage values for all. Use a minimum attractive rate of return of 15%.

16–18. A study of the costs of operating a 4-year-old piece of construction equipment indicates that the only costs variable with age are repairs and losses due to lost time. These have been as follows:

Year	Repair Cost	Cost of Lost Time
1	$ 88	$ 0
2	132	50
3	415	150
4	640	300

The present realizable value of this piece of equipment is $1,100. The first cost of a new one is $3,820. Due to certain improvements in design it is believed that the new one will reduce annual costs for fuel and supplies by $150; however, it is expected that repair costs and lost time will behave about as before. If the old unit is kept in service, it is guessed that repairs and cost of lost time next year will be 20% higher than last year. An estimate of the net realizable value at the end of the 3rd year of life is $1,500; at the end of the 5th year it is $900. Assume these salvage values apply to both old and new assets. Compare the annual cost of extending the service of the old asset one year more with the annual cost over the number of years (3, 4, or 5) that gives the lowest figure for the new asset. Make your comparison before income taxes using a minimum attractive rate of return of 12%.

16–19. A company engaged in the canning of food uses machine filling rather than hand filling for a certain product. The machine filler now in use was purchased 6 years ago at an installed cost of $3,600. Recently this machine has experienced lubrication troubles that have caused frequent breakdowns. The maintenance engineer considers these troubles to be due to a fundamental defect in the design of the machine. However, the machine manufacturer has developed a new design that eliminates this defect. A new machine of this design would cost $5,400 installed. It is believed that such a machine would be much more reliable because of the elimination of the lubrication difficulties.

When the machine filler breaks down, hand filling must be used temporarily until the machine is repaired. It is difficult to determine the exact cost occasioned by a breakdown. A brief shutdown is more costly per hour than a long-continued one; on a shutdown for an entire shift, it is possible to change assignments of workers in the cannery in a way that takes account of the lower filling rate. But a careful analysis of the situation by the plant industrial engineer leads to the conclusion that the extra labor cost created by a shutdown of the machine filler is, on the average, at least $5.50 per hour. In order to meet government specifications on minimum filling weights, it is necessary to overfill somewhat more with hand filling than with machine filling. The plant quality control engineer estimates the cost of this additional overfill as $2 for each hour that hand filling is used.

During last year's pack, the machine filler was shut down for a total of 320 hours. It is estimated that with the greater reliability of the new machine the average hours of breakdown can be reduced to 100 or less, and that annual repair costs, now $850, can be reduced to $200.

Income tax authorities require the use of a 12-year estimated average life for machine fillers for tax accounting purposes. The present machine has been depreciated on the books at $8\frac{1}{3}\%$ a year. It has no secondhand resale value. As its scrap value will not be appreciably more than the cost of removal, its net realizable value is assumed to be zero both now and later.

The required payoff period for the new machine is assumed as 4 years. It is understood that another new design for an improved machine filler suitable for this operation is currently in the development stage. When and if this design is perfected by the manufacturer, it will increase the rated output by about 50%. It seems probable that whenever such an improved machine should become available, it will make possible enough cost reduction so that any machine purchased today would be retired in its favor. For this reason the analysis is to be based on a 4-year challenger life with zero salvage value.

It is believed that property taxes and insurance will not be affected by the change in the machine filler. As the rated output of the new machine is the same as that of the old one, it is assumed that the only savings due to the change will be in the costs incident to breakdowns and in repair costs.

(a) Compute comparative annual costs before income taxes for the next 4 years assuming a minimum attractive rate of return of 20%.

(b) Compute comparative annual costs after income taxes for the next 4 years using a tax rate of 50% and a minimum attractive rate of return of 10%. Assume that the $8\frac{1}{3}\%$ straight-line depreciation rate will also be used for the new filler. Assume that because of the use of group depreciation accounting, no "loss" on disposal will be allowable for tax purposes either on disposal of defender or challenger. The retirement of either will terminate the depreciation charge against it. (The 12-year life is in fact the approximate average service life of machine fillers owned by this particular taxpayer. Retirements at ages of less than 12 years are offset by other retirements at ages greater than 12 years. Under the rules of straight-line group accounting, the $8\frac{1}{3}\%$ rate continues to be charged as long as a machine filler continues in service even though it is more than 12 years old.)

16–20. A manufacturer must double his press brake capacity for making certain sheet metal parts. Two plans are set up for comparison:

A. Continue the present XY–10 press brake in service, and supplement it by an XY–12 (a newer model) of equal capacity. The XY–10 cost $9,000 5 years ago. It has been depreciated for tax purposes by the straight-line item method assuming a 15-year life and zero salvage value. A new XY–12 model will cost $12,000. If purchased, it will be depreciated for tax purposes by the years-digits item method assuming a 15-year life and zero salvage value.

B. Sell the XY–10 for $4,500. Buy an XZ–20 model press brake that has double the capacity of the XY–10. The first cost of the XZ–20 is $24,000. If purchased, it will be depreciated for tax purposes by the years-digits item method assuming a 15-year life and zero salvage value.

It is desired to compare these two plans on the assumption that the need for this particular operation will terminate after 5 years. Expected salvage values 5 years hence are $3,000 for the present XY–10, $5,500 for the XY–12, and $11,000 for the XZ–20. Average annual operating disbursements for the three press brakes are estimated as follows:

	XY–10	XY–12	XZ–20
Direct labor	$6,200	$5,800	$10,000
Labor extras	1,550	1,450	2,500
Maintenance	1,800	1,200	2,000
Power	200	150	250
Taxes and insurance	140	240	480

The XZ–20 has the same space requirements as the total of XY–10 and XY–12. Receipts from the sale of product are not expected to be influenced by the choice between A and B. The manufacturer's effective tax rate is 50% on ordinary income and 25% on capital gains.

(a) For years 0 to 5, both inclusive, tabulate the difference in prospective cash flow before income taxes. What interest rate makes plans A and B equivalent to one another?

(b) For years 0 to 5, both inclusive, tabulate the difference in prospective cash flow after income taxes. Assume that any "loss" on disposal can be treated as a deduction from taxable income in the year of disposal. What interest rate makes plans A and B equivalent to one another?

(c) Discuss the interpretation of your computed interest rates in (a) and (b) as a basis for the choice between the two plans.

16–21. The following problem deals with a decision that it was necessary to make in the RST Company in November of 1957.

Early in 1956, the maintenance department of this company ordered a specially designed machine, Machine X, costing $120,000. Nearly 2 years was needed to secure delivery of Machine X. It was delivered and paid for in mid-November 1957. However, it could not be used until it was installed. The installation period would require another month and the estimated cost of installation was $24,000.

The maintenance department had two objectives in mind when Machine X was originally ordered. The primary objective was to improve the diagnosis of certain types of troubles that had occurred in equipment subject to periodic overhaul. A secondary objective was to effect a moderate reduction in the labor, fuel, and power costs in the testing of overhauled equipment. This secondary objective alone was not sufficient to have justified the purchase of Machine X.

When Machine X was ordered, the management of the RST Company knew that the equipment that Machine X was designed to service would gradually be superseded by a different type of equipment by the end of 1965. It was believed that after 1965, Machine X could no longer be used and that it would have a negligible salvage value at that time.

In the period of nearly 2 years that had elapsed between the order date and the delivery date of Machine X, other methods had been developed for diagnosing the troubles in the equipment Machine X was designed to service. It was believed that these other methods were satisfactory enough that Machine X was not actually needed for purpose of diagnosis.

Mr. A, the controller of the RST Company, was therefore opposed to spending the $24,000 to install Machine X. He said: "We are always short of funds for plant investment. Why send good money after bad?" He favored disposing of Machine X at the best available price. A prospective buyer was found who was willing to pay $36,000 for this machine. The market for specialized machines of this type was quite limited, and it seemed unlikely that Machine X could be sold for more than this figure.

Mr. B, the superintendent of the maintenance department, favored keeping Machine X. He pointed out that there would be substantial savings in disbursements for the testing of overhauled equipment if Machine X was installed. The industrial engineering department made careful estimates of these savings, as follows:

1958.........$32,000	1961..........$19,000	1964..........$10,000
1959.......... 25,000	1962.......... 16,000	1965.......... 7,000
1960.......... 22,000	1963.......... 13,000	

The following questions are to be answered as if it were November of 1957. They deal with various aspects of the choice between the alternatives, I, to sell Machine X at once for $36,000, and II, to install Machine X and operate it for the next 8 years. Where necessary to make assumptions about the timing of receipts and disbursements, assume that money payments near the end of 1957 are made on January 1, 1958 (i.e., at zero date on your time scale). Assume the end-of-year convention with respect to the savings in annual disbursements. In answering questions that involve income taxes, assume an end-of-year convention with regard to tax payments. For example, assume that anything that affects 1957 taxable income influences a tax payment at the end of 1957; anything that affects 1958 taxable income influences a tax payment at the end of 1958, etc.

(a) Assume Alternative II is selected. At what rate of return will the *total* investment in the purchase and installation of Machine X be recovered?

(b) Discuss the relevance of the rate of return computed in your answer to (a) in the decision between Alternatives I and II.

(c) Determine the year-by-year differences between Alternatives I and II in cash flow before income taxes.

(d) Use compound interest calculations to make an analysis of the cash flow series in your answer to (c) in a way that would provide a rational basis for choice between Alternatives I and II if the RST Company were not subject to income taxes.

(e) Analyze the effect of the choice between I and II on cash flow for income taxes. Assume an effective tax rate of 50% throughout the period of the study. Assume that if Machine X is installed, it will be depreciated for tax purposes by the years-digits method using a life of 8 years with zero salvage value. Assume that depreciation charges will start with the year 1958 and that a full-year's depreciation will be charged in 1958. Assume that if Machine X is sold at once, any loss sustained will be deductible from 1957 taxable income. Tabulate the differences between I and II in cash flow after income taxes.

(f) Use compound interest calculations to make an analysis of the final cash flow series in your answer to (e) in a way that provides a rational basis for choice between I and II.

(g) How would you recommend that your analysis in your answer to (f) be used by the management of the RST Company in choosing between Alternatives I and II?

17

The Influence on Economy Studies
of Sources of Investment Funds

Engineering economy impinges on many other fields. We have seen some relationships between engineering economy and accounting and income taxation. In this chapter we shall examine some relationships between engineering economy and certain aspects of business finance and government finance. Some additional aspects of government finance are discussed in the next chapter.

We shall see how certain types of confused reasoning may be introduced into economy studies where calculations appropriate for judging long-run economy of proposed investments in physical assets are combined with calculations related to the financing of these assets. We shall also see how certain techniques of engineering economy, particularly cash flow analysis and rate of return calculations, can be used to help in comparing the merits of alternative financing plans.

Possible Sources of Funds for Financing of Fixed Assets. Plant and equipment may be financed by (1) ownership funds or by (2) borrowed funds or by a combination of the two. In many cases another possible source of funds is (3) long-term leasing.

As the name implies, ownership funds are those furnished by the owners of an enterprise. In the case of an individual this is limited by his personal resources. A partnership may secure ownership funds from the existing partners, or it may possibly reorganize by taking another partner—a new owner. Similarly, a corporation may secure ownership funds in various ways from its existing stockholders, or it may acquire some more owners by selling stock to new stockholders. The ownership funds of governmental bodies are those supplied by current taxation and other current revenues.

Before we can discuss the relationship between borrowing and economy studies, some general background material is needed.

Borrowing. For funds to be borrowed, some security is usually required by lenders. This may be specific property that is put up as collateral. Thus, an individual may finance the purchase of a home by giving the lender a mortgage—a deed that conveys title to the lender (after appropriate legal action) in case the borrower fails to pay interest or principal on his note in accordance with his promise. Similarly, by means of somewhat more elaborate legal devices, a corporation may give a mortgage on specific physical property as security for a bond issue. Often, however, borrowing takes place without specific collateral, the security being the general credit of the borrower; this is the case with nearly all governmental loans.

Whatever the security, borrowed money must ultimately be repaid. It follows that if a proposed investment is to be financed by borrowing, two questions must be answered regarding it:

1. Is it economical in the long run as compared to other possible alternatives?
2. Do the conditions of repayment make it advisable in the short run?

Various Possible Plans for Repayment of Borrowed Money. Table 3–1 (page 36) described four different ways in which money borrowed for a period of several years or more might be repaid. These are representative of the ways of repaying personal loans, business loans (including corporate borrowings through bond issues), and government loans.

In Plan I, interest was paid each year.[1] No annual payments at all were made on the principal of the debt that was to be repaid in a lump sum at the end of a stipulated number of years. This is a common plan of repayment for corporate bond issues as well as for secured loans for business and personal purposes.

Where money is borrowed to be repaid in a lump sum, some plan is necessary for securing the lump sum to make the repayment. There are two possibilities here: (a) refunding, or (b) the accumulation of the necessary funds through the use of a sinking fund.

Refunding means that the money for repayment is secured through a new borrowing. This is common in corporate bond issues, particularly those of public utilities (including railroads) where the public regulation of rates generally makes it impracticable to accumulate sufficient funds to pay off bonds out of earnings. Although individual bonds carry a definite maturity date[2] and there is an

---

[1] As brought out in Chapter 7, the almost universal practice in bond issues of private corporations is for interest to be payable semiannually. This is also a common practice in other types of long-term loans.

[2] As brought out in Chapter 9, interest rates in the United States were declining throughout the 1930's and early 1940's. During this period much refunding of bond issues took place in advance of specified maturity dates in order to reduce interest charges. Such refunding is possible only when bonds are made callable (usually at a slight premium) at the election of the borrower in advance of the maturity date. Corporation bonds are generally issued with this callable feature. Most government bonds, on the other hand, have not been made callable.

obligation to pay the bondholders on that date, it is merely a case of borrowing from Peter to pay Paul. When the refunding of a bond issue is contemplated, there are no short-run burdensome repayment obligations to influence decisions between engineering alternatives. From the viewpoint of the engineer at the time the money is borrowed, the debt may be thought of as perpetual. Whenever refunding is contemplated, the managerial problem is to maintain the company's assets and earning power so that the company's credit position will permit a new borrowing at the time refunding is necessary.

Plans II and III in Table 3–1 called for annual payments on the principal of the debt. In Plan II the debt repayment was uniform from year to year with a resulting steady decrease in the annual interest payment. In Plan III the debt repayment increased from year to year in a way that permitted the sum of the principal and interest payments to be constant.

Where a bond issue provides for *serial maturities*, repayment plans similar to Plans II and III are used. For example, a $500,000, 20-year bond issue might consist of 500 bonds, each of $1,000 denomination. Of these, 25 might mature at the end of the 1st year, 25 more at the end of the 2nd, and so on until the 20th year when the final 25 bonds would mature. Each separate bond with its definite maturity date would be comparable to Plan I. However, the bond issue as a whole would be comparable to Plan II. This type of uniform serial maturities is characteristic of bond issues by states, counties, cities, school districts, and the many special types of local improvement districts. In such public borrowing, the use of serial maturities often is required by law in order to prevent the diversion of sinking funds to other purposes than debt repayment.

If uniform annual payments of principal plus interest are desired in a bond issue, it is possible to schedule serial maturities so that these payments are roughly uniform, approximating the equivalent uniform annual cost of capital recovery. This is sometimes done in real estate bond issues and in bond issues by local governments. The Plan III type of uniform payment is also characteristic of real estate loans to individuals.

In Plan IV no current interest was paid during the life of the loan and the final lump-sum payment covered both principal and compound interest. The well-known and popular Series E United States Savings Bonds are of this type. However, this scheme of payment is seldom used by business.

The different plans of debt repayment may sometimes be combined. For instance, a bond issue might run "flat" without repayment for 5 years, after which time uniform serial maturities start. Or half the bonds might mature serially, the other half coming due in a lump sum at the end of 20 years, with refunding contemplated.

Serial Maturities vs. Sinking Funds. Where a bond issue is to be paid off in a lump sum and refunding is not contemplated, it is necessary to establish a sinking fund to provide the lump sum. This involves the use of current receipts to amortize the debt just as is necessary when serial maturities are used. A sinking fund to pay off a bond issue might involve uniform annual deposits such as were discussed in the chapters on compound interest. However, it is also possible for the sinking fund deposits to be variable, possibly depending on net earnings each year.

One difficulty with sinking funds is that if they are conservatively invested with a view to maximum safety, the interest rate is likely to be considerably less than that which is being paid on the outstanding debt. For instance, a corporation with 5% bonds outstanding might be able to invest with safety at only $3\frac{1}{2}\%$. For this reason the best investment for current revenues intended for ultimate debt repayment is to pay off some of that debt immediately. This means that a borrowing corporation or public body may best invest its sinking fund in its own outstanding bonds, provided they can be purchased without paying too high a premium above par. If a borrower purchases his own bonds at par, this amounts to an investment of his sinking fund at the coupon rate of the bond issue.

The adoption of a plan calling for serial maturities has the same effect as if a regular sinking fund investment were made each year in the borrower's bonds at par. The serial maturities insure that such bonds will be available, and thus avoid all possibility of loss of interest due to the difference between what the borrower pays and what he can get on a conservative sinking fund.

From the standpoint of keeping to a minimum the total disbursements on account of the bond issue, the serial maturity plan would thus seem to have a definite advantage over the plan of establishing a sinking fund to provide for lump-sum repayment. In cases where either plan might be used, the choice between the two plans should depend somewhat on the prospective relative difficulty of meeting serial repayments and of maintaining a sinking fund. In the case of an industrial borrower anticipating wide fluctuations in annual earnings, a fixed annual repayment obligation may be a severe burden in bad years, and a sinking fund plan in which deposits (if possible in the form of purchases of outstanding bonds) vary with earnings may be advantageous. On the other hand, the tax revenues of local governments may be expected to be reasonably stable; here serial maturities on public bond issues prevent the possibility of pressure on public officials to appropriate existing sinking funds to current needs. Thus, serial maturities are advantageous in bond issues by cities, counties, states, and special improvement districts.

Many enterprises, if they are to finance at all, must do so on a serial repayment basis in order to satisfy the lender's requirements that the margin of security behind the loan be maintained or increased. This is particularly true if the loan is secured by a single property (such as an office building subject to depreciation). It is also likely to be true of hazardous enterprises or relatively small enterprises; in such cases the required repayment period is likely to be much shorter than the estimated life of the property being financed.

The Relationship Between Debt Repayment and Economy Studies. Many economy studies relate to the proposed acquisition of fixed assets that must be financed by borrowing. In such studies, in addition to considering the question "Will it pay in the long run?" it is also necessary to consider the question "Can the required repayment obligation be met?" If short-run repayment obligations for a proposed alternative are such as to prevent ever reaching the "long run," it is impractical to select that alternative even though it may show theoretical long-run economy.

However, the two questions of long-run economy and practicability of debt repayment should not be confused. It is only in those rare cases in which a proposed plant is to be financed entirely by borrowing, with the debt repayment spread fairly uniformly over its entire estimated life, that the debt charges may be correctly substituted for the annual cost of capital recovery (depreciation plus interest) in a study of long-run economy. This situation occurs in connection with some public improvements made by cities and other local governmental units, but seldom happens in private enterprise.

The mistake is sometimes made of including both debt repayment and depreciation as "costs" in an economy study. It should be obvious that the estimator who does this is badly confused in his reasoning, and that his calculations serve to answer neither the question of long-run economy nor the one of practicability of debt repayment.

A General Principle—Debt Charges Are Equal to the Annual Cost of Capital Recovery Where the Life of the Debt Is Equal to the Capital Recovery Period and the Interest Rate on the Debt Is Used as the Minimum Attractive Rate of Return. A city owns its electric distribution system, generating part of the electric energy that it distributes and purchasing the rest. It is proposed to increase the capacity of the generating station to eliminate the necessity of purchasing energy. An economy study is to be made to determine whether or not this will be economical.

The estimated cost of the new generating facilities is $2,000,000. If constructed, they will be financed entirely by long-term borrowing repayable from the revenues of the electric system. The proposed bonds will mature serially, with the entire issue to be paid off at the end of 20 years. Consultation with investment bankers indicates that such a $2,000,000 bond issue will need to have an interest rate of 4%. Serial maturities are to be scheduled in a way so that the sum of interest and bond repayment will be as nearly uniform as possible throughout the 20-year period. This annual payment of interest plus principal will, of course, be approximately $2,000,-000(crf–4%–20) = $2,000,000(0.07358) = $147,000.

If the estimated life of the generating plant is 20 years, with zero terminal salvage value, and if 4% is used as the minimum attractive rate of return, this annual outlay for debt service is exactly equal to the annual cost of capital recovery that should be used in the economy study. In an engineer's presentation to city officials of his analysis of the proposed investment, it may be more understandable if he shows this annual charge for debt service instead of an annual figure for capital recovery with a 4% return (or an annual figure for depreciation plus 4% interest). But it would be double counting to include *both* a figure for bond repayment with interest and a figure for depreciation plus interest. This would be charging the proposed generation of power with the investment costs of two generating stations during the life of one.

However, in this connection we should mention that in Chapter 9 we explained that the minimum attractive rate of return used in economy studies should ordinarily be greater than the bare cost of borrowed money. Further comments on this point, with particular reference to governmental projects, are made in Chapter 18.

Advantages and Hazards of Doing Business on Borrowed Money. Consider a business enterprise financed entirely by ownership funds and earning a 12% return after taxes. Assume that this business expands by borrowing money at 6% interest and that the after-tax cost of this borrowed money is 3%. If the new funds are as productive as the old ones, the owners will earn 9% (i.e., 12% — 3%) on the borrowed money without increasing their personal investments in the enterprise.

Using an ownership investment as a basis for borrowing is referred to as "trading on the equity." In effect, the owners' equity in an enterprise provides a margin of security that makes it possible to secure a loan. It is a general principle that trading on the equity makes good business better and bad business worse. The owners who succeed in earning more on the borrowed funds than the cost of the borrowed money will, of course, increase the rate of return on their own investments. On the other hand, if such an enterprise does not continue to be prosperous, all of its earnings may have to go to pay interest and principal on the debt, and the owners will have no return at all; in the absence of sufficient earnings to meet the debt charges, foreclosure on the part of the lenders may result in the owners losing their entire investment.

The foregoing comments about financing by borrowing are also applicable—with some modifications—to financing by long-term leases of fixed assets. The question of whether any particular business enterprise ought to finance in part by long-term loans and/or long-term leases cannot be analyzed without considering many aspects of business finance that are outside the scope of this book. However, it should be evident that long-term obligations are less suitable to enterprises of the feast-or-famine type than to enterprises with stable earning power. An enterprise financed entirely by ownership funds may weather a few bad years that could be fatal to an enterprise that has substantial fixed obligations.

When rate-of-return studies are made assuming financing by borrowing or by leasing, there is danger of an incorrect interpretation of computed rates of return. However, a rate-of-return-type analysis of alternate possible financing plans is an extremely useful tool to aid decisions on methods of financing. The foregoing ideas can be explained to best advantage with the help of numerical examples. Examples 17–1 and 17–2 are designed for this purpose.

EXAMPLE 17–1. ANALYSIS OF BEFORE-TAX AND AFTER-TAX EFFECTS OF EQUIPMENT PURCHASE USING DEBT FINANCING

Facts of the Case. It is proposed to acquire certain equipment having a first cost of $20,000, an estimated life of 8 years, and an estimated zero terminal salvage value. (These estimates of life and salvage value will be used for income tax purposes as well as in the economy study.) It is estimated that this equipment will reduce disbursements for labor and related costs by $6,000 a year. This saving in annual disbursements will be partially offset by increased expenditures of $800 a year for maintenance and property taxes. The net reduction in estimated annual disbursements (disregarding capital costs and income taxes) is therefore $5,200. It is believed this saving will continue throughout the 8-year life.

Straight-line depreciation will be used for accounting and income tax purposes. An effective income tax rate of 50% is to be assumed throughout the 8-year period.

This equipment might be purchased from equity funds. An alternative proposal calls for buying the equipment on time. The initial payment will be $8,000, with the remaining $12,000 to be paid off over the 8-year period. At the end of each year, $1,500 will be paid on the principal of the debt plus 8% interest on the unpaid balance. Thus the payments will decline uniformly from $2,460 at the end of the first year to $1,620 at the end of the 8th year.

Rate of Return Assuming Purchase from Equity Funds. Interpolation indicates a rate of return before income taxes of approximately 19.9% (crf = $5,200 ÷ $20,000 = 0.260).

The investment will increase annual taxable income by $5,200 − $\dfrac{\$20,000}{8}$ = $2,700. Annual disbursements for income taxes will therefore be 0.50($2,700) = $1,350. Annual cash flow after income taxes will be $5,200 − $1,350 = $3,850. Interpolation indicates a rate of return after taxes of approximately 10.7% (crf = 0.1925).

Rate of Return Assuming Purchase on Time. To compute rate of return before income taxes, the cash flow series (0, −$20,000; 1 to 8, +$5,200) must be combined with the cash flow associated with the $12,000 debt. The resulting cash flow series is 0, −$8,000; 1, +$2,740; 2, +$2,860; and so on, increasing $120 a year to +$3,580 at year 8. A trial-and-error calculation with the aid of the table of gradient present worth factors is:

PW at 30% = −$8,000 + $2,740(pwf-30%-8) + $120(gpwf-30%-8) = +$792

PW at 35% = −$8,000 + $2,740(pwf-35%-8) + $120(gpwf-35%-8) = −$239

The approximate before-tax rate of return on equity capital is 33.8%.

To compute rate of return after income taxes, an analysis is needed along the lines of Table 15–8 (page 339). Such an analysis will indicate cash flow at 0 date of −$8,000. The positive cash flow at date 1 will be $1,870; this will increase by $60 a year to $2,290 at date 8. (In each year from 1 to 8, there will be negative cash flow for debt repayment with interest. This will be partially offset because disbursements for income taxes will be reduced by 50% of the interest. For example, in year 1, the cash flow after income taxes is +$3,850 − $2,460 + 0.50($960) = $1,870.)

Trial-and-error calculations are:

PW at 15% = −$8,000 + $1,870(pwf-15%-8) + $60(gpwf-15%-8) = +$1,140

PW at 20% = −$8,000 + $1,870(pwf-20%-8) + $60(gpwf-20%-8) = −$ 232

The approximate after-tax rate of return on equity capital is 19.2%.

After-Tax Cost of Borrowed Money. It is of interest to compare the after-tax cash flow under complete equity financing with that under partial debt financing, as follows:

Year	After-Tax Cash Flow, Equity Financing	After-Tax Cash Flow, Purchase on Time	Difference in After-Tax Cash Flow
0	−$20,000	−$8,000	+$12,000
1	+3,850	+1,870	−1,980
2	+3,850	+1,930	−1,920
3	+3,850	+1,990	−1,860
4	+3,850	+2,050	−1,800
5	+3,850	+2,110	−1,740
6	+3,850	+2,170	−1,680
7	+3,850	+2,230	−1,620
8	+3,850	+2,290	−1,560

No trial-and-error present worth calculations are needed here to see that 4% is the interest rate that will make the present worth of the final column equal to zero. That is, the series of disbursements from years 1 to 8 would repay $1,500 of principal of a $12,000 debt each year with 4% interest on the unpaid balance, so that the debt would be completely repaid with 4% interest at the end of 8 years.

It should also be obvious that our final column of differences in cash flow is unrelated to the merits of the equipment that it is proposed to finance. The figures in the column depend only on the amount borrowed, the repayment schedule, the interest rate on the loan, and the effective income tax rate.

Our tabulation of difference in after-tax cash flow between equity financing and purchase on time was really unnecessary in this simple case. If we borrow money at 8% and if our effective income tax rate is 50%, the after-tax cost of our borrowed money obviously is 4%. However, we shall see in Example 17–2 that a similar tabulation will be a useful tool in the more complex circumstances that exist in many leasing agreements.

EXAMPLE 17–2. ANALYSIS OF BEFORE-TAX AND AFTER-TAX EFFECTS OF PROPOSED ACQUISITION OF EQUIPMENT BY LEASING

Facts of the Case. The equipment in Example 17–1 can also be acquired under an 8-year lease. The proposed lease contract calls for an initial deposit of $2,000, which will be returned at the end of the period of the lease. Rental charges will be $6,000 at the *beginning* of each of the first 3 years and $2,000 at the *beginning* of each of the remaining 5 years. Under this contract the lessee will pay all maintenance, insurance, and property taxes just as if he owned the equipment.

Rate of Return Before Income Taxes. Table 17–1 shows before-tax cash flow and calculation of present worths at 15% and 20%. Interpolation indicates a rate of return of approximately 17.8%.

Rate of Return After Income Taxes. Table 17–2 develops the year-by-year effect on taxable income of the proposal to lease the equipment. The taxable income each year will be increased by the $5,200 operating saving and decreased

TABLE 17–1

BEFORE-TAX ANALYSIS OF A PROPOSAL TO LEASE CERTAIN EQUIPMENT

Year	Effect on Cash Flow of Use of Equipment	Cash Flow for Payments Related to Lease	Combined Cash Flow	Present Worth at 15%	Present Worth at 20%
0		−$8,000	−$8,000	−$8,000	−$8,000
1	+$5,200	−6,000	−800	−696	−666
2	+5,200	−6,000	−800	−605	−556
3	+5,200	−2,000	+3,200	+2,104	+1,852
4	+5,200	−2,000	+3,200	+1,830	+1,543
5	+5,200	−2,000	+3,200	+1,591	+1,286
6	+5,200	−2,000	+3,200	+1,383	+1,072
7	+5,200	−2,000	+3,200	+1,203	+893
8	+5,200	+2,000	+7,200	+2,354	+1,675
Totals	+$41,600	−$28,000	+$13,600	+$1,164	−$ 901

by the rental payment applicable to the particular year. It should be noted that because each year's rental is *prepaid*, the effect on taxable income applies to the year following the payment date; the influence on cash flow for income taxes of each item of cash flow for rental occurs one year after the rental payment. (Under our end-of-year convention, we assign cash flow for income taxes to the end of the tax year. It was pointed out in Chapter 15 that tax payments by corporations in the United States tend to be centered at a date slightly later than this.) Of course the $2,000 negative cash flow for the deposit at zero date and

TABLE 17–2

AFTER-TAX ANALYSIS OF A PROPOSAL TO LEASE CERTAIN EQUIPMENT

Year	A Effect of Proposal on Cash Flow Before Income Taxes	B Effect of Use of Equipment on Taxable Income	C Effect of Rental Payment on Taxable Income	D Combined Effect on Taxable Income (B + C)	E Effect on Cash Flow for Income Taxes (−0.5D)	F Effect on Cash Flow After Income Taxes (A + E)
0	−$ 8,000					−$8,000
1	−800	+$ 5,200	−$ 6,000	−$ 800	+$ 400	−400
2	−800	+5,200	−6,000	−800	+400	−400
3	+3,200	+5,200	−6,000	−800	+400	+3,600
4	+3,200	+5,200	−2,000	+3,200	−1,600	+1,600
5	+3,200	+5,200	−2,000	+3,200	−1,600	+1,600
6	+3,200	+5,200	−2,000	+3,200	−1,600	+1,600
7	+3,200	+5,200	−2,000	+3,200	−1,600	+1,600
8	+7,200	+5,200	−2,000	+3,200	−1,600	+5,600
Totals	+$13,600	+$41,600	−$28,000	+$13,600	−$6,800	+$6,800

the $2,000 positive cash flow for the refund at date 8 have no effect on taxable income. As the equipment is not owned, no depreciation is recognized in computing taxable income. (Depreciation will enter into the *lessor's* taxable income but not the lessee's.)

The present worth of the cash flow series in column F of Table 17–2 may be computed to be +$432 at 10% and −$392 at 12%. The approximate after-tax rate of return on equity funds is 11.0%.

Cost of Money Provided by the Lessor. The following tabulation shows the differences in cash flow before and after income taxes between financing by the proposed lease agreement and financing entirely from ownership funds.

Year	Before-Tax Difference in Cash Flow Between Equity Financing and Leasing	After-Tax Difference in Cash Flow Between Equity Financing and Leasing
0	+$12,000	+$12,000
1	−6,000	−4,250
2	−6,000	−4,250
3	−2,000	−250
4	−2,000	−2,250
5	−2,000	−2,250
6	−2,000	−2,250
7	−2,000	−2,250
8	+2,000	+1,750
Totals	−$ 8,000	−$ 4,000

The present worth of the before-tax series is −$855 at 20% and +$225 at 25%. In effect, the funds made available by the lessor will cost the owners approximately 23.9% before taxes. The present worth of the after-tax series is −$106 at 10% and +$481 at 12%. Considered after income taxes, the cost of money provided by the lessor is approximately 10.4%.

It will be noted that, although $20,000 worth of equipment is being leased, the effect of the leasing agreement is to make only $12,000 of cash available to the lessor. Because of the requirement of a $2,000 deposit and a prepayment of $6,000 for the first year's rent, an initial outlay of $8,000 of ownership funds is required under the leasing agreement.

It will also be noted that Example 17–2 is like Example 17–1 in that the difference in cash flow between equity financing and outside financing is unrelated to the merits of the equipment that it is proposed to acquire. The before-tax and after-tax series of cash flow differences can be derived solely from the terms of the leasing agreement, the allowable depreciation if the equipment is to be owned, and the effective tax rate. However, unlike the case of debt financing in Example 17–1, the after-tax cost of money with a 50% tax rate is not exactly half of the before-tax cost. The favorable timing of the tax consequences of this particular leasing agreement is such that the after-tax cost of the money (10.4%) is considerably *less* than half the before-tax cost (23.9%).

Some Comments on Examples 17–1 and 17–2. The facts of these two examples have been deliberately simplified by assuming

straight-line depreciation, zero salvage value, a 50% tax rate, and a uniform saving in operating disbursements. This simplification permits the reader to concentrate attention on the methods of analysis and the points at issue in interpretation. The techniques illustrated are, of course, applicable in more complex circumstances. A more complex example involving debt financing has already been given (Example 15–8).

Example 17–1 illustrates the way in which trading on the equity can "make good business better." The equipment was productive enough to yield a prospective over-all rate of return of 10.7% after taxes. With debt financing of $12,000 of the total $20,000 investment at an after-tax cost of 4%, the rate of return on the required $8,000 of equity funds was 19.2%.

In contrast, in Example 17–2, the after-tax cost of the $12,000 secured by the leasing agreement was 10.4%. The leverage provided in Example 17–1 by the difference between the 10.7% and 4% figures did not exist in Example 17–2; here the rate of return on the required equity funds was only 11.0%.

Desirability of Separating Decision Making on Physical Plant from Decision Making on Methods of Financing. Throughout this book, the general principle has been stressed that separable decisions should be made separately. Some cases occur where a decision to acquire the use of certain fixed assets is inseparably linked with one particular plan for financing the assets. In such instances it is rational to apply a single analysis to the proposed acquisition and financing. But in the more common case where decisions among alternative fixed assets are clearly separable from decisions regarding policies on methods of financing, both types of decisions are likely to be made more intelligently if the analyses are separated.

Difficulties in Judging Merits of Proposed Plant Investments on the Basis of Prospective Rate of Return to Equity Capital Where It Is Assumed That a Portion of Financing Will Be by Borrowing or Leasing. In Examples 15–8, 17–1, and 17–2 we have computed rates of return to the portion of a proposed investment to be made from ownership funds—12.2% to the $6,000 equity investment in Example 15–8, and 19.2% and 11.0% to the respective equity investments in Examples 17–1 and 17–2. Calculations such as these are often made in industry. Given the assumptions regarding income taxation and method of financing, these are unquestionably valid as exercises in the mathematics of compound interest.

Nevertheless, the authors recommend against using such computed rates of return on equity investments as guides to decisions about the acquisition of fixed assets. Their objections to such use are as follows:

1. Because such computed rates of return depend on the fraction of equity funds assumed, they are not appropriate to determine the relative merits of types of plant that are to be financed in different ways.
2. In the common case where the cost of outside money (secured by borrowing or leasing) is less than the return earned by the equipment itself (as computed under the assumption of equity financing), a computed rate of return on a fractional equity investment tends to give an unduly favorable impression of the productivity of the equipment.

The foregoing objections apply to studies made either before or after income taxes. A numerical example may help to clarify the reasoning underlying the objections. We shall use the after-tax analysis from Example 17–1.

It will be recalled that with complete equity financing, the after-tax return was 10.7%. With 60% of the cost of the equipment borrowed at an after-tax cost of 4%, the return on the remaining 40% of equity capital was 19.2%.

Now let us change the leverage exerted by the low after-tax cost of borrowed money by assuming that 80% ($16,000) can be borrowed at 8% (before taxes). A calculation similar to that made in Example 17–1 will show that the after-tax return on the 20% ($4,000) of equity capital is approximately 30.6%. If we assume 90% can be borrowed, the return on the remaining 10% of equity capital can be computed to be approximately 49.6%. If we assume that 100% can be borrowed, the absurdity of the rate of return analysis is evident because the computed rate of return is infinite. (That is, there is a money return even though no equity investment is attributed to the proposed equipment.)

The Usefulness of Computed After-Tax Costs of Money. Throughout this book, we have stressed the point that interest rates are not always what they seem. In this connection we strongly recommend calculation of the after-tax cost of money to be borrowed or secured through leasing agreements, with such costs expressed as an interest rate in the manner illustrated at the ends of Examples 17–1 and 17–2. In these two examples it is evident that leasing at an after-tax cost of 10.4% is unattractive if we can borrow at an after-tax cost of 4.0%. In general such calculations are a great help in comparing the merits of alternate plans of financing.

Such calculations employ techniques that are similar to the ones we use in engineering economy, since they start with estimates of differences in cash flow and apply compound interest mathematics to these differences to find unknown interest rates.

The calculation of the after-tax cost of borrowed money is not always as simple as in Example 17–1. Some sources of complications in finding the true cost of borrowed money were illustrated in Chapter 8. These included the difference between a cash price and a price on terms, initial disbursements incident to securing a loan, and required annual disbursements throughout the life of a loan. Although the illustrations in Chapter 8 dealt with the before-tax cost of borrowed money, the same complications arise in computing after-tax costs. Several of the problems at the end of this chapter illustrate after-tax calculations where these complications exist.

Some Aspects of the Analysis of Proposed Leasing Agreements. There is great variety in the types of leasing agreements made in industry. In many cases both the lessor and lessee recognize that the lease may continue only for a relatively short term; such leases are terminable by the lessee on short notice.

The more interesting problems for the student of engineering economy arise where the lease is used as a device for long-term financing. In such cases it often is true that the same assets would be acquired with leasing or outright ownership and that the assets would be continued in service for the same number of years whether leased or owned. From the viewpoint of the lessee, the long-term lease is a fixed obligation not unlike an obligation for debt interest and repayment.[3]

Frequently the analysis of difference in cash flow before income taxes between leasing and ownership is more complicated than in Example 17–2. Certain disbursements necessary if an asset were owned (e.g., major maintenance overhauls, property taxes, insurance) may be made by the lessor—not by the lessee as stipulated in Example 17–2. There may be substantial prospective salvage values, realizable under ownership but not under leasing. These matters are illustrated in some of the problems at the end of this chapter.

An analysis of the difference in cash flow for income taxes requires a tabulation of deductions from taxable income under ownership and leasing. The after-tax analysis made at the end of Exam-

---

[3] For a good discussion of this point and of other aspects of leasing, see D. R. Gant, "Illusion in Lease Financing," *Harvard Business Review*, XXXVII, No. 2 (March–April, 1959), 121–42.

ple 17-2 could also have been obtained by means of the following tabulation:

Year	Deduction for Depreciation	Deduction for Rental	Difference in Taxable Income	Difference in Cash Flow for Income Taxes
1	$ 2,500	$ 6,000	−$3,500	+$1,750
2	2,500	6,000	−3,500	+1,750
3	2,500	6,000	−3,500	+1,750
4	2,500	2,000	+500	−250
5	2,500	2,000	+500	−250
6	2,500	2,000	+500	−250
7	2,500	2,000	+500	−250
8	2,500	2,000	+500	−250
Totals	$20,000	$28,000	−$8,000	+$4,000

Long-term leases of machinery and equipment generally are like Example 17-2 in requiring the highest rental charges during the early years. As illustrated in the foregoing tabulation, such an arrangement leads to a favorable timing of the tax consequences of leasing. The large difference between the before-tax cost and after-tax cost of money secured by leasing in Example 17-2 was due to the fact that a tax credit in the near future is more valuable than one in the more distant future. The longer the expected life of the equipment to be leased, the more favorable to leasing may be the tax consequences of the difference in timing of tax deductions under leasing and ownership.

When Is an Agreement That Purports To Be a Lease Not Recognized as a Lease for Income Tax Purposes? In order to secure the advantage of larger tax deductions in the early years of life, some agreements that are—in effect—sales on time are drawn in a way that makes them appear to be leases. Such agreements are viewed critically by taxing authorities in the United States. A Treasury publication contained the following advice to taxpayers on this topic: [4]

If you decide to lease equipment, rather than purchase it, you should determine whether the agreement is actually a lease or is, in reality, a conditional sales contract.

If the agreement is a lease, you will be entitled to deduct rental payments for the use of such equipment in your trade or business.

If the agreement is a conditional sales contract and you have acquired, or will acquire, title to or equity in the equipment, the payments under the agreement, to the extent they do not represent interest or other charges, will be considered as payments for the purchase of the equipment. You may not deduct these payments as rentals, but must capitalize them and recover them through deductions for depreciation over the life of the equipment.

[4] *Tax Guide for Small Business,* Internal Revenue Service Publication No. 334 (Washington, D.C.: Government Printing Office, 1959).

Look to the agreement, because whatever interest you obtain is acquired under the terms of the agreement itself. Whether the agreement, which in form is a lease, is in substance a conditional sales contract, depends upon the intent of the parties as shown by the agreement, read in the light of the facts and circumstances existing at the time the agreement was executed.

In ascertaining such intent, no single test, or special combination of tests is absolutely determinative. However, in the absence of compelling persuasive factors to the contrary, an agreement is considered a conditional sales contract rather than a lease if one or more of the following conditions are present:

1. Portions of the periodic payments are made specifically applicable to an equity to be acquired by you.
2. Title will be acquired upon payment of a stated amount of rentals which you are required to make under the contract.
3. The total amount which you are required to pay for a relatively short period of use constitutes an excessively large proportion of the total sum required to be paid to secure the transfer of the title.
4. The agreed rental payments materially exceed the current fair rental value. This may be indicative that the payments include an element other than compensation for the use of the property.
5. The property may be acquired under a purchase option at a price which is nominal in relation to the value of the property at the time when you may exercise the option, as determined at the time of entering into the original agreement, or which is a relatively small amount when compared with the total payments you are required to make.
6. Some portion of the periodic payments is specifically designated as interest or is otherwise readily recognizable as the equivalent of interest.
7. Title will be acquired upon payment of an aggregate amount (that is, the total of the rental payments plus the option price, if any) which approximates the price at which you could have purchased the equipment when you entered into the agreemnt, plus interest and carrying charges.

In the problems at the end of this chapter requiring the after-tax analysis of various leasing agreements, it will be assumed that the agreements described are legitimate leases and not conditional sales contracts.

A Classification of Sources of Equity Funds in Business Enterprise. Although the issues involved in choosing between equity financing, on the one hand, and long-term obligations involving borrowing or leasing, on the other hand, are beyond the scope of this book, it is helpful to classify sources of equity funds as follows:

1. New equity money (e.g., the sale of new stock by a corporation)
2. Profits retained in the business
3. Capital recovered through the depreciation charge

The relationship between depreciation charges and the financing of fixed assets is not always clear to persons who have not studied accounting. Example 17–3 presents this topic in a simplified form.

EXAMPLE 17-3. FINANCING FIXED ASSETS WITH CAPITAL
RECOVERED THROUGH THE DEPRECIATION CHARGE [5]

Facts of the Case. The accounting expense of depreciation was discussed in Chapter 10. One of the reasons for recognizing depreciation in the accounts is to include it in the selling price of the product or service. A concern that includes an adequate amount for depreciation in its selling price year after year will at least succeed in recovering the invested capital that is being used up through the decrease in value of its plant and machinery. In such a concern a part (or all) of the excess of income currently received over expenses currently paid out (i.e., expenses not including depreciation) will not be profit but will be recovered capital.

Assume that on January 1 of some specified year, a manufacturing company has the following balance sheet:

Assets

Current Assets

Cash		$ 300,000	
Accounts Receivable		500,000	
Inventories		600,000	$1,400,000

Fixed Assets

Land		150,000	
Plant and Machinery	$2,000,000		
Less			
Allowance for Depreciation	800,000	1,200,000	1,350,000
			$2,750,000

Liabilities and Owners' Equity

Current Liabilities

Accounts Payable	$ 300,000	
Notes Payable	200,000	$ 500,000

Fixed Liabilities

Mortgage Bonds Outstanding	500,000

Owners' Equity

Capital Stock	1,500,000	
Surplus	250,000	1,750,000
		$2,750,000

Suppose there is no profit or loss for the year, the company just clearing its expenses including estimated depreciation. A condensed form of its profit and loss statement for the year might be as follows:

Sales	$1,200,000
Less	
Cost of Goods Sold (including $100,000 Depreciation Expense)	850,000
Gross Profit on Sales	$ 350,000
Less	
Selling, Administrative, and Financial Expense (including Bond Interest)	350,000
Net Profit for Year	—

[5] For a more complete version of this same example and a more detailed discussion of this subject, see E. L. Grant and P. T. Norton, Jr., *Depreciation* (rev. prtg., New York: The Ronald Press Co., 1955), chap. xiv.

The cost of goods sold includes $750,000 currently paid out and $100,000 of depreciation expense, prepaid in previous years, which is balanced by a $100,000 increase in allowance for depreciation. Thus total expenses currently paid out are $1,100,000 ($750,000 + $350,000); with revenues of $1,200,000 there remains $100,000 of additional assets in the business to compensate for the estimated decrease in value of plant and machinery.

For the capital invested in the business to be conserved, this $100,000 must be left in the enterprise in some form. Conceivably it might all be an addition to cash. Or it might increase other current assets through financing additional accounts receivable, or financing a larger investment in inventories. Or the cash might be applied to decrease liabilities, reducing accounts or notes payable or paying off some of the mortgage bonds. In certain circumstances one of these uses or some combination of them might be imperative. But it is generally recognized that the primary use for such recovered capital should be the financing of fixed assets. This includes both those assets needed to replace those retired and other fixed assets acquired to reduce operating costs or increase revenues. If $30,000 of the $100,000 should be devoted to the replacement of assets having an original cost of $20,000 that were retired during the year, $50,000 to the acquisition of other new plant and machinery, $15,000 to financing increased inventories, and $5,000 to an increase of cash, and if the receivables and payables should be the same at the year end as at the start of the year, the year-end balance sheet will be as follows:

Assets

Current Assets

Cash	$ 305,000	
Accounts Receivable	500,000	
Inventories	615,000	$1,420,000

Fixed Assets

Land		150,000	
Plant and Machinery	$2,060,000		
Less			
Allowance for Depreciation	880,000	1,180,000	1,330,000
			$2,750,000

Liabilities and Owners' Equity

Current Liabilities

Accounts Payable	$ 300,000	
Notes Payable	200,000	$ 500,000

Fixed Liabilities

Mortgage Bonds Outstanding	500,000

Owners' Equity

Capital Stock	1,500,000	
Surplus	250,000	1,750,000
		$2,750,000

This corporation has made no profit during the year. If, as may well be the case, it is impossible to borrow more money or to sell more stock, the capital recovered through the depreciation charge is the only possible source of ownership funds to finance the purchase of plant and machinery. These funds are therefore of great importance in the continuation of the business.

As pointed out in Chapter 16, the factors that make replacements economical do not usually make them imperative. Machines and structures do not collapse like the "one hoss shay"; it is possible to continue them in service for a long time after it has become economical to replace them.

A business cannot continue indefinitely to operate profitably with an uneconomical plant; if its plant is worn out or obsolete, the concern is likely to have difficulty competing with rival concerns that have lower operating costs because their plants are new and modern. A manufacturing company that year after year diverts its recovered capital to uses other than the financing of fixed assets may ultimately find itself in this unfavorable competitive position. The difficulty of securing funds for other capital requirements (such as financing receivables and inventories or reducing debt) and the ease of putting off plant modernization may combine to bring about such diversion of funds.

Deferring replacements beyond the date when they are economical not only results in an uneconomical plant; it also has the hazard of causing depreciation rates that are much too low. Such low rates cause an overstatement of profits; the possible unfortunate consequences of such overstatement are obvious.

Complications in the Financing of Fixed Assets Created by a Rise in Price Levels.

A rise in price levels creates special difficulties in the way of financing new fixed assets. As pointed out in Chapter 10, the depreciation charge in the accounts is a writing-off of *cost*. In the years immediately following a price-level rise, the depreciation charges in the accounts apply in large measure to assets acquired before price levels had risen. Hence the funds made available through the depreciation charge tend to remain nearly constant whereas the funds needed to finance the replacement of any asset are greatly increased. At the same time, rising price levels create an increased demand for funds to finance inventories and accounts receivable. In such a period the funds needed for investment in fixed assets often cannot be secured without either a substantial diversion of profits to this purpose or the issuance of new securities or both.

Some Ways in Which Proposed Investments May Be Vetoed Because of Considerations of Financing.

If it is impossible to finance proposed physical assets in some way—either from equity funds, borrowing, or leasing—it is merely of academic interest that they would earn a good rate of return. And it is not only the proposals that *cannot* be financed that are eliminated due to considerations related to their financing. It often happens that one or more ways exist in which assets might be financed, but that for one reason or another these ways are unattractive from the viewpoint of the decision maker. This point is illustrated in Examples 17–4 and 17–5.

Moreover, as pointed out in Chapter 9, any limitation of investment funds tends to increase the appropriate minimum attractive rate of return. Some additional aspects of this matter are illustrated in Examples 17–5 and 17–6.

EXAMPLE 17–4. EFFECT ON AN INVESTMENT DECISION OF A REQUIREMENT FOR RAPID DEBT REPAYMENT

Facts of the Case. A family living in a rented house was offered a chance to purchase this house at a favorable price. However, because the house was an old one, only 50% of the purchase price could be borrowed on a long-term first mortgage. The family had funds for only a 10% down payment. The present owner agreed to take a second mortgage for the remaining 40%. But he insisted that one-fifth of the principal of this second mortgage be repaid each year. No better source of money could be found for this 40% of the purchase price.

An analysis of the long-run economy of home ownership and renting was favorable to home ownership. However, because of the high repayment requirements on the second mortgage, the money outlays to finance home ownership would be much higher than rent. These outlays included principal and interest payments on both mortgages, maintenance, property taxes, and insurance. When these outlays were considered with relation to the prospective family income, it was evident that not enough money would be left for the other necessary family living expenses during the next 5 years. Therefore, it was advisable to continue to rent.

EXAMPLE 17–5. EFFECT ON CHOICE OF INVESTMENT ALTERNATIVES OF DECISION MAKING FROM VIEWPOINT OF PERSONS HOLDING A CONTROLLING INTEREST IN A CLOSELY HELD CORPORATION

Facts of the Case. Three members of a family held slightly more than half of the stock of a successful small manufacturing company. This company had no long-term debt. These controlling stockholders were active officers of the corporation. As the company made capital goods, its profits fluctuated considerably; although its over-all profit record had been excellent, there had been occasional loss years.

The proposal was made to expand by manufacturing certain new products. An analysis of the proposal indicated that there was a good prospective rate of return. However, all the moneys for plant investment that became available each year from retained earnings and depreciation charges were being absorbed by replacements and plant modernization in connection with the present product line. A substantial investment in plant and equipment was needed to undertake the new product line. Therefore, it was necessary to raise new capital if this proposal for business expansion were to be accepted.

Investigation disclosed that this capital could be raised either by the sale of new stock to certain persons interested in the company or by a 10-year loan from an individual investor. The proposal to make the new products was finally rejected by the three controlling stockholders on the grounds that neither type of financing was acceptable to them.

The objection to the sale of stock was that the three stockholders would no longer have a majority stock interest that made it certain they could control the company's affairs. The 10-year loan also involved certain restrictions on their control through stipulations (such as one limiting dividend payments while the loan was outstanding). However, their chief objection to the loan was that the required annual payments of principal and interest made them much more vulnerable to any business recession that might cause one or more loss years.

In effect, this decision, based on considerations related to financing, caused the rejection of an investment proposal (plant expansion) yielding a high prospective rate of return even though other investment proposals (replacements and modernization) were being accepted yielding lower rates of return.

EXAMPLE 17–6. CRITERIA FOR INVESTMENT DECISIONS IN AN UNDERFINANCED MANUFACTURING BUSINESS

Facts of the Case. Two partners purchased a small manufacturing enterprise. They used their entire personal savings for a payment to the former proprietor of half the purchase price. The remainder of the purchase price was to be paid from a stipulated percentage of the profits.

During its initial years, the partnership was always short of cash. The partners saw many chances to reduce production costs by moderate outlays for new equipment or for changes in existing equipment. Because of the cash shortage and because it was impracticable to bring new money into the business, every proposal had to be judged primarily with relation to its effect on the short-term cash position of the business. During the first year, it was not possible to adopt any proposal that—in terms of cash flow—would not "pay for itself" in three months.

Comment on Examples 17–4 to 17–6. Whenever proposed plant is to be financed largely by borrowing, as in Example 17–4, a requirement for rapid debt repayment may prevent the acquisition of plant that would be economical in the long run. This condition occurs not only for individuals and for business enterprises; it also occurs for local governmental works where 100% debt financing is common. Further comment on this matter is made in Chapter 18.

A striking aspect of Example 17–5 was that a larger attractive project was vetoed because it needed new financing even though smaller less attractive projects were approved where they could be financed from funds generated within the business enterprise.

Example 17–6 dealt with rather specialized circumstances of capital rationing in which no investments could be undertaken that did not have a prospective rate of return of several hundred per cent. In such circumstances it was appropriate to express the criterion for decision making as a "payout" requirement. For reasons explained in Chapter 19, the payout requirement is not a sound criterion for making investment decisions under more normal circumstances.

Summary. Some of the points brought out in this chapter may be restated for emphasis as follows:

In most instances where it is expected that the major part of the cost of fixed assets will be financed by borrowing or leasing, the prospective rate of return on a small increment of equity capital is not a sound guide to investment decisions.

In comparing different possible schemes of financing through borrowing or leasing, it is desirable to compute an after-tax cost of money for each scheme. A tabulation should be made of prospective differences in cash flow after taxes between equity financing and each other proposed scheme of financing. Appropriate compound interest calculations should then be made to find the unknown interest rate in each case.

Whenever it is proposed to acquire the ownership of property through the borrowing of money, consideration should always be given to the question of whether or not it is practicable to meet the repayment obligations.

The question of the practicability of debt repayment should not be confused with the question of long-run economy; repayment obligations and depreciation should not appear as "costs" in the same study.

The problem of meeting short-run repayment obligations does not arise in connection with a bond issue on which refunding is contemplated; it does arise whenever bonds mature serially.

Doing business on borrowed money has the tendency to make good business better and bad business worse.

Available funds for plant expansion and replacement are often limited; if so, the problem is likely to be to select, from a number of desirable uses for these funds, those which seem likely to yield the highest returns.

Where for some reason it is impossible or undesirable to secure funds by borrowing or to secure new ownership funds, the sources of financing for new fixed assets are limited to profits and to capital recovered through the depreciation charge. It often happens that such funds are practically limited to the latter source by company policies or by income tax considerations influencing the use of profits.

A limitation of funds for investment in fixed assets may result in the requirement of a high minimum attractive return or a short payoff period or both.

Problems

17–1. A machine tool builder will rent new machine tools for 3 years under the following rental contract:

The purchase price of a tool is designated as 100N. The lessee must deposit 10N at the start of the rental period; when the tool is returned to the lessor in good condition at the end of 3 years, this deposit is refunded to the lessee. Annual rental payments are 24N, payable at the start of each year. Lessee pays all operation and maintenance costs, including property taxes and insurance.

A user of machine tools has determined that he intends to use a certain machine tool for a 3-year period. He is undecided whether to purchase the machine and sell it in the secondhand market at the end of 3 years or to rent it. Designate purchase as Plan P and rental as Plan R. Show the year-by-year differences in cash flow before income taxes for these two plans. Assume that the machine can be sold for a net figure of 55N after 3 years of use. Find the interest rate that makes the two plans have equal present worths of net cash flow before income taxes. (This rate might be interpreted as a basis for decision making in an organization not subject to income taxes—such as a nonprofit organization.) (*Ans.* = (P − R) cash flow: 0, −66N; 1, +24N; 2, +24N; 3, +45N; interest rate, 17.2%.)

17-2. (a) In Problem 17–1, assume an effective tax rate of 50%. If Plan P is selected, years-digits depreciation will be used for tax purposes assuming a 3-year life and 55% salvage value. If Plan R is selected, assume that rental paid for a particular year will affect taxes paid at the year end. What is the after-tax cost of the money made available by the lease agreement? (*Ans.* = 9.1%.)

(b) What would be the after-tax cost of the money made available by the lease agrement if straight-line depreciation were to be used? (*Ans.* = 8.6%.)

17-3. (a) It is estimated that a proposed equipment investment of $30,000 to be financed from equity funds will cause an excess of receipts over disbursements of $9,000 a year for 5 years. The equipment will have zero salvage value at the end of 5 years. What is the prospective rate of return before income taxes? (*Ans.* = 15.2%.)

(b) Assume that this equipment can be financed by a $15,000 down payment from equity funds. The remainder will be paid off at $3,000 a year plus 8% interest on the unpaid balance. What is the prospective before-tax rate of return on the equity investment? (*Ans.* = 21.6%.)

(c) Assume that the equipment can be financed by a $5,000 down payment from equity funds. The remainder will be paid off at $5,000 a year plus 8% interest on the unpaid balance. What is the prospective before-tax rate of return on the equity investment? (*Ans.* = 42.0%.)

17-4. Find the after-tax rates of return on equity investment in parts (a), (b), and (c) of Problem 17–3, assuming a 50% effective tax rate and years-digits depreciation based on a 5-year life and zero salvage value. (*Ans.* = (a) 8.8%; (b) 14.0%; (c) 38.7%.)

17-5. A home may be purchased for cash for $20,000. Or it may be purchased by a $6,000 down payment and a $15,000 mortgage loan with interest at 6%. The loan is scheduled to be paid off in 15 years by payments of $1,000 at the end of each year plus interest on the balance that was unpaid at the start of the year. A "gift" of $500 must be made to a "financial consultant" to secure this loan. The homeowner will itemize his nonbusiness deductions and will, therefore, secure a tax deduction for interest paid. No tax deduction will be available for the higher purchase price on time or for the $500 "gift."

(a) Compute the true cost of this borrowed money before income taxes, analyzing the matter along the lines explained in Chapter 8. (*Ans.* = 7.9%.)

(b) Compute the after-tax cost of this borrowed money, assuming an effective tax rate of 25% throughout the 15 years. (*Ans.* = 6.2%.)

17-6. Mrs. Z is a widow, 62 years old, who must live on a modest life annuity supplemented by social security payments, plus the moneys received from investment of the $24,000 proceeds of an insurance policy. She has decided to invest the $24,000 in an apartment rental property. She is giving serious consideration to purchasing either apartment house S or apartment house T.

The asking price of S is $60,000. To finance this project, she will assume an existing $36,000 mortgage on the property and pay the remaining $24,000. The mortgage must be paid off at $2,400 a year for 15 years with interest at 6% on the unpaid balance. With all apartments rented, the rental income is $7,500 a year. Her financial adviser tells her that it is conservative to assume that in the long run there will be an average occupancy of 90%. In addition to the payments of interest and principal on the debt, estimated annual disbursements are $900 for property taxes, $150 for insurance, and $750 for other operation and maintenance, a total of $1,800.

Since the asking price of T is $24,000, it can be purchased free of debt. With all apartments rented, the rental income is $3,000 a year. An average occupancy of 90% is to be assumed in the following analysis. Property taxes, insurance, and other annual disbursements are estimated to be a total of $720.

Either apartment will have to be depreciated for income tax purposes by the straight-line method, assuming a remaining life of 50 years with zero salvage value. In S, the investment is divisible into $10,000 for the land (nondepreciable) and $50,000 for the building. In T, the division is $4,000 for the land and $20,000 for the building. For the purpose of the following analysis, assume Mrs. Z's effective tax rate to be 20%.

(a) Assume that the criterion for decision making is after-tax rate of return on equity investment. What will this be for each apartment house, based on the assumed 90% occupancy. Base your analysis on the assumption of a 15-year period of ownership (approximately equal to Mrs. Z's life expectancy). Assume that the resale value 15 years hence of each apartment house will be equal to its present purchase price, on the grounds that population growth and price level increases will offset the obsolescence and deterioration of the properties. Neglect any possible taxes (e.g., capital gains taxes or estate taxes) on disposal of the properties at the end of 15 years. (*Ans.* = S, 8.3%; T, 6.9%.)

(b) Compute the cash flow after income taxes for each property for the first year and for the 5th year of ownership, assuming 90% of occupancy in these years. (*Ans.* = first year, S, +$32, T, +$1,664; 5th year, S, +$492.8, T, +$1,664.)

17–7. In order to judge the sensitivity of the conclusions in Problem 17–6 to the assumption of 90% occupancy, compute prospective rates of return on equity capital for S and T assuming average occupancy rates of 100% and 80%. Compute cash flow for the 5th year of ownership on the assumption of 60% of occupancy during this year.

17–8. Discuss the issues involved in Mrs. Z's choice of the major criterion for decision making between investments S and T in Problem 17–6. Under what circumstances would prospective positive cash flow in the next few years be a superior criterion to rate of return? What weight in the choice do you think should be given to the matter of differences in sensitivity to percentage of occupancy, examined in your solution of Problem 17–7?

17–9. Find the after-tax cost of the borrowed money in Problem 8–11 (page 133), assuming the corporation's effective tax rate to be 50%. The $1,250,000 difference between the amount received and the face amount of the bonds will be prorated equally among the 30 years as a tax deduction. (*Ans.* = 2.5%.)

17–10. A proposal is made for a city-owned public garage to be built in the business district of a certain city. The purchase price of the required land is $500,000 and the estimated first cost of the garage building is $1,000,000. The proponents of this garage project suggest that it be financed by $1,500,000 of general obligation bonds of the city. These bonds would mature at $75,000 a year for 20 years and would pay 4% interest per annum. The estimated life of the garage building is 50 years.

A committee from a local garage owners' association has submitted a report on this project. This report, given to the city council, seems to show that the expenses of the project will exceed its revenues. The tabulated annual expenses include the following items:

Building depreciation ($1,000,000 ÷ 50) $20,000
Bond repayment   75,000
Bond interest   60,000
Sinking fund at 3% for building replacement   8,870

Comment on the relevance of these items in the economic analysis of this project. Discuss also the question of the different types of economic analysis that it might be appropriate to make and the relevance of various items based on the capital investment in each type of economic analysis.

17-11. (a) It is estimated that a proposed equipment investment of $39,000 to be financed from equity funds will cause an excess of receipts over disbursements of $8,800 a year for 12 years. The equipment will have zero salvage value at the end of 12 years. What is the prospective rate of return before income taxes?

(b) Assume that this equipment can be financed by a $15,000 down payment from equity funds. The remainder will be paid off at $2,000 a year plus 8% interest on the unpaid balance. What is the prospective before-tax rate of return on the equity investment?

(c) Assume that the equipment can be financed by a $9,000 down payment from equity funds. The remainder will be paid off at $2,500 a year plus 8% interest on the unpaid balance. What is the prospective before-tax rate of return on the equity investment?

17-12. Find the after-tax rates of return on equity investment in parts (a), (b), and (c) of Problem 17-11, assuming a 30% effective tax rate and years-digits depreciation based on a 12-year life and zero salvage value.

17-13. Two alternate sites for a new service station for an oil company are under consideration. Site A is on leased land; site B is on land that will be purchased. Each site requires an investment of $60,000 in the service station itself, assumed to have zero salvage value at the end of the 15-year life. Each site requires a commitment of $20,000 of working capital, assumed to be fully recoverable (i.e., to have a 100% salvage value) at the end of the 15-year life. Site B requires an investment of $40,000 in land; it is estimated that this land can be sold for $80,000 at the end of the 15 years. The estimated annual excess of receipts over disbursements for either station in connection with service station operation is $25,000. At site A there will be an additional annual disbursement of $5,000 for land rental. At site B, there will be an annual disbursement of $1,000 for property taxes on the land owned.

Straight-line depreciation on the service station itself will be used for income tax purposes, assuming a 15-year life and zero salvage value. Effective tax rates of 50% on ordinary income and 25% on capital gains are to be assumed.

(a) Compute the prospective rate of return after income taxes on the investment at site A.

(b) Compute the prospective rate of return after income taxes on the investment at site B.

(c) Compute the prospective rate of return after income taxes on the extra investment required by site B over the investment needed at site A.

(d) Discuss the relevance of the rates of return computed in (a), (b), and (c) with reference to the choice between sites A and B. What other information, if any, would you want before deciding which of these two sites you believe to be preferable?

17–14. The four parts of this problem all deal with different aspects of an agreement under which Company B, the lessee, rents certain machine tools from Company A, the lessor. The particular agreement deals with a 5-year lease of tools that have a first cost of $100,000. Company B pays $25,000 rental at the start of the first year, $24,000 at the start of the second, $23,000 at the start of the third, $22,000 at the start of the fourth, and $21,000 at the start of the fifth year. (The annual figures were computed as if $100,000 had been borrowed to be repaid by 5 annual payments of $20,000 plus 5% interest on the unpaid principal; however, the rental is paid at the start of each year rather than at the end of each year as would be the case if a debt were repaid with interest.) There are many other equipment rental agreements between Companies A and B that are similar to the one cited. Under all of these agreements, Company B pays all insurance, repairs, and property taxes.

(a) On the assumption that the machine tools will be scrapped with a zero net salvage value at the end of the 5-year period, compute the rate of return before income taxes that Company A will earn on its investment.

(b) On the assumption that the machine tools will be removed from the premises of Company B at the end of the 5-year lease and immediately sold in the secondhand market, compute the rate of return before income taxes that Company A will earn on its investment. Assume a net realized value of $25,000. (This figure is based on an estimate that the tools can be sold for $30,000 and that necessary disbursements in connection with their sale will be $5,000.)

(c) For the assumptions of part (b), compute Company A's rate of return after income taxes. Assume an effective tax rate of 50%. Assume that tax payments are made at the end of the year in which taxable income is received. Company A uses years-digits depreciation accounting. Assume that an estimate of a 5-year life and 25% net salvage value will be acceptable to the taxing authorities.

(d) For nearly all of the equipment that it leases from Company A, Company B terminates its use of the equipment at the end of its 5-year rental period. However, for certain equipment, it is probable that Company B will require 20 years of service. It is therefore desired to compare an outright immediate purchase from equity funds for $100,000 with the plan of leasing for 5 years and then purchasing the equipment from Company A at the going secondhand market price. It is estimated that this purchase price 5 years hence will be $30,000. A comparison of estimated cash flow before income taxes for the two plans of financing the 20 years of service is as follows:

Year	Plan I—Lease Now; Purchase in 5 Years	Plan II— Purchase Now
0	−$25,000	−$100,000
1	−24,000	
2	−23,000	
3	−22,000	
4	−21,000	
5	−30,000	

It is desired to compare Plans I and II after income taxes. Assume that Company B will have an effective tax rate of 50% of taxable income for the next 20 years. It uses straight-line depreciation for tax purposes. Assume that if Plan I is adopted, the depreciation write-off from years 6 to 20 will be based on an estimate of a 15-year remaining life and zero salvage value. Assume that if Plan II is adopted, the depreciation write-off from years 1 to 20 will be based on an estimate of a 20-year life and zero salvage value. Compute an interest rate that makes Plans I and II equivalent after income taxes. Give your interpretation of your computed rate as a basis for a choice between the two plans by the management of Company B.

17–15. Company X is a lessor of capital assets. This company holds title to office buildings, hotels, warehouses, stores, machine tools, construction equipment, slot machines, and various other types of assets intended to produce income for their lessees. All of the assets are leased to the respective operators under an agreement that requires the lessee to pay all upkeep, property taxes, and insurance. Mr. A, one of the officials of Company X, is very articulate in pointing out why he believes it is to the advantage of the operators of capital assets to acquire the use of such assets by means of leasing rather than by outright ownership. He states that working capital usually is the most productive capital invested in a business enterprise and that leasing agreements (such as those made by Company X) have the effect of making more working capital available to the lessee. He uses the following example to compare a 10-year lease of a fixed asset with outright ownership of the same asset:

An asset having a first cost of $110,000, a life of 10 years, and zero salvage value may be purchased or leased. If leased, the lessor requires an initial deposit of $10,000 to be refunded at the end of the term of the lease. The rental charge will be $2,500 a month for the first 5 years and $500 a month over the final 5 years. If purchased, the asset will be depreciated for tax purposes by the years-digits method. If leased, the rental charge will be deductible from taxable income for the year in which it is made. For the sake of simplicity in Mr. A's example, an effective tax rate of 50% is used. He assumes that any funds made available by choosing the lease rather than outright purchase will serve to increase working capital. Because Mr. A contends that working capital generally earns at least 20% after income taxes, his example assumes that all funds made available by the choice of the lease agreement will earn a rate of 20%. His conclusion from the following table is that the decision to lease this $110,000 asset rather than to own it outright will yield the company leasing the asset an additional $149,300 after income taxes in 10 years. Therefore, he asserts, it is better to lease than to own.

Year	Difference in Cash Flow Before Income Taxes Between Leasing and Ownership	Difference in Cash Flow for Income Taxes	Difference in Cash Flow After Income Taxes	Cash Accumulation from Differences After Allowing for 20% Return Each Year		
0	+$100,000		+$100,000			$100,000
1	−30,000	+$5,000	−25,000	1.2(100,000)	− 25,000 =	95,000
2	−30,000	+6,000	−24,000	1.2(95,000)	− 24,000 =	90,000
3	−30,000	+7,000	−23,000	1.2(90,000)	− 23,000 =	85,000
4	−30,000	+8,000	−22,000	1.2(85,000)	− 22,000 =	80,000
5	−30,000	+9,000	−21,000	1.2(80,000)	− 21,000 =	75,000
6	−6,000	−2,000	−8,000	1.2(75,000)	− 8,000 =	82,000
7	−6,000	−1,000	−7,000	1.2(82,000)	− 7,000 =	91,400
8	−6,000	0	−6,000	1.2(91,400)	− 6,000 =	103,680
9	−6,000	+1,000	−5,000	1.2(103,680)	− 5,000 =	119,416
10	+4,000	+2,000	+6,000	1.2(119,416)	+ 6,000 =	149,300

(a) Has Mr. A made a correct analysis of the prospective differences in cash flow after income taxes? Given his figures for differences in cash flow, is his figure of a difference of $149,300 in compound amount at the end of 10 years consistent with his assumptions? Explain your answers. (It will be noted that he has used an end-of-year convention with respect to monthly rental payments to be made during a year and with respect to the payment of income taxes on each year's income. In your analysis of this problem, assume that this end-of-year convention is satisfactory.)

(b) The leasing agreement may be viewed as providing a source of investment capital for the lessee. Disregarding the effect of the leasing agreement on income taxes, express the cost of this capital as an interest rate.

(c) Considering the effect on income taxes of the difference between leasing and outright purchase, express the cost of this capital as an interest rate. Accept the assumptions of years-digits depreciation and an effective tax rate of 50% throughout the 10-year period.

(d) Discuss the relevance of Mr. A's analysis and of the two interest rates that you computed in your answers to (b) and (c) as a basis for a decision between leasing and outright ownership to be made by the prospective lessee. Assume that equity funds can be made available for the purchase of this $110,000 asset if it is decided that outright purchase is more advantageous than leasing. What information other than leasing terms, tax rate, and depreciation method, if any, would you need before deciding on your recommendation between leasing and ownership? How would this additional information influence your recommendation?

17-16. A manufacturer of machine tools offers the folllowing plan for the rental of his product. The outright price of a tool is designated as 100C. Upon rental, a deposit of 10C is required, to be returned upon termination of the rental. For the first 4 years, the rental charge, payable at the *start* of each year, is 18C. For the next 3 years, the rental charge, payable at the start of each year, is 14C. Thereafter, the annual prepaid rental is 6C. The lessee may terminate the agreement at the end of the 4th year, at the end of the 7th year, or at the end of any year thereafter.

The GH Company uses many of these tools that have been purchased outright. These have typically been retired when 9 years old with a 10% salvage value. This company's effective tax rate is 50%. Consideration is being given to a change in policy to rental for a 9-year period rather than outright purchase from equity funds. If purchased, tools are depreciated for tax purposes by the years-digits method using the life and salvage value based on the company's experience. On the assumption that tools will be leased, compute the after-tax cost of the money made available by the leasing agreement.

17-17. A municipally owned water plant showed in its report the following figures for January 1, 1959:

A. Total investment in plant now in service $426,415
B. Estimated depreciation to date on plant now in service 151,200
C. Net present value (A — B) 275,215
D. Bonds outstanding against the plant 180,000

The accounts of the plant were kept on a "cash" basis, so that this figure for net present value was merely a statistical figure built up from past records of the cost of plant additions and the city engineer's estimates of the amount of depreciation chargeable each year. The cash receipts and disbursements from the water department fund for the year 1959 were as follows:

Receipts		*Disbursements*	
Sale of water to private customers	$68,300	Labor	$ 7,800
		Miscellaneous operating supplies	1,500
Sale of water to city departments including hydrant rental	5,600	New well	5,000
		Power for pumping	10,240
		Pump house and pump at new well	3,200
		Repairs to pumps	1,870
		Maintenance of distribution system	4,100
		Cost of new water mains	1,580
		Interest on bonds	9,000
		Repayment of bonds	10,000
		Transfers to other city departments (used for general city offices, police department, and street lighting)	19,610
	$73,900		$73,900

The city engineer's figure for depreciation chargeable in 1959 was $20,120.

A committee of citizens, criticizing the financial policy of the city in running the water department, point out that since no sinking fund has ever been maintained, there has been no financial provision made to take care of the depreciation of the plant. Discuss the topic of whether this criticism is sound, giving specific answers to the following questions:

(a) What outlays, if any, during 1959, do you think should be viewed as financial provision for depreciation? If the city engineer's figure for 1959 depreciation is accepted, do you think this financial provision has been adequate? Why or why not?

(b) It is known that the original construction of this plant was financed entirely by a bond issue. If operation and maintenance, debt service, and plant additions have been financed solely from the sale of water, and if the city engineer's over-all depreciation figure is accepted as reasonable, what can you say about the over-all financial provision for depreciation up to the end of 1959?

17–18. A writer on the subject of the determination of the costs of public hydroelectric power projects included the following items as costs: (1) interest on the first cost of the project; (2) depreciation by the straight-line method based on the estimated life of the project; (3) an annual deposit in an amortization sinking fund sufficient to amount to the first cost of the project at the end of 50 years (or at the end of the life of the project if that should be less than 50 years); (4) where money is borrowed, the annual disbursements for bond interest and bond repayment; (5) all actual annual disbursements for operation and maintenance of the project.

Do you believe that annual cost should properly be considered as the sum of these items? Explain your answer.

18

Some Aspects of Economy Studies
for Governmental Activities

We started this book with General Carty's questions "Why at all?" "Why now?" "Why this way?" These questions are just as relevant in government as in private enterprise. The basic procedures in decision making about proposed governmental outlays for fixed assets ought to be the same as in proposed outlays in private business, namely:

1. Define alternatives clearly and try to determine the differences in consequences of various alternatives.
2. In so far as practicable, make these differences commensurable by expressing them in terms of money.
3. Apply some criterion to the monetary figures to provide a basis for judgment whether proposed investments are justified. The time value of money should be recognized in establishing this criterion.
4. Choose among alternatives applying the foregoing criterion but also giving consideration to the differences among alternatives that were not reduced to money terms.

Special Difficulties in the Way of Economy in Governmental Activities. Nevertheless, the securing of maximum economy in public works is often a more complex and troublesome matter than in private enterprise. Some special difficulties are as follows:

1. In private business, the securing of profits is generally accepted by those responsible for decisions as the standard of business success. There is no such general acceptance of any standard of success of public works by either the public officials immediately responsible for decisions or the general public that is ultimately responsible for them.

2. In private business there is a unified owner interest—the interest in the securing of profits—and ownership control of decisions on technical matters, at least in the case of large corporations.

is comparatively remote. (That is, the individual stockholder is not likely to be greatly concerned about technical decisions under the jurisdiction of the chief engineer; even if concerned, he is not in a position to do much about it.) In public works there may be a wide variety of owner interests (assuming that the citizens of a community bear a relation to its government similar to the relation of the stockholders to their corporation) that are often in conflict with one another, and individual owners are much more articulate about decisions on technical matters and their control of such matters is fairly direct.

3. The customers of a private business are generally in the position of making a voluntary purchase of goods or services for which they make payment in the form of a price that is presumably less than their valuations of the benefits they receive. The beneficiaries of public works, on the other hand, generally receive their services without any specific voluntary purchase; payment that is made for these services in the form of taxes does not bear any necessary relation to benefits received by the individual taxpayer. This tends to accentuate the diversity of owner interests above mentioned. Because the beneficiaries of public works do not pay for their benefits directly in the form of a price, there is a constant pressure on public officials to undertake projects and activities that are decidedly uneconomical from any common-sense viewpoint. This pressure for an unreasonably high standard of service is much less likely to exist from the customers of a private enterprise. On the other hand, because there are always a few taxpayers who do not receive, from public works projects, benefits that are in excess of their payments for those projects, there is frequently determined opposition by influential taxpaying groups to projects that are sound and economical.

4. Politics is always a factor in public business, and even in cases where political favoritism or locality favoritism of the "pork barrel legislation" type does not enter into the picture, this political control is operative. In addition to the question of whether an expenditure is really desirable from the standpoint of community economy, the question always arises whether it will appear justifiable to the general public and to boards of aldermen or legislative bodies that may not have the technical background or openness of mind for proper appreciation of all of the factors in the case. This point of view underlies the thinking of nearly all heads of government departments and is often a serious preventive of proper decisions from the standpoint of engineering economy. Particularly does it create difficulties in the way of getting a planned coordinated development

for the future, as contrasted with piecemeal construction where each decision is made only to meet a present emergency.

5. The short and uncertain tenure of office of many public officials is an obstacle to a carrying out of a consistent policy that is not so likely to exist in private business.

6. The legal limitations on what may be done in public works are in many respects much more severe than those encountered in private enterprise.

7. It often is more difficult to secure reliable estimates regarding relevant matters in public works economy studies than in similar studies for private enterprise. Moreover, the dangers of double-counting and other types of incorrect reasoning are much greater in economy studies for public works. Matters that cannot readily be reduced to estimated money receipts and disbursements (i.e., irreducibles) are properly given more consideration in arriving at decisions between alternatives. All in all, it is more difficult to make satisfactory economy studies for public works than to make satisfactory economy studies in private enterprise.

8. The complications involved in financing public works are often greater than the complications involved in financing the assets of private industry.

The Benefit-Cost Ratio in Economy Studies for Public Works. In certain types of public works projects, engineers tend to use the ratio of estimated benefits to estimated costs as the major criterion in determining whether or not to recommend expenditures that have been proposed. In some instances a comparison of benefits and costs is dictated by law. For example, the Flood Control Act of June 22, 1936, contained the following statement:

It is hereby recognized that destructive floods upon the rivers of the United States, upsetting orderly processes and causing loss of life and property, including the erosion of lands, and impairing and obstructing navigation, highways, railroads, and other channels of commerce between the States, constitute a menace to national welfare; that it is the sense of Congress that flood control on navigable waters or their tributaries is a proper activity of the Federal Government in cooperation with States, their political subdivisions, and localities thereof; that investigations and improvements of rivers and other waterways, including watersheds thereof, for flood-control purposes are in the interest of the general welfare; that the Federal Government should improve or participate in the improvement of navigable waters or their tributaries, including watersheds thereof, for flood-control purposes if the benefits to whomsoever they may accrue are in excess of the estimated costs, and if the lives and social security of people are otherwise adversely affected.[1]

[1] *United States Code,* 1940 ed. (Washington, D.C.: Government Printing Office), p. 2964.

Up to this point, the examples of economy studies in this book have been based on comparisons of equivalent annual costs or present worths or on calculations of prospective rates of return. These methods are as appropriate for most economy studies for governments as they are in private enterprise.

The student of engineering economy needs to understand the relationship between the foregoing methods of analysis and the benefit-cost technique. Such an understanding is particularly desirable because the benefit-cost technique contains certain pitfalls that may lead to an incorrect interpretation of benefit-cost ratios as a basis for action.

Example 18–1 is designed to bring out the relationships between these various methods of analysis. The example also provides a basis for further comment on several special aspects of governmental projects.

EXAMPLE 18–1. ANALYSIS OF ALTERNATIVE PLANS FOR A PROPOSED FLOOD CONTROL PROJECT

Facts of the Case. The flood plain in the lower reaches of the Rattlesnake River is subject to occasional severe floods. A flood control district has been organized that includes all of the area subject to flood damages. Engineers for the district have found four feasible sites for dams and detention reservoirs. Site A is on the main river just below the junction of the three forks of the river. Sites B and C are on the North Fork and Middle Fork respectively, not far above the junction point. Neither B nor C can be used if A is used, because the reservoir area from A will extend above these two sites. Site D is some distance upstream on the South Fork and can be combined with A, B, or C. The first cost at each site (including interest during construction) has been estimated, and annual operation and maintenance (O & M) costs also estimated, as follows:

	First Cost	Annual O & M
Site A	$20,000,000	$50,000
Site B	4,700,000	20,000
Site C	4,400,000	20,000
Site D	4,200,000	20,000

For any practicable combination of sites (such as A and D, or B and C), the total first cost will be the sum of the first costs at the respective sites, and the total O & M will be the sum of the respective O & M costs. For purposes of an economic analysis, the life of each dam and reservoir is assumed to be 50 years with zero salvage value. The funds to provide the needed first costs will be secured entirely from general obligation bonds to be voted by the flood control district. It is believed that the district can borrow at $3\frac{1}{2}\%$ interest. Bonds will mature serially over a 50-year period, with a maturity schedule that will result in a fairly uniform annual total of principal repayment plus interest. Bond interest, repayments of principal, and payment of O & M costs, will all come from ad valorem taxes levied on the property in the flood control district.

The consulting hydrologist for the district has estimated the probabilities of floods of various magnitudes with no flood control and with each reservoir and combination of reservoirs. Estimates have been made of the relationship between flood stages and the monetary cost of damage caused by floods. The district's engineers have analyzed these figures (along the lines explained in Chapter 13) and have estimated average annual flood damages within the district under each of the feasible plans, as follows:

Plan Number	Plan	Average Annual Flood Damages
1	No flood control	$1,600,000
2	A alone	300,000
3	B alone	800,000
4	C alone	900,000
5	D alone	850,000
6	A and D	250,000
7	B and D	580,000
8	C and D	700,000
9	B and C	640,000
10	B, C, and D	450,000

Comparison of Annual Costs. Table 18–1 compares the annual costs of no flood control (Plan 1) and the 9 different possible combinations of reservoirs (Plans 2 to 10). The minimum attractive rate of return is assumed to be $3\frac{1}{2}\%$, the cost of money to the flood control district. The final column of the table adds the annual costs to the taxpayers of the district (capital recovery plus O & M) to the average annual costs caused by floods within the district. Any of Plans 2 to 10 will reduce the annual cost below the $1,600,000 occurring with no flood control at all. However, the lowest annual cost is obtained with Plan 7, a combination of sites B and D.

TABLE 18–1

ANNUAL COST COMPARISON IN FORMULATION OF A FLOOD CONTROL PROJECT

(000 omitted from all dollar figures)

Plan	Total First Cost	Annual Capital Recovery Cost at $3\frac{1}{2}\%$	Annual O & M Cost	Total Annual Cost of Project Works	Average Annual Cost of Flood Damage	Total Annual Cost
1	$ 0	$ 0	$ 0	$ 0	$1,600	$1,600
5	4,200	179	20	199	850	1,049
4	4,400	188	20	208	900	1,108
3	4,700	200	20	220	800	1,020
8	8,600	367	40	407	700	1,107
7	8,900	379	40	419	580	999
9	9,100	388	40	428	640	1,068
10	13,300	567	60	627	450	1,077
2	20,000	853	50	903	300	1,203
6	24,200	1,032	70	1,102	250	1,352

The reader will note that this is the type of case referred to in Chapter 17 where the first cost of a project is financed entirely by borrowing, the assumed life of the project is the same as the period of a serial bond issue, and the minimum attractive rate of return is assumed to be the interest rate on the bonds. In this special case the annual cost of capital recovery is equal to the annual cost of debt service.

Benefit-Cost Analysis. In this case the annual benefits from each plan are the prospective reductions in the average annual damages caused by floods. These are tabulated in Table 18–2. (For each plan, the annual benefit is $1,600,-000 minus the expected average annual flood damages with the plan.) The annual project costs (capital recovery plus O & M) are also tabulated. The benefit-cost ratio for each plan is the annual benefit divided by the annual cost.

TABLE 18–2

COMPARISON OF BENEFIT-COST RATIOS IN FORMULATION
OF A FLOOD CONTROL PROJECT

(000 omitted from all dollar figures)

Plan	Annual Project Benefits	Annual Project Costs	Benefit-Cost Ratio
5	$ 750	$ 199	3.77
4	700	208	3.37
3	800	220	3.64
8	900	407	2.21
7	1,020	419	2.43
9	960	428	2.24
10	1,150	627	1.83
2	1,300	903	1.44
6	1,350	1,102	1.23

By themselves, such benefit-cost ratios do not provide sufficient guidance to enable an analyst to pick out the best of the various plans. This weakness of over-all benefit-cost ratios is not always understood by persons who employ benefit-cost analysis. One person, examining Table 18–2, might favor Plan 5, which gives the highest benefit-cost ratio, 3.77. Another person might favor the plan having the highest benefits that had a benefit-cost ratio greater than one; this would lead to the selection of Plan 6 with its $1,350,000 of annual benefits and its ratio of 1.23. Neither person would be correct.

The reader may recall that in Chapter 12 we discussed certain possible sources of errors in reasoning where rates of return are used in the analysis of multiple alternatives. We noted that it was necessary to compute rates of return on increments of investment as well as rates of return on total investment. For the same kinds of reasons, ratios of increments of benefits to increments of costs should be computed in any analysis by means of benefit-cost ratios. Table 18–3 shows the incremental ratios needed for decision making in Example 18–1.

In Table 18–1, the implied criterion for decision making was to minimize total annual costs, considering both project costs and costs of flood damages. This criterion led to the selection of Plan 7 (sites B and D) as the most economical alternative.

The data for Tables 18–2 and 18–3 are the same as for Table 18–1, even though they are expressed in different language, and the conclusion favoring Plan 7 is also the same. In these tables of benefit-cost ratios, reductions in costs of

TABLE 18–3

CALCULATION OF INCREMENTAL BENEFIT-COST RATIOS TO AID IN
FORMULATION OF A FLOOD CONTROL PROJECT

(000 omitted from all dollar figures)

Plans Compared	Increment of Annual Benefits	Increment of Annual Costs	Incremental Benefit-Cost Ratio
5 over 1......................	$750	$199	3.77
4 over 5......................	−50	9	negative
3 over 5......................	50	21	2.38
8 over 3......................	100	187	0.53
7 over 3......................	220	199	1.11
9 over 7......................	−60	9	negative
10 over 7......................	130	208	0.62
2 over 7......................	280	484	0.58
6 over 7......................	330	683	0.48

flood damages have been designated as *benefits*. Total costs, including project costs and costs of flood damages, will be minimized if the plan is selected that yields the maximum excess of benefits over costs.

It follows that no separable increment of project costs is justified unless it yields at least an equal increment of benefits. In other words, its incremental benefit-cost ratio over any project having lower costs must be at least unity. Table 18–3 illustrates the way in which plans should be analyzed in order of increasing costs. Plan 5 is superior to Plan 1 on the basis of its incremental B/C ratio of 3.77. Plan 4 is discarded because of its negative incremental B/C ratio. Plan 3 is superior to Plan 5 because its incremental B/C ratio is 2.38. Plan 8 is discarded because its incremental B/C ratio over Plan 3 (0.53) is less than unity. Plan 7 is superior to Plan 3 because its incremental ratio of 1.11 exceeds unity. The extra costs of Plans 9, 10, 2, and 6 over Plan 7 are not justified, because the respective incremental B/C ratios of these plans (negative, 0.62, 0.58, and 0.48) are less than unity when the plans are compared to Plan 7.

Some Other Methods of Comparison of the Different Plans. Table 18–4 shows a simpler method of analysis employing the terminology of benefits and costs. The excess of benefits over costs is tabulated for each plan. It is evident this excess is maximized by the selection of Plan 7.

The final two columns of Table 18–4 show an analysis based on rate of return along the lines explained in Chapter 12 in our discussion of economy studies for multiple alternatives. All of the proposed flood control plans show rates of return on total investment that exceed 3.5%, the stipulated minimum attractive rate of return. However, an analysis of rates of return on increments of investment indicates that Plan 7 should be selected. None of the plans having higher investments (Plans 9, 10, 2, and 6) come close to a 3.5% return on their respective increments of investment over Plan 7.

Some Comments on Example 18–1. Although Example 18–1 illustrates the types of alternatives present in many actual proposals for flood control, it does not describe an actual case. It should be

TABLE 18–4

SOME OTHER APPROACHES TO FORMULATION OF THE PROPOSED FLOOD CONTROL
PROJECT OF EXAMPLE 18–1

Plan	Benefits Minus Costs (000 omitted)	Rate of Return on Total Investment	Rate of Return on Increment of Investment
1	$ 0	–	–
5	551	17.4%	17.4% over Plan 1
4	492	15.4%	negative over Plan 5
3	580	16.6%	9.9% over Plan 5
8	493	9.9%	0.1% over Plan 3
7	601	10.9%	4.1% over Plan 3
9	532	10.0%	negative over Plan 7
10	523	8.0%	0.9% over Plan 7
2	397	5.9%	0.8% over Plan 7
6	248	4.8%	negative over Plan 7

viewed by the reader as an artificially simple case, designed to bring out certain aspects of the benefit-cost ratio as a technique of analysis of government projects and to compare this technique with the methods of analysis that have been illustrated throughout this book.

The various simplifications in Example 18–1 do not affect the validity of the comparison of the different techniques of analysis. It does not matter that this is a single-purpose flood control project rather than a multiple-purpose water project including other objectives (such as navigation, power, irrigation, or recreation). Neither does it matter that the payment of costs is to be solely by the taxpayers of the benefited area rather than by the taxpayers of the entire country. Neither does it matter that the annual cost of capital recovery happens to be equal to the annual payments of principal and interest on the bonds that will be used to finance the project.

An essential point in Example 18–1 was that all techniques of analysis—when correctly applied—led to the same conclusion, namely, that Plan 7 should be selected. (If we had also illustrated a present worth comparison at 3½%, the respective present worths would have been the product of our computed annual costs and pwf–3.5%–50, and the same conclusion favoring Plan 7 would have been reached.) However, this conclusion, whether reached via benefit-cost analysis, annual costs, present worths, or rates of return, depends on our selection of 3½% as the minimum attractive rate of return. If we had used, say, 4½%, Plan 3 rather than Plan 7 would have been selected by all of the methods.

The favorable consequences of flood control in Example 18–1— the so-called project benefits—all consist of cost reductions to someone. Hence, it was possible to use annual cost as one of our techniques of analysis, adding the annual project costs to the annual costs of flood damages. If the benefits had been of a type that did not permit a comparison of annual costs, correct analyses by the benefit-cost technique and by rate of return would have yielded the same conclusion, provided the minimum attractive rate of return had been used as the interest rate in the benefit-cost analysis.

Use of the Expressions "Project Formulation" and "Project Justification." Most proposals for public works are similar to Example 18–1 in having many different physically feasible designs that are sufficiently promising to need economic analysis on the design level. Many of the choices among the design alternatives are made by the engineers who make the designs. Other such choices are made, usually with due consideration of the engineers' recommendations, by the administrative bodies who employ the engineers. In certain government agencies in the United States, economic analysis aimed at guiding these design decisions is described as dealing with *project formulation*.

In cases such as Example 18–1, some one plan will generally be chosen for submission to the legislative body that will vote on an appropriation for the project or to the electorate that will vote on the project bonds. Economic analysis to be presented to such bodies is referred to as dealing with *project justification*.

Much of the literature dealing with the economic analysis of public works projects in the United States has dealt chiefly with project justification, with only an incidental glance, if any, at problems of project formulation. A critical look at the subject should convince the reader that the criteria for answering the "Why at all?" and "Why this way?" questions should be the same in public works, just as they ought to be the same in private enterprise.

If a government agency is interested only in economic analysis with reference to project justification and not with reference to project formulation, the projects that it submits for approval by legislative bodies or by the electorate are likely to contain elements that are economically unsound. For example, if Plan 6 should be the one project submitted in Example 18–1, it would show a B/C ratio of 1.23 and therefore meet the criterion that the B/C ratio should exceed unity. Nevertheless, as compared to Plan 7—not submitted for approval—this project would contain $683,000 of avoidable annual costs that would add annual benefits of only $330,-000; it would contain an avoidable extra investment of $15,300,000 (nearly two-thirds of the total proposed investment) that would yield a negative return.

In discussions of the economics of government projects, criteria for project justification have often been matters of controversy. It is the authors' view that one test that should always be applied to judge the soundness of criteria proposed for project justification ought to be whether or not these criteria are appropriate for project formulation.

Types of Governmental Activity. Primarily, governmental activity deals with the satisfaction of fundamental group wants that can be satisfied best by the association of all of the individuals in a community. Activities of this sort from which there are no specific measurable benefits to any individual are necessarily financed by taxes of some sort, presumably levied more or less on the principle of ability to pay, and with no particular relation to benefits received by the individual taxpayer.

However, governmental bodies also undertake the satisfaction of individual wants where the social interest is somehow involved. Such activities are frequently financed by a tax or charge that is essentially a price intended to be based as nearly as possible on benefits received or perhaps on the costs of providing those benefits. This frequently creates a problem of allocating joint costs and benefits to particular individuals or groups. A good example of this type of activity is the construction of those highways that are financed largely or entirely by user taxes.

Whose Point of View? It is possible to consider the economy of a public works proposal from several viewpoints:

1. That of the particular governmental body (or governmental department) concerned
2. That of all of the people of a particular area (such as a state, county, city, or special district)
3. That of all of the people in the country

It is necessary to have clearly in mind whose viewpoint is being taken, before it is possible to proceed with such an economy study.

In many cases the first impulse of the engineer will be to take viewpoint 1, considering only the prospective receipts and disbursements by the governmental body—or, in some cases, merely the particular governmental department—concerned. This appears to be comparable to an economy study for a private corporation in which the relevant matters are the prospective receipts and disbursements of that corporation. It should be clear that this viewpoint is a sound one in public works economy studies only when the alternatives being compared provide identical services to the people whom the government is organized to serve. For instance, this viewpoint might be correct in the choice between centrifugal pumps and reciprocating pumps for a municipal water works if it appeared that the service received by the water users would be equally satisfactory with either; the differences between the alternatives would then merely be differences in costs to the city's water department.

But where there are differences in the service provided by two alternatives, it is necessary to recognize the broader viewpoint that what the government does is simply something done collectively by all the people. If the ideal of democratic government that it is the objective of government to "promote the general welfare" is to be followed, it is necessary to consider the probable effects of alternative governmental policies on all of the people, not merely on the income and expenditures of a particular governmental unit.

Ideally, perhaps, it should be viewpoint 3 rather than 2 that should be considered in the public works policies of cities, counties, and states. For example, in comparing alternative plans for sewage treatment and disposal, a city should give consideration to the differences in their effects on downstream communities that take their water supply from the stream into which the sewage is discharged. Practically, however, experience indicates that the public officials and people of a community look at matters from the standpoint of what they consider to be the self-interest of their own community. Usually, the most that can be hoped for in economy studies for local governmental units is viewpoint 2 rather than viewpoint 1. If the broader question of the effect of one community's action on other communities is to be considered, it must be by the governmental authority of an area that includes both. Thus, a state board of health may regulate the sewage treatment policies of individual communities from the standpoint of the interests of all of the people of a state.

Viewpoint 3 definitely seems to be the correct one in all federally financed public works. Nevertheless, because the direct effects of most of this character (e.g., navigation, flood control, reclamation), seem to be concentrated in a particular locality, there may be difficulty in applying this broad viewpoint even here. All of the effects on the people of a nation of a particular public improvement may be hard to trace, and doubly hard to evaluate quantitatively, even though the prospective local effects are fairly clear.

Evaluation of Consequences of Public Works in Money Terms. In economy studies for private enterprises, it seems natural that alternatives should be evaluated in money terms so far as possible. Private enterprises are organized and operated for the purpose of securing a profit for their owners, a profit that is necessarily expressed in terms of money. Profits are an essential condition for the existence of private enterprise; those that show a loss year after year will finally cease to exist. Because the standard of business success is in money terms, economy studies for private enterprise must necessarily be in such terms.

The reason for trying to evaluate consequences of public works in money terms is somewhat different. It is true that governments are not organized to make a profit—that the standard of success that applies to private enterprise does not apply in the same way to public enterprise. Nevertheless, when the government collects taxes or other revenues, it is taking funds that otherwise might be either invested productively by the taxpayers or used to increase their immediate standards of living by expenditures for consumers' goods and services. It follows that public works so financed are not socially advantageous unless they yield a return in goods and services as high as the return from the private investments that are displaced by the diversion of taxpayers' funds to public uses.

If it is determined whether specific public works do, in fact, yield such a return, it becomes necessary to place a value on the services that they perform. This requires the use of some standard of value; the only standard that we have that may be used to measure all kinds of goods and services is the standard of the market place, a monetary standard. Thus, because money is the only standard of value that can make commensurable the benefits and the costs of public works, economy studies for public works should be made in monetary terms so far as is practicable.

Who Gets the Benefits and Who Is Responsible for the Costs? As has been suggested, certain public works may be a benefit to some people, a matter of indifference to others, and possibly a detriment to others. This raises the question not only of what are the benefits, but who gets them.

The effort is frequently made in public works to allocate taxes or other charges according to a price principle that recognizes benefits and responsibility for costs. This is likely to involve somewhat arbitrary allocations of joint benefits and joint costs; in some instances, however, it is necessary to recognize increment costs in such studies.

Consider, for example, the case of a trunk-line sewer that, in addition to collecting the sewage of the buildings on its own street, also carries the sewage from a large tributary area. Here, the only charge that may be made legitimately in the form of a special assessment against the abutting property is a charge sufficient to build a sewer of the size necessary to serve that property. The difference between the actual cost of the trunk sewer and the estimated cost of a sewer adequate to serve the local needs should be financed in some other way, perhaps by considering it as a general benefit to the entire community and paying for it out of general taxation, or perhaps by considering it as a special benefit to the entire area tributary to the trunk sewer and distributing it over the property in that area in the form of a special assessment.

Economy Studies for Highway Improvement. The contrast between economy studies for private enterprise and economy studies for public works is strikingly illustrated in the difference between two transportation systems, railways and highways. A railway company owns both the roadway and the vehicles that operate over it; if it spends money to make improvements in the roadway—for instance, by reducing grades or shortening the length of its line— it is compensated by saving money in vehicle operating costs. In the case of a highway system, on the other hand, the money for road improvements is spent by many governmental units—federal, state, county, and city; vehicle operating costs, however, are paid by the many individual vehicle owners rather than by these governmental units as such. In one case the design of the works and their utilization are under control of one group of officials; in the other case the design of the works is under the control of many groups of officials none of whom has direct control over the utilization.

Even though governmental officials cannot control highway utilization, they must consider prospective utilization in arriving at economical highway design. The general principle that all differences between alternatives are relevant to their comparison makes it necessary to consider the probable consequences to the highway users and to the general public from any proposal for the expenditure of highway funds. In order that these consequences be commensurable with the costs, they should be expressed in money terms wherever practicable.

EXAMPLE 18–2. A HIGHWAY ECONOMY STUDY

Facts and Estimates. In the relocation of a rural highway two alternative locations are under consideration.

Location A involves a distance of 8.6 miles with an estimated total cost for right-of-way, grading, drainage structures, and paving of $682,000. Resurfacing will be required every 10 years at an estimated cost of $160,000; extensive reconstruction of the base will be required every 20 years at an estimated cost of $125,000. In addition to this, the ordinary annual cost of maintenance is estimated at $800 per mile.

Location B involves a distance of 7.1 miles. Because of the much heavier grading required to shorten the distance, its estimated total cost is $940,000. Resurfacing will be required every 10 years at an estimated cost of $132,000; extensive reconstruction of the base will be required every 20 years at an estimated cost of $103,000. The ordinary annual cost of maintenance is estimated at $1,800 per mile; this is higher than the estimate for Location A because of deeper cuts and the consequent possibility of earth slides.

In comparing the economy of these two locations, annual costs to the state are to be based on a minimum attractive rate of return (interest rate) of 6%. Calculations are based on an assumed life of 40 years for the highway as a whole, considering the possibility of obsolescence of location.

The estimated average annual traffic over this highway for the next few years is as follows:

Passenger cars	420,000
Light trucks (under 2 tons)	45,000
Heavy trucks	20,000

Average figures for the increment cost per mile of operation for these three types of vehicles are estimated to be 4, 9, and 30 cents respectively. Therefore, the difference of 1.5 miles in distance between Locations A and B involves a difference in cost of vehicle operation of:

Passenger cars—420,000(1.5)($0.04)	$25,200
Light trucks—45,000(1.5)($0.09)	6,070
Heavy trucks—20,000(1.5)($0.30)	9,000
Total	$40,270

For 1.2 miles of Location A, there are 4% grades which are avoided in Location B. These grades will not affect the cost of operation of the passenger cars or the light trucks; it is estimated they will require an average increase in cost of 3 cents per mile for heavy trucks. This is a total money difference due to gradient of 20,000(1.2)($0.03) = $720.

Because of the shorter distance there will be a time saving to all traffic. The value of this saving is arbitrarily estimated at 4 cents per vehicle minute for all commercial traffic, assuming average drivers' wages or salaries at $2.40 per hour. The possible influence of a time saving in reducing investment charges on motor vehicles by decreasing the number of vehicles required is to be neglected. It is estimated that 20% of the passenger cars are commercial. Passenger cars and light trucks are estimated to travel on this road at an average speed of 40 miles per hour, and will thus save 2.25 minutes each if Location B is selected. Heavy trucks are estimated to travel at an average speed of 25 miles per hour and will thus save 3.6 minutes each with Location B. The total money value of time saved by commercial vehicles is:

Passenger cars—84,000(2.25)($0.04)	$ 7,560
Light trucks—45,000(2.25)($0.04)	4,050
Heavy trucks—20,000(3.6)($0.04)	2,880
Total	$14,490

Comparison of Alternatives. The annual capital costs and maintenance costs for the two locations are as follows, assuming the 6% interest rate:

Annual Cost to State—Location A

CR—Surface = $160,000(crf–6%–10)	$21,740
CR—Base = $125,000(crf–6%–20)	10,900
CR—Remainder of investment = $397,000(crf–6%–40)	26,380
Maintenance cost = 8.6($800)	6,880
Total	$65,900

Annual Cost to State—Location B

CR—Surface = $132,000(crf–6%–10)	$17,930
CR—Base = $103,000(crf–6%–20)	8,980
CR—Remainder of investment = $705,000(crf–6%–40)	46,850
Maintenance cost = 7.1($1,800)	12,780
Total	$86,540

A comparison of the annual costs of the two locations considering the total highway costs and the differences in highway user costs is as follows:

	Location A	Location B
Highway costs	$ 65,900	$86,540
Extra vehicle costs due to distance	40,270	
Extra vehicle costs due to gradient	720	
Extra vehicle costs due to time	14,490	
Totals	$121,380	$86,540

If comparison by the B/C ratio is desired, the savings to highway users from the choice of Location B would be viewed as the benefits, namely, $40,270 + $720 + $14,490 = $55,480. This figure is to be compared with the extra highway costs of Location B, namely, $86,540 − $65,900 = $20,640.

The B/C ratio is, therefore, $55,480 ÷ $20,640 = 2.69.

A trial-and-error calculation for rate of return will show that the rate of return on extra investment in Location B is nearly 20%.

Regardless of the method of comparison, it is apparent that Location B is clearly superior to Location A, provided consideration is given to the prospective highway user costs associated with the two locations. One element omitted from the preceding analysis is the saving in time by pleasure traffic. If this time saving is evaluated at a figure of, say, 1.5 cent per vehicle minute, the resulting annual figure is 336,000(2.25)($0.015) = $11,340. By adding this to the benefits, the benefit-cost ratio is increased from 2.69 to 3.24.

Special Problems of Public Borrowing.

When cities, counties, or special improvement districts (such as water districts, sanitary districts, irrigation and drainage districts, and bridge districts) wish to construct public works of any substantial magnitude, it is often necessary to finance such works by borrowing 100% of their cost. In many instances only minor works can be financed out of current taxes and revenues.

In order to prevent excessive borrowing and assure systematic repayment, the states of the United States, either through constitutional provisions or legislative enactments, have put various restrictions on borrowing by local governments. These restrictions are commonly of three types:

1. The total borrowing power of a local government is limited to a specified percentage of the assessed valuation of the property within its area.
2. No bonds may be issued without the approval of the voters at an election; with the exception of "revenue bonds" in certain jurisdictions, it is usually specified that this approval must be by a two-thirds affirmative vote.
3. Repayment must be within a specified number of years, and must be in accordance with a specified plan. This plan often requires uniform serial maturities over the life of a bond issue.

In considering any proposal for local public works to be financed by bond issues, the effect of these legal restrictions must be considered. Will borrowing power, considering probable future needs, be impaired by the proposed issue? Are the chances good for a two-thirds favorable vote? Can required obligations for interest and repayment be met, particularly in the earlier years when they are the greatest?

The necessity for 100% borrowing to finance many local public works, and the requirement that the bonds be completely paid off within a limited period, usually 40 years or less, makes the financial background quite different from that found in private enterprise. Private enterprises seldom have the opportunity for 100% borrowing; on the other hand, they are not confronted with the necessity for retiring all of their capital obligations within a limited period.

Borrowings by states are generally subject to restrictions similar to those enforced on cities, counties, and special districts. However, state highway improvements, which are the major state-financed public works, are now generally financed on a pay-as-you-go plan through the proceeds of gasoline taxes and other forms of motor vehicle taxation. Thus the problems of debt limit, bond elections, and debt repayment, which are so common in connection with municipal public works, arise less frequently in connection with state works.

The situation with respect to borrowing by the federal government is entirely different from that existing in other governmental units. Whereas each bond issue by a state, city, county, or special district is for a definitely specified purpose, borrowings by the federal government are for the general purpose of supplying funds to take care of the excess of current disbursements over current receipts.

The relationship between the financing of federal deficits, the banking and credit mechanism, and the general price structure, is much too complex for discussion here. Let it suffice to point out that federal borrowing (except that engaged in for purposes of debt refunding) serves to create purchasing power and is thus a stimulant to business activity that may be used for the purpose of promoting recovery from periods of business depression. Federal borrowing also, if carried on in large amounts, has the tendency to cause a great rise in price levels with all of the ills that the experience of the world has demonstrated to be attendant upon inflation. Both of these effects—one good, the other bad—are decidedly relevant in connection with any federal public works proposal made when the federal government is operating at or near a deficit. They are, however, a long way removed from matters of engineering technology.

The Controversial Question of the Treatment of Interest in Economy Studies for Public Works. Engineers do not agree on the point of view that should be taken toward the treatment of interest in judging the soundness of proposed public works expenditures. Some different viewpoints on this subject are as follows:

1. Costs should, in effect, be computed at zero interest rate. The advocates of this viewpoint generally limit its application to those public works that are financed out of current taxation rather than by borrowing.
2. Costs should be computed, using an interest rate equal to the rate paid on borrowings by the particular unit of government in question. If the proposed public works are to be financed by borrowing, the probable cost of the borrowed money should be used. Otherwise the average cost of money for long-term borrowings should be used.
3. Just as in private enterprise, the question of the interest rate to be used in an economy study is essentially the question of what is a minimum attractive return under the circumstances. Although the cost of borrowed money is one appropriate element in determining the minimum attractive return, it is not the sole element to be considered. In most instances the appropriate minimum attractive return should be somewhat higher than the cost of borrowed money.

Our discussion of capital rationing in Chapter 9 made it clear that the authors of this book favor the view stated under heading 3. Some further aspects of the case supporting this view are developed in Example 18–3 and the subsequent discussion.

EXAMPLE 18–3. THE EFFECT OF THE SELECTION OF THE
MINIMUM ATTRACTIVE RATE OF RETURN ON A
COMPARISON OF HIGHWAY BRIDGE TYPES

Facts of the Case. In a certain location near the Pacific Ocean, two alternative types of highway bridge are under consideration for the replacement of an existing timber trestle bridge on a state highway in a rural area. The first cost of a steel bridge will be $340,000; the first cost of a concrete arch bridge will be $390,000. Maintenance costs for the steel bridge consist chiefly of painting; the average annual figure is estimated to be $3,000. Maintenance costs on the concrete arch bridge are assumed to be negligible over the life of the bridge. Either bridge has an estimated life of 50 years. The two bridges have no differences in their prospective services to the highway users.

It is evident that in this instance the choice between the two types depends on the assumed interest rate or minimum attractive return. A tabulation of annual costs with various interest rates is as follows:

Interest Rate	Annual Cost		Difference in Annual Cost	
	Steel	Concrete	Favoring Steel	Favoring Concrete
0%	$ 9,800	$ 7,800		$2,000
2%	13,820	12,410		1,410
4%	18,830	18,150		680
5%	21,630	21,360		270
6%	24,570	24,740	$ 170	
8%	30,790	31,880	1,090	
10%	37,290	39,340	2,050	
12%	43,940	46,960	3,020	

If the minimum attractive return is below 5.6%, the concrete bridge is more economical for this location. If above 5.6%, the steel bridge is more economical.

The Need for a Minimum Attractive Rate of Return in Economy Studies for Public Works.

Examples 18–2 and 18–3 deal with economy studies for state highway projects. In general, such projects in the United States are financed entirely by current highway user taxes and involve no public borrowing. This is the field in which the advocates of 0% interest rate in public works projects have been most articulate. It is also a field in which the funds available in any year are limited by current tax collections, and in which the typical situation is that at any given time there are many economically justifiable projects that cannot be constructed because of the limitation on current funds.

Examples 18–2 and 18–3 were alike in representing the type of decision that usually is made on the level of engineering design rather than on the policy level of determining the order of priority of projects competing for funds. If each authorized project is to be designed to best advantage, it is essential that economy studies be made to compare the various alternative features in the design. If such studies were made at 0% interest, and if the conclusions of the studies were accepted in determining the design, many extra investments would be made that would yield relatively small returns (such as 1% or 2%). These extra investments in the projects actually undertaken would absorb funds that might otherwise have been used for additional highway projects. If the additional projects put off by a shortage of funds should be ones where the benefits to highway users represented a return of, say, 15%, on the highway investment, it is clearly not in the over-all interest of highway users to have invested funds where the return was only 2%. In other words, where available funds are limited, the selection of an appropriate minimum attractive return calls for consideration of the prospective returns obtainable from alternative investments. This is as sound a principle in public works as it is in private enterprise.

If the time should ever be reached when economy studies indicate that all the highway funds currently available in any state cannot be used without undertaking a number of highway investments yielding very low returns (such as 2%), a fair conclusion would be that highway user taxes should be lowered. In such a case the alternative investments would be those that might be made by individual taxpayers if taxes should be reduced. Money has a time value to the taxpayers; this is a fact that should be recognized in the use of funds collected from taxpayers.

Some Considerations in the Selection of an Interest Rate or Minimum Attractive Rate of Return. Even though it is agreed that *some* interest rate or minimum attractive return greater than 0% should be used in economy studies for public works, it may be troublesome to decide just what rate is appropriate in any given case. The rate is appropriately lower in studies similar to Example 18–3 than in studies similar to Example 18–2.

In Example 18–3 construction of the steel bridge would commit the state highway department to a $3,000 annual maintenance expense. The annual funds available to the department must first be used to cover necessary maintenance expenses. Hence the greater the maintenance cost of the highway system, the less will be the funds available for new construction. The extra $50,000 investment required now to build the concrete bridge rather than the steel one may therefore be thought of as increasing the amount available for new construction by $3,000 a year for the next 50 years. In general, any investment that reduces annual maintenance cost may be thought of as providing funds for needed construction to meet the changing traffic requirements of future years. Presumably these funds will yield high returns in reduced highway user costs.

One reason, therefore, why investments that reduce those highway costs that are paid by the government should be accepted with a lower required rate of return than investments reducing highway costs paid by the public is that the former may be expected to result in a long series of future productive investments that will be advantageous to the public. Another reason is that the savings in the former case may be estimated with much greater precision than in the latter case.

Just as in economy studies for private enterprise, any minimum attractive return used in public works should include a safety factor that gives recognition to the fact that even the best engineering estimates are subject to a margin of error. In economy studies for local governments in the United States, consideration should also be given to the fact that these interest rates are artificially low because of the exemption of this interest from federal income taxation.

Where certain public works clearly benefit a limited group of individuals who are asked to repay the costs of these works, the question of interest rate also arises. Here the required interest rate may properly equal the cost of money to the governmental body in question. This is not comparable to an economy study in which a factor of safety is desirable and in which the question of alternative investments requires consideration. Where policy dictates that such works be subsidized in part out of general taxation, and that the remainder of the cost be paid by the special beneficiaries of the works, it is better that the subsidy take the form of an outright grant of a fraction of the construction cost than that the subsidy be concealed through the omission of an interest charge.

Systematic Fact Finding Is Needed To Permit Reliable Estimates of Probable Consequences from Public Works Expenditures. Many types of data required for economic planning of public works cannot be secured on the spur of the moment when the decision is made to consider the merits of some proposed expenditure. This fact is recognized by many government agencies dealing with public works.

For example, one of the objectives in many highway investments is the improvement of highway safety. The influence of alternative proposals on highway accidents cannot be judged without a complete and accurate system of reporting highway accidents whenever they occur. Regular traffic counts carried out on a routine basis throughout a highway system are essential for this purpose as well as for other aspects of the economic planning of highways.

Another good example is the recognized need for systematic collection of information regarding flood damages. This information is difficult to secure with reasonable accuracy except immediately following a flood; memories of specific aspects of a flood become dimmed after a very few years.

Double-Counting in Economy Studies for Public Works. Without careful reasoning there is danger that the same benefits from a public works project may be measured in different ways and added together.

For example, the common approach to estimating the benefits of flood protection works lies in making estimates of the flood damages that they will eliminate. An alternative approach, possible only in those circumstances where an extreme flood has followed a long period without any floods, is to determine the reduction in property values that has taken place as a result of the flood. In this approach it is reasoned that property values before the flood were based on the assumption that no destructive flood would ever occur; property values shortly after the flood (assuming reconstruction has restored property to something like its preflood condition) discount the expected damages from future floods.

It should be clear that these two approaches are alternative ways of trying to measure the same thing. Because both are imperfect measures they will not agree; nevertheless, the reduction in property values represents a collective estimate of the present worth of the costs of future flood damages. However, in some studies of flood protection economy these two measures were added together to determine the prospective benefits of flood protection!

Irreducibles in Economy Studies for Public Works. Although measurements of benefits of public works in money terms make it possible to take many decisions out of the "hunch" class, such measurements have obvious limitations. These limitations lie not only in the difficulties of measurement, but also in the much greater importance of irreducibles in public works than in private enterprise.

In many respects the irreducibles in public works projects create problems of judgment similar to those that arise in personal economy studies. The best that an individual can do in dealing with his personal problems of economy may be to note the satisfactions that will come from particular expenditures, and to consider them in the light of their long-run costs and in the light of his capacity to pay.

A similar analysis may be applied to such a public works project as one for park improvement. Even though the services provided by the park are not expressible in money terms, it is pertinent to estimate how many people will use the proposed facilities, and in what ways. It is also pertinent to estimate the long-run cost of the park improvement, considering not only the immediate investment (translated into annual cost in the conventional manner) but also the necessary annual expenditures for upkeep. The annual cost of the service of the proposed park improvement may even be expressed as so much money per unit of use in order to permit its comparison with other improvement proposals. Finally, any such proposed expenditure must always be considered in relation to the capacity of the community to pay for it, particularly in the light of other possible uses for available public funds.

"Hunch" Decisions in Public Works vs. Decisions Based on Economy Studies. If, as was suggested in Chapter 1, the managers of private enterprises often elect to choose between technical alternatives by "going into a trance and coming out with an answer," it is no wonder that, confronted with choices which are both more complex and more controversial, public officials frequently also elect to do so. Nevertheless, if public funds are to be spent to the best advantage, decisions in the public works field should be based on economy studies that attempt as far as possible to make benefits commensurable with costs. This objective cannot be realized merely by engineers in public service becoming convinced it is desirable; it requires the active cooperation of other public officials, executive, legislative, and judicial.

For this reason the presentation of the results of such economy studies to legislative bodies and to the general public by engineers in public employment usually must start from the fundamentals of cost comparisons. Such presentations should, if possible, steer a course between two extremes; one, the implication that a choice between engineering alternatives in public works should be made on the basis of conversation rather than calculation; the other, the implication that measurements of benefits from public works are exact and that there are no unmeasured irreducibles that should also be considered. Special administrative difficulties in realizing maximum economy in public works were discussed at the beginning of this chapter.

Many Situations Call for Joint Action by Two or More Governmental Bodies. In the planning of many public works, unified administrative control is of the greatest importance. This is particularly true in planning highway transportation systems around our congested metropolitan areas.

The necessity for a comprehensive plan and a unified administrative control of developments regarding the transportation needs of the metropolitan area of New York City was recognized by the states of New York and New Jersey when, by joint action, they established the Port of New York Authority. This administrative board, with three members from each state, has dealt with such related matters as improved facilities for the handling of railway freight, facilities for suburban passenger transportation, and the location and construction of highway toll bridges and tunnels between the two states. The provision of the compact between the states that allowed the Port Authority to acquire property and to borrow money on its own credit has made possible the construction of a number of bridges and tunnels connecting New Jersey with various parts of New York City. A similar example of interstate cooperation is the construction of the bridge across the Delaware River connecting Philadelphia and Camden, built by joint action of the states of Pennsylvania and New Jersey.

There are frequent conflicts between various interests in the utilization of natural resources. Thus, stream flow may be controlled in the interests of navigation, power, irrigation, or flood control, and each of these interests requires a different sort of regulation. The interests of land transportation conflict with the interests of navigation in any project for the construction of a bridge over navigable waters. There is a definite need for the development of standards of social utility that will enable some coordinating agency to make intelligent decisions between the demands of the various interests involved in any such situation.

Summary. Certain points brought out in this chapter may be restated for emphasis as follows:

In economy studies for public works, it is necessary to recognize that governmental activities are undertaken to serve all the people. Thus the consequences of various alternatives should be evaluated from a broader viewpoint than that of mere governmental receipts and disbursements. Whenever reasonable, a monetary valuation should be placed on consequences of alternatives to the general public in order to make these consequences commensurable with differences in costs to the government. To make such valuations, considerable effort may be needed in finding the facts about the effects of public works and the ways in which these effects are likely to be influenced by changes in design.

In the United States many proposals for public works are judged in terms of their prospective benefit-cost ratios. There are certain difficulties of interpretation of these ratios that sometimes are responsible for incorrect conclusions, particularly on matters of project formulation. Nevertheless, correctly interpreted, benefit-cost ratios will yield the same conclusions that will be reached by analysis by annual cost or rate of return.

The choice of a minimum attractive rate of return is as important in economy studies for governments as in studies for private enterprise. The capital rationing viewpoint that aims to make the best possible use of a limited resource, namely, investment funds, is appropriate in government just as in competitive industry.

Public works involve special problems of financing. In connection with local works these problems relate to such matters as bond elections, debt limits, and mandatory provisons for repayment. In connection with federal public works they deal with the relation of federal fiscal policy to the system of money and credit and to business stabilization.

Special problems arise in connection with the apportionment of charges for public works among different taxpayers and taxpaying groups. Studies of increment costs may be helpful in establishing limits in dealing with these problems, even though their final solution must be based on public policy that is not determinable by methods of engineering economy.

Problems

18–1. Two alternative locations for a new highway are to be compared.

Location X involves a distance of 11.3 miles. Total first cost is estimated to be $1,694,000. The location and grading are assumed to be permanent. Resurfacing and reconstruction of the base will be required every 15 years at an estimated cost of $40,000 per mile. In addition, annual maintenance cost will be $1,000 per mile.

Location Y involves a distance of 13.5 miles. Total first cost is estimated at $1,160,000. Costs per mile for resurfacing and annual maintenance are the same as in X.

The estimated average traffic over this highway for the next few years is 1,100 vehicles per day, of which about 15% will be trucks and an additional 10% will be commercial passenger cars. The increment cost per mile of vehicle operation is assumed as 5.4 cents for passenger cars and 20 cents for trucks. Traffic will travel at an average speed of 40 miles per hour. The money value of a time saving to the commercial traffic is estimated as 2 cents per vehicle minute.

Assuming interest at 6%, compute a benefit-cost ratio applicable to the extra investment in Location X. (*Ans.* = 2.84.)

18–2. Solve Problem 18–1 by determining the approximate interest rate (i.e., rate of return) at which Locations X and Y will be equally economical. (*Ans.* = 14.6%.)

18–3. The elimination of a certain level crossing of a highway and railway is under consideration. The total cost of this grade crossing elimination is estimated as $479,000. Although the improvement is assumed to be permanent, it involves estimated repair and renewal expenditures every 20 years of $35,000, and an annual cost for energy for pumping drainage water of $300.

The highway traffic is 3,000 vehicles per day, and the railway carries 70 trains per day. Time studies indicate that on the average a train stops 12 vehicles with an average delay per vehicle of 2.5 minutes. The cost of a vehicle stop (applicable to all cars stopped) is estimated as 0.15 cent. The cost of lost time (applicable to the 25% of commercial vehicles only) is estimated as 4 cents per vehicle minute.

Based on past accident statistics, it is estimated that if this grade crossing is continued it will be responsible for 1 fatal accident every 2 years and 5 nonfatal accidents per year. Make the arbitrary assumption of a "cost" of $25,000 for a fatal accident and $500 for a nonfatal one.

The railway company has maintained a watchman at this crossing for 14 hours per day at an annual cost of $4,800.

In order to determine which of a number of proposed grade-crossing elimination projects are to receive limited available funds, it is desired to compare annual benefits with annual costs for each. Compute the benefit-cost ratio for this project, assuming an interest rate of 5%. (Ans. = 1.10.)

18–4. Discuss the sensitivity of the benefit-cost ratio in Problem 18–3 to the various estimates and assumptions used in the analysis. Discuss the irreducible elements in the choice of the grade-crossing elimination projects that are to receive the limited funds.

18–5. A city of 40,000 population uses an average of 150 gallons of water per capita per day. Its water supply has a total hardness of 320 parts per million (p.p.m.). A municipal water softening plant is proposed to reduce this to 70 p.p.m.

The plant capacity must be double the average daily consumption; the plant will cost $25,000 per millions of gallons per day (m.g.d.) of capacity. The plant would be financed by 20-year 3½% serial bonds, with a uniform number of bonds maturing each year. Chemicals are estimated to cost 12 cents per m.g. per p.p.m. of hardness removed. Plant labor costs at the water treatment plant will be increased by $6,000 a year. Pumping in the softening plant will cost $1.60 per m.g. pumped. Average annual maintenance cost is estimated as 3% of investment. The life of the plant is estimated as 20 years with a negligible salvage value. The city will raise water rates sufficiently to cover the extra operating costs for water softening plus first year's bond interest and repayment.

Assume a saving in annual per capita soap consumption from 38.5 lb. to 30.8 lb. as a result of the water softening, with an average retail soap price of 20 cents per lb. Assume a saving in cost of chemicals to customers already softening their water of 18 cents per m.g. per p.p.m. of hardness removed; this applies to 110 m.g. per year. It is estimated that the life will be doubled for 4,000 storage water heaters having an average life of 8 years under present conditions; the average investment per heater is $65.

Estimate the required increase in water rate per 1,000 gallons. Make an analysis to determine whether the foregoing estimated monetary savings are sufficient to justify water softening.

18–6. Two alternative locations for a new highway are to be compared. Location A involves a distance of 12.1 miles with a total first cost of $1,600,000. The location and grading are assumed to be permanent. Resurfacing and reconstruction of the base will be required every 18 years at an estimated cost of $40,000 per mile. Annual maintenance cost will be $1,000 per mile. Location B involves a distance of 14.1 miles with a total first cost of $900,000. Assumptions regarding life and cost per mile for resurfacing and annual maintenance are the same as for Location A.

The estimated average traffic over this highway for the next few years is 1,200 vehicles per day, of which 15% is truck traffic. The increment cost per mile for the average truck is estimated to be 15 cents; for other vehicles it is estimated to be 4 cents. Value of time saved per minute is estimated as 4 cents for trucks and 1.25 cents for other vehicles. It is estimated that accident costs and other vehicle operation costs will be the same for the two locations. Average vehicle speed is 40 miles per hour. Assuming interest at 4%, compute a benefit-cost ratio applicable to the extra investment in Location A.

18–7. A state highway department is considering the installation of an overpass and cloverleaves to eliminate a grade crossing at the intersection of two main highways. The installation will cost $500,000. An economy study to consider the desirability of this investment will use a capital recovery period of 25 years as it is likely one of these highways will ultimately be relocated. A minimum attractive return of 5% is to be used.

The average traffic is 3,000 vehicles per day on one of the highways and 2,000 vehicles per day on the other. Traffic is made up of 20% trucks, 20% light commercial, and 60% private passenger vehicles. Increment costs of operation are assumed to be 20 cents per mile for the trucks and 5 cents per mile for all others. Time is valued at 3 cents per minute for the drivers of trucks and light commercial vehicles and one cent per mile for drivers of other vehicles. It is estimated that the cloverleaf arrangement will increase the mileage traveled by 0.3 mile for 25% of the vehicles. The average time saving per vehicle is estimated to be 1.5 minutes. The installation will eliminate an annual expense by the state of $6,000 now spent for patroling the intersection. Annual highway maintenance costs will be increased by $1,500. It is forecast that the installation will effect a 75% reduction in the accident rate at the intersection. During the past 5 years, there have been two fatal accidents and 31 accidents involving personal injury at this intersection. A fatal accident is to be estimated as a $14,000 cost; a nonfatal one as a $700 cost.

Determine the benefit-cost ratio for this proposed installation.

18–8. In a proposed flood control project, there are two possible sites, A and B, for a dam and storage reservoir. One or the other of these sites may be used but not both. Certain channel improvement is also considered; this will increase the capacity of the stream to carry flood discharge. Estimated first costs, lives, and operation and maintenance costs are as follows:

	Site A	Site B	Channel Improvement
First cost	$6,000,000	$8,000,000	$1,000,000
Life	75 years	75 years	25 years
Annual O & M	$120,000	$160,000	$200,000

Annual capital recovery costs are to be computed using an interest rate of 4%. Assume zero salvage values at the end of the estimated lives.

The average annual amount of damages due to floods are estimated under various possible plans of development, as follows:

No flood control works at all..	$1,100,000
Development at Site A alone..	380,000
Development at Site B alone..	260,000
Channel improvement alone...	500,000
Site A plus channel improvement.....................................	200,000
Site B plus channel improvement.....................................	120,000

Compute a benefit-cost ratio for each of the five plans of development. Assume that the annual costs of a dam and reservoir plus channel improvement will be the sum of the costs of the dam and reservoir alone plus channel improvement alone. Make any other analysis that you think is desirable. Which plan of development, if any, would you recommend? Why?

18–9. In a proposed flood control project, there are two possible sites for a dam and storage reservoir, designated as the Willow and Cottonwood sites. One or the other of these sites may be used but not both. A small hydroelectric power development may be added at the Willow site. Certain channel improvements are also considered. Seven alternate projects are set up for analysis and average annual damages due to floods under each plan estimated as follows:

Plan	Damages
A Willow dam and reservoir alone	$110,000
B Willow dam, reservoir, and power plant	130,000
C Willow dam and reservoir, with channel improvement	40,000
D Willow dam, reservoir, and power plant with channel improvement	60,000
E Cottonwood dam and reservoir alone	180,000
F Cottonwood dam and reservoir, with channel improvement	90,000
G Channel improvement alone	330,000

With no flood control works at all, the average annual amount of flood damages is estimated as $680,000.

The estimated first cost of the Willow dam and reservoir is $5,000,000. The power plant will increase this first cost by $1,000,000. The estimated first cost of the Cottonwood dam and reservoir is $3,000,000. The estimated first cost of the channel improvement is $800,000. In the economic analysis a 100-year life with zero salvage value is to be used for the two dams and reservoirs, a 50-year life with zero salvage value is to be used for the power plant, and a 20-year life with $300,000 salvage value is to be used for the channel improvement. All equivalence calculations are to use an interest rate of $3\frac{1}{2}\%$.

On the basis of the cost of equal power from a steam electric plant, the "benefits" from the hydroelectric power are estimated to be $70,000 a year. Annual operation and maintenance costs will be:

Willow dam and reservoir	$60,000
Power plant	25,000
Cottonwood dam and reservoir	50,000
Channel improvement	70,000

Compute a benefit-cost ratio for each of the seven plans of development. Make any other calculations that you think are desirable to aid a choice among the different plans. Do you recommend that one of these plans be adopted? If so, which one? Why?

18–10. The following question is adapted from one used in a state examination for registration as a professional engineer:

Estimates are made for the first costs of various elements of a new highway assuming designs for different numbers of lanes, as follows:

	4 Lanes	6 Lanes
Right of way	$ 240,000	$ 320,000
Pavement	960,000	1,440,000
All other elements of first cost	1,200,000	1,440,000
Total	$2,400,000	$3,200,000

It is estimated that 4 traffic lanes will be sufficient for the next 10 years; after that, 6 lanes will be required. The interest rate is 4%. How much money, in addition to the cost of a 4-lane highway, can be spent economically at once? How should your recommended total be divided among the foregoing elements of first cost? Explain your answers.

Give the solution that you think was expected by the examiner.

Assume that you are confronted by this type of problem in an actual case. What additional data and estimates, if any, would you want before arriving at your recommendations? How would you use the additional data in your analysis?

18–11. In a growing city decisions must be made from time to time whether various physical means of traffic control are to be used at specific street intersections to control motor vehicle traffic and pedestrian traffic. The various possibilities at an intersection may include:

1. No control devices
2. Arterial stop sign on one street but not on the other
3. Arterial stop signs on both streets
4. Traffic lights with duration of signals in each direction controlled by preset timing devices
5. Traffic lights in which the frequency and duration of the traffic signals are determined by traffic activated devices on one of the intersecting streets
6. Traffic lights in which the frequency and duration of the traffic signals are determined by traffic activated devices on both of the intersecting streets

Decisions by city officials among such alternatives often are made largely by intuition, although weight may be given to such matters as traffic counts of motor vehicles, the current state of the city budget, the occurrence of recent accidents at a particular intersection, and pressures from residents living near the various intersections. It has been suggested that decision making might be improved by the practice of using formal economy studies requiring an evaluation (in money terms as far as practicable) of the various benefits and costs associated with each alternative.

Assume an intersection that is now in condition (2) above. Make arbitrary numerical estimates of the various physical matters that you would deem relevant in deciding among alternatives (2), (3), (4), (5), and (6). Make the necessary estimates to convert into money amounts all physical differences that you believe ought to be so converted. (Arbitrary assumptions may be made of the unit cost figures that you need.) Using your own figures, make a formal economy study leading to a recommendation for action.

Briefly discuss the issues involved in deciding (a) whether or not economy studies of this type should be made at all, and (b) how they should be made if it is decided to use economy studies for this purpose.

18–12. A steel bridge on a county highway near the ocean cost $230,000 12 years ago. Although the average annual maintenance costs of $7,200 a year have seemed excessive to the county supervisors, these costs, mostly for painting, have been necessary to prevent severe corrosion in this particular location.

A consulting structural engineer proposes to the county supervisors that he be employed to design and to supervise the construction of a reinforced concrete bridge to replace this steel bridge. He estimates the total first cost of the concrete bridge to be $420,000 and the net salvage from the steel bridge to be $20,000. The required net outlay is therefore $400,000. Since the county receives $500,000 a year from state gas tax funds to be used for county highway improvement, the engineer points out that this bridge could be financed without borrowing. His economic comparison is as follows:

Annual Cost of Proposed Bridge

Depreciation (based on 100-year life) = $400,000 ÷ 100 = $4,000

Annual maintenance cost .... =   200

Total annual cost .... = $4,200

Annual Cost of Present Bridge

Depreciation (based on 50-year life) = $230,000 ÷ 50 = $4,600

Annual maintenance cost .... =   7,200

Total annual cost .... = $11,800

Comment on the engineer's analysis. Explain how you would approach this problem.

19

Establishing Criteria and Procedures
for Investment Decisions

The earliest book on engineering economy was Wellington's *The Economic Theory of Railway Location*. Wellington wrote in a missionary spirit in a day when investments in railway plant were greater than the aggregate of all other investments in industrial assets. Railway location obviously is a field in which many alternatives are likely to be available. Nevertheless, Wellington observed what seemed to him to be an almost complete disregard by many locating engineers of the influence of their locations on the prospective costs and revenues of the railways. In his first edition (1877) he said of railway location, "And yet there is no field of professional labor in which a limited amount of modest incompetency at $150 per month can set so many picks and shovels and locomotives at work to no purpose whatever."

Management's Responsibility for Decisions on Plant Investment. Although salary rates and many other things have changed since Wellington's time, the type of problem that he recognized is an ever present one in an industrialized civilization. If, in a business enterprise or in government, many important decisions that in the aggregate can have a major influence on the success (and sometimes on the survival) of the enterprise are badly made by persons of "modest incompetence," these bad decisions are not primarily the fault of those persons; they are the fault of top management.

This chapter briefly discusses the steps that management ought to take to avoid bad decisions on matters related to plant investment. It is convenient to consider the subject with reference to the following topics:

1. Choice of procedures and criteria for decision making
2. Need to recognize that the chosen criteria must be implemented at various levels in an organization and that the expression of the

465

criteria and the methods of implementation may reasonably be different at different levels
3. Implementation of criteria at the level of capital budgeting
4. Implementation of criteria below the capital budgeting level
5. Personal bias as a factor in decisions on plant investment
6. Post-audit of decisions on plant investment

Selecting Procedures and Criteria To Arrive at Sound Decisions on Plant Investment. Various aspects of the topic of procedures for investment decisions have been discussed throughout this book. Stress has been placed on the need to hunt for good alternatives, the need for a clear definition of alternatives, the need to recognize that it is prospective *differences* between alternatives that are relevant in their comparison, the desirability of converting physical differences to differences in cash flow to the extent practicable, and the desirability of making separable decisions separately.

In most instances the primary criterion for judging the relative merits of proposed investments should be prospective rate of return. It has been pointed out that the rate-of-return criterion can be applied using several different methods of computation. Rates of return can be computed and compared with one another or with some standard. Or a standard, which we have referred to as the minimum attractive rate of return, can be established and equivalent uniform annual costs or present worths can be compared using this standard as the interest rate in compound interest conversions.

It has been stressed that the rate-of-return criterion should be applied using compound interest methods. Chapter 10 pointed out the deficiencies of the average book method, the original book method, and other so-called rates of return that sometimes are computed in industry.

We have also stressed the need for decisions among alternatives to give weight to the various prospective differences that have not been converted into money estimates and thus included into the rate-of-return analysis. Chapter 13 presented some useful supplementary criteria for this purpose, based on the concept of sensitivity.

Comment on Weakness of the Payout Period as the Primary Criterion for Investment Decisions. In small enterprises it is common to use some variant of the payout (or payback) period as the primary criterion to compare the merits of proposed investments, particularly where the comparisons are made at the level of capital budgeting. Some large industrial enterprises also base decisions on comparisons of payout periods.[1] In this book, the only references to payout calculations up to this point have been in Chapters 15 and 17. In Chapter 15 we illustrated the calculation of crude payout after income taxes (page 318) and in Chapter 17 we discussed the usefulness of this crude payout as a supplementary criterion for decisions, particularly where there is a serious shortage of funds for plant investment.

Except for the special case where funds are so limited that *no* outlay can be made unless the money can be recovered in a very short time (for example, 6 months), the payout period is *never* an appropriate way to rank a group of proposed investment proposals in order of merit. The objection is that the payout period fails to give weight to the difference in consequences of different investment proposals after the date of payout. Thus a proposal for an investment in jigs and fixtures might pay out in 2 years but have no useful results after the end of the 2 years. Such a proposal would provide recovery of capital with no return whatsoever. Clearly it would not be superior to a proposal for a new production machine having a longer payout period, say 4 years, but favorable enough consequences for many years thereafter to give it an over-all rate of return of 20%. Some numerical examples involving payout calculations and illustrating this deficiency are given at the end of this chapter (Problems 19–1 to 19–4).

Some analysts, attempting to correct the foregoing bias of crude payout in favor of short-lived alternatives, modify the payout calculation by computing so-called payout after depreciation, or, sometimes, after both depreciation and interest. Such modified payout figures are meaningless as they involve a double counting of the first cost of plant. Some illustrations of this point are given at the end of this chapter (Problems 19–5 to 19–7). There are, in fact, many variants of the payout method in use in industry, none of them providing a sound basis for ranking alternative investment proposals.

Often there is merit in the idea of computing payout in addition to rate of return and using payout as a supplementary criterion for investment decisions. Such a use of payout may be justified partly on the grounds of judging the sensitivity of proposals to the estimates of duration of their favorable consequences and partly on the grounds that proposals should be examined in relation to their

---

[1] For an excellent statement from an industrial source of the case for rate of return as compared to payout, see J. G. McLean, "How To Evaluate New Capital Investments," *Harvard Business Review*, XXXVI, No. 6 (November–December, 1958), pp. 59–69.

probable effects on the cash budget. However, if payout is to be used in this way, the authors recommend that it should always be crude payout after income taxes, calculated in the way illustrated in Chapter 15. The various modifications of the payout period using depreciation or interest are less meaningful than crude payout and are less reliable guides to the purposes that may legitimately be served by a payout analysis.

Use of Unreasonably Short Payout Periods. Sometimes the payout technique is combined with the stipulation that no proposal will be accepted unless it has an extremely short payout period, such as one year or two years. Such a stipulation, if rigidly adhered to, tends to block the approval of projects that would earn excellent returns. As applied to replacement decisions, this type of stipulation tends to perpetuate the use of obsolete and uneconomical plant. George Terborgh's forceful writings on this subject were referred to in Chapter 16.

Implementation of Criteria for Investment Decisions at Various Levels in an Organization. Generally speaking, proposals for appropriation of funds to acquire physical plant are subject to review and approval by top management as part of a system of budgetary control. The segment of the budget that deals with such appropriations is referred to as the capital budget or investment budget. Good literature is available on this subject.[2] It was pointed out in Chapter 9 that it is a common experience for the aggregate of the capital budget proposals to greatly exceed the funds that can be made available.

Although it is common to have procedures for the budgeting of investment funds, it often happens that there are no established criteria for comparing proposals. Of course each proposal will contain the necessary estimates of first costs. But the supporting material may vary greatly from one proposal to another, and there may be no recognized method for evaluating the relative merits of different proposals. Under such circumstances the choice by top management among proposals may depend on the skill with which they are supported by department heads rather than on the productivity of the different proposed investments.

However, it is not sufficient merely to establish sound criteria for decision making at the level of capital budgeting. The criteria need to be implemented by prescribing consistent methods of presenting

[2] See particularly Joel Dean, *Capital Budgeting* (New York: Columbia University Press, 1951).

the relevant estimates and of showing the analysis of these estimates. Certain forms used for this purpose in one organization are presented and discussed later in this chapter.

There are likely to be a great many decisions between alternatives on the design level for each investment proposal submitted in the capital budget. (In the language of the economics of public works, referred to in Chapter 18, there are many decisions required in project formulation for every decision in project justification.) The majority of the examples and problems in this book relate to economic decisions on the level of engineering design rather than on the level of capital budgeting.

Usually it is a physical impossibility for most of the economic decisions on the design level to be reviewed at the level of capital budgeting. Moreover, in a large organization, hundreds of persons are likely to be involved in design level decisions regarding physical plant. What is needed is a feedback to these persons of the criteria for decision making established at the capital budgeting level. The quotation from Robert F. Barrell in Chapter 9 (page 145) stressed the importance of consistency of criteria throughout an organization. It is the authors' observation that Mr. Barrell is correct in his view that a sound and uniform basis for decision making on the capital budgeting level is much more common than on the design level.

If engineers are left to their own inclinations on design alternatives regarding physical plant, some may greatly overdesign in the sense of making large uneconomic increases in first costs and others may greatly underdesign in the sense of keeping first costs uneconomically low. To offset these extreme tendencies, some written material is needed stating the rules to govern economic design in the particular organization and giving some typical examples of economic comparisons of alternate designs. In some cases this material may take the form of a company manual on engineering economy. Such a manual may well be supplemented by short courses on company time for engineers and other persons concerned with decisions among investment alternatives. A case where a manual and courses were both used is briefly discussed later in this chapter.

An Example of Forms for Presentation of Investment Proposals. A number of facets of the review of investment proposals on the capital budgeting level can be illustrated by a brief description of certain forms and methods of analysis developed for the Chemical Division of Food Machinery and Chemical Corporation.

The forms (Figures 19–1 to 19–3) and the descriptive material are reproduced by permission from an article by Ray I. Reul.[3]

Discussion of Figures 19–1 to 19–3. These three forms contain a worked-out example of a hypothetical proposal for facilities to produce a new product. In this example the proposed investment starts in 1956 with the purchase of a site, and the plant construction occurs in 1957 and 1958. Sales of the product start in 1958 at 600 tons and reach a plateau of 1,200 tons per year in the sixth year. Although the analysis assumes sales for only 20 years, the tax consequences of the depreciation deductions are shown for 30 years.

In Figure 19–1, the estimated investment requirements are classified by years and by various categories. The reader will note that different categories have different income tax consequences. Thus "land" and "working funds" have no income tax effects. Items listed as "expense" can be charged off for tax purposes in the year in which the expenditure is made. Mr. Reul's suggested treatment of "future obligations" was discussed in Chapter 13. In this instance the project will employ existing unused warehouse and office space and existing surplus steam and compressed air capacity; the analysis assumes that, in this expanding enterprise, the commitment of these presently unused facilities to this proposed project will result in construction of new similar facilities in 1962.

The *Harvard Business Review* article reproduced a "depreciation and depletion work sheet" not shown here. On this sheet the income tax deductions for depreciation (and depletion, where applicable) are shown on a year-by-year basis. Any investment-type outlay chargeable as a current expense for tax purposes (such as the $50,000 for site preparation in this example) is tabulated on this work sheet in the year of its occurrence. In this example years-digits depreciation is assumed for all depreciable assets. Assumed lives are 40 years for buildings, 15 years for process equipment, and 20 years for future requirements.

Figure 19–2 is a general summary of expected cash flow resulting from the proposal, including investment-type disbursements, receipts from the sale of the product, operating disbursements (referred to as "plant cost before depreciation"), and income taxes. The end product of the tabulation and calculation in this form is a year-by-year listing of certain disbursements in the right-hand column under "investment" and of certain net receipts in the two right-hand columns under "receipts."

---

[3] R. I. Reul, "Profitability Index for Investments," *Harvard Business Review*, XXXV, No. 4 (July–August, 1957), 116–32.

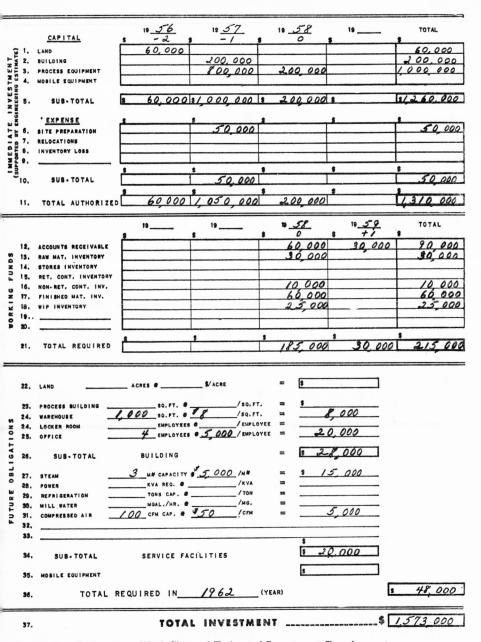

FIGURE 19–1. Work Sheet of Estimated Investment Requirements

SOURCE: R. I. Reul, "Profitability Index for Investments," *Harvard Business Review*, XXXV, No. 4 (July–August, 1957), 123.

INVESTMENT

CAL. YEAR	PERIOD		CAPITAL		EXPENSED	WORKING FUND	TOTAL
			LAND	FACILITIES			
	3RD YR.	AT START					
		DURING					
56	2ND YR.	AT START	$ 60,000				$60,000
		DURING					
57	1ST YR.	AT START					
		DURING		$1,000,000	$50,000		1,050,000
58	1ST YR.	AT START					
		DURING		200,000		$185,000	385,000
59	2ND YEAR DURING					30,000	30,000
60	3RD YEAR DURING						
61	4TH YEAR DURING						
62	5TH YEAR DURING			48,000			48,000
	6TH YEAR DURING						
	7TH YEAR DURING						
	8TH YEAR DURING						
	9TH YEAR DURING						
	10TH YEAR DURING						
TOTALS			$ 60,000	$1,248,000	$ 50,000	$ 215,000	$1,573,000

RECEIPTS

CAL. YEAR	ANNUAL PERIOD	ANNUAL VOLUME IN TONS	PLANT NET INCOME	PLANT COST BEFORE DEPRECIATION	PROFIT BEFORE DEPRECIATION	DEPRECIATION & DEPLETION DEDUCTION	CASH FLOW BACK AFTER 50 % INCOME TAX	
							ON INCOME	ON DEDUCTION
						$ 50,000		$ 25,000
	1ST	600	$ 1,200,000	$1,000,000	$200,000	136,800	$ 100,000	68,400
	2ND	800	1,600,000	1,200,000	400,000	126,600	200,000	63,300
	3RD	1,000	2,000,000	1,600,000	400,000	114,300	200,000	57,100
	4TH	1,000	2,000,000	1,600,000	400,000	110,200	200,000	55,100
	5TH	1,000	2,000,000	1,600,000	400,000	105,400	200,000	52,700
	6TH	1,200	2,400,000	1,800,000	600,000	95,900	300,000	48,000
	7TH	1,200	2,400,000	1,800,000	600,000	87,400	300,000	43,000
	8TH	1,200	2,400,000	1,800,000	600,000	79,000	300,000	39,500
	9TH	1,200	2,400,000	1,800,000	600,000	69,500	300,000	34,800
	10TH	1,200	2,400,000	1,800,000	600,000	61,000	300,000	30,500
	11TH	1,200	2,400,000	1,800,000	600,000	52,500	300,000	26,300
	12TH	1,200	2,400,000	1,800,000	600,000	43,100	300,000	21,600
	13TH	1,200	2,400,000	1,800,000	600,000	34,600	300,000	17,300
	14TH	1,200	2,400,000	1,800,000	600,000	26,100	300,000	13,100
	15TH	1,200	2,400,000	1,800,000	600,000	16,700	300,000	8,300
	16TH	1,200	2,400,000	1,800,000	600,000	8,700	300,000	4,100
	17TH	1,200	2,400,000	1,800,000	600,000	7,700	300,000	3,800
	18TH	1,200	2,400,000	1,800,000	600,000	7,200	300,000	3,600
	19TH	1,200	2,400,000	1,800,000	600,000	6,800	300,000	3,200
	20TH	1,200	2,615,000	1,800,000	600,000	6,100	515,000	3,000
	21ST					5,800		2,900
	22ND					5,300		2,700
	23RD					5,000		2,500
	24TH					4,400		2,200
	25TH					3,900		2,000
	26TH					3,700		1,800
	27TH					3,400		1,700
	28TH					3,200		1,600
	29TH					2,900		1,500
	30TH					2,700		1,400

✳ NOTE: INCLUDES $215,000 WORKING FUNDS RECOVERED—NOT SUBJECT TO INCOME TAX

FIGURE 19-2. Time Schedule of Expenditures and Receipts

SOURCE: R. I. Reul, "Profitability Index for Investments," *Harvard Business Review*, XXXV. No. 4 (July–August, 1957), 126.

TIMING			TRIAL #1 0% INTEREST RATE	TRIAL #2 10% INTEREST RATE		TRIAL #3 15% INTEREST RATE		TRIAL #4 25% INTEREST RATE		TRIAL #5 40% INTEREST RATE	
CAL. YEAR	PERIOD		ACTUAL AMOUNT OF DISBURSEMENTS	FACTOR	PRESENT WORTH	FACTOR	PRESENT WORTH	FACTOR	PRESENT WORTH	FACTOR	PRESENT WORTH
	3RD YR.	AT ST.		1.350		1.568		2.117		3.320	
		DURING		1.285		1.456		1.873		2.736	
56	2ND YR.	AT ST.	$ 60,000	1.221	$ 73,300	1.350	$ 81,000	1.649	$ 98,000	2.225	$ 133,500
		DURING		1.162		1.253		1.459		1.834	
57	1ST YR.	AT ST.		1.105		1.162		1.284		1.492	
		DURING	$1,050,000	1.052	$1,104,600	1.079	$1,133,000	1.136	$1,192,800	1.230	$1,291,500
58	1ST YR.	AT ST.		1.000		1.000		1.000		1.000	
		DURING	385,000	.952	366,500	.929	357,700	.885	340,700	.824	317,200
59	2ND YEAR DURING		30,000	.861	25,800	.799	24,000	.689	20,700	.553	16,600
60	3RD " "			.779		.688		.537		.370	
61	4TH " "			.705		.592		.418		.248	
62	5TH " "		48,000	.638	30,600	.510	24,500	.326	15,600	.166	8,000
	6TH " "			.577		.439		.254		.112	
	7TH " "			.522		.378		.197		.075	
	8TH " "			.473		.325		.154		.050	
	9TH " "			.428		.280		.120		.034	
	10TH " "			.387		.241		.093		.023	
TOTALS (A)			$1,573,000		$1,600,800		$1,620,200		$1,668,700		$1,766,800

CAL. YEAR	PERIOD		ACTUAL AMOUNT OF RECEIPTS	FACTOR	PRESENT WORTH	FACTOR	PRESENT WORTH	FACTOR	PRESENT WORTH	FACTOR	PRESENT WORTH
57	1ST YR. BEFORE DURING		25,000	1.052	26,300	1.079	27,000	1.136	28,400	1.230	30,800
58	1ST YEAR DURING		168,400	.952	160,300	.929	156,400	.885	149,000	.824	138,800
59	2ND " "		263,300	.861	226,700	.799	210,400	.689	181,400	.553	145,600
60	3RD " "		257,200	.779	205,500	.688	177,000	.537	138,100	.370	95,200
61	4TH " "		255,100	.705	179,800	.592	151,000	.418	106,600	.248	63,300
62	5TH " "		252,700	.638	161,200	.510	128,900	.326	82,400	.166	41,900
63	6TH " "		348,000	.577	200,800	.439	152,800	.254	88,400	.112	39,000
64	7TH " "		343,700	.522	179,400	.378	129,900	.197	67,700	.075	25,800
65	8TH " "		339,500	.473	160,600	.325	110,300	.154	52,300	.050	17,000
66	9TH " "		334,800	.428	143,300	.280	93,700	.119	39,800	.034	11,400
67	10TH " "		330,500	.387	127,900	.241	79,700	.093	30,700	.023	7,000
68	11TH " "		326,300	.350	114,200	.207	67,500	.073	23,800	.015	4,900
69	12TH " "		321,600	.317	101,900	.178	57,200	.057	18,300	.010	3,200
70	13TH " "		317,300	.287	91,100	.154	48,900	.044	14,000	.007	2,200
71	14TH " "		313,100	.259	81,100	.132	41,300	.034	10,600	.005	1,600
72	15TH " "		308,300	.235	72,500	.114	35,100	.027	8,300	.003	900
73	16TH " "		304,100	.212	64,500	.098	29,800	.021	6,400	.002	600
74	17TH " "		303,800	.192	58,300	.084	25,500	.016	4,900	.001	300
75	18TH " "		303,600	.174	52,800	.073	22,200	.013	3,900	.001	300
76	19TH " "		303,200	.157	47,600	.062	18,800	.010	3,000	.001	300
77	20TH " "		517,900	.142	73,500	.054	28,000	.008	4,100		
78	21ST " "		2,900	.129	400	.046	100	.006			
79	22ND " "		2,700	.117	300	.040		.005			
80	23RD " "		2,500	.105	300	.034		.004			
81	24TH " "		2,200	.095	200	.029		.003			
82	25TH " "		2,000	.086	200	.025		.002			
83	26TH " "		1,800	.078	100	.022		.002			
84	27TH " "		1,700	.071		.019		.001			
85	28TH " "		1,600	.064		.016		.001			
86	29TH " "		1,500	.058		.014		.001			
87	30TH " "		1,400	.052		.012		.001			
TOTALS (B)			6,257,700		2,530,800		1,791,500		1,062,100		630,100
RATIO A/B			.25		.63		.90		1.57		2.80

FIGURE 19–3. Calculation of the Profitability Index

SOURCE: R. I. Reul, "Profitability Index for Investments," *Harvard Business Review*, XXXV, No. 4 (July–August, 1957), 127.

Although the information and calculations in Figure 19–2 are organized differently from the tables in Chapter 15 that showed calculation of cash flow after income taxes, the end product of the two different types of analysis is identical. This point may be illustrated by computing the net cash flow for 1961 (the fourth year) by the method used in Chapter 15, as follows:

A	Receipts	$2,000,000
B	Operating disbursements	1,600,000
C	Cash flow before income taxes (A − B)............................	$ 400,000
D	Depreciation write-off for tax purposes	110,200
E	Taxable income (C − D)...	$ 289,800
F	Cash flow for income taxes (50% of E)............................	144,900
G	Cash flow after income taxes (C − F).............................	$ 255,100

In Figure 19–2, the same $255,100 is shown in two parts, $200,000 and $55,100. In effect the $400,000 cash flow before depreciation is assumed to be cut in half by the 50% tax, and then half of the $110,200 depreciation tax deduction is restored as positive cash flow.

Figure 19–3 contains the necessary present worth calculations to convert cash flow after income taxes into rate of return. (The phrase "profitability index" is used here to mean rate of return computed by compound interest methods.) The tabulation of cash flow itself, transferred from Figure 19–2, provides the basis for computing present worth at zero interest rate. Present worth factors for interest rates of 10%, 15%, 25%, and 40% are printed on the forms; the necessary multiplications and additions to compute present worths are obvious.

Certain points of difference should be noted from the many calculations of unknown rates of return that have been illustrated throughout this book. One point, a minor one, relates to the method of interpolation used. The unknown rate of return is, of course, the interest rate that makes the algebraic sum of the present worths of all cash flows equal to zero. We have ordinarily computed present worths for one interest rate giving a positive sum and another interest rate giving a negative sum and interpolated between these two present worth figures to find the unknown rate of return.

Another way to state that the algebraic sum of present worths of all cash flows is equal to zero is to say that the present worth of receipts is equal to the present worth of disbursements. In the analysis illustrated in Figure 19–3, the ratio is computed of present worth of investment-type disbursements to present worth of net operating receipts for each of the five interest rates used. These ratios, designated as A/B at the bottom of Figure 19–3, are plotted against interest rate on a sheet of graph paper. This graph is shown in the *Harvard Business Review* article but is not reproduced here. The rate of return (profitability index) is the interest rate for which the ratio A/B is 1.0. This graphical interpolation gives 16.5% as the rate of return for the data of Figure 19–3. A linear interpolation between the ratios 0.90 for 15% and 1.57 for 25% will also give 16.5% as the rate of return.

A more important difference from the methods illustrated throughout this book is that Figure 19–3 does not use the end-of-year convention. For all of the receipts and most of the investments, the assumption is made that the cash flow occurs uniformly throughout the year in question. To use this uniform-flow convention, it is necessary to use present worth factors computed on the assumption of continuous compounding of interest. The continuous-compounding present worth factors shown in Figure 19–3 differ from the factors for the same interest rates shown in Table E–25 of this book because the interest rates in Figure 19–3 are *nominal* rates whereas those in Table E–25 are *effective* rates. This particular aspect of Figure 19–3 is discussed in Appendix B.

Some Differences Between Economy Studies on the Capital Budgeting Level and on the Design Level. In administering a capital budget in competitive industry there are obvious advantages in having a prospective rate of return after income taxes computed for each major investment proposal. Proposals can be arrayed in order of rate of return in the manner illustrated in Table 9–1 (page 138). Such an array helps in establishing an order of priority where funds are limited. Moreover, management can weigh risks and other irreducible data in relation to prospective rates of return. No formal decision needs to be made regarding a single minimum attractive rate of return to be applied to all projects. The desire to avoid any firm decision about minimum attractive rate of return is perhaps the most important reason for using rate of return studies at the level of capital budgeting.

As previously mentioned, every project submitted for the capital budget is likely to have its subalternatives, and each subalternative will have its own subalternatives, and so on. Most of the decisions among subalternatives and among sub-subalternatives must necessarily be made at organizational levels below that of capital budgeting. For simplicity in discussion here, such decisions are referred to as being at the design level, although it is recognized that not all of the decisions involve alternative engineering designs.

Often it is completely impracticable to compare all subalternatives and sub-subalternatives within an organization in the way illustrated in Table 9–1. For this reason the case for making economy studies by the rate of return method is not nearly as strong on the design level as on the capital budgeting level. As a practical matter, to secure rough consistency in the criteria for decision making at the two levels, some figure for minimum attractive rate of return should be established by management to be used in economy studies made at the design level. Conceivably, this figure may be different for different divisions of an organization, or for different design problems, but it should be definite for any particular case.

Once the minimum attractive rate of return is stipulated, there may be an advantage in using the annual cost method (occasionally supplemented by the present worth method) to make economy studies at the design level. This advantage is that the annual cost and present worth methods are somewhat easier to apply because of the absence of the trial-and-error calculations needed in computing rates of return. Designers may offer less resistance to the making of economy studies based on annual costs than they would offer to studies based on rate of return.

Designers may also be resistant to requirements that they make studies involving specific consideration of the income tax consequences of design decisions. Moreover, they are not always competent to judge the effect on income taxes of different alternatives. For these reasons, and because of greater simplicity, it may be desirable that many economy studies at the design level be based on a minimum attractive rate of return *before* income taxes. In general, someone who understands the income tax aspects of the subject should make a sufficient review of such studies to be sure that they are made in circumstances where the before-tax and after-tax analysis will lead to the same design decisions.

The foregoing comments regarding differences in methods for economy studies at the two levels are not applicable to regulated public utilities that make economy studies based on minimizing revenue requirements. Generally speaking, the same "fair return" (based on the utility's over-all cost of money) should be used as the interest rate in economy studies at all levels; income taxes can be introduced in a simple manner as a percentage of first cost of plant by the type of formula explained in Chapter 15.

Use of Company Manuals and In-Plant Courses To Implement Criteria for Decision Making at the Design Level. The public utility industry contains a number of good examples of procedures aimed to secure effective economy studies at the design level. A case in point is that of the Pacific Telephone and Telegraph Company.

During the mid-1950's and thereafter, this company was spending several hundred million dollars a year for new plant. Decisions on the selection of plant were made by many engineers and others throughout the organization. It was decided to conduct a series of courses or seminars to help to ensure that the desired criteria were used for economic selection of plant.

Text material for the seminars included a pamphlet entitled "Engineering Economy" issued in 1952 by the Department of Operation and Engineering of the American Telephone and Telegraph Company for use by the member companies of the Bell Telephone System. As the seminars developed, this pamphlet from the parent company was supplemented by a pair of pamphlets of the same title issued in 1956 by Pacific Telephone and Telegraph Company.

The seminars were held on company time and occupied half a day a week for 10 or 12 weeks. The usual seminar group consisted of 10 persons. Several hundred persons participated in the initial series of seminars that took place over a period of two or three years. Although most of these were engineering personnel, there were also a few persons from related departments (such as accounting and budgeting). In many cases the leaders for the later seminars were selected from the membership of the earlier ones.

The topics covered in these seminars are indicated by the following chapter titles from Pacific Telephone's two "Engineering Economy" pamphlets:

Volume 1—Fundamentals
1 Corporate organization and financial structure
2 Accounting methods and techniques
3 Taxes, interest, and depreciation
4 Construction program

Volume 2—Economic Selection Studies
1 Depreciation, service life and salvage
2 Mathematics of money
3 Taxes
4 The cost study and its elements
5 Techniques of economic selection studies
6 Study procedures
7 Interpretation of results
8 Cost studies involving outside parties

Personal Bias as a Factor in Some Decisions on Plant Investment. Where decisions among investment alternatives are made on intuitive grounds, or where the pros and cons of the various alternatives are stated only in words rather than in monetary figures, personal bias often plays a large part in the decision making. Many psychological and personal interest factors, often unconscious, are likely to weigh against a choice for greatest long-run economy.

Particularly insidious among such factors is the desire for personal importance on the part of someone who has the responsibility for an investment decision. Such a desire may lead an individual to make the decision that increases the size of the activities under his own control regardless of considerations of economy.

For example, a mechanical engineer for a municipal waterworks was responsible for the design of a new pumping station. He had to choose between installation of boiler equipment with steam-driven pumps, and motor-driven pumps with electricity supplied by the local electric light and power company. The power company offered the city a rate for electrical energy that made the operating cost of motor-driven pumps about half that of the steam-driven pumps. Nevertheless, the engineer selected the steam-driven equipment, giving the excuse that it had the advantage of greater reliability of service. This excuse was made despite the fact that the city had pumping plants of both sorts, and breakdowns were as frequent in the steam stations as were interruptions of electrical service in the electrically operated stations. It was quite clear to observers that this steam engineer's desire for more activities under his own control was the chief factor in the decision.

Managers with a purely financial outlook sometimes think in terms of immediate least cost. Occasionally the engineer may go to the opposite extreme. He may think in terms of the most permanent structure, the latest and most mechanically efficient machine; he wants the thing that is the best mechanical job or the most monumental engineering achievement. To be sure, this choice may result in long-run economy in some instances. But there are also cases where the economical thing to do is to choose the temporary installation, or the installation with a low mechanical efficiency and a correspondingly low first cost.

The managerial requirement that decisions among investment alternatives be based on formal economy studies may prevent many bad decisions that would otherwise be based on personal bias. This desirable influence of economy studies may be greatest where they are subject to the possibility of post-audit.

Post-Audit of Decisions on Plant Investment. Two useful purposes may be served by an organized program for an audit of past investment decisions:

1. The expectation that audits will be undertaken may cause more careful estimates to be made for all economy studies. That is, estimators will take more care if they anticipate that their estimates will be checked against performance. This influence may apply to many different kinds of estimates—first costs, savings in annual operating costs, sales, prices at which products can be sold, and so on.

2. The information gained in auditing past decisions may be fed back to estimators and analysts and persons reviewing capital budgets in a way that makes it possible to prepare better estimates in the future and to do a better job of reviewing future investment proposals.

Nevertheless, a systematic program for auditing past economy studies should not be undertaken by management without a clear idea regarding the limitations of post-audits. An economy study deals with prospective differences among alternative courses of action. In principle an audit should aim to analyze the difference between what happened with the decision as actually made and what would have happened if some other different decision had been made. But it is rarely possible to be *sure* what would have happened with the other decision. Therefore, a past *decision* is not really subject to audit. Moreover, an uncritical use of accounting allocations —among activities or among different periods of time—can be as misleading in an audit as in an economy study.

Generally speaking, where audit procedures are used, they should be applied to various elements of a group of economy studies rather than to each study as a whole. For example, it is useful to know that particular individuals consistently overestimate or underestimate on certain items.

Only in a limited number of cases is it possible to make a valid audit of a past estimate of a rate of return. This may be done only for projects that are clearly separable from the other activities of an enterprise and where it is possible to carry the analysis to the date of termination of consequences of an investment. Of course, short of the terminal date, it frequently may be evident that a project is turning out approximately as estimated, or much better, or much worse.

Post-audit procedures are most readily applied to projects for which estimates have been submitted at the level of capital budgeting. In some cases they might be applied on a sampling basis to certain aspects of economy studies made on the design level.

Summary. This chapter has given a brief introduction to the topic of the steps that may be taken by management to ensure that sound decisions are made regarding proposed plant investments. The basic criteria for decision making should be consistent throughout an organization. Nevertheless, it is helpful to make a distinction between decision making at the level of capital budgeting and at the level of engineering design. It often is advantageous to use different methods of implementing decision making criteria at different levels in an organization.

Problems

19–1. Three proposals, each for the immediate disbursement of $10,000, are to be compared in crude payout before income taxes and in rate of return before income taxes. Proposal A has a net positive cash flow of $3,500 a year for 3 years. Proposal B has a net positive cash flow of $2,000 a year for 6 years. Proposal C has a net positive cash flow of $1,200 a year for 20 years. All three proposals have zero salvage values. (*Ans.* = A, 2.9 years, 2.5%; B, 5.0 years, 5.5%; C, 8.3 years, 10.3%.)

19–2. Compare the proposals in Problem 19–1 by crude payout after income taxes and rate of return after income taxes. Assume an effective tax rate of 50%. Assume straight-line depreciation and that the lives and salvage values used in the economy study are also used for tax purposes. (*Ans.* = A, 2.9 years, 1.2%; B, 5.5 years, 2.8%; C, 11.8 years, 5.7%.)

19–3. Two proposals, each for the immediate disbursement of $20,000, are to be compared in crude payout before income taxes and in rate of return before income taxes. Both proposals have a 5-year life. Proposal D has a net positive cash flow of $6,000 a year for 5 years and zero salvage value. Proposal E has a net positive cash flow of $4,200 a year for 5 years and a $20,000 salvage value. (*Ans.* = D, 3.3 years, 15.2%; E, 4.8 years, 21.0%.)

19–4. Compare the proposals in Problem 19–3 by crude payout after income taxes and rate of return after income taxes. Assume an effective tax rate of 50%. Assume straight-line depreciation and that the lives and salvage values used in the economy study are also used for tax purposes. (*Ans.* = D, 4.0 years, 7.9%; E, 5.0 years, 10.5%.)

19–5. For each proposal of Problem 19–1, subtract annual straight-line depreciation from annual cash flow before income taxes. Divide the resulting figure into the investment to obtain a so-called payoff period after depreciation. (*Ans.:* In A and B, the respective answers of 60 years and 30 years obviously are meaningless as they are much longer than the estimated lives of the projects. As the answer in C is 14.3 years, the double counting of the depreciation is not so obvious.)

19–6. Two investment proposals are to be compared. Each requires the immediate disbursement of $30,000. Both proposals have a 5-year life. Proposal J has a net positive cash flow of $9,600 a year and a zero salvage value. Proposal K has a net positive cash flow of $4,500 a year and a $30,000 salvage value. It may be shown by simple calculation that J will yield a rate of return of 17.6% as compared to 15.0% for K. However, in this organization proposals are compared on the basis of payout period (so-called) after straight-line depreciation. Compute for each proposal the number of years required for the excess of positive cash flow above straight-line depreciation to equal the original investment. Which proposal appears superior by this distorted criterion? (*Ans.:* K, as its payout is computed to be 6.7 years as compared to 8.3 years for J.)

19–7. A certain project has a first cost of $100,000, a 5-year life with zero salvage value, and estimated excess of receipts over disbursements of $42,000 a year throughout the life. In computing "payout," it is proposed to subtract straight-line depreciation and 6% interest on the depreciated book value from the positive cash flow each year. The payout period is defined as the number of years needed for the results of these annual subtractions to add up to the original investment. With this definition, what is the prospective payout period? Also compute the prospective rate of return by correct compound interest methods. (*Ans.:* According to this definition, the investment will never pay out; the double counting of the depreciation leaves an apparent shortage of $8,000 at the end of the 5 years. However, the rate of return is 31.2%.)

19–8. In Figure 19–3, the interpolation between the ratios of A/B for 15% and 25% indicated a rate of return of 16.5%. Compute the ratios of B/A for 15% and 25% and make a linear interpolation to find the rate of return. Add algebraically the present worths of investments and receipts at 15% and 25% in the manner illustrated throughout this book and make a linear interpolation to find rate of return. Discuss your results.

19–9. The computed rate of return (profitability index) was 16.5% in the example developed in Figures 19–1 to 19–3. Discuss the sensitivity of this index to changes made in the estimates of occurrences during the later years of this study. For example, Figure 19–2 shows $215,000 of positive cash flow in 1977 (year 20) due to recovery of "working funds." How would the index have been changed if this estimated recovery had been omitted? How would it have been changed if the forecast had been made that the land and building would be sold for their book value (about $110,000) at the end of 20 years? How could it have been changed if the residual depreciation tax credits in years 21 to 30 had been omitted? How would it have been changed if the study had assumed that sales of this product would terminate after 15 years rather than after 20 years?

19–10. (This is suggested as a possible term report problem for a course in engineering economy.)

An economy study requires a clear definition either of some proposal for action that is to be considered, or of alternative proposals that are to be compared. It then requires estimates to translate such proposals as far as possible into terms of future money receipts and disbursements, accompanied by estimates of other relevant matters (so-called irreducibles) not so translated. Financial calculations are then necessary to provide a basis for judgment. Finally there must be a decision or recommendation as to action that gives weight both to the financial calculations and to the irreducibles. In preliminary studies to determine whether or not any proposal is really promising, the result of a study may be a recommendation for or against the expenditure of time and money for a more detailed study. This problem is intended as a brief exercise in the carrying out of all of these steps.

Selection of Subject. Choose some proposal or set of alternatives for consideration. Two general types of study are possible:

1. A rough preliminary study of some proposed project or set of alternatives. The result of such a study should generally be a recommendation that the project is or is not worthy of more detailed investigation, or a recommendation that certain alternatives be selected for detailed study.
   Example: Proposal for a group of small furnished apartments as housing for married students, research assistants, instructors, etc., at your college or university.
2. A complete study of some fairly simple problem of engineering alternatives.
   Example: Selection of an electric motor for a given service.

Because the time available for this report is necessarily limited, you are likely to be better satisfied with your results if you do not undertake too complicated a problem. Wherever practicable, it is a good plan to select a problem dealing with some actual situation of which you have personal knowledge. If you wish to make an economy study in some field in which you do not have access to data on an actual situation, it is necessary to set up a hypothetical case for study.

Collection of Data. Investigation of an actual case may require you to do some legwork collecting information. Any problem may involve some library work. The best sources of reference on technical papers and articles are the *Engineering Index* and the *Industrial Arts Index*. Books on cost estimating give general guidance on methods of making preliminary and detailed cost estimates. Some up-to-date price information may be found in the current issues of a number of technical and trade journals.

Report. The report should start with a clear statement of your problem. It should give your analysis of the problem and should state your definite recommendation for action. The sources of all of your estimates should be given.

APPENDIXES

A
Certain Alternate Methods of Computing Annual Capital Recovery Cost

One of the topics presented in Chapter 6 was the conversion of a first cost, P, into an equivalent uniform annual figure over a life or study period. To make this conversion, it is necessary to have a stipulated minimum attractive rate of return or interest rate, i, an estimated life or study period, n, and an estimated salvage value, L, at the end of the life or study period.

Throughout this book, we have used the following equation to compute this annual cost of capital recovery with a return:

$$CR = (P - L)(\text{crf-}i\%\text{-}n) + Li$$

This equation, which involves the use of the capital recovery factor, obviously is independent of the depreciation accounts.

Some Methods That Appear To Tie Annual Capital Recovery Costs to the Depreciation Accounts. In some economy studies that use the method of annual costs, various combinations of depreciation figures and interest figures are used. The total of depreciation plus interest is intended to serve the same purpose as our annual cost of capital recovery with a return. Three methods that sometimes are used are as follows:

1. Sinking-fund depreciation plus interest on first cost
2. Straight-line depreciation plus interest on first cost
3. Straight-line depreciation plus average interest

These methods give satisfactory results in some cases and misleading results in others.

Sinking-Fund Depreciation Plus Interest on First Cost. This is a correct compound interest method that gives the same annual cost of capital recovery as our conventional method provided the assumed interest rate on the sinking fund is equal to the stipulated minimum attractive rate of return. Sometimes the method is referred to as *interest plus amortization.*

As explained in Chapter 4, the capital recovery factor is always equal to the sinking fund factor plus the interest rate. An alternate way of writing our basic equation for capital recovery at interest rate i is therefore:

$$CR = (P - L)(\text{sff–}i\text{–}n) + (P - L)i + Li = (P - L)(\text{sff–}i\text{–}n) + Pi$$

In effect, the method of sinking-fund depreciation plus interest on first cost is based on this latter formula. A numerical example will help to show the relationship between this method and the conventional method. Let us assume an asset with a first cost of $22,000, an estimated life of 10 years, and an estimated salvage value of $2,000. We shall use a minimum attractive rate of return of 10%. By the conventional method that has been used throughout this book:

$$CR = (\$22,000 - \$2,000)(\text{crf–}10\%\text{–}10) + \$2,000(0.10)$$

$$= \$20,000(0.16275) + \$2,000(0.10) = \$3,255 + \$200 = \$3,455$$

Assuming the use of a 10% interest rate in computing sinking-fund depreciation, the calculation by the method of sinking-fund depreciation plus interest on first cost reaches an identical result, as follows:

Sinking-fund depreciation $= (P - L)(\text{sff–}i\text{–}n)$
$\quad = (\$22,000 - \$2,000)(\text{sff–}10\%\text{–}10) = \$20,000(0.06275)$ $\qquad = \$1,255$
Interest on first cost $= Pi = \$22,000(0.10)$ $\qquad = \underline{\ \ 2,200}$

Total annual cost of capital recovery with a 10% return $\qquad = \$3,455$

The sinking-fund method of depreciation accounting was described in Chapter 10. It should be noted that the figure for so-called sinking-fund depreciation in the foregoing calculation of capital recovery cost is not the full depreciation charge that would be made in the books if the sinking-fund method should be used; it is merely the *annuity* portion of the depreciation charge. If we should calculate year-by-year depreciation charges in the manner illustrated in Table 10–2, we would see that the sinking-fund depreciation charge for our $22,000 asset would vary from $1,255 in the first year to $2,959 in the 10th year; in our calculation of sinking-fund depreciation plus interest on first cost, only the $1,255 figure was used.

This annuity portion of the sinking-fund depreciation charge is sometimes referred to as *amortization*.[1] (The verb *amortize* comes from the same root as *mortal* and literally means "to make dead or destroy." It is applied to the provision for extinguishment of a debt or other obligation, particularly through periodic payments into a sinking fund.)

If the interest rate used on the amortization fund differs from the interest rate on first cost, the capital recovery cost obtained by this method obviously will differ from the one obtained by a conventional calculation using only one interest rate. For example, assume that a 10% rate is used to compute interest on first cost and a 3% rate is used in the sinking fund calculation. The capital recovery cost for our $22,000 asset will then appear to be:

Sinking-fund depreciation = ($22,000 − $2,000)(sff–3%–10)
= $20,000(0.08723)   = $1,745
Interest on first cost = $22,000(0.10)   = 2,200

Total   = $3,945

Some Pros and Cons on the Method of Sinking-Fund Depreciation Plus Interest on First Cost. Although this method has not been common in economy studies in competitive industry, it has been widely used in economy studies for regulated public utilities and for governments. In such studies it is usual to assume the same interest rate on first cost and on the sinking fund—often 7% in public utilities and from 2½% to 4% for governments.

Where used in this manner with a single interest rate, the method gives exactly the same annual cost figure as the method employing the capital recovery factor, which has been used throughout this book. The choice between these two methods of computing annual cost must therefore be based on other grounds than the correctness of the results given by the two methods.

If sinking-fund depreciation accounting were actually to be used in the accounts, the use in economy studies of sinking-fund depreciation plus interest on first cost would serve the purpose of helping to reconcile economy studies with the accounts of the enterprise. But this method of depreciation accounting, once used by a few regulated public utilities, has largely been abandoned. As pointed out in Chapter 10, this method is subject to the objection that it gives an unrealistically high proportion of the total write off in the final years of the life of an asset.

---

[1] For some reason this word is often mispronounced. The correct division into syllables is a-mor-ti-za-tion, with the second and fourth syllables accented. The common mispronunciation assumes the first syllable is *am* and accents the *am*.

Or sinking-fund depreciation plus interest on first cost might tie an economy study to the financial policies of an enterprise if an actual sinking fund were to be established to recover an investment (less salvage, if any) in a fixed asset at the end of its life. But such sinking funds are rarely used.

In most cases, therefore, this method should be viewed as a compound interest conversion unrelated to the accounts or to the establishment of any actual fund. Viewed in this way, the method of sinking-fund depreciation plus interest on first cost does not seem to the authors to have any advantage over the conventional method of computing the annual cost of capital recovery with a return illustrated throughout this book. Often the method using sinking-fund depreciation is harder to explain than the conventional method because critics may make such comments as "There will be no actual sinking fund" or "We are not actually using this method of depreciation accounting." It is hard to give a satisfactory answer to these comments.

Valid objections may be raised to this method where two interest rates are used. A discussion of these objections follows the explanation of the method of straight-line depreciation plus interest on first cost because this latter method is really a special case of the analysis using two interest rates.

Straight-Line Depreciation Plus Interest on First Cost. If this method were used, the annual capital recovery cost of our $22,000 asset would be computed as follows:

$$\text{Straight-line depreciation} = \frac{P - L}{n}$$

$$= \frac{\$22,000 - \$2,000}{10} = \frac{\$20,000}{10} \qquad\qquad = \$2,000$$

$$\text{Interest on first cost} = Pi = \$22,000\,(0.10) \qquad = \underline{2,200}$$

Total $= \$4,200$

Except in the special case of a salvage value of 100% (or more), this method invariably gives too high a figure for equivalent annual cost. The $4,200 a year that the method indicates is needed to recover our proposed $22,000 investment with a 10% return is, in fact sufficient to permit recovery with a return of about 14.5%.

It was pointed out in Chapter 10 that the straight-line method of depreciation accounting may be thought of as a limiting case of the sinking-fund method in which the interest rate on the sinking fund has been assumed to be 0%. Similarly, straight-line depreciation plus interest on first cost may be viewed as a special case of sinking-fund depreciation plus interest on first cost in which the sinking-fund interest rate is 0%.

Objection to Annual Cost Calculations Using Two Interest Rates. We have computed three different figures for the annual cost of capital recovery with a 10% return for our proposed $22,000 investment in equipment. The conventional method using the capital recovery factor gave us a figure of $3,455; this same figure was obtained with 10% sinking-fund depreciation plus 10% interest on first cost. But 3% sinking-fund depreciation plus 10% interest on first cost gave us an annual capital recovery cost of $3,945. And straight-line depreciation plus interest on first cost gave us $4,200.

The usual objective of comparing equivalent annual costs in an economy study is to judge whether or not certain proposed investments will yield at least a minimum attractive rate of return. Assume that our proposed $22,000 asset is expected to be responsible for increased receipts (or reduced disbursements) of $3,800 a year for 10 years. This annual $3,800 plus the final $2,000 salvage value will in fact be sufficient to recover the $22,000 investment with interest at 12.1%.

If we should compare this annual figure of $3,800 with our computed annual capital recovery cost of $3,455, we would obtain the correct conclusion that the asset would yield more than a 10% return. But if we should compare the $3,800 with $3,945 or with $4,200, we would obtain the incorrect conclusion that the proposed investment was not justified because it would not yield 10%.

The reader may recall our discussion in Chapter 8 of the misleading conclusions obtainable from the calculation of an unknown rate of return by the Hoskold method, where reinvestment was assumed in an imaginary sinking fund bearing a low interest rate. The fallacy in the annual cost calculation using two interest rates (e.g., 3% and 10%, or 0% and 10%) is the same one that we examined in Chapter 8 in our discussion of the Hoskold method.

Consider the following possible interpretation of a comparison of the $3,800 annual receipts with the $3,945 figure obtained by the method of 3% depreciation and 10% interest on first cost: "To judge whether our proposed $22,000 investment will give us a 10% return, the positive cash flow that it will cause is divided into two parts. One part, $2,200, is 10% on our investment. The other part must be enough so that we can invest it at 3% and (with the prospective terminal salvage value) have $22,000 back at the end of the 10 years. As the $3,800 will not be enough to permit us to do this, we should view this proposed investment as yielding less than 10%."

The error here is that the merits of *one* investment, the proposed $22,000 asset, are to be judged on the basis of the combined consequences of *two* investments, the asset and the 3% sinking fund. It is true that the asset, yielding 12.1%, and the sinking fund, yielding 3%, will not combine to give an over-all rate of return of 10%. A total of $3,945 a year will be needed for the combined rate of return to be 10%; $3,800 is not enough. But, unless there is to be an actual 3% sinking fund investment that *must* be made if the asset is acquired, this deficiency of the combined rate of return below 10% has no bearing on the merits of the proposed investment in the asset.

The foregoing two paragraphs may be altered so that they become a comment on the method of straight-line depreciation plus interest on first cost if 0% is substituted for 3% and $4,200 for $3,945.

Straight-Line Depreciation Plus Average Interest. This method of computing the annual cost of capital recovery with a return was widely used in economy studies in the United States in the 1930's and 1940's. Its use was illustrated in many examples and problems in the second (1938) and third (1950) editions of this book. Where straight-line depreciation was actually to be used in the accounts and where the assumed life and salvage value in the economy study were the same as used in the accounts, the method had the advantage of helping to reconcile economy studies with the accounts of an enterprise. The method is a close approximation to true equivalent annual cost in certain cases but a poor approximation in others.

With the decline in the application of straight-line depreciation accounting to new assets that started in 1954 in the United States, the use of this method no longer is justified on the basis of reconciling economy studies with the accounts except in a minority of cases.

A good way for the reader to compare this method with the conventional method is to look back at Table 3–1 (page 36) which compares different schemes of repaying (or recovering) $10,000 in 10 years with interest at 6%. Plan III in this table corresponds to the conventional viewpoint on computing the annual cost of capital recovery with a return. It is evident that the $1,358.68 a year for 10 years (obtained as the product of $10,000 and crf–6%–10) will exactly repay $10,000 with 6% interest.

Plan II is representative of another approach to the annual cost of capital recovery with interest. In this plan the annual payment on principal is uniform but the interest paid each year diminishes. With $10,000 paid in 10 equal installments, each installment is $1,000. Interest the first year is $600, which is 6% of the full $10,000, but diminishes by $60 each year as the principal is repaid until in the tenth year it is only $60. The average interest is $330.

These interest payments form an arithmetic progression the first term of which is Pi and the final term of which is $(P/n)i$. The average interest is the average of the first and last terms or $\dfrac{Pi}{2}\left(\dfrac{n+1}{n}\right)$.

The method of straight-line depreciation plus average interest always computes an *average* (rather than an equivalent) annual figure for a repayment plan devised along the lines of Plan II in Table 3–1. In the general case with a first cost, P, an estimated terminal salvage value, L, an estimated life in n years, and an interest rate, i, straight-line depreciation is $\dfrac{P-L}{n}$ and average interest is $(P-L)\left(\dfrac{i}{2}\right)\left(\dfrac{n+1}{n}\right)+Li$. As applied to our $22,000 asset, the calculation is:

Straight-line depreciation $= \dfrac{\$22{,}000 - \$2{,}000}{10}$ $= \$2{,}000$

Average interest $= \left[\,(\$22{,}000 - \$2{,}000)\left(\dfrac{0.10}{2}\right)\left(\dfrac{11}{10}\right)\right]$
$+ \$2{,}000(0.10) = \$1{,}100 + \$200$ $= \underline{\ \ 1{,}300\ }$
$\$3{,}300$

This is somewhat less than the exact equivalent uniform annual cost, which we computed to be $3,455.

Limitations of Methods of Straight-Line Depreciation Plus Average Interest. Wherever the prospective terminal salvage is less than 100% of first cost, this method yields a figure for capital recovery cost that is too low. The method is an approximate one because it assumes the simple average of a diminishing series of payments to be the equivalent uniform annual payment. The error involved in its use increases with the length of the period of time considered and also increases with an increase in the interest rate. This variation is illustrated in Table A–1.

Where annual cost methods are used to compare assets having approximately the same lives, where the lives are not too long, and where the minimum attractive rate of return is low, this method often gives satisfactory results. The greater the disparity in the lives of assets being compared and the higher the minimum attractive rate of return, the more likely it is that economy studies using this method will yield misleading conclusions.

TABLE A–1

CAPITAL RECOVERY FACTORS BY EXACT AND APPROXIMATE METHODS

Re-covery Period, Years n	4% INTEREST			8% INTEREST		
	Exact Method $\dfrac{i}{(1+i)^n - 1} + i$	Approx. Method $\dfrac{1}{n} + \dfrac{i}{2}\left(\dfrac{n+1}{n}\right)$	% Error	Exact Method $\dfrac{i}{(1+i)^n - 1} + i$	Approx. Method $\dfrac{1}{n} + \dfrac{i}{2}\left(\dfrac{n+1}{n}\right)$	% Error
5	0.22463	0.22400	− 0.3	0.25046	0.24800	− 1.0
10	0.12329	0.12200	− 1	0.14903	0.14400	− 3
15	0.08994	0.08800	− 2	0.11683	0.10933	− 6
20	0.07358	0.07100	− 4	0.10185	0.09200	−10
50	0.04655	0.04040	−13	0.08174	0.06080	−26
100	0.04081	0.03020	−26	0.08004	0.05040	−37

Recovery Period, Years n	12% INTEREST		
	Exact Method $\dfrac{i}{(1+i)^n - 1} + i$	Approx. Method $\dfrac{1}{n} + \dfrac{i}{2}\left(\dfrac{n+1}{n}\right)$	% Error
5	0.27741	0.27200	− 2.0
10	0.17698	0.16600	− 6
15	0.14682	0.13067	−11
20	0.13388	0.11300	−16
50	0.12042	0.08120	−33
100	0.12000	0.07060	−41

Problems

A–1. Solve Problem 6–1 (page 92), computing capital recovery costs by the method of straight-line depreciation plus average interest. Compare your results with those obtained by the methods used in Chapter 6.

A–2. Solve Problem 6–2 (page 92), computing capital recovery costs by the method of straight-line depreciation plus average interest. Compare your results with those obtained by the methods used in Chapter 6.

A–3. Solve Problem 6–5 (page 93), computing capital recovery costs by the method of straight-line depreciation plus average interest. Compare your results with those obtained by the methods used in Chapter 6.

A–4. The following estimates were made to compare a timber trestle with a steel bridge for a certain drainage crossing:

	Trestle	Steel Bridge
First cost	$9,000	$24,000
Life	10 years	60 years
Annual maintenance cost	$ 500	$ 350

Salvage values are assumed to be negligible.

A comparison of annual costs using an interest rate of 8% was made as follows:

	Trestle	Steel Bridge
Depreciation	$ 900	$ 400
Average interest	396	976
Annual maintenance	500	350
Total annual cost	$1,796	$1,726

Assuming all estimates (i.e., first cost, life, salvage value, maintenance cost, and interest rate) to be acceptable, is this a satisfactory comparison of the economy of these two alternatives? Explain your answer. If you disagree with this comparison, give your solution of this problem.

B

Continuous Compounding of Interest and the Uniform-Flow Convention

Throughout this book, we have used the end-of-year convention, making compound interest conversions as if cash flow occurring throughout a year were concentrated at the year end. An alternate convention was mentioned in Chapter 6—namely, that certain cash flow taking place during a year occurs uniformly throughout the year. To use this alternate convention in trial-and-error calculations of unknown rates of return, it is necessary to assume continuous compounding of interest. Tables E–25 and E–26, based on continuous compounding, may be used for calculations employing this uniform-flow convention.

A Present Worth Formula That Assumes Continuous Compounding. To explain Tables E–25 and E–26, it is necessary to develop the formula for present worth of $1 flowing uniformly throughout one year.

The concept of the present worth at zero date of money flowing uniformly throughout a year may be introduced by a numerical example assuming money flowing at different specified intervals during a year. Certain aspects of the subject are illustrated to better advantage if a high interest rate is used and if the rate is specified as a nominal (rather than an effective) rate per annum. The following example assumes a nominal rate of 30% per annum and assumes a total cash flow of $1 during the year.

If the entire $1 flows at year end, the present worth at zero date is $1(pwf–30%–1) = $1(0.769) = $0.769. If there are payments of $½ at the ends of half-year intervals and if interest is compounded semiannually, the present worth at zero date is ($½)(pwf–15%–2) = ($0.50)(1.626) = $0.813. If there are payments of $⅙ at the ends of 2-month intervals and interest is compounded every 2 months, the present worth is ($⅙)(pwf–5%–6) = ($0.1667)(5.076)

= \$0.846. If there are monthly payments of $\$\frac{1}{12}$ and interest is compounded monthly, the present worth is $(\$\frac{1}{12})(\text{pwf–}2.5\%\text{–}12)$ = (\$0.0833)(10.258) = \$0.855. If payments of $\$\frac{1}{24}$ are made at half-month intervals and interest is compounded 24 times a year, the present worth is $(\$\frac{1}{24})(\text{pwf–}1.25\%\text{–}24)$ = (\$0.04167)(20.624) = \$0.859. It may be shown that as the frequency of payments and compounding periods increases indefinitely, this present worth approaches a limit of \$0.864. The formula for this present worth is $\dfrac{e^r - 1}{re^r}$ where r is the *nominal* interest rate per annum.

Derivations in Chapter 4 showed that with continuous compounding, the single payment compound amount factor is e^{rn} and the single payment present worth factor is e^{-rn}. The formula for the present worth of \$1 flowing uniformly throughout a year may be derived along lines similar to the derivations in Chapter 4, as follows:

With regular end-of-period payments R and an interest rate of i per period:

$$P = R\,\frac{(1+i)^n - 1}{i(1+i)^n}$$

If \$1 is divided into m end-of-period payments a year, each payment R is $\dfrac{\$1}{m}$. If the nominal interest rate per annum is r, the interest rate i per compounding period is $\dfrac{r}{m}$. Therefore:

$$P = \frac{\$1}{m}\,\frac{\left(1+\dfrac{r}{m}\right)^m - 1}{\dfrac{r}{m}\left(1+\dfrac{r}{m}\right)^m}$$

Now designate $\dfrac{m}{r}$ by the symbol k as we did in the derivation in Chapter 4.

$$P = \$1\,\frac{\left[\left(1+\dfrac{1}{k}\right)^k\right]^r - 1}{r\left[\left(1+\dfrac{1}{k}\right)^k\right]^r}$$

As the number of compounding periods per year, m, increases without limit, so also must k. It follows that the bracketed quantities in the numerator and denominator approach the limit e. Therefore the limiting value of P is

$$P = \$1\,\frac{e^r - 1}{re^r}$$

Relationship Between Nominal and Effective Rates Per Annum Assuming Continuous Compounding.

It was pointed out in Chapter 4 that the more frequent the number of compoundings during the year, the greater the difference between the values of nominal and effective rate per annum. This difference is greatest in continuous compounding, where an infinite number of compoundings is assumed. In the language of the mathematics of finance, the nominal rate r used in continuous compounding is referred to as the *force of interest*.

For high interest rates the effective rate per annum is considerably higher than the force of interest. For example, assume $1 at zero date accumulating interest for one year at a force of interest of 30%. At the end of the year the compound amount will be 1(e^{0.30})$ = $1.3498. The effective rate is 34.98%, nearly 5% more than the nominal rate.

Table B–1 shows the values of force of interest to yield various integral values of effective interest rates from 1% to 50%. These values of r were used in computing Tables E–25 and E–26.

TABLE B–1

Force of Interest, r, To Be Used in Interest Formulas Involving Continuous Compounding in Order To Yield Various Effective Interest Rates per Annum

Effective Rate per Annum	Force of Interest (i.e., nominal rate compounded continuously to yield the stated effective rate)	Effective Rate per Annum	Force of Interest (i.e., nominal rate compounded continuously to yield the stated effective rate)
1%	0.995033%	15%	13.976194%
2%	1.980263%	20%	18.232156%
3%	2.955880%	25%	22.314355%
4%	3.922071%	30%	26.236426%
5%	4.879016%	35%	30.010459%
6%	5.826891%	40%	33.647224%
7%	6.765865%	45%	37.156356%
8%	7.696104%	50%	40.546511%
10%	9.531018%		
12%	11.332869%		

Explanation of Tables E–25 and E–26.

Table E–25 (in Appendix E) converts $1 flowing uniformly throughout stated one-year periods to the corresponding present worth at zero date, with continuous compounding at effective rates from 1% to 50%.

For example, the first figure in the 30% column is 0.8796, the present worth at the start of a year of $1 flowing uniformly throughout the year. This was computed by the formula we have just derived, using an r of 0.26236426. (It will be recalled that when we used an r of 0.30, the present worth was 0.864.) All subsequent figures in the 30% column are the product of 0.8796 and the appropriate single payment present worth factor. For instance, the figure of 0.4004 for the period 3 to 4 is $0.8796(\text{pwf}'-30\%-3) = 0.8796-(0.4552)$.

Table E–26 gives the present worth at zero date of $1 per year flowing uniformly through various stated periods, all starting with zero date and terminating at various dates from 1 to 100. The figures in E–26 may be obtained by adding the appropriate figures in the corresponding column of E–25. For instance, the figure 2.477 for 30% and the period 0 to 4 is the sum of figures 0.8796, 0.6766, 0.5205, and 0.4004 from E–25.

Application of Uniform-Flow Convention in Computing Rate of Return. Consider a cost-reduction proposal to purchase certain machinery for $50,000. This proposal is to be analyzed before income taxes. It is estimated that this machinery will reduce disbursements in connection with certain operations by $10,000 a year for the

TABLE B–2

PRESENT WORTH CALCULATIONS APPLYING UNIFORM-FLOW CONVENTION

Time Period	Cash Flow	Assuming 12%		Assuming 15%	
		Present Worth Factor	Present Worth	Present Worth Factor	Present Worth
0	−$50,000	1.000	−$50,000	1.000	−$50,000
0 to 4	+10,000 per year	3.216	+32,160	3.064	+30,640
4 to 5	+8,000	0.6008	+4,810	0.5336	+4,270
5 to 6	+6,000	0.5365	+3,220	0.4640	+2,780
6 to 7	+4,000	0.4790	+1,920	0.4035	+1,610
7 to 8	+2,000	0.4277	+860	0.3508	+700
8	+25,000	0.4039	+10,100	0.3269	+8,070
Totals	+$35,000		+$ 3,070		−$ 1,930

next 4 years. The reduction in disbursements is estimated as $8,000 for the 5th year, $6,000 for the 6th, $4,000 for the 7th, and $2,000 for the 8th. The estimated salvage value at the end of 5 years is $25,000. Table B–2 shows calculations to determine rate of return before income taxes with the uniform-flow convention applied to each year's reduction in disbursements.

The present worth factors for the 4-year period 0 to 4 are taken from Table E–26. The present worth factors for the one-year periods 4 to 5, 5 to 6, etc. are taken from Table E–25. The present worth factors applied to the salvage value at date 8 are taken from the regular 12% and 15% tables, E–17 and E–18.

Interpolation between the present worth of +$3,070 at 12% and −$1,930 at 15% indicates a before-tax rate of return of approximately 13.8%. If the same cash flow series had been analyzed using an end-of-year convention, the computed rate of return would have been 12.4%. In general, rates of return computed with the uniform-flow convention tend to be slightly higher than with the end-of-year convention.

Application of the Uniform-Flow Convention to Proposed Investments. Table B–2 assumes that all the $50,000 investment was made at zero date on the time scale. As it was stipulated that the machinery was to be purchased, this assumption presumably was reasonably close to the facts.

However, if proposed fixed assets are to be constructed or otherwise acquired over a period of time, it often is reasonable to apply a uniform-flow convention to the investment as well as to the cash flow subsequent to the investment. For example, assume that the machinery in Table B–2 will be built over the one-year period prior to zero date on our time scale. The compound amount of $1 flowing uniformly throughout a year is, of course, the reciprocal of the present worth of $1 so flowing. Table B–2 might therefore be modified to show a cash flow of −$50,000 for the period −1 to 0 rather than for date 0. By dividing $50,000 by the appropriate 0-to-1 present worth factors from Table E–25, the equivalent figure at date 0 may be computed to be −$52,890 at 12% and −$53,570 at 15%. The resulting figures for total present worth are +$180 at 12% and −$5,500 at 15%. Interpolation now indicates a rate of return of 12.1%.

The concept of uniform flow as applicable to proposed investments (as well as to the consequences of investments) was illustrated in Chapter 19 by Figures 19–1, 19–2, and 19–3 taken from the article by R. I. Reul in *Harvard Business Review.*

Choosing Between the End-of-Year Convention and the Uniform-Flow Convention. In most compound interest conversions in economy studies, the year is adopted as a unit of time that is not to be subdivided. Therefore *some* convention is necessary regarding receipts and disbursements that occur each year. For many items in economy studies (e.g., receipts from the sale of a product or service, routine operating disbursements), the uniform-flow convention is somewhat closer to the facts than the end-of-year convention. But there may be other items where the end-of-year convention may be a better approximation to the facts (e.g., corporate income taxes, annual or semiannual interest, or rental payments). Moreover, in many economy studies there are many receipts and disbursements that clearly apply to a point in time rather than to a period of time.

All things considered, the uniform-flow convention probably comes somewhat closer to describing the way most cash flow occurs than does the end-of-year convention. Nevertheless, it is desirable to recognize that either is merely a *convention* to facilitate compound interest conversions; neither is a completely accurate reflection of the way in which cash flow is expected to take place.

The authors have observed a number of instances in which the uniform-flow convention is used. But it is their impression that there are a great many organizations using the end-of-year convention for every one that uses uniform-flow.

The greater use of the end-of-year convention doubtless is based largely on grounds of its greater convenience. Standard interest tables and formulas may be used with this convention. In the numerous cases where annual cost comparisons are made, this convention has the advantage of being better adapted to such comparisons. Where compound interest methods require explanation in presenting the results of economy studies, it is easier to explain periodic compounding of interest than to explain continuous compounding.

Compound interest conversions in economy studies constitute one of the steps in providing a rational basis for decisions among alternatives. In most cases the *decisions* will be the same regardless of the convention used. That is, both conventions will normally array a series of investment proposals in the same order.

However, there are certain cases where the two conventions might lead to different recommendations for a decision between alternative investments and where the recommendation based on the uniform-flow convention will be sounder than the one based on the end-of-year convention. These cases occur particularly where an investment leading to positive cash flow concentrated in the near future is being compared with one leading to positive cash flow spread over a considerably longer period. Several examples of such cases are illustrated in the problems at the end of this appendix.

Comparison of Continuous Compounding Tables Based on Nominal and Effective Rates of Interest. The present worth factors in Tables E–25 and E–26 are given for various effective rates. In contrast, the present worth factors in one of the forms shown in

Chapter 19 (Figure 19–3) were based on nominal rates. Both sets of factors are based on continuous compounding and the uniform-flow convention.

Certain differences between uniform-flow analyses using nominal and effective rates and between these analyses and the end-of-year analyses are brought out in Table B–3.

TABLE B–3

COMPARISON OF CERTAIN PRESENT WORTH FACTORS

Period	Present Worth Factors with Nominal 25% Interest (from Figure 19–3) A	Present Worth Factors with Effective 25% Interest (from Table E–25) B	End of Year	Present Worth Factors with Effective 25% Interest (from Table E–21) C
0 to 1	0.885	0.896	1	0.800
1 to 2	0.689	0.717	2	0.640
2 to 3	0.537	0.574	3	0.512
3 to 4	0.418	0.459	4	0.410
4 to 5	0.326	0.367	5	0.328
9 to 10	0.093	0.120	10	0.107
14 to 15	0.027	0.039	15	0.035
19 to 20	0.008	0.013	20	0.012
24 to 25	0.002	0.004	25	0.004

It will be observed that the figures in column A of Table B–3 are always less than the corresponding figures in column B and that the proportionate difference increases as the period becomes more distant from zero date. The differences here are due entirely to difference in interest rate. Column A, based on a nominal rate of 25%, used an effective rate of approximately 28.4%. The lower effective rate used in column B of course gives higher present worths, particularly at more distant dates.

The ratio of each figure in column B to the corresponding figure in column C is constant (0.896 to 0.800). Both columns are computed at the same interest rate, an effective 25%. The present worths in column B are higher than those in C because the cash flow is sooner—uniformly during a year rather than at year end.

The most striking comparison is between the corresponding figures in columns A and C. The present worth factors in A are greater in the first few lines of the table, approximately equal at the 5th year, and less thereafter. As time goes on, the assumption in A that cash flow occurs sooner is more than offset by the use of a higher effective interest rate.

Reasons for Using Effective Interest Rates Rather Than Nominal Rates When the Uniform-Flow Convention Is Adopted. Wherever the decision is made to use the uniform-flow convention in economy studies, there are two advantages in using continuous compounding tables such as E–25 and E–26 rather than similar tables based on nominal rates.

One advantage is that the reporting of prospective rates of return in terms of effective rates gives a more realistic picture of the productivity of an investment than the reporting of a nominal rate that assumes continuous compounding. For instance, it will be recalled that with continuous compounding a nominal 30% yields an effective 35% per annum. For a proposed business investment with this prospective yield, management will have a better basis for decision making if the yield is reported as 35% rather than as a nominal 30% compounded continuously.

(This desirability of identifying effective rates applies to personal loans as well as to business investments. Both lenders and borrowers should be aware of effective rates. The officials of a bank that establishes a credit card plan calling for the payment of interest at $1\frac{1}{2}\%$ per month are doubtless aware that the effective rate is 19.6% per annum; creditors under this plan should also know that they are paying an effective 19.6%.)

Another advantage of using such tables as E–25 and E–26 is that these tables can be used in combination with conventional interest tables such as are found in standard handbooks and textbooks on the mathematics of finance (or in Appendix E of this book). That is, the conventional tables can be used for all conversions that do not assume uniform flow of funds. If an analysis is to be based on continuous compounding at nominal rates it is necessary to substitute for the conventional tables a complete set of continuous compounding tables applicable to all types of conversions. All factors in such specialized tables will differ from the corresponding factors in conventional tables.

The authors' observation has been that a certain amount of confusion may arise in organizations where special tables are prepared based on continuous compounding at nominal rates. Some persons in the organization will use the special tables and others will use conventional tables. Difficulties may arise in checking the analysis of investment proposals and in discussion or other communications among persons using the different types of tables.

Problems

B–1. Proposal X involves an investment of $10,000 at zero date. The expected excess of receipts over disbursements is $6,200 a year for 2 years. The expected life is 2 years with zero salvage value. Proposition Y also involves an investment of $10,000 at zero date. Its expected excess of receipts over disbursements is $2,050 a year for 20 years; the life is 20 years with zero salvage value. Compute the prospective before-tax rates of return for each proposal, using (a) the uniform-flow convention and (b) the end-of-year convention. (*Ans.* = (a) X, 25%; Y, 22.5%; (b) X, 15.6%; Y, 20%.)

B–2. Proposal V involves an investment of $100,000 at zero date. The expected excess of receipts over disbursements is $15,780 a year for 5 years. The expected life is 5 years with a $60,000 terminal salvage value at the end of the 5-year period. Proposal W involves an investment of $100,000 at zero date. The expected excess of receipts over disbursements is $10,000 a year for 25 years with a $40,000 terminal salvage value at the end of the 25-year period. Compute the before-tax rate of return for each proposal, (a) using the uniform-flow convention for annual excess of receipts over disbursements and (b) using the end-of-year convention throughout. (*Ans.* = (a) V, 10%; W, 9.9%; (b) V, 9.1%; W, 9.4%.)

B–3. Compute the prospective before-tax rates of return in Problem B–2 assuming that the $100,000 investment is made uniformly throughout the year prior to zero date. Apply the uniform-flow convention to annual excess of receipts over disbursements (but, of course, not to terminal salvage values). (*Ans.* = V, 8.0%; W, 9.4%.)

B–4. The answers to Problems B–1, B–2, and B–3 illustrate certain differences between rates of return computed using the two conventions. Discuss the points that seem to you to be illustrated by these examples.

B–5. Solve Problem 8–5, page 133, assuming a uniform-flow convention for annual receipts and disbursements.

B–6. Solve Problem 8–12, page 133, assuming a uniform-flow convention for annual receipts and disbursements.

B–7. Solve Problem 8–13, page 133, assuming a uniform-flow convention for annual receipts and disbursements.

B–8. Solve Problem 8–33, page 136, assuming a uniform-flow convention for annual receipts and for the annual disbursements for maintenance, property taxes, and insurance. Use the end-of-year convention for salvage value and for the nonrecurrent outlay for maintenance at the end of the 5th year.

B–9. Solve Problem 15–1, page 354, assuming a uniform-flow convention for the reduction in annual disbursements and for the effect of the investment on income tax payments.

B–10. Solve Problem 15–1, page 354, applying the uniform-flow convention to the reduction in annual disbursements but using an end-of-year convention for the effect of the investment on income tax payments.

C

Certain Compound Interest Analyses Involving Two Interest Rates

Much of the discussion in this book has dealt with decision making among alternatives where the forecast differences between any two alternatives could be expressed as an estimated cash flow series. Generally speaking, we have advocated the application to such series of analyses based on the mathematics of compound interest. Some of our compound interest analyses have called for computing equivalent annual costs or present worths; here we generally have used a stipulated minimum attractive rate of return as our interest rate. Other compound interest analyses have called for using trial-and-error calculations to find prospective rates of return on proposed investments; such computed rates for competing investment proposals could be compared with one another or with a stipulated minimum attractive rate of return.

We have made the point (particularly in Chapter 5 and Appendix A) that it normally is undesirable to use two rates of interest in a single set of annual cost or present worth conversions. And we have made the point (particularly in Chapter 8) that it normally is undesirable to stipulate an interest rate to be used in a portion of the trial-and-error calculations to find an unknown rate of return. (In effect, this amounts to the use of two interest rates in one set of calculations; one rate is the stipulated rate and the other is the unknown one computed by the trial-and-error analysis.) The limitations of analyses involving two interest rates are considered further in this appendix.

Nevertheless, special circumstances occur where decision making regarding proposed investments may sometimes require the use of two interest rates. This appendix includes a brief discussion of two types of circumstances of this kind, namely:

1. Where it is desired to compare investments that will have consequences for different lengths of time and where it is expected that rates of return available at the conclusion of the shorter-lived investment will differ substantially from rates of return presently available from similar investments
2. Where there are one or more reversals of the direction of change of the net cash flow in a cash flow series that represents the difference between two alternatives. For some series of this type the present worth of cash flow will be zero at two or more interest rates.

An Underestimate of Present Worth Due to the Use of Two Interest Rates in One Series of Conversions. Appendix A illustrated how too high a figure for equivalent annual cost of a proposal was obtained by a particular type of use of two interest rates in one set of conversions. In the example given, the use of two interest rates made an investment proposal look less attractive than it really was. It is also worth while to be aware that two interest rates are sometimes used in a way that makes a proposal look more attractive than it ought to. For instance, this result occurs when present worths are computed from figures that are assumed to be taken from the books of account where the accounting figures include a charge for depreciation.

As an example, consider a proposed investment of $100,000 in a property expected to have a life of 20 years, zero salvage value, and annual disbursements of $5,000 throughout the life. It is desired to compute the present worth of all costs, using an interest rate of 8%. The correct total is figured as follows:

$$PW = \$100,000 + \$5,000(\text{pwf–}8\%\text{–}20)$$
$$= \$100,000 + \$5,000(9.818) = \$149,090$$

However, assume that straight-line depreciation of $5,000 a year is to be used in the accounts. The annual costs shown in the accounts will be $100,000/20 + $5,000 = $10,000. The present worth of this annual figure might be computed as

$$PW = \$10,000(\text{pwf–}8\%\text{–}20)$$
$$= \$10,000(9.818) = \$98,180$$

It should be obvious at a glance that this $98,180 figure that purports to be the present worth of the costs is incorrect and misleading; it makes the present worth of investment and operating costs appear to be less than the investment itself. The difficulty, of course, is that the $100,000 outlay at zero date was, in effect, converted to $5,000 a year from years 1 to 20, using an interest rate of 0%. When an 8% interest rate was used in converting the $5,000 a year back to zero date, the original $100,000 at zero date was, in a roundabout way, converted to $49,090 at zero date.

In this particular case the numerical value of the present worth made it evident that some type of error had been made. But the authors have seen conversions of this type made in analyses for industry and government where the existence of an error in principle could not have been discovered merely by looking at the results of the analyst's calculations.

EXAMPLE C–1. MISUSE OF AN AUXILIARY INTEREST RATE IN COMPUTING PROSPECTIVE RATES OF RETURN

Misleading Analysis of Two Investment Proposals. The discussion of Hoskold's method in Chapter 8 explained how a proposed investment sometimes is judged by calculating a rate of return that combines the consequences of two investments, the proposed one under review and an investment in an imaginary sinking fund. It was pointed out that, in general, the return from an unrelated investment—either real or imaginary—is irrelevant in judging the merits of a proposed investment under review. The basic error of the Hoskold-type analysis appears in many settings.

For instance, consider an investment proposal that has the following estimates of after-tax cash flow: [1]

Year	Cash Flow for Investment	Cash Flow from Excess of Operating Receipts over Disbursements
0	−$450,000	
1		+$270,000
2		+220,000
3		+170,000
4		+120,000
5		+70,000
Totals (PW at 0%)	−$450,000	+$850,000

A conventional analysis along the lines used in Chapter 8 and thereafter in this book indicates that the prospective rate of return is 33.8%. That is, if the funds indicated in the investment column were loaned and if the borrower made the payments shown in the right-hand column, he would pay back the loan with interest at 33.8%.

However, a proposed method of computing rate of return uses as an auxiliary interest rate "the average rate of return which the company is making on its investment." Assume this rate is 10%. The investment outlays are then discounted to zero date at this rate and the cash flow from the project is compounded to the final date of the study period at the same rate. At date zero the present worth of the investment obviously is $450,000. At date 5, the compound amount at 10% interest of the positive cash flows may be computed to be

[1] Example C–1 was suggested by a method of analysis proposed in an article by R. H. Baldwin, "How To Assess Investment Proposals," *Harvard Business Review*, XXXVII, No. 3 (May–June, 1959), 98–104.

$1,095,900. A single payment compound amount factor for 5 years is then computed as $1,095,900 ÷ $450,000 = 2.435. Interpolation between 2.011 (caf'–15%–5) and 2.488 (caf'–20%–5) indicates a return of 19.4%.

The foregoing proposed method of analysis underestimates the rate of return from the proposed investment by more than 14%. The error in principle here is the same one discussed in Chapter 8 in connection with the Hoskold formula; the computed 19.4% is, in effect, the result of two separable investments, the proposed $450,000 investment yielding 33.8% and an investment of varying amount elsewhere in the business enterprise assumed to yield 10%.

The fallacy in this type of analysis may be even more evident if we apply the method to the following estimates for another investment proposal:

Year	Cash Flow for Investment	Cash Flow from Excess of Operating Receipts over Disbursements
0	−$200,000	
1	−250,000	+$130,000
2		+110,000
3		+90,000
4		+70,000
5		+50,000
Totals (PW at 0%)	−$450,000	+$450,000

A simple inspection of the figures shows that the prospective rate of return is 0%; the $450,000 investment will be recovered with nothing left over. But if we use the 10% rate that the company is expected to make on other investments, the present worth of the investments at date zero is $427,300 and the compound amount of the positive cash flows at the end of 5 years is $572,600. If (caf'–$i$%–5) is computed as $572,600 ÷ $427,300 = 1.340, interpolation in our interest tables indicates a prospective rate of return of 6.0%. In effect, the investment proposal yielding 0% has been combined with the 10% assumed to be earned elsewhere in the enterprise to give the misleading conclusion that the proposal will yield 6%.

Comparing Investment Proposals When Future Rates of Return Are Expected To Differ Substantially from Present Rates.

Chapter 9 introduced the problem of choosing among investment proposals in circumstances where available funds are limited. Table 9–1 (page 138) described an assumed situation in which 8 proposals requiring a total investment of $207,000 were under consideration and in which the available funds were limited to $90,000. The prospective after-tax rates of return had been computed for each proposal and were arrayed in order of descending magnitude. It was evident that the available funds would be exhausted by proposals U, Y, Z, and S, which had prospective rates of return of 15% or more. Our discussion in Chapter 9 indicated that if the maximum possible return should be desired from the available funds, it would be necessary to reject proposals X, T, U, and W, all of which had prospective rates of return of 12% or less.

The cutoff point in Table 9–1 was 15%; this was the minimum attractive rate of return because the selection of any project yielding less than 15% would force the elimination of some project having a prospective yield of 15% or more. However, our discussion in Chapter 9 gave no consideration to one aspect of capital rationing that sometimes is important. When we selected certain projects and rejected others, we gave no consideration to the duration of the favorable consequences of each project except as this duration influenced the computed rate of return. (Although our array in Table 9–1 did not show the expected pattern of future cash flow from each project, such supporting information would necessarily be available in any actual case as the source of the calculation of the respective rates of return.)

Assume that it is expected that the typical rate of return available from future investment proposals will be considerably higher or considerably lower than the rate obtainable from present proposals. To maximize the long-run rate of return on available investment funds, it is necessary to consider the duration of the expected consequences of each present proposal. In general, the prospect of lower future rates of return favors the longer-lived of the projects under present consideration; the prospect of higher future rates of return favors the shorter-lived projects (or sometimes the approval of no present projects at all).

For example, suppose that Project S in Table 9–1, yielding 15%, has a life of 2 years whereas Project X, yielding 12%, had a life of 12 years. Assume that it is believed that rates of return from projects that will be proposed in the next few years will not exceed 8%. The combination of S with its 15% and a subsequent investment yielding 8% may result in a lower over-all rate of return over the next 12 years than the 12% obtainable from X.

Or—in contrast—suppose it is expected that if sufficient funds are available in a year or two, a large project can be undertaken that will yield a 25% rate of return. The acceptance of too many long-lived proposals now may make it impracticable to finance this desirable future project. A present capital rationing analysis may therefore favor projects with short capital recovery periods even though they have relatively low rates of return in order to make funds available for this attractive future project.

Occasionally circumstances arise where such forecasts of future rates of return are deemed appropriate in making decisions about present proposals for investment. If the forecasts are specific enough, it is possible to make the necessary calculations to find an over-all rate of return from a proposed present investment and its successors. Such calculations would, in effect, make use of two or more interest rates. However, in most cases the best thing to do with forecasts about upward or downward trends in rates of return is to consider these forecasts on a qualitative basis, using them as irreducibles to influence capital rationing decisions in borderline cases.

Certain Difficulties in Analyzing Proposals That Involve Reversals of the Direction of Change of Net Cash Flow. Our first discussion of the subject of compound interest in Chapter 3 dealt with loan transactions. Although we examined a number of different possible cash flow patterns that occur in various types of loans, these patterns had certain characteristics in common. From the lender's viewpoint, there was an initial negative cash flow followed by one or more positive cash flows; if cash flows should be added algebraically starting with the initial negative cash flow at zero date, there would be an increase each year in the algebraic sum of the cash flows to date.

The various types of proposals for investments by business enterprises that we have discussed throughout this book have been similar to loans in their expected patterns of cash flow. Investment in business assets is generally undertaken with the expectation that the business enterprise will gradually recover the investment plus a return. By stretching the concept of a loan, we can say that—in effect—the enterprise loans its funds to the various assets which are expected to repay the loan with interest. Generally speaking, compound interest techniques that are appropriate for analysis of proposed loans are also applicable to the analysis of proposals for investments in business assets.

However, particularly in the mineral industry and the petroleum industry, proposals for investments sometimes occur in which the business enterprise may be viewed as a lender to the project during one period of time and as a borrower from the project at another period of time. A characteristic of such proposals is that the year by year cumulation of net cash flow attributed to the proposal will change its direction one or more times. For some such proposals conventional methods of compound interest analysis may not provide an adequate guide to decision making.

This topic can be discussed to better advantage with the aid of some numerical illustrations. We shall use Example C–2 for this purpose. This example contains conventional rate of return calculations that are obviously inconclusive. Our discussion of the problem of decision making in such cases is deferred until after the example has been described and analyzed by conventional compound interest methods.

EXAMPLE C–2. COMPUTING RATE OF RETURN FROM A PROPOSAL INVOLVING A DEFERRED INVESTMENT

Facts of the Case. An oil company is offered a lease of a group of oil wells on which the primary reserves are close to exhaustion. The major condition of the purchase is that the oil company must agree to undertake the injection of water into the underground reservoir in order to make possible a secondary recovery at such time as the primary reserves are exhausted. The lessor will receive a standard royalty from all oil produced from the property whether from primary or secondary reserves. No immediate payment by the oil company is required.

The production department of the oil company estimates the after-tax positive cash flow from the property (after considering all production expenses and royalty payments) as $50,000 a year for the next 5 years. This will exhaust the primary reserves. At the end of the 5th year of ownership, an expenditure of $800,000 will be required for the water flooding project. It is expected that this project will cause a net positive cash flow of $100,000 a year for the following 15 years (years 6 to 20) due to the recovery of secondary reserves.[2]

Trial-and-Error Calculations To Find Prospective Rate of Return. Table C–1 shows the present worths of cash flow computed at various interest rates. The present worth starts with a positive value (+$950,000) at 0% interest. It declines to zero at slightly less than 25% interest, continues to decline to about 30% interest, and then increases. The present worth is zero again at slightly more than 40% interest.

TABLE C–1

PRESENT WORTH OF ESTIMATED CASH FLOW FROM AGREEMENT TO UNDERTAKE PROPOSED WATER FLOODING PROJECT, ASSUMING VARIOUS INTEREST RATES

(000 omitted)

Year	Net Cash Flow (and PW at 0%)	Present Worth						
		at 10%	at 20%	at 25%	at 30%	at 40%	at 45%	at 50%
1 to 5	+$ 50 per year	+$189.6	+$149.6	+$134.4	+$121.8	+$101.8	+$ 93.8	+$ 86.8
5	−$800	−496.7	−321.5	−262.2	−215.4	−148.7	−124.8	−105.4
6 to 20	+$100 per year	+472.3	+187.9	+126.5	+88.0	+46.2	+34.5	+26.2
Total PW	+$950.0	+$165.2	+$ 16.0	−$ 1.3	−$ 5.6	−$ 0.7	+$ 3.5	+$ 7.6

A Way To Compute a Unique Answer for Prospective Rate of Return. We can convert cases such as Example C–2 into problems giving only one figure for prospective rate of return if we make appropriate use of an auxiliary interest rate. Let us first view this merely as a problem in computation without worrying

[2] This example was suggested by an example of a water flooding project described in J. G. McLean's article "How To Evaluate New Capital Investments," *Harvard Business Review*, XXXVI, No. 6 (November–December, 1958), 67–68. The McLean example shows cash flow declining from year to year in the primary recovery period and again in the period of secondary recovery. Such a decline would be the usual condition. However, in order to make it somewhat easier for the reader to follow the arithmetic of our example, we have assumed uniform cash flow during each period.

about the difficulties of selecting the right auxiliary interest rate or interpreting the results of the calculations.

The objective of the conversion with the auxiliary interest rate should be to obtain a money time series in which there is no reversal of the direction of change of net cash flow. In effect, we aim to make a conversion that gives us a usable figure for an initial investment that will be recovered by positive cash flow over a period of years. In this case we can convert the positive cash flow in years 1 to 5 to compound amount at date 5. For purposes of illustration let us make this conversion with an interest rate of 8%.

The compound amount at date 5 of the series in years 1 to 5 is $50,000(caf–8%–5) = +$50,000(5.867) = $293,400. We now have a series: 5, −$506,600 (i.e., −$800,000 + $293,400); 6 to 20, + $100,000 a year. The pwf–$i$%–15 is evidently 5.066. Interpolation in our interest tables indicates a prospective rate of return of about 18%.

It is evident that although the foregoing type of analysis will give us a unique answer for the prospective rate of return, this answer depends on the auxiliary interest rate that was selected. In reviewing the following additional comments about this example, the reader should keep in mind that the really important question is the *decision* regarding a proposed investment. The computation of a prospective rate of return should be viewed merely as one of the desirable steps in reaching a sound decision.

A Useful Viewpoint in Examining Proposals Such as Example C–2.

The chief source of the difficulty of analysis in such cases is the shifting position of the business enterprise with respect to the proposed project—at one or more times as a "borrower" from the project and at one or more other times as an investor in it. The most useful advice that the authors can give about the analysis of such projects is for the analyst to take a critical look at the question of whether different interest rates (or rates of return) are applicable to the different time periods.

In Example C–2, the heart of the analysis is deciding on an interest rate that is deemed applicable to the period from years 1 to 5, when the oil company receives $50,000 a year from the project without having made any investment. When we compounded this series to date 5 at 8% interest, we assumed—in effect—that the oil company would invest these funds at an after-tax rate of return of 8% during years 1 to 5. When we combined the computed compound amount of +$293,400 with the −$800,000 cash flow at date 5 for the water flooding project, we assumed that this compound amount would provide partial financing for this project so that only $506,600 of funds from other oil company sources would be needed for the water flooding investment. Our figure of 18% for the prospective rate of return was the rate at which the $100,000 a year positive cash flow from secondary recovery during years 6 to 20 would repay $506,600 invested at date 5.

The basis for decision making will be improved if we investigate the sensitivity of our computed rate of return to the rate of earnings assumed on the $50,000 a year during years 1 to 5. Suppose we conclude that this assumed rate should be not less than 3% (a rate believed obtainable from investment in short-term tax-exempt bonds) or more than 12% (the average after-tax rate currently being earned on new investments in the oil company). If we recompute using 3%, we will conclude that the rate of return on the water flooding investment is approximately 17%. If we recompute using 12%, we will conclude that the rate is approximately 19%. In this particular example the prospective rate of return is relatively insensitive to variations in the auxiliary interest rate within the range deemed appropriate for this auxiliary rate. If the oil company management believes that, 5 years hence, a prospective rate of return from 17% to 19% in a secondary recovery investment will be attractive, the oil well lease should be acquired and the commitment made to undertake the water flooding project.

Why an Auxiliary Interest Rate May Be Appropriate in Analyzing an Investment Proposal That Involves a "Borrowing" Period. Let us look back for a moment at the present worth calculations in Table C–1. From these calculations we had obtained the ambiguous conclusion that the rate of return was either a little less than 25% or a little over 40%. In spite of the ambiguous nature of this conclusion, either of these two figures for rate of return can be supported if we assume the respective figures as rates obtainable on investment of the positive cash flow in years 1 to 5.

Thus if we should assume that the oil company could invest at a 25% after-tax rate of return the $50,000 a year received during years 1 to 5, the company would have $410,000 at the end of the 5 years. The company funds from other sources required for the water flooding would be only $390,000; the expected $100,000 a year for the following 15 years would recover this amount with a return of about 25%.

Or if we assume a 40% after-tax rate of return on the investment of the $50,000 a year, the oil company would have $547,000 at the end of the 5 years; only $253,000 extra would be needed to finance the water flooding project; the $100,000 a year would provide recovery of this investment with a return of about 40%.

If we should assume a 30% rate of return on the cash receipts during years 1 to 5, our computed rate of return would be approximately 28%. If we should assume a 50% rate during years 1 to 5, our computed rate would be approximately 71%.

In this example it is apparent that the difficulty of computing rate of return by a conventional trial-and-error calculation (such as Table C–1) is that this calculation—in effect—assumes that the interest rate at which the present worth of net cash flow equals zero is the rate of return that could be earned on the funds received by the oil company during its "borrowing" period. But the rates at which the present worth of all cash flow is zero are unrealistically high as estimates of the rate of return obtainable from some other investment during the first 5 years. Moreover, for high values of assumed rates of return during years 1 to 5, the computed rates of return for the entire project depend largely on the assumed rate of return on some unspecified investment elsewhere in the business enterprise during the first 5 years.

Example C–1 represented the usual type of case of proposed investment in physical assets. Example C–2 represents a specialized and exceptional type of case. The difference between the two examples should be clear with respect to the reason for not using an auxiliary interest rate to compute the prospective rate of return in Example C–1 and using such a rate in Example C–2.

In Example C–1, the merits of the two projects discussed were obscured by the introduction of the 10% auxiliary interest rate. The project earning 33.8% appeared to earn only 19.4% because the consequences of the investment in the project were combined with the consequences of unspecified subsequent investments yielding 10%. In contrast, the project earning 0% appeared to earn 6% because its consequences were combined with consequences of assumed investments at 10%.

But in Example C–2 it was not possible to obtain a realistic figure for the actual investment by the oil company required to finance the project without the use of an auxiliary interest rate applicable to the oil company's positive cash flow from the project in years 1 to 5.

Further Comments on Cases Such as Example C–2. If $\dfrac{1}{1+i}$ is designated as x, the usual analysis to find an unknown rate of return may be thought of as a trial-and-error solution of an equation:

$$c_n x^n + c_{n-1} x^{n-1} + \ldots c_1 x + c_0 = 0$$

where the values of c are the estimated cash flows at dates 0 to n. Anyone familiar with the principles of algebra will recognize that such an equation may have n different roots. In general, where algebraic equations are used to represent physical situations, it may be evident from the physical circumstances that certain roots are meaningless. For example, it may be clear in certain cases that there is no meaning to the solution where x is negative or is an imaginary number.

Where two or more different roots exist and where it is not possible to rule out all but one of the roots by inspection, a critical look at the physical circumstances is needed to determine which of the two or more roots is the correct one. In our critical look at Example C–2, we concluded that *neither* of our two answers gave us a sound guide to action. In effect, we concluded that our original algebraic equation was not the equation that we needed to solve in order to guide our decision on the proposed investment.

Not all cases where there is a reversal of the direction of change of net cash flow will cause difficulties in analysis. The indicator that a particular analysis is a troublesome one is an increase in the value of present worth with an increase in interest rate (such as occurred from 30% to 50% in Table C–1). The occurrence of such an increase should always suggest to an analyst that he is probably trying to solve the wrong equation. In normal investment proposals the present worth will continue to decrease algebraically as the interest rate is increased.

It cannot be emphasized too strongly that cases such as Example C–2 are rare outside of the mineral industry and the petroleum industry. Even in these industries, cases of this type arise only in quite specialized circumstances.

Rate of Return vs. Present Worth as a Technique for Investment Analysis. Some analysts have contended that because conventional compound interest calculations to find an unknown rate of return occasionally give ambiguous conclusions (e.g., in Example C–2), the method of rate of return should be abandoned in all cases as a technique for analyzing proposals for investments. It is contended that such proposals should always be analyzed by the method of present worth because a present worth analysis always gives a definite answer favorable to a project or against it. If the present worth of the cash flow resulting from an investment (or series of investments) is equal to or greater than the present worth of the investments, a project should be accepted; otherwise it should be rejected. The foregoing contention assumes that the minimum attractive rate of return is used as the interest rate in the present worth calculation.

We may use Example C–2 to demonstrate that, although a present worth analysis always gives an unambiguous answer to the question of whether or not a proposed investment should be undertaken, the answer obtained by the present worth analysis may be just as unreliable in cases like Example C–2 as the answer obtained by a rate of return analysis.

For instance, let us assume that the present worth study is made using an interest rate of 50%. This study will show the present worth of net receipts to be $113,000 and the present worth of the investment to be $105,400. The present worth study will therefore favor the project as yielding more than the stipulated minimum attractive rate of return of 50%. But we have already seen that this favorable conclusion is not a sound one unless we are sure that the $50,000 a year to be received during the first 5 years can be invested elsewhere at an after-tax yield of at least 50%. Thus the present worth analysis has the same basic defects as the rate of return analysis.

In general, all cases similar to Example C–2 require a critical look at the difference between the "borrowing" period of years and the investment period of years, regardless of the method of analysis employed.

Problems

C–1. An investment of $75,700 proposed to be made at zero date is expected to cause a net positive after-tax cash flow of $20,000 in the first year of the 20-year life of the asset. This positive cash flow is expected to decrease by $1,000 a year to $1,000 in the 20th year. There is no estimated terminal salvage value.

(a) At what interest rate will the positive cash flow repay the investment? (*Ans.* = 20%.)

(b) Compute the prospective rate of return by the proposed method illustrated in Example C–1, assuming reinvestment at 3% interest of all positive cash flows until the end of the 20-year study period. (*Ans.* = 7.3%.)

(c) Explain the reason for the difference in the answers in (a) and (b).

C–2. An investment of $170,750 proposed to be made at zero date is expected to cause the same series of net positive after-tax cash flows described in Problem C–1. The estimated life of this asset is also 20 years with zero terminal salvage value.

(a) At what interest rate will the positive cash flow repay this investment? (*Ans.* = 3%.)

(b) Compute the prospective rate of return by the proposed method illustrated in Example C–1, assuming reinvestment throughout the 20-year period of all positive cash flows at the 12% average rate of return that is being earned by this business enterprise. (*Ans.* = 9.2%.)

(c) Explain the reason for the difference in the answers in (a) and (b).

C–3. Change the data of Example C–2 so that the estimated disbursement for the water flooding project at the end of the 5th year is $700,000. Make a trial-and-error calculation similar to Table C–1 to find the interest rate at which the present worth of cash flow is zero. (*Ans.*: There is no interest rate for which the present worth is zero.)

C–4. Use an auxiliary interest rate of 8% to compute the compound amount at date 5 of the positive cash flow from years 1 to 5 in Problem C–3. Subtract this compound amount from the $700,000 figure at date 5 to find the net investment in the water flooding project required from other oil company funds. At what rate of return will this net investment be recovered? (*Ans.* = 24%.)

C–5. In the light of the answers in Problems C–3 and C–4, discuss the topic of decision making about the investment proposal in Problem C–3.

C–6. In Example C–2, use an auxiliary interest rate of 8% to convert the negative cash flow of $800,000 at date 5 to an equivalent negative cash flow at zero date. Using this figure at zero date as the investment in the project, find the interest rate at which this investment would be recovered by the estimated positive cash flows from years 1 to 20. Why does your answer differ from the 18% obtained in Example C–2 when the $50,000 a year positive cash flow from years 1 to 5 was compounded to date 5? Discuss the relative merits of the 18% and the answer you have found in this problem as guides to the oil company's decision regarding the leasing of this group of oil wells.

C–7. Alter the data of Example C–2 in two ways. Assume that an immediate payment of $100,000 is required to secure the lease on the oil wells. Assume that the purchase of the lease does not involve any agreement to undertake the water flooding project to secure the secondary recovery; the oil company can make its own decision about whether or not to undertake the water flooding at such time as the primary reserves are exhausted. Make no change in the estimates of the after-tax positive cash flows from primary recovery or from secondary recovery (if undertaken) or in the estimate of the cost of water flooding at date 5. Discuss the question of how to analyze this altered proposal, making any calculations that you consider to be relevant.

C–8. Alter the data of Example C–2 by assuming an immediate payment of $100,000 is required to secure the lease. Assume that the oil company must agree to undertake the water flooding at date 5, just as stipulated in Example C–2. Discuss the question of how this analysis should differ from the one appropriate for Problem C–7. Make any calculations that you believe are called for to guide the oil company's decision in this case.

D

Certain Mathematical Models
in Replacement Economy

This appendix describes certain aspects of a number of mathematical models for replacement economy developed over a period of years by the research staff of the Machinery and Allied Products Institute.[1] In order to illustrate certain characteristics of mathematical models of this type, the formula for one of the simplest models is derived and a numerical example is used to show how to interpret a replacement study using this simple model. Other more complex models are briefly mentioned, and the use of one of them is illustrated.

The words *challenger* and *defender,* coined by George Terborgh for discussion of replacement economy, were defined and used in Chapter 16. These words also are used throughout this appendix.

Examples 16–4, 16–5, and 16–6 described cases in which the expected remaining life of the defender was shorter than the expected economic life of the challenger. The discussion in Chapter 16 pointed out that a possible consideration in such cases is the likelihood that if replacement is deferred, a better challenger than the present one will be available. However, no general rules for making a monetary allowance for this matter were developed in Chapter 16. We shall see that an important aspect of the mathematical models mentioned in this appendix is that they contain a formalized allowance for the superiority of future challengers to present ones.

The Concept of an Annual Gradient That Describes the Operating Advantage of Future Challengers as Compared to the Present One. A present challenger may have various advantages over a

---

[1] In chronological order, the books describing these models are: George Terborgh, *Dynamic Equipment Policy* (New York: McGraw-Hill Book Co., Inc., 1949); Machinery and Allied Products Institute, *MAPI Replacement Manual* (Washington, D.C.: Machinery and Allied Products Institute, 1950); George Terborgh, *Business Investment Policy* (Washington, D.C.: Machinery and Allied Products Institute, 1958).

defender that will influence prospective year-by-year cash flow. These advantages may lead to lower disbursements to provide a given service, higher receipts from the sale of that service, or both. Similarly, future challengers may have such advantages over the present challenger. For simplicity, the following example assumes that defender, present challenger, and future challengers will all have the same receipts and that the year-by-year differences in cash flow are caused solely by differences in disbursements. However, the analysis is entirely general and may be applied to differences in receipts as well as to differences in disbursements.

Assume that the present challenger for a given service has estimated first-year disbursements of $3,500. Assume that each year these disbursements are expected to increase by $20 so that they will be $3,520 in the second year of service, $3,540 in the third year, etc.

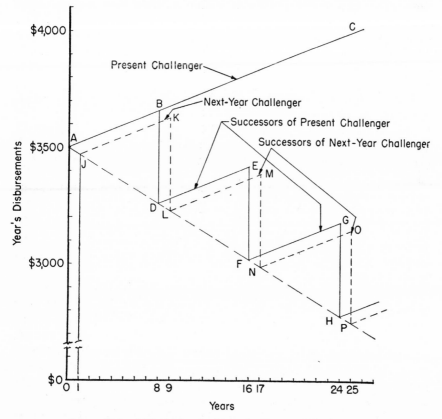

FIGURE D–1. A Model for Analysis of a Proposed Replacement

SOURCE: Adapted from A. A. Alchian, *Economic Replacement Policy,* Publication R–224 (Santa Monica, Calif.: The Rand Corporation, 1952), Fig. 2.1, p. 8.

Assume that a steady improvement in future challengers is anticipated so that the first-year disbursements will be $3,470 for next-
year's challenger, $3,440 for the challenger available 2 years hence,
and will continue to decrease by $30 a year. Assume that disburse-
ments for all future challengers, like those for the present one, will
increase at $20 a year. Assume that the first cost of the present
challenger is $1,000 and that this will be the first cost of all future
challengers. Assume that all challengers will have zero salvage
values at all times. Assume that decisions on plant investments are
to be made by before-tax analyses using a minimum attractive rate
of return (interest rate) of 15%.

In the foregoing assumptions it will be noted that the present
challenger accumulates inferiority to future challengers at a rate of
$50 per year. The expected behavior of annual disbursements for
the present challenger is shown by line ABC in Figure D–1. Line
JK, for the next-year challenger, is always $50 below line ABC.
Line DE, for the challenger 8 years hence, is always $400 below line
ABC. And so on. In Terborgh's *Dynamic Equipment Policy*, such
a $50 figure is referred to as an *inferiority gradient*.

Calculation of Economic Life. If all challengers have the same
first cost ($1,000 in our example) and zero salvage at all times, the
economic life may be shown to depend on the ratio of inferiority
gradient to first cost. In our example the gradient-cost ratio is 5%
(i.e., $50 ÷ $1,000). Table D–1 shows the economic life to be 8
years.[2]

Line C in this table is simply the product of $1,000 and the capi-
tal recovery factor for n years. Line D is the product of $50 and the
gradient factor for n years. Line E is the sum of lines C and D.
The minimum value in line E, $362, occurs for a life of 8 years. In
Dynamic Equipment Policy, such a minimum value is referred to
as the challenger's *adverse minimum*.

In our discussion of the gas main example in Chapter 16, we
noted that as long as the cost of extending the service another year
(column B of Table 16–1, page 382) was less than the equivalent
uniform cost up to date (column E), the equivalent uniform annual
cost would continue to decrease; once the figure in column B was
greater than the column E figure on the preceding line, the figures
in column E started to increase. Columns B and E in Table D–1
are, in this respect, comparable to the corresponding figures in Table
16–1. Thus the adverse minimum is reached at the end of 8 years

---

[2] Table D–1 is computed along the same lines as Table 1 in Terborgh, *Dynamic Equipment Policy, op. cit.,* p. 78.

when the 9th-year inferiority in column B, $400, exceeds $362, the 8th-year figure in column E.

An Independent Check on the Comparative Cost Figures Given in Table D–1. The figure in any line of column B of Table D–1 does not represent the current year's operating cost of any particular

TABLE D–1

DETERMINATION OF ECONOMIC LIFE OF A $1,000 ASSET WITH A $50 GRADIENT
ASSUMING ZERO SALVAGE VALUE AT ALL TIMES AND INTEREST AT 15%

Year n	Excess of Disbursements for Year Indicated Over First Year's Disbursements for New Asset	Equivalent Annual Cost—n Year Life		
		Capital Recovery Cost	Excess of Annual Disbursements	Total
A	B	C	D	E
1	$ 0	$1,150	$ 0	$1,150
2	50	615	24	639
3	100	438	46	484
4	150	350	67	417
5	200	298	86	384
6	250	264	105	369
7	300	240	123	363
8	350	223	139	362
9	400	210	155	365
10	450	199	169	368
11	500	191	183	374
12	550	184	196	380
13	600	179	207	386
14	650	175	218	393
15	700	171	228	399
16	750	168	238	406
17	800	165	247	412
18	850	163	254	417
19	900	161	262	423
20	950	160	269	429

asset; it is, as stated in the column heading, the excess of disbursements for the year indicated over the first year's disbursements for the best new asset expected to be available in that year. It follows that the total figure in column E does not represent equivalent annual cost for any particular asset. At first glance it may be hard to see why these figures, which depend on the shifting standard of the first year's performance of a different new asset every year, can give a correct comparison of the relative economy of different service lives. Nevertheless, the differences between the figures in column E for different assumed lives are the long-run differences in equivalent annual costs for these lives that would exist if costs should behave as assumed.

For example, let us compare the equivalent annual costs to be realized over a 16-year period on the assumption that the present challenger is continued in service for 16 years, that it is replaced after 8 years, and that there is a replacement every 4 years. By appropriate manipulations of compound interest factors, such costs may be computed to be as follows:

Life in Years	Capital Recovery	Equivalent Annual Disbursements	Total Equivalent Annual Cost	Excess Over Annual Cost for 8-Yr. Life
4	$350	$2,924	$3,274	$55
8	223	2,996	3,219	
16	168	3,095	3,263	44

The excesses over the equivalent annual cost for the economic life of 8 years are exactly the same as the excesses over the $362 adverse minimum as they may be observed in column E of Table D–1.

Use of the Challenger's Adverse Minimum in a Replacement Study. Assume that a certain defender has estimated next-year disbursements of $3,800, that subsequent years' disbursements will be higher than this, and that there is no salvage value now or later. If this defender is to be compared with the present challenger of Figure D–1 and Table D–1 by the method of analysis developed in *Dynamic Equipment Policy,* the comparison is:

Defender

Next-year capital costs (zero because of zero salvage values now and next year) .... $ 0
Next-year operating inferiority to present challenger = $3,800 − $3,500   300

Total is *defender's adverse minimum* $300

Challenger

Challenger's adverse minimum (from Table D–1) $362

This comparison favors the defender by $62. It may be contrasted with the following comparison of next-year costs along conventional lines, assuming an 8-year life and zero salvage value for the $1,000 challenger.

Defender

CR .... $ 0
Next-year disbursements   3,800
                                                                            ———
                                                                            $3,800

Challenger

CR = $1,000(crf–15%–8) = $1,000(0.22285) .... $ 223
Next-year disbursements 3,500
_____
$3,723

This next-year comparison favors the challenger by $77.

The algebraic difference between these two results, $139, consists of a formalized allowance for the prospect that if the defender is kept another year, it will be followed by the next-year challenger and its successors and that the next-year challenger and its successors will, on balance, be superior to the present challenger and its successors.

Figure D–1 shows a graphical comparison of year-by-year disbursements for the present challenger and its successors (solid line ABDEFGH, etc.) and the next-year challenger and its successors (dash line JKLMNOP, etc.). Although the graph only goes for 25 years or so, this difference is a perpetual series that may be tabulated as follows:

Years	Advantage of Next-Year Challenger and Its Successors as Compared to Present Challenger and Its Successors
2 to 8	+$ 50 a year
9	−350
10 to 16	+50 a year
17	−350
18 to 24	+50 a year
25	−350
26 to 32	+50 a year
33	−350

and so on, ad infinitum

If we assume that all future challengers will have first costs of $1,000, 8-year lives, and zero salvage values, and if we accept the other implications of the mathematical model illustrated in Figure D–1, we may modify the next-year comparison of $3,800 for defender and $3,723 for challenger by charging the present challenger with the present worth (one year from zero date) of the infinite series of subsequent differences between the present challenger and its successors and the next-year challenger and its successors. To simplify calculations of present worth, the infinite series may be viewed as +$50 a year forever and −$400 at the end of every 8th year. The present worth at 15% may then be computed as follows:

$$PW = \frac{\$50}{0.15} - \frac{\$400\,(\text{sff}–15\%–8)}{0.15}$$

$$= \$333 - \frac{\$400\,(0.07285)}{0.15} = \$333 - \$194 = \$139$$

Adding this $139 to the challenger's next-year costs of $3,723 in order to equalize matters over all subsequent years, we now have a next-year $3,800 figure for the defender to compare with a $3,862 figure for the challenger. If we subtract the common element in next year's disbursements, $3,500, we have the MAPI-type comparison of $300 for defender's adverse minimum with $362 for challenger's adverse minimum.

If instead of our specific figures of $50 for inferiority gradient, 0.15 for interest rate, and 8 years for life, we use the symbols g, i, and n, we note that

$$\text{PW} = \frac{g}{i} - \frac{ng(\text{sff–}i\text{–}n)}{i}$$

This expression happens to be identical with the expression for the factor to convert a gradient to an equivalent uniform annual series developed in Chapter 4. It follows that under certain circumstances our table of gradient factors, Table E–23, could be used in computing a challenger's adverse minimum.

The total challenger's adverse minimum is the sum of challenger's capital recovery cost and a figure for the present worth of the advantage gained by having the next-year challenger and its successors rather than the present challenger and its successors. To use Table E–23 in computing the latter figure, we need the interest rate, the inferiority gradient, and the challenger's economic life. For instance, in our example the adverse minimum is $1,000(\text{crf–}15\%\text{–}8) + 50(\text{gf–}15\%\text{–}8) = \$1,000(0.22285) + \$50(2.78) = \$223 + \$139 = \$362$.

Usually the foregoing scheme for computing challenger's adverse minimum is not feasible because it assumes that both the inferiority gradient and the economic life are known. But these are not independent figures. Under the conditions of the mathematical model, the gradient determines the economic life, as brought out in Table D–1. Conversely, an assumed economic life implies a particular value of gradient. *Dynamic Equipment Policy* and *MAPI Replacement Manual* contain various formulas and diagrams for calculation of a challenger's adverse minimum without the detailed arithmetic of a table such as D–1.

An Approximate Formula for Challenger's Adverse Minimum as a Function of the Gradient. The recommendation in *Dynamic Equipment Policy* was that, wherever practicable in a replacement economy study, the challenger's adverse minimum should be based on its estimated gradient. Often the data of a study will supply a basis for computing the past gradient. Sometimes there may be reasons for expecting that the future gradient will be greater or smaller than the past one; sometimes it will be reasonable to assume that the past gradient will continue in the future.

For a first cost c, a gradient g, and an interest rate i, *Dynamic Equipment Policy* gave the following approximate formula:

$$\text{Challenger's adverse minimum} = \sqrt{2cg} + \frac{ic - g}{2}$$

This formula was based on average (rather than equivalent) annual disbursements with capital recovery costs computed by straight-line depreciation plus average interest. It assumed a zero salvage value at the end of the challenger's economic life.

Applied to our example of Table D–1, this gives

$$\text{Adverse minimum} = \sqrt{2(\$1{,}000)(\$50)} + \frac{0.15(\$1{,}000) - \$50}{2}$$

$$= \$316 + \$50 = \$366$$

Derivation of an Expression for the Relationship Between Adverse Minimum and Economic Life. In contrast to *Dynamic Equipment Policy*, no estimate of the gradient was needed to apply the methods of analysis advocated in *MAPI Replacement Manual;* a challenger's adverse minimum was computed from its estimated life and terminal salvage value. The formula used for adverse minimum in the zero-salvage case may be derived fairly simply, as follows:

The total equivalent annual figure, U, for n years in a calculation such as the one illustrated in Table D–1 is the sum of the annual cost of capital recovery and the equivalent annual operating inferiority.

$$U = c\frac{i(1+i)^n}{(1+i)^n - 1} + \frac{g}{i} - \frac{ng}{i}\left[\frac{i}{(1+i)^n - 1}\right]$$

The operating inferiority for any year, n, is $(n-1)g$. The operating inferiority for the year following the nth year is ng. As long as the next-year operating inferiority, ng, is less than U, the value of U for the year $(n+1)$ will obviously be less than for year n. The first year for which the next-year operating inferiority is equal to or greater than U is the year corresponding to the minimum value of U. For a specified first cost, c, with any specified economic life there will be a possible range of values of U_{min} corresponding to the range of values of g that will result in the particular economic life. The lowest possible value of g that will result in the particular economic life will be that for which $U = ng$.

To find the value of U corresponding to this particular value of g, $\frac{U}{n}$ may be substituted for g in the general expression for U, as follows:

$$U = \frac{ci(1+i)^n}{(1+i)^n - 1} + \frac{U}{in} - \frac{U}{i}\left[\frac{i}{(1+i)^n - 1}\right]$$

$$U + \frac{U}{(1+i)^n - 1} - \frac{U}{in} = \frac{ci(1+i)^n}{(1+i)^n - 1}$$

Multiply both sides of this equation by $in\,[(1+i)^n - 1]$,

$$Uin(1+i)^n - Uin + Uin - U(1+i)^n + U = cni^2(1+i)^n$$

Divide by $(1+i)^n$

$$U\left(in + \frac{1}{(1+i)^n} - 1\right) = cni^2$$

$$U = \frac{cni^2}{in + \dfrac{1}{(1+i)^n} - 1}$$

A minor limitation on the use of this formula for challenger's adverse minimum as a function of estimated economic life may be brought out by the following example. Assume $c = \$1,000$, $n = 8$, and $i = 0.15$.

$$U_{min} = \frac{\$1,000\,(8)\,(0.15)^2}{(0.15)\,(8) + 0.3269 - 1} = \frac{\$180}{0.5269} = \$342$$

It will be observed that, although the economic life is 8 years as in Table D–1 and the values of first cost and interest rate are the same ones used in that table, this adverse minimum of \$342 is somewhat less than the figure of \$362 computed for a gradient of \$50 in Table D–1. The \$342 adverse minimum corresponds to a gradient of $\$342 \div 8 = \$43$, the lowest possible gradient that will give an 8-year economic life with a first cost of \$1,000 and an interest rate of 15%.

With any given first cost and interest rate there will be a range of values of gradient that will result in any designated economic life. This formula for adverse minimum as a function of economic life always implies the lowest possible gradient within this range. The upper end of the range may be determined in any case by using the formula to compute adverse minimum for a life of one year less.

For instance if $c = \$1,000$, $n = 7$, and $i = 0.15$, $U_{min} = \$370$. The corresponding gradient is $\$370 \div 7 = \$53$. It follows that any gradient above \$43 and below \$53 will give an economic life of 8 years.

Salvage Values in the Methods of *Dynamic Equipment Policy* **and** *MAPI Replacement Manual.* The schemes of analysis presented in these two volumes were identical in their method of calculation of the defender's adverse minimum. This consisted of two parts, the defender's next-year operating inferiority to the challenger and the defender's next-year capital cost. This next-year capital cost was a conventional capital recovery cost made up of one year's interest on present salvage value plus the prospective decline in salvage value during the next year. (See the discussion in Example 16–6 under the heading "Calculation of Annual Cost of Defender.") This use of defender's present and next-year salvage values in computing defender's adverse minimum is illustrated in Example D–1.

Where challenger's adverse minimum was computed from the prospective gradient by the formula we have quoted from *Dynamic Equipment Policy*, a zero challenger salvage value was assumed. It will be recalled that this adverse minimum is, in principle, made up of two parts, the challenger's capital recovery cost and a figure that can be computed from the gradient. With relatively high interest rates (say 10% or more), the influence of a moderate terminal salvage value on capital recovery cost was relatively small and a negligible error was introduced by the arbitrary assumption of zero terminal salvage value (particularly so for the longer-lived challengers).

In contrast, *MAPI Replacement Manual* used the challenger's estimated life and terminal salvage value to determine its adverse minimum; in effect, as we have seen in the derivation of the no-salvage formula, the gradient was inferred from the life and salvage value. The following formula for adverse minimum with a positive salvage value was derived on the assumption that challengers' salvage values would decline at a uniform rate (i.e., according to a declining-balance curve):

$$U_{\min} = \frac{in\left[ci + rs \dfrac{1}{(1+i)^n} \right] - s(i+r)\left[1 - \dfrac{1}{(1+i)^n} \right]}{in + \dfrac{1}{(1+i)^n} - 1}$$

where c is challenger's first cost, n is estimated service life, s is estimated terminal salvage value, i is interest rate expressed as a decimal, and r is a symbol for $\dfrac{2.30259}{n}$ ($\log c - \log s$).

In the formulas used in *MAPI Replacement Manual*, both the challenger's adverse minimum and its implied gradient were quite sensitive to differences in estimated terminal salvage percentages. For example, consider three $10,000 challengers each with an 8-year estimated life and with respective estimated terminal salvage values of 0%, 20%, and 40%. Values of adverse minimum using an interest rate of 15% may be computed and broken down into their elements as follows:

Estimated Terminal Salvage	Total Adverse Minimum	Portion of Adverse Minimum Due to Capital Recovery Cost	Portion of Adverse Minimum Due to Advantage of Next-Year Challenger and Its Successors over Present Challenger and Its Successors
0%	$3,416	$2,228	$1,188
20%	2,818	2,083	735
40%	2,406	1,937	469

It is evident that moderate differences in assumed challenger salvage values cause substantial differences in the allowances for future technological progress due to the expected superiority of future challengers.

Some Changes in the Mathematical Model Incorporated into Business Investment Policy. This 1958 version of the MAPI techniques had many points in common with the mathematical models described in the earlier MAPI volumes. Just as in the earlier books, a formal allowance was made for the prospect that future challengers will be superior to present ones. And this prospect of superiority of future challengers was, in effect, converted to a single equivalent monetary amount to permit a next-year comparison between the alternatives of (A) retiring the defender at once in favor of the present challenger and (B) continuing the defender in service one more year and then retiring it in favor of the next-year challenger. *Business Investment Policy* was like *MAPI Replacement Manual* in basing its assumptions regarding the superiority of future challengers on the estimated life and salvage value of the present one; the two volumes were alike in making the conclusions of a replacement study quite sensitive to the estimated salvage percentage of a challenger.

(Some of the specialized terminology developed for the earlier volumes was abandoned in the 1958 publication; for instance, the words *challenger, defender,* and *gradient* do not appear in *Business Investment Policy.* Nevertheless, although not mentioned by the original names, these useful concepts continued to be employed in the 1958 volume.)

However, these 1958 MAPI methods had a number of points of difference from the earlier ones. Some important differences were:

1. The previous techniques involved comparisons before income taxes; the 1958 techniques involved after-tax comparisons. A tax rate of 50% was assumed. An analyst could apply the techniques either with years-digits or straight-line depreciation assumed for tax purposes. (Where the declining-balance method was to be used in tax returns, the economy study was to be based on the years-digits method. The reader may recall that a similar recommendation was made in Chapter 15 of this book.)
2. Whereas the previous techniques had compared next-year dollar figures for challenger and defender, the 1958 techniques computed a next-year rate of return. This rate was called the "MAPI urgency rating."
3. Certain aspects of the mathematical models assumed in the earlier methods were illustrated in Figure D–1. Technological progress was assumed to take place by a constant amount each year (indicated on the graph by the straight line AJDLFNHP). This same general assumption about technological progress was made in the 1958 methods.

In the earlier methods the gradual increase of operation and maintenance costs (or decrease of revenues) with the age of an asset was also assumed to follow a uniform gradient. This increase was shown in Figure D–1 by the parallel straight lines ABC, JK, DE, LM, FG, and NO. In *Business Investment Policy*, such a uniform increase is described as the "standard" projection pattern. But other projection patterns also were made available in the 1958 volume; it was possible to assume that annual disbursements increase either at a decreasing rate or an increasing rate.[3] Figure D–2 is a chart based on the standard projection pattern. Other similar charts, not reproduced here, were available for use with the other projection patterns. The use of Figure D–2 in a replacement study is described in Example D–1.

All of these charts were based on the assumption that 75% of the capital for proposed investments would come from equity sources and that the remaining 25% would be borrowed at an average interest rate of 3%. Compound interest conversions were made on the assumption that equity funds would yield a 10% return; the weighted average return on all funds would therefore be 8.25%.

[3] An earlier mathematical model assuming that annual disbursements for operation and maintenance increase at a decreasing rate was described in A. A. Alchian's *Economic Replacement Policy*, Publication R–224 (Santa Monica, Calif.: The Rand Corporation, 1952). Our Figure D–1 was suggested by Figure 2.1, p. 8 of the Alchian pamphlet.

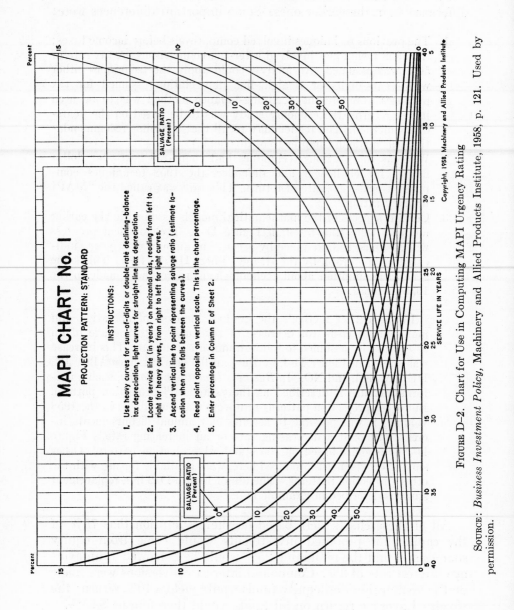

FIGURE D-2. Chart for Use in Computing MAPI Urgency Rating

SOURCE: *Business Investment Policy*, Machinery and Allied Products Institute, 1958, p. 121. Used by permission.

EXAMPLE D-1. A SIMPLE REPLACEMENT STUDY
ILLUSTRATING DIFFERENT MAPI TECHNIQUES

Facts of the Case. This example is based on Case 1 of *Business Investment Policy* (pages 153–57). Certain additions to data and minor changes have been made in order to illustrate the analysis of this case by the earlier MAPI techniques as well as by the 1958 methods.

The first cost installed of a proposed new cutter grinder is $6,124. The present salvage value of the existing cutter grinder is $400; this is expected to decline to $200 next year. Because the challenger can grind to closer tolerances, it is expected to increase next-year revenues by $500. Expected savings in next-year operating disbursements are $2,255 in direct labor, $565 in fringe benefits, and $150 in maintenance. Next-year insurance will be $60 higher with the challenger.

The analysis of this case in *Business Investment Policy* is based on a "standard" projection pattern, a 15-year challenger service life with 7% terminal salvage value, and declining-balance depreciation.

To illustrate the before-tax type of analysis used in *Dynamic Equipment Policy* and *MAPI Replacement Manual*, we shall simplify matters by assuming a zero salvage value for the challenger (rather than 7%). We shall use an interest rate (in effect, a before-tax minimum attractive rate of return) of 15%. In order to have a basis for estimating the past gradient, we shall assume that the defender is 12 years old.

Defender's Adverse Minimum. This is the sum of the defender's next-year operating inferiority and its next-year capital costs. The calculation of operating inferiority may be tabulated as follows:

	Next-Year Operating Advantage	
	Defender	Challenger
Increased receipts due to quality improvement		$ 500
Direct labor costs		2,255
Fringe benefits		565
Maintenance		150
Insurance	$60	
	$60	$3,470

Net challenger advantage (defender inferiority) = $3,470 − $60 = $3,410

The next-year capital costs for the defender are interest on present salvage value plus decline in salvage value. This sum is $400(0.15) + ($400 − $200) = $60 + $200 = $260.

The defender's adverse minimum is $3,410 + $260 = $3,670.

Challenger's Adverse Minimum Based on Estimated Challenger Gradient. To find the past gradient, we divide the defender's operating inferiority, $3,410, by its age, 12 years, and secure a figure of $282. If we assume that this gradient will continue in the future, we can use it in the approximate zero-salvage formula from *Dynamic Equipment Policy,* as follows:

$$U_{min} = \sqrt{2cg} + \frac{ic - g}{2}$$

$$= \sqrt{2(\$6,124)(\$282)} + \frac{0.15(\$6,124) - \$282}{2}$$

$$= \$1,858 + \$318 = \$2,176$$

```
PROJECT NO.    I                                                          SHEET I

                             SUMMARY OF ANALYSIS
                    (SEE ACCOMPANYING WORK SHEETS FOR DETAIL)

                             I.  REQUIRED INVESTMENT

 I  INSTALLED COST OF PROJECT                                      $    6,124    I
 2  DISPOSAL VALUE OF ASSETS TO BE RETIRED BY PROJECT             $      400    2
 3  CAPITAL ADDITIONS REQUIRED IN ABSENCE OF PROJECT              $             3
 4  INVESTMENT RELEASED OR AVOIDED BY PROJECT (2+3)               $      400    4
 5  NET INVESTMENT REQUIRED (1-4)                                 $    5,724    5

                    II.  NEXT-YEAR ADVANTAGE FROM PROJECT
                           A.  OPERATING ADVANTAGE
                       (USE FIRST YEAR OF PROJECT OPERATION)*

 6  ASSUMED OPERATING RATE OF PROJECT  (HOURS PER YEAR)                2,400    6

    EFFECT OF PROJECT ON REVENUE                  Increase      Decrease
 7  FROM CHANGE IN QUALITY OF PRODUCTS          $    500    $                   7
 8  FROM CHANGE IN VOLUME OF OUTPUT                                             8
 9  TOTAL                                       $    500  A $            B      9

    EFFECT OF PROJECT ON OPERATING COSTS
10  DIRECT LABOR                                $          $    2,255          10
11  INDIRECT LABOR                                                            11
12  FRINGE BENEFITS                                              565          12
13  MAINTENANCE                                                  150          13
14  TOOLING                                                                  14
15  SUPPLIES                                                                 15
16  SCRAP AND REWORK                                                         16
17  DOWN TIME                                                                17
18  POWER                                                                    18
19  FLOOR SPACE                                                              19
20  PROPERTY TAXES AND INSURANCE                       60                    20
21  SUBCONTRACTING                                                           21
22  INVENTORY                                                                22
23  SAFETY                                                                   23
24  FLEXIBILITY                                                              24
25  OTHER                                                                    25
26  TOTAL                                       $     60  A $    2,970  B     26

27  NET INCREASE IN REVENUE (9A-9B)                            $      500     27
28  NET DECREASE IN OPERATING COST (26B-26A)                   $    2,910     28
29  NEXT-YEAR OPERATING ADVANTAGE (27+28)                      $    3,410     29

                         B.  NON-OPERATING ADVANTAGE
                    (USE ONLY IF THERE IS AN ENTRY IN LINE 4)

30  NEXT-YEAR CAPITAL CONSUMPTION AVOIDED BY PROJECT:                        30
       A  DECLINE OF DISPOSAL VALUE DURING THE YEAR           $      200      A
       B  NEXT-YEAR ALLOCATION OF CAPITAL ADDITIONS           $              B
                                              TOTAL $      200

                           C.  TOTAL ADVANTAGE
31  TOTAL NEXT-YEAR ADVANTAGE FROM PROJECT (29+30)            $    3,610     31

 * For projects with a significant break-in period, use performance after break-in.
```

FIGURE D–3. First Sheet of Analysis To Compute MAPI Urgency Rating

SOURCE: *Business Investment Policy,* Machinery and Allied Products Institute, 1958, p. 156. Used by permission.

PROJECT NO. 1   SHEET 2

III. COMPUTATION OF MAPI URGENCY RATING

32   TOTAL NEXT-YEAR ADVANTAGE AFTER INCOME TAX (31 − TAX) $ 1,805

33   MAPI CHART ALLOWANCE FOR PROJECT (TOTAL OF COLUMN F, BELOW) $ 214 *

(ENTER DEPRECIABLE ASSETS ONLY)

Item or Group	Installed Cost of Item or Group A	Estimated Service Life (Years) B	Estimated Terminal Salvage (Percent of Cost) C	MAPI Chart Number D	Chart Percentage E	Chart Percentage × Cost (E × A) F
Cutter Grinder	$ 6,124	15	7	1	3.5	$ 214
					TOTAL	$ 214

34   AMOUNT AVAILABLE FOR RETURN ON INVESTMENT (32−33) $ 1,591

35   **MAPI URGENCY RATING** (34÷5) · 100   %   28

* Since the chart allowance does not cover future capital additions to project assets, add an annual proration of such additions, if any, to the figure in Line 33.

FIGURE D–4. Second Sheet of Analysis To Compute MAPI Urgency Rating

SOURCE: *Business Investment Policy,* Machinery and Allied Products Institute, 1958, p. 157. Used by permission.

This $2,176 should be compared with $3,670, the defender's adverse minimum. The comparison favors the challenger by $1,494. The $1,494 should be interpreted as a one-year difference favoring immediate replacement in comparison with replacement one year hence.

In this analysis assuming zero salvage value, the implied challenger life is the adverse minimum, $2,176, divided by the gradient, $282; this is between 7 and 8 years.

Challenger's Adverse Minimum Based on Estimated Service Life and Salvage Value. As we are assuming zero salvage value, we may use the no-salvage version of the formula from *MAPI Replacement Manual*, as follows:

$$U_{min} = \frac{cni^2}{in + \dfrac{1}{(1+i)^n} - 1}$$

$$= \frac{(\$6,124)(15)(0.15)^2}{0.15(15) + 0.1229 - 1} = \$1,505$$

A comparison of this $1,505 with the $3,670 defender's adverse minimum favors the challenger by $2,165.

In this analysis assuming zero salvage value, the implied gradient is the adverse minimum, $1,505, divided by the life, 15 years; this is $100.

Calculation of MAPI Urgency Rating. Figures D–3 and D–4, reproduced from *Business Investment Policy*, illustrate the application of the 1958 MAPI methods to the data of this example. These forms are largely self-explanatory.

It will be noted that the next-year before-tax operating advantage, $3,410, is computed just as it was in the earlier MAPI methods. However, both present and next-year defender salvage values are handled somewhat differently. The present defender salvage value, $400, is subtracted from the challenger investment to obtain the $5,724 denominator (line 5 of Figure D–3) used in computing the "urgency rating." The next-year decline in salvage value, $200, is added to the $3,410 operating advantage to obtain line 31, the total next-year advantage from the project.

Because the assumed tax rate is 50%, the after-tax figure on line 32 (at the top of Figure D–4) is half of the $3,610 in line 31. In this mathematical model, the use of the MAPI Chart No. 1 (our Figure D–2) has an effect somewhat comparable to the use of the earlier formulas for challenger's adverse minimum.

Space is not available here for a detailed discussion of this 1958 MAPI mathematical model as this model is much more complicated than the earlier ones. However, it should be emphasized that the 28% urgency rating should not be interpreted as an expected rate of return over the life of the challenger. It is a prospective next-year rate, just as the difference between values of challenger's and defender's adverse minimum was a next-year difference. In discounting expected future events subsequent to a date one year hence, the MAPI charts have been based on the assumption of a rate of return of 10% from the assumed 75% of equity funds and a 3% interest cost for the assumed 25% of borrowed capital.

The Issue of How To Consider the Prospect of Future Technological Change in Making Present Replacement Decisions. Although the various MAPI methods have differed from one another, one element that they have had in common has been the use of a formal monetary figure—usually implied rather than explicitly stated—to reflect the likelihood that future challengers will be superior to present ones. In fact, this formal allowance has been the new element that these mathematical models have introduced into replacement economy.

In the common case where replacement decisions are made without the use of a mathematical model of this type, one possibility is to make the required monetary comparisons with no special allowance for the prospect that there will be a better challenger in the near future. Then, whenever deemed relevant, this prospect can be recognized as a nonmonetary element in making the decision. In effect, this prospect is viewed as part of the irreducible data for decision making.

An alternate possibility is to require challengers in replacement studies to meet more severe criteria than are imposed on other proposals for new assets. For example, somewhat higher minimum attractive rates of return might be used in replacement studies than in other studies. More commonly, this device of using severe criteria takes the form of shortening the estimated service life of the challenger.

An extreme shortening of challenger service life in replacement studies constitutes an irrational obstacle to technological progress. If old assets are kept in service until new ones will "pay for themselves" in one or two years, the old assets will generally be kept for much too long a time. The adverse social consequences to be expected from a widespread use of extreme short payoff periods were stressed by George Terborgh in *Dynamic Equipment Policy*.

On the other hand, *some* shortening of the estimated life of a challenger in its initial or primary service has an effect not unlike the one obtained from using certain MAPI models. It is roughly true, although not exactly so, that a comparison using the zero-salvage formula from *MAPI Replacement Manual* and a challenger service life of n will give the same results as a conventional economy study using a challenger service life of $n/2$ and zero salvage. For example, we computed the challenger's adverse minimum to be $342 where first cost was $1,000, life was 8 years, salvage was zero, and interest was 15%. For the same asset the capital recovery cost is $350 for a 4-year life and zero salvage value.

Some General Comments on the Use of Complex Mathematical Models as Aids in Making Economic Decisions. If the use of a mathematical model is under consideration as a possible basis for decision making—either on a proposed replacement or on any other matter—certain questions need to be examined. One question is which of the available models seems to be best adapted to the particular circumstances. (It sometimes happens that although no available model is suitable, a new one can be devised that is more nearly adequate.) Another question is whether or not the formalized assumptions of the best model are close enough to the facts. In general, these questions cannot be answered in a satisfactory way except by someone who understands both the facts and the assumptions underlying the various models. Judgment on these questions is more difficult for complex mathematical models than for simple ones.

It is not a valid objection to a particular model to point out some way in which the model fails to fit the exact circumstances of a case. Assumptions that can be incorporated into mathematical formulas will seldom fit economic facts perfectly. In judging the suitability of a certain model to a particular case, the important matter is to judge whether the *decision* based on the use of the model is likely to be sensitive to the various ways in which the assumptions depart from the facts of the case.

The foregoing comment about the importance of sensitivity may be illustrated with reference to several of the assumptions made in all of the MAPI models. Consider the assumptions (1) that the service period is perpetual, (2) that all future challengers will have the same first costs, salvage values, and lives as the present one and that technological progress will occur at a uniform rate, and (3) that the appropriate comparison is between replacement at once with the present challenger and continuing the defender in service one year more and then replacing it with the next-year challenger.

1. In general, with the interest rates of 8% or more commonly used in replacement studies, the present worth of the assumed distant consequences of present decisions is quite small. If a service is likely to be needed for a fairly long time, no serious error in decision making will be caused by using a model that assumes perpetual service. But such a model clearly is inappropriate whenever it is expected that the service will terminate at a forseeable date in the near future.

2. It was pointed out in Chapter 16 (following the discussion of Example 16–6) that there sometimes is a reasonable basis for making specific forecasts about the challengers to be expected in the next few years. Different forecasts have different implications regarding the present replacement decision. For example, the expectation that challengers in the near future will have considerably higher first costs than the present challenger is favorable to immediate

replacement; the expectation of substantial technological improvement in the near future is favorable to putting off replacement. Where a basis exists for such specific forecasts, better decisions are likely to be made by an analysis incorporating these forecasts than by an analysis using a mathematical model that depends on generalized forecasts about future challengers.

3. The question of selecting the defender remaining life that is most favorable to the defender was discussed in Chapter 16 (following Example 16–6). It was pointed out that under certain circumstances this life is one year; under other circumstances it may be considerably longer. In those circumstances where a defender life of more than one year should be used in a replacement study, a next-year analysis may lead to an incorrect decision favorable to the challenger.

In general, it should be emphasized that a prerequisite to the use of *any* mathematical model to guide an economic decision should be a clear understanding of the assumptions of the particular model by the person who makes (or recommends) the decision.

Problems

The following problems are all based on a single replacement proposal, for which the circumstances have been suggested by an example on pages 136–39 of *Dynamic Equipment Policy*. The purpose of the problems is to help the reader to examine certain aspects of various replacement models by making a series of calculations about a specific case. The facts and estimates regarding the replacement proposal are as follows:

The management of a metalworking plant is considering the replacement of a 19-year old planer. The proposed new planer (challenger) has a first cost of $30,000. The old planer (defender) has a net salvage value of $6,000. It is estimated that this salvage value will decline to $5,000 one year hence. The challenger will save $1,550 a year in direct labor cost and labor extras on the planing operation. Moreover, the greater precision of the challenger reduces the amount of work needed on subsequent operations, with a resulting annual saving of $2,440 in direct labor cost and labor extras. It is estimated the maintenance cost for the challenger next year will be $250 less than the maintenance cost for the defender; however, this saving in maintenance costs will be offset by $250 higher challenger costs for property taxes and insurance.

The original cost of the defender 19 years ago was $14,400. It has been depreciated for accounting and income tax purposes by the straight-line item method assuming a 24-year life with zero terminal salvage value. If the challenger is purchased, it will be depreciated for accounting and income tax purposes by the years-digits item method assuming a 24-year life with zero terminal salvage value. The effective tax rate is 50% on ordinary income and 25% on long-term gains on disposal of depreciable assets used in the trade or business.

D–1. Assume that a before-tax comparison is to be made, computing challenger's adverse minimum by the approximate no-salvage formula from *Dynamic*

Equipment Policy, $U_{min} = \sqrt{2cg} + \dfrac{ic - g}{2}$. An interest rate (minimum attractive rate of return before income taxes) of 10% is to be used. The future gradient is to be assumed the same as the past gradient.

(a) What is the gradient? (*Ans.* = $210.)

(b) What is the defender's adverse minimum? (*Ans.* = $5,590.)

(c) What is the challenger's adverse minimum? (*Ans.* = $4,945.)

(d) What challenger service life can be derived from the challenger's adverse minimum? (*Ans.* = between 23 and 24 years.)

D–2. Assume that a before-tax comparison is to be made, computing challenger's adverse minimum by the no-salvage formula used in *MAPI Replacement Manual,* $U_{min} = \dfrac{cni^2}{in + (1 + i)^{-n} - 1}$. An interest rate of 10% is to be used. The estimated challenger life is 24 years.

(a) What is the defender's adverse minimum? (*Ans.* = $5,590.)

(b) What is the challenger's adverse minimum? (*Ans.* = $4,795.)

(c) What gradient is implied by the challenger's adverse minimum? (*Ans.* = $200.)

D–3. It is evident that the past gradient has been due entirely to obsolescence. (The lower prospective next-year maintenance costs for the challenger are offset by equal higher prospective next-year costs for property taxes and insurance.) What is the excess of the total $4,795 challenger's adverse minimum in Problem D–2 over the challenger's capital recovery cost? Show that this excess is equal to the present worth one year hence of the advantage gained thereafter by an infinite series of challengers starting a year hence and having 24-year lives, as compared to a similar infinite series starting at once with the present challenger. In this calculation, assume that the superiority of future challengers will correspond to the gradient computed in Problem D–2.

D–4. Solve Problem D–1, using an interest rate (minimum attractive rate of return before income taxes) of 20%.

D–5. Solve Problem D–2, using an interest rate of 20%.

D–6. On the basis of your analysis of Problems D–1 to D–5 and any further analysis that you believe is appropriate, discuss the sensitivity of the choice between challenger and defender to (a) present defender salvage value; (b) estimated decline in defender salvage value during the coming year; and (c) assumed interest rate. Discuss the sensitivity of the choice to assumed gradient where the challenger's adverse minimum is based on estimated gradient, as in Problems D–1 and D–4. Discuss the sensitivity of the choice to assumed challenger service life where challenger's adverse minimum is based on service life, as in Problems D–2 and D–5.

D–7. Analyze the proposed replacement by the method described in *Business Investment Policy,* using the "standard projection pattern." (This pattern assumes a uniform gradient.) Assume a 24-year challenger life. MAPI Chart No. 1, based on this pattern, indicates an allowance for capital consumption of 1.9%. Disregard the tax consequences of the gain on disposal of defender this year and also next year. Compute the MAPI urgency rating. (*Ans.* = 8.0%.)

D–8. Solve Problem D–7, considering the tax consequences of the gain on disposal of defender. (*Ans.* = 7.6%.)

D–9. Tabulate the prospective differences in cash flow after taxes between retiring the defender at once and retiring it one year hence in favor of a challenger that will reduce annual operating disbursements $200 below those expected with the present challenger. Assume that the first cost of the new challenger will also be $30,000. Compute figures for each of the next 5 years and indicate the pattern of differences thereafter.

D–10. Assume that the present defender can be kept in service for, say, the next 10 years with substantially the same annual disbursements as at present, but that its salvage value will be zero when finally retired. Compute the year-by-year differences in cash flow after taxes for each of the next 10 years. (Assume that differences in challenger and defender maintenance cost will continue to be offset by differences in property taxes.) Compute the period for crude payout after taxes. (*Ans.* = 8.8 years.)

E

Interest Tables

TABLE E–1

1% COMPOUND INTEREST FACTORS

	SINGLE PAYMENT		UNIFORM SERIES				
	Compound Amount Factor caf'	Present Worth Factor pwf'	Sinking Fund Factor sff	Capital Recovery Factor crf	Compound Amount Factor caf	Present Worth Factor pwf	
n	Given P To find S $(1+i)^n$	Given S To find P $\dfrac{1}{(1+i)^n}$	Given S To find R $\dfrac{i}{(1+i)^n-1}$	Given P To find R $\dfrac{i(1+i)^n}{(1+i)^n-1}$	Given R To find S $\dfrac{(1+i)^n-1}{i}$	Given R To find P $\dfrac{(1+i)^n-1}{i(1+i)^n}$	n
1	1.010	0.9901	1.00000	1.01000	1.000	0.990	1
2	1.020	0.9803	0.49751	0.50751	2.010	1.970	2
3	1.030	0.9706	0.33002	0.34002	3.030	2.941	3
4	1.041	0.9610	0.24628	0.25628	4.060	3.902	4
5	1.051	0.9515	0.19604	0.20604	5.101	4.853	5
6	1.062	0.9420	0.16255	0.17255	6.152	5.795	6
7	1.072	0.9327	0.13863	0.14863	7.214	6.728	7
8	1.083	0.9235	0.12069	0.13069	8.286	7.652	8
9	1.094	0.9143	0.10674	0.11674	9.369	8.566	9
10	1.105	0.9053	0.09558	0.10558	10.462	9.471	10
11	1.116	0.8963	0.08645	0.09645	11.567	10.368	11
12	1.127	0.8874	0.07885	0.08885	12.683	11.255	12
13	1.138	0.8787	0.07241	0.08241	13.809	12.134	13
14	1.149	0.8700	0.06690	0.07690	14.947	13.004	14
15	1.161	0.8613	0.06212	0.07212	16.097	13.865	15
16	1.173	0.8528	0.05794	0.06794	17.258	14.718	16
17	1.184	0.8444	0.05426	0.06426	18.430	15.562	17
18	1.196	0.8360	0.05098	0.06098	19.615	16.398	18
19	1.208	0.8277	0.04805	0.05805	20.811	17.226	19
20	1.220	0.8195	0.04542	0.05542	22.019	18.046	20
21	1.232	0.8114	0.04303	0.05303	23.239	18.857	21
22	1.245	0.8034	0.04086	0.05086	24.472	19.660	22
23	1.257	0.7954	0.03889	0.04889	25.716	20.456	23
24	1.270	0.7876	0.03707	0.04707	26.973	21.243	24
25	1.282	0.7798	0.03541	0.04541	28.243	22.023	25
26	1.295	0.7720	0.03387	0.04387	29.526	22.795	26
27	1.308	0.7644	0.03245	0.04245	30.821	23.560	27
28	1.321	0.7568	0.03112	0.04112	32.129	24.316	28
29	1.335	0.7493	0.02990	0.03990	33.450	25.066	29
30	1.348	0.7419	0.02875	0.03875	34.785	25.808	30
31	1.361	0.7346	0.02768	0.03768	36.133	26.542	31
32	1.375	0.7273	0.02667	0.03667	37.494	27.270	32
33	1.389	0.7201	0.02573	0.03573	38.869	27.990	33
34	1.403	0.7130	0.02484	0.03484	40.258	28.703	34
35	1.417	0.7059	0.02400	0.03400	41.660	29.409	35
40	1.489	0.6717	0.02046	0.03046	48.886	32.835	40
45	1.565	0.6391	0.01771	0.02771	56.481	36.095	45
50	1.645	0.6080	0.01551	0.02551	64.463	39.196	50
55	1.729	0.5785	0.01373	0.02373	72.852	42.147	55
60	1.817	0.5504	0.01224	0.02224	81.670	44.955	60
65	1.909	0.5237	0.01100	0.02100	90.937	47.627	65
70	2.007	0.4983	0.00993	0.01993	100.676	50.169	70
75	2.109	0.4741	0.00902	0.01902	110.913	52.587	75
80	2.217	0.4511	0.00822	0.01822	121.672	54.888	80
85	2.330	0.4292	0.00752	0.01752	132.979	57.078	85
90	2.449	0.4084	0.00690	0.01690	144.863	59.161	90
95	2.574	0.3886	0.00636	0.01636	157.354	61.143	95
100	2.705	0.3697	0.00587	0.01587	170.481	63.029	100

TABLE E–2

1¼% Compound Interest Factors

	Single Payment		Uniform Series				
n	Compound Amount Factor caf'	Present Worth Factor pwf'	Sinking Fund Factor sff	Capital Recovery Factor crf	Compound Amount Factor caf	Present Worth Factor pwf	n
	Given P To find S $(1+i)^n$	Given S To find P $\dfrac{1}{(1+i)^n}$	Given S To find R $\dfrac{i}{(1+i)^n-1}$	Given P To find R $\dfrac{i(1+i)^n}{(1+i)^n-1}$	Given R To find S $\dfrac{(1+i)^n-1}{i}$	Given R To find P $\dfrac{(1+i)^n-1}{i(1+i)^n}$	
1	1.012	0.9877	1.00000	1.01250	1.000	0.988	1
2	1.025	0.9755	0.49689	0.50939	2.012	1.963	2
3	1.038	0.9634	0.32920	0.34170	3.038	2.927	3
4	1.051	0.9515	0.24536	0.25786	4.076	3.878	4
5	1.064	0.9398	0.19506	0.20756	5.127	4.818	5
6	1.077	0.9282	0.16153	0.17403	6.191	5.746	6
7	1.091	0.9167	0.13759	0.15009	7.268	6.663	7
8	1.104	0.9054	0.11963	0.13213	8.359	7.568	8
9	1.118	0.8942	0.10567	0.11817	9.463	8.462	9
10	1.132	0.8832	0.09450	0.10700	10.582	9.346	10
11	1.146	0.8723	0.08537	0.09787	11.714	10.218	11
12	1.161	0.8615	0.07776	0.09026	12.860	11.079	12
13	1.175	0.8509	0.07132	0.08382	14.021	11.930	13
14	1.190	0.8404	0.06581	0.07831	15.196	12.771	14
15	1.205	0.8300	0.06103	0.07353	16.386	13.601	15
16	1.220	0.8197	0.05685	0.06935	17.591	14.420	16
17	1.235	0.8096	0.05316	0.06566	18.811	15.230	17
18	1.251	0.7996	0.04988	0.06238	20.046	16.030	18
19	1.266	0.7898	0.04696	0.05946	21.297	16.819	19
20	1.282	0.7800	0.04432	0.05682	22.563	17.599	20
21	1.298	0.7704	0.04194	0.05444	23.845	18.370	21
22	1.314	0.7609	0.03977	0.05227	25.143	19.131	22
23	1.331	0.7515	0.03780	0.05030	26.457	19.882	23
24	1.347	0.7422	0.03599	0.04849	27.788	20.624	24
25	1.364	0.7330	0.03432	0.04682	29.135	21.357	25
26	1.381	0.7240	0.03279	0.04529	30.500	22.081	26
27	1.399	0.7150	0.03137	0.04387	31.881	22.796	27
28	1.416	0.7062	0.03005	0.04255	33.279	23.503	28
29	1.434	0.6975	0.02882	0.04132	34.695	24.200	29
30	1.452	0.6889	0.02768	0.04018	36.129	24.889	30
31	1.470	0.6804	0.02661	0.03911	37.581	25.569	31
32	1.488	0.6720	0.02561	0.03811	39.050	26.241	32
33	1.507	0.6637	0.02467	0.03717	40.539	26.905	33
34	1.526	0.6555	0.02378	0.03628	42.045	27.560	34
35	1.545	0.6474	0.02295	0.03545	43.571	28.208	35
40	1.644	0.6084	0.01942	0.03192	51.490	31.327	40
45	1.749	0.5718	0.01669	0.02919	59.916	34.258	45
50	1.861	0.5373	0.01452	0.02702	68.882	37.013	50
55	1.980	0.5050	0.01275	0.02525	78.422	39.602	55
60	2.107	0.4746	0.01129	0.02379	88.575	42.035	60
65	2.242	0.4460	0.01006	0.02256	99.377	44.321	65
70	2.386	0.4191	0.00902	0.02152	110.872	46.470	70
75	2.539	0.3939	0.00812	0.02062	123.103	48.489	75
80	2.701	0.3702	0.00735	0.01985	136.119	50.387	80
85	2.875	0.3479	0.00667	0.01917	149.968	52.170	85
90	3.059	0.3269	0.00607	0.01857	164.705	53.846	90
95	3.255	0.3072	0.00554	0.01804	180.386	55.421	95
100	3.463	0.2887	0.00507	0.01757	197.072	56.901	100

TABLE E–3

1½% Compound Interest Factors

	Single Payment		Uniform Series				
n	Compound Amount Factor caf'	Present Worth Factor pwf'	Sinking Fund Factor sff	Capital Recovery Factor crf	Compound Amount Factor caf	Present Worth Factor pwf	n
	Given P To find S $(1+i)^n$	Given S To find P $\dfrac{1}{(1+i)^n}$	Given S To find R $\dfrac{i}{(1+i)^n-1}$	Given P To find R $\dfrac{i(1+i)^n}{(1+i)^n-1}$	Given R To find S $\dfrac{(1+i)^n-1}{i}$	Given R To find P $\dfrac{(1+i)^n-1}{i(1+i)^n}$	
1	1.015	0.9852	1.00000	1.01500	1.000	0.985	1
2	1.030	0.9707	0.49628	0.51128	2.015	1.956	2
3	1.046	0.9563	0.32838	0.34338	3.045	2.912	3
4	1.061	0.9422	0.24444	0.25944	4.091	3.854	4
5	1.077	0.9283	0.19409	0.20909	5.152	4.783	5
6	1.093	0.9145	0.16053	0.17553	6.230	5.697	6
7	1.110	0.9010	0.13656	0.15156	7.323	6.598	7
8	1.126	0.8877	0.11858	0.13358	8.433	7.486	8
9	1.143	0.8746	0.10461	0.11961	9.559	8.361	9
10	1.161	0.8617	0.09343	0.10843	10.703	9.222	10
11	1.178	0.8489	0.08429	0.09929	11.863	10.071	11
12	1.196	0.8364	0.07668	0.09168	13.041	10.908	12
13	1.214	0.8240	0.07024	0.08524	14.237	11.732	13
14	1.232	0.8118	0.06472	0.07972	15.450	12.543	14
15	1.250	0.7999	0.05994	0.07494	16.682	13.343	15
16	1.269	0.7880	0.05577	0.07077	17.932	14.131	16
17	1.288	0.7764	0.05208	0.06708	19.201	14.908	17
18	1.307	0.7649	0.04881	0.06381	20.489	15.673	18
19	1.327	0.7536	0.04588	0.06088	21.797	16.426	19
20	1.347	0.7425	0.04325	0.05825	23.124	17.169	20
21	1.367	0.7315	0.04087	0.05587	24.471	17.900	21
22	1.388	0.7207	0.03870	0.05370	25.838	18.621	22
23	1.408	0.7100	0.03673	0.05173	27.225	19.331	23
24	1.430	0.6995	0.03492	0.04992	28.634	20.030	24
25	1.451	0.6892	0.03326	0.04826	30.063	20.720	25
26	1.473	0.6790	0.03173	0.04673	31.514	21.399	26
27	1.495	0.6690	0.03032	0.04532	32.987	22.068	27
28	1.517	0.6591	0.02900	0.04400	34.481	22.727	28
29	1.540	0.6494	0.02778	0.04278	35.999	23.376	29
30	1.563	0.6398	0.02664	0.04164	37.539	24.016	30
31	1.587	0.6303	0.02557	0.04057	39.102	24.646	31
32	1.610	0.6210	0.02458	0.03958	40.688	25.267	32
33	1.634	0.6118	0.02364	0.03864	42.299	25.879	33
34	1.659	0.6028	0.02276	0.03776	43.933	26.482	34
35	1.684	0.5939	0.02193	0.03693	45.592	27.076	35
40	1.814	0.5513	0.01843	0.03343	54.268	29.916	40
45	1.954	0.5117	0.01572	0.03072	63.614	32.552	45
50	2.105	0.4750	0.01357	0.02857	73.683	35.000	50
55	2.268	0.4409	0.01183	0.02683	84.530	37.271	55
60	2.443	0.4093	0.01039	0.02539	96.215	39.380	60
65	2.632	0.3799	0.00919	0.02419	108.803	41.338	65
70	2.835	0.3527	0.00817	0.02317	122.364	43.155	70
75	3.055	0.3274	0.00730	0.02230	136.973	44.842	75
80	3.291	0.3039	0.00655	0.02155	152.711	46.407	80
85	3.545	0.2821	0.00589	0.02089	169.665	47.861	85
90	3.819	0.2619	0.00532	0.02032	187.930	49.210	90
95	4.114	0.2431	0.00482	0.01982	207.606	50.462	95
100	4.432	0.2256	0.00437	0.01937	228.803	51.625	100

TABLE E–4

1¾% Compound Interest Factors

	Single Payment		Uniform Series				
	Compound Amount Factor caf′	Present Worth Factor pwf′	Sinking Fund Factor sff	Capital Recovery Factor crf	Compound Amount Factor caf	Present Worth Factor pwf	
n	Given P To find S $(1+i)^n$	Given S To find P $\dfrac{1}{(1+i)^n}$	Given S To find R $\dfrac{i}{(1+i)^n-1}$	Given P To find R $\dfrac{i(1+i)^n}{(1+i)^n-1}$	Given R To find S $\dfrac{(1+i)^n-1}{i}$	Given R To find P $\dfrac{(1+i)^n-1}{i(1+i)^n}$	n
1	1.018	0.9828	1.00000	1.01750	1.000	0.983	1
2	1.035	0.9659	0.49566	0.51316	2.018	1.949	2
3	1.053	0.9493	0.32757	0.34507	3.053	2.898	3
4	1.072	0.9330	0.24353	0.26103	4.106	3.831	4
5	1.091	0.9169	0.19312	0.21062	5.178	4.748	5
6	1.110	0.9011	0.15952	0.17702	6.269	5.649	6
7	1.129	0.8856	0.13553	0.15303	7.378	6.535	7
8	1.149	0.8704	0.11754	0.13504	8.508	7.405	8
9	1.169	0.8554	0.10356	0.12106	9.656	8.260	9
10	1.189	0.8407	0.09238	0.10988	10.825	9.101	10
11	1.210	0.8263	0.08323	0.10073	12.015	9.927	11
12	1.231	0.8121	0.07561	0.09311	13.225	10.740	12
13	1.253	0.7981	0.06917	0.08667	14.457	11.538	13
14	1.275	0.7844	0.06366	0.08116	15.710	12.322	14
15	1.297	0.7709	0.05888	0.07638	16.984	13.093	15
16	1.320	0.7576	0.05470	0.07220	18.282	13.850	16
17	1.343	0.7446	0.05102	0.06852	19.602	14.595	17
18	1.367	0.7318	0.04774	0.06524	20.945	15.327	18
19	1.390	0.7192	0.04482	0.06232	22.311	16.046	19
20	1.415	0.7068	0.04219	0.05969	23.702	16.753	20
21	1.440	0.6947	0.03981	0.05731	25.116	17.448	21
22	1.465	0.6827	0.03766	0.05516	26.556	18.130	22
23	1.490	0.6710	0.03569	0.05319	28.021	18.801	23
24	1.516	0.6594	0.03389	0.05139	29.511	19.461	24
25	1.543	0.6481	0.03223	0.04973	31.027	20.109	25
26	1.570	0.6369	0.03070	0.04820	32.570	20.746	26
27	1.597	0.6260	0.02929	0.04679	34.140	21.372	27
28	1.625	0.6152	0.02798	0.04548	35.738	21.987	28
29	1.654	0.6046	0.02676	0.04426	37.363	22.592	29
30	1.683	0.5942	0.02563	0.04313	39.017	23.186	30
31	1.712	0.5840	0.02457	0.04207	40.700	23.770	31
32	1.742	0.5740	0.02358	0.04108	42.412	24.344	32
33	1.773	0.5641	0.02265	0.04015	44.154	24.908	33
34	1.804	0.5544	0.02177	0.03927	45.927	25.462	34
35	1.835	0.5449	0.02095	0.03845	47.731	26.007	35
40	2.002	0.4996	0.01747	0.03497	57.234	28.594	40
45	2.183	0.4581	0.01479	0.03229	67.599	30.966	45
50	2.381	0.4200	0.01267	0.03017	78.902	33.141	50
55	2.597	0.3851	0.01096	0.02846	91.230	35.135	55
60	2.832	0.3531	0.00955	0.02705	104.675	36.964	60
65	3.088	0.3238	0.00838	0.02588	119.339	38.641	65
70	3.368	0.2969	0.00739	0.02489	135.331	40.178	70
75	3.674	0.2722	0.00655	0.02405	152.772	41.587	75
80	4.006	0.2496	0.00582	0.02332	171.794	42.880	80
85	4.369	0.2289	0.00519	0.02269	192.539	44.065	85
90	4.765	0.2098	0.00465	0.02215	215.165	45.152	90
95	5.197	0.1924	0.00417	0.02167	239.840	46.148	95
100	5.668	0.1764	0.00375	0.02125	266.752	47.061	100

TABLE E–5

2% Compound Interest Factors

	Single Payment		Uniform Series				
	Compound Amount Factor caf′	Present Worth Factor pwf′	Sinking Fund Factor sff	Capital Recovery Factor crf	Compound Amount Factor caf	Present Worth Factor pwf	
n	Given P To find S $(1+i)^n$	Given S To find P $\dfrac{1}{(1+i)^n}$	Given S To find R $\dfrac{i}{(1+i)^n-1}$	Given P To find R $\dfrac{i(1+i)^n}{(1+i)^n-1}$	Given R To find S $\dfrac{(1+i)^n-1}{i}$	Given R To find P $\dfrac{(1+i)^n-1}{i(1+i)^n}$	n
1	1.020	0.9804	1.00000	1.02000	1.000	0.980	1
2	1.040	0.9612	0.49505	0.51505	2.020	1.942	2
3	1.061	0.9423	0.32675	0.34675	3.060	2.884	3
4	1.082	0.9238	0.24262	0.26262	4.122	3.808	4
5	1.104	0.9057	0.19216	0.21216	5.204	4.713	5
6	1.126	0.8880	0.15853	0.17853	6.308	5.601	6
7	1.149	0.8706	0.13451	0.15451	7.434	6.472	7
8	1.172	0.8535	0.11651	0.13651	8.583	7.325	8
9	1.195	0.8368	0.10252	0.12252	9.755	8.162	9
10	1.219	0.8203	0.09133	0.11133	10.950	8.983	10
11	1.243	0.8043	0.08218	0.10218	12.169	9.787	11
12	1.268	0.7885	0.07456	0.09456	13.412	10.575	12
13	1.294	0.7730	0.06812	0.08812	14.680	11.348	13
14	1.319	0.7579	0.06260	0.08260	15.974	12.106	14
15	1.346	0.7430	0.05783	0.07783	17.293	12.849	15
16	1.373	0.7284	0.05365	0.07365	18.639	13.578	16
17	1.400	0.7142	0.04997	0.06997	20.012	14.292	17
18	1.428	0.7002	0.04670	0.06670	21.412	14.992	18
19	1.457	0.6864	0.04378	0.06378	22.841	15.678	19
20	1.486	0.6730	0.04116	0.06116	24.297	16.351	20
21	1.516	0.6598	0.03878	0.05878	25.783	17.011	21
22	1.546	0.6468	0.03663	0.05663	27.299	17.658	22
23	1.577	0.6342	0.03467	0.05467	28.845	18.292	23
24	1.608	0.6217	0.03287	0.05287	30.422	18.914	24
25	1.641	0.6095	0.03122	0.05122	32.030	19.523	25
26	1.673	0.5976	0.02970	0.04970	33.671	20.121	26
27	1.707	0.5859	0.02829	0.04829	35.344	20.707	27
28	1.741	0.5744	0.02699	0.04699	37.051	21.281	28
29	1.776	0.5631	0.02578	0.04578	38.792	21.844	29
30	1.811	0.5521	0.02465	0.04465	40.568	22.396	30
31	1.848	0.5412	0.02360	0.04360	42.379	22.938	31
32	1.885	0.5306	0.02261	0.04261	44.227	23.468	32
33	1.922	0.5202	0.02169	0.04169	46.112	23.989	33
34	1.961	0.5100	0.02082	0.04082	48.034	24.499	34
35	2.000	0.5000	0.02000	0.04000	49.994	24.999	35
40	2.208	0.4529	0.01656	0.03656	60.402	27.355	40
45	2.438	0.4102	0.01391	0.03391	71.893	29.490	45
50	2.692	0.3715	0.01182	0.03182	84.579	31.424	50
55	2.972	0.3365	0.01014	0.03014	98.587	33.175	55
60	3.281	0.3048	0.00877	0.02877	114.052	34.761	60
65	3.623	0.2761	0.00763	0.02763	131.126	36.197	65
70	4.000	0.2500	0.00667	0.02667	149.978	37.499	70
75	4.416	0.2265	0.00586	0.02586	170.792	38.677	75
80	4.875	0.2051	0.00516	0.02516	193.772	39.745	80
85	5.383	0.1858	0.00456	0.02456	219.144	40.711	85
90	5.943	0.1683	0.00405	0.02405	247.157	41.587	90
95	6.562	0.1524	0.00360	0.02360	278.085	42.380	95
100	7.245	0.1380	0.00320	0.02320	312.232	43.098	100

TABLE E–6

2½% Compound Interest Factors

	Single Payment		Uniform Series				
n	Compound Amount Factor caf'	Present Worth Factor pwf'	Sinking Fund Factor sff	Capital Recovery Factor crf	Compound Amount Factor caf	Present Worth Factor pwf	n
	Given P To find S $(1+i)^n$	Given S To find P $\dfrac{1}{(1+i)^n}$	Given S To find R $\dfrac{i}{(1+i)^n-1}$	Given P To find R $\dfrac{i(1+i)^n}{(1+i)^n-1}$	Given R To find S $\dfrac{(1+i)^n-1}{i}$	Given R To find P $\dfrac{(1+i)^n-1}{i(1+i)^n}$	
1	1.025	0.9756	1.00000	1.02500	1.000	0.976	1
2	1.051	0.9518	0.49383	0.51883	2.025	1.927	2
3	1.077	0.9286	0.32514	0.35014	3.076	2.856	3
4	1.104	0.9060	0.24082	0.26582	4.153	3.762	4
5	1.131	0.8839	0.19025	0.21525	5.256	4.646	5
6	1.160	0.8623	0.15655	0.18155	6.388	5.508	6
7	1.189	0.8413	0.13250	0.15750	7.547	6.349	7
8	1.218	0.8207	0.11447	0.13947	8.736	7.170	8
9	1.249	0.8007	0.10046	0.12546	9.955	7.971	9
10	1.280	0.7812	0.08926	0.11426	11.203	8.752	10
11	1.312	0.7621	0.08011	0.10511	12.483	9.514	11
12	1.345	0.7436	0.07249	0.09749	13.796	10.258	12
13	1.379	0.7254	0.06605	0.09105	15.140	10.983	13
14	1.413	0.7077	0.06054	0.08554	16.519	11.691	14
15	1.448	0.6905	0.05577	0.08077	17.932	12.381	15
16	1.485	0.6736	0.05160	0.07660	19.380	13.055	16
17	1.522	0.6572	0.04793	0.07293	20.865	13.712	17
18	1.560	0.6412	0.04467	0.06967	22.386	14.353	18
19	1.599	0.6255	0.04176	0.06676	23.946	14.979	19
20	1.639	0.6103	0.03915	0.06415	25.545	15.589	20
21	1.680	0.5954	0.03679	0.06179	27.183	16.185	21
22	1.722	0.5809	0.03465	0.05965	28.863	16.765	22
23	1.765	0.5667	0.03270	0.05770	30.584	17.332	23
24	1.809	0.5529	0.03091	0.05591	32.349	17.885	24
25	1.854	0.5394	0.02928	0.05428	34.158	18.424	25
26	1.900	0.5262	0.02777	0.05277	36.012	18.951	26
27	1.948	0.5134	0.02638	0.05138	37.912	19.464	27
28	1.996	0.5009	0.02509	0.05009	39.860	19.965	28
29	2.046	0.4887	0.02389	0.04889	41.856	20.454	29
30	2.098	0.4767	0.02278	0.04778	43.903	20.930	30
31	2.150	0.4651	0.02174	0.04674	46.000	21.395	31
32	2.204	0.4538	0.02077	0.04577	48.150	21.849	32
33	2.259	0.4427	0.01986	0.04486	50.354	22.292	33
34	2.315	0.4319	0.01901	0.04401	52.613	22.724	34
35	2.373	0.4214	0.01821	0.04321	54.928	23.145	35
40	2.685	0.3724	0.01484	0.03984	67.403	25.103	40
45	3.038	0.3292	0.01227	0.03727	81.516	26.833	45
50	3.437	0.2909	0.01026	0.03526	97.484	28.362	50
55	3.889	0.2572	0.00865	0.03365	115.551	29.714	55
60	4.400	0.2273	0.00735	0.03235	135.992	30.909	60
65	4.978	0.2009	0.00628	0.03128	159.118	31.965	65
70	5.632	0.1776	0.00540	0.03040	185.284	32.898	70
75	6.372	0.1569	0.00465	0.02965	214.888	33.723	75
80	7.210	0.1387	0.00403	0.02903	248.383	34.452	80
85	8.157	0.1226	0.00349	0.02849	286.279	35.096	85
90	9.229	0.1084	0.00304	0.02804	329.154	35.666	90
95	10.442	0.0958	0.00265	0.02765	377.664	36.169	95
100	11.814	0.0846	0.00231	0.02731	432.549	36.614	100

APPENDIX E

TABLE E–7

3% COMPOUND INTEREST FACTORS

	SINGLE PAYMENT		UNIFORM SERIES				
n	Compound Amount Factor caf'	Present Worth Factor pwf'	Sinking Fund Factor sff	Capital Recovery Factor crf	Compound Amount Factor caf	Present Worth Factor pwf	n
	Given P To find S $(1+i)^n$	Given S To find P $\dfrac{1}{(1+i)^n}$	Given S To find R $\dfrac{i}{(1+i)^n-1}$	Given P To find R $\dfrac{i(1+i)^n}{(1+i)^n-1}$	Given R To find S $\dfrac{(1+i)^n-1}{i}$	Given R To find P $\dfrac{(1+i)^n-1}{i(1+i)^n}$	
1	1.030	0.9709	1.00000	1.03000	1.000	0.971	1
2	1.061	0.9426	0.49261	0.52261	2.030	1.913	2
3	1.093	0.9151	0.32353	0.35353	3.091	2.829	3
4	1.126	0.8885	0.23903	0.26903	4.184	3.717	4
5	1.159	0.8626	0.18835	0.21835	5.309	4.580	5
6	1.194	0.8375	0.15460	0.18460	6.468	5.417	6
7	1.230	0.8131	0.13051	0.16051	7.662	6.230	7
8	1.267	0.7894	0.11246	0.14246	8.892	7.020	8
9	1.305	0.7664	0.09843	0.12843	10.159	7.786	9
10	1.344	0.7441	0.08723	0.11723	11.464	8.530	10
11	1.384	0.7224	0.07808	0.10808	12.808	9.253	11
12	1.426	0.7014	0.07046	0.10046	14.192	9.954	12
13	1.469	0.6810	0.06403	0.09403	15.618	10.635	13
14	1.513	0.6611	0.05853	0.08853	17.086	11.296	14
15	1.558	0.6419	0.05377	0.08377	18.599	11.938	15
16	1.605	0.6232	0.04961	0.07961	20.157	12.561	16
17	1.653	0.6050	0.04595	0.07595	21.762	13.166	17
18	1.702	0.5874	0.04271	0.07271	23.414	13.754	18
19	1.754	0.5703	0.03981	0.06981	25.117	14.324	19
20	1.806	0.5537	0.03722	0.06722	26.870	14.877	20
21	1.860	0.5375	0.03487	0.06487	28.676	15.415	21
22	1.916	0.5219	0.03275	0.06275	30.537	15.937	22
23	1.974	0.5067	0.03081	0.06081	32.453	16.444	23
24	2.033	0.4919	0.02905	0.05905	34.426	16.936	24
25	2.094	0.4776	0.02743	0.05743	36.459	17.413	25
26	2.157	0.4637	0.02594	0.05594	38.553	17.877	26
27	2.221	0.4502	0.02456	0.05456	40.710	18.327	27
28	2.288	0.4371	0.02329	0.05329	42.931	18.764	28
29	2.357	0.4243	0.02211	0.05211	45.219	19.188	29
30	2.427	0.4120	0.02102	0.05102	47.575	19.600	30
31	2.500	0.4000	0.02000	0.05000	50.003	20.000	31
32	2.575	0.3883	0.01905	0.04905	52.503	20.389	32
33	2.652	0.3770	0.01816	0.04816	55.078	20.766	33
34	2.732	0.3660	0.01732	0.04732	57.730	21.132	34
35	2.814	0.3554	0.01654	0.04654	60.462	21.487	35
40	3.262	0.3066	0.01326	0.04326	75.401	23.115	40
45	3.782	0.2644	0.01079	0.04079	92.720	24.519	45
50	4.384	0.2281	0.00887	0.03887	112.797	25.730	50
55	5.082	0.1968	0.00735	0.03735	136.072	26.774	55
60	5.892	0.1697	0.00613	0.03613	163.053	27.676	60
65	6.830	0.1464	0.00515	0.03515	194.333	28.453	65
70	7.918	0.1263	0.00434	0.03434	230.594	29.123	70
75	9.179	0.1089	0.00367	0.03367	272.631	29.702	75
80	10.641	0.0940	0.00311	0.03311	321.363	30.201	80
85	12.336	0.0811	0.00265	0.03265	377.857	30.631	85
90	14.300	0.0699	0.00226	0.03226	443.349	31.002	90
95	16.578	0.0603	0.00193	0.03193	519.272	31.323	95
100	19.219	0.0520	0.00165	0.03165	607.288	31.599	100

TABLE E–8

3½% Compound Interest Factors

	SINGLE PAYMENT		UNIFORM SERIES				
	Compound Amount Factor caf'	Present Worth Factor pwf'	Sinking Fund Factor sff	Capital Recovery Factor crf	Compound Amount Factor caf	Present Worth Factor pwf	
n	Given P To find S $(1+i)^n$	Given S To find P $\dfrac{1}{(1+i)^n}$	Given S To find R $\dfrac{i}{(1+i)^n-1}$	Given P To find R $\dfrac{i(1+i)^n}{(1+i)^n-1}$	Given R To find S $\dfrac{(1+i)^n-1}{i}$	Given R To find P $\dfrac{(1+i)^n-1}{i(1+i)^n}$	n
1	1.035	0.9662	1.00000	1.03500	1.000	0.966	1
2	1.071	0.9335	0.49140	0.52640	2.035	1.900	2
3	1.109	0.9019	0.32193	0.35693	3.106	2.802	3
4	1.148	0.8714	0.23725	0.27225	4.215	3.673	4
5	1.188	0.8420	0.18648	0.22148	5.362	4.515	5
6	1.229	0.8135	0.15267	0.18767	6.550	5.329	6
7	1.272	0.7860	0.12854	0.16354	7.779	6.115	7
8	1.317	0.7594	0.11048	0.14548	9.052	6.874	8
9	1.363	0.7337	0.09645	0.13145	10.368	7.608	9
10	1.411	0.7089	0.08524	0.12024	11.731	8.317	10
11	1.460	0.6849	0.07609	0.11109	13.142	9.002	11
12	1.511	0.6618	0.06848	0.10348	14.602	9.663	12
13	1.564	0.6394	0.06206	0.09706	16.113	10.303	13
14	1.619	0.6178	0.05657	0.09157	17.677	10.921	14
15	1.675	0.5969	0.05183	0.08683	19.296	11.517	15
16	1.734	0.5767	0.04768	0.08268	20.971	12.094	16
17	1.795	0.5572	0.04404	0.07904	22.705	12.651	17
18	1.857	0.5384	0.04082	0.07582	24.500	13.190	18
19	1.923	0.5202	0.03794	0.07294	26.357	13.710	19
20	1.990	0.5026	0.03536	0.07036	28.280	14.212	20
21	2.059	0.4856	0.03304	0.06804	30.269	14.698	21
22	2.132	0.4692	0.03093	0.06593	32.329	15.167	22
23	2.206	0.4533	0.02902	0.06402	34.460	15.620	23
24	2.283	0.4380	0.02727	0.06227	36.667	16.058	24
25	2.363	0.4231	0.02567	0.06067	38.950	16.482	25
26	2.446	0.4088	0.02421	0.05921	41.313	16.890	26
27	2.532	0.3950	0.02285	0.05785	43.759	17.285	27
28	2.620	0.3817	0.02160	0.05660	46.291	17.667	28
29	2.712	0.3687	0.02045	0.05545	48.911	18.036	29
30	2.807	0.3563	0.01937	0.05437	51.623	18.392	30
31	2.905	0.3442	0.01837	0.05337	54.429	18.736	31
32	3.007	0.3326	0.01744	0.05244	57.335	19.069	32
33	3.112	0.3213	0.01657	0.05157	60.341	19.390	33
34	3.221	0.3105	0.01576	0.05076	63.453	19.701	34
35	3.334	0.3000	0.01500	0.05000	66.674	20.001	35
40	3.959	0.2526	0.01183	0.04683	84.550	21.355	40
45	4.702	0.2127	0.00945	0.04445	105.782	22.495	45
50	5.585	0.1791	0.00763	0.04263	130.998	23.456	50
55	6.633	0.1508	0.00621	0.04121	160.947	24.264	55
60	7.878	0.1269	0.00509	0.04009	196.517	24.945	60
65	9.357	0.1069	0.00419	0.03919	238.763	25.518	65
70	11.113	0.0900	0.00346	0.03846	288.938	26.000	70
75	13.199	0.0758	0.00287	0.03787	348.530	26.407	75
80	15.676	0.0638	0.00238	0.03738	419.307	26.749	80
85	18.618	0.0537	0.00199	0.03699	503.367	27.037	85
90	22.112	0.0452	0.00166	0.03666	603.205	27.279	90
95	26.262	0.0381	0.00139	0.03639	721.781	27.484	95
100	31.191	0.0321	0.00116	0.03616	862.612	27.655	100

APPENDIX E

TABLE E–9

4% Compound Interest Factors

n	Single Payment		Uniform Series				n
	Compound Amount Factor caf'	Present Worth Factor pwf'	Sinking Fund Factor sff	Capital Recovery Factor crf	Compound Amount Factor caf	Present Worth Factor pwf	
	Given P To find S $(1+i)^n$	Given S To find P $\dfrac{1}{(1+i)^n}$	Given S To find R $\dfrac{i}{(1+i)^n-1}$	Given P To find R $\dfrac{i(1+i)^n}{(1+i)^n-1}$	Given R To find S $\dfrac{(1+i)^n-1}{i}$	Given R To find P $\dfrac{(1+i)^n-1}{i(1+i)^n}$	
1	1.040	0.9615	1.00000	1.04000	1.000	0.962	1
2	1.082	0.9246	0.49020	0.53020	2.040	1.886	2
3	1.125	0.8890	0.32035	0.36035	3.122	2.775	3
4	1.170	0.8548	0.23549	0.27549	4.246	3.630	4
5	1.217	0.8219	0.18463	0.22463	5.416	4.452	5
6	1.265	0.7903	0.15076	0.19076	6.633	5.242	6
7	1.316	0.7599	0.12661	0.16661	7.898	6.002	7
8	1.369	0.7307	0.10853	0.14853	9.214	6.733	8
9	1.423	0.7026	0.09449	0.13449	10.583	7.435	9
10	1.480	0.6756	0.08329	0.12329	12.006	8.111	10
11	1.539	0.6496	0.07415	0.11415	13.486	8.760	11
12	1.601	0.6246	0.06655	0.10655	15.026	9.385	12
13	1.665	0.6006	0.06014	0.10014	16.627	9.986	13
14	1.732	0.5775	0.05467	0.09467	18.292	10.563	14
15	1.801	0.5553	0.04994	0.08994	20.024	11.118	15
16	1.873	0.5339	0.04582	0.08582	21.825	11.652	16
17	1.948	0.5134	0.04220	0.08220	23.698	12.166	17
18	2.026	0.4936	0.03899	0.07899	25.645	12.659	18
19	2.107	0.4746	0.03614	0.07614	27.671	13.134	19
20	2.191	0.4564	0.03358	0.07358	29.778	13.590	20
21	2.279	0.4388	0.03128	0.07128	31.969	14.029	21
22	2.370	0.4220	0.02920	0.06920	34.248	14.451	22
23	2.465	0.4057	0.02731	0.06731	36.618	14.857	23
24	2.563	0.3901	0.02559	0.06559	39.083	15.247	24
25	2.666	0.3751	0.02401	0.06401	41.646	15.622	25
26	2.772	0.3607	0.02257	0.06257	44.312	15.983	26
27	2.883	0.3468	0.02124	0.06124	47.084	16.330	27
28	2.999	0.3335	0.02001	0.06001	49.968	16.663	28
29	3.119	0.3207	0.01888	0.05888	52.966	16.984	29
30	3.243	0.3083	0.01783	0.05783	56.085	17.292	30
31	3.373	0.2965	0.01686	0.05686	59.328	17.588	31
32	3.508	0.2851	0.01595	0.05595	62.701	17.874	32
33	3.648	0.2741	0.01510	0.05510	66.210	18.148	33
34	3.794	0.2636	0.01431	0.05431	69.858	18.411	34
35	3.946	0.2534	0.01358	0.05358	73.652	18.665	35
40	4.801	0.2083	0.01052	0.05052	95.026	19.793	40
45	5.841	0.1712	0.00826	0.04826	121.029	20.720	45
50	7.107	0.1407	0.00655	0.04655	152.667	21.482	50
55	8.646	0.1157	0.00523	0.04523	191.159	22.109	55
60	10.520	0.0951	0.00420	0.04420	237.991	22.623	60
65	12.799	0.0781	0.00339	0.04339	294.968	23.047	65
70	15.572	0.0642	0.00275	0.04275	364.290	23.395	70
75	18.945	0.0528	0.00223	0.04223	448.631	23.680	75
80	23.050	0.0434	0.00181	0.04181	551.245	23.915	80
85	28.044	0.0357	0.00148	0.04148	676.090	24.109	85
90	34.119	0.0293	0.00121	0.04121	827.983	24.267	90
95	41.511	0.0241	0.00099	0.04099	1012.785	24.398	95
100	50.505	0.0198	0.00081	0.04081	1237.624	24.505	100

TABLE E–10

4½% Compound Interest Factors

	Single Payment		Uniform Series				
n	Compound Amount Factor caf'	Present Worth Factor pwf'	Sinking Fund Factor sff	Capital Recovery Factor crf	Compound Amount Factor caf	Present Worth Factor pwf	n
	Given P To find S $(1+i)^n$	Given S To find P $\dfrac{1}{(1+i)^n}$	Given S To find R $\dfrac{i}{(1+i)^n-1}$	Given P To find R $\dfrac{i(1+i)^n}{(1+i)^n-1}$	Given R To find S $\dfrac{(1+i)^n-1}{i}$	Given R To find P $\dfrac{(1+i)^n-1}{i(1+i)^n}$	
1	1.045	0.9569	1.00000	1.04500	1.000	0.957	1
2	1.092	0.9157	0.48900	0.53400	2.045	1.873	2
3	1.141	0.8763	0.31877	0.36377	3.137	2.749	3
4	1.193	0.8386	0.23374	0.27874	4.278	3.588	4
5	1.246	0.8025	0.18279	0.22779	5.471	4.390	5
6	1.302	0.7679	0.14888	0.19388	6.717	5.158	6
7	1.361	0.7348	0.12470	0.16970	8.019	5.893	7
8	1.422	0.7032	0.10661	0.15161	9.380	6.596	8
9	1.486	0.6729	0.09257	0.13757	10.802	7.269	9
10	1.553	0.6439	0.08138	0.12638	12.288	7.913	10
11	1.623	0.6162	0.07225	0.11725	13.841	8.529	11
12	1.696	0.5897	0.06467	0.10967	15.464	9.119	12
13	1.772	0.5643	0.05828	0.10328	17.160	9.683	13
14	1.852	0.5400	0.05282	0.09782	18.932	10.223	14
15	1.935	0.5167	0.04811	0.09311	20.784	10.740	15
16	2.022	0.4945	0.04402	0.08902	22.719	11.234	16
17	2.113	0.4732	0.04042	0.08542	24.742	11.707	17
18	2.208	0.4528	0.03724	0.08224	26.855	12.160	18
19	2.308	0.4333	0.03441	0.07941	29.064	12.593	19
20	2.412	0.4146	0.03188	0.07688	31.371	13.008	20
21	2.520	0.3968	0.02960	0.07460	33.783	13.405	21
22	2.634	0.3797	0.02755	0.07255	36.303	13.784	22
23	2.752	0.3634	0.02568	0.07068	38.937	14.148	23
24	2.876	0.3477	0.02399	0.06899	41.689	14.495	24
25	3.005	0.3327	0.02244	0.06744	44.565	14.828	25
26	3.141	0.3184	0.02102	0.06602	47.571	15.147	26
27	3.282	0.3047	0.01972	0.06472	50.711	15.451	27
28	3.430	0.2916	0.01852	0.06352	53.993	15.743	28
29	3.584	0.2790	0.01741	0.06241	57.423	16.022	29
30	3.745	0.2670	0.01639	0.06139	61.007	16.289	30
31	3.914	0.2555	0.01544	0.06044	64.752	16.544	31
32	4.090	0.2445	0.01456	0.05956	68.666	16.789	32
33	4.274	0.2340	0.01374	0.05874	72.756	17.023	33
34	4.466	0.2239	0.01298	0.05798	77.030	17.247	34
35	4.667	0.2143	0.01227	0.05727	81.497	17.461	35
40	5.816	0.1719	0.00934	0.05434	107.030	18.402	40
45	7.248	0.1380	0.00720	0.05220	138.850	19.156	45
50	9.033	0.1107	0.00560	0.05060	178.503	19.762	50
55	11.256	0.0888	0.00439	0.04939	227.918	20.248	55
60	14.027	0.0713	0.00345	0.04845	289.498	20.638	60
65	17.481	0.0572	0.00273	0.04773	366.238	20.951	65
70	21.784	0.0459	0.00217	0.04717	461.870	21.202	70
75	27.147	0.0368	0.00172	0.04672	581.044	21.404	75
80	33.830	0.0296	0.00137	0.04637	729.558	21.565	80
85	42.158	0.0237	0.00109	0.04609	914.632	21.695	85
90	52.537	0.0190	0.00087	0.04587	1145.269	21.799	90
95	65.471	0.0153	0.00070	0.04570	1432.684	21.883	95
100	81.589	0.0123	0.00056	0.04556	1790.856	21.950	100

TABLE E–11

5% COMPOUND INTEREST FACTORS

	SINGLE PAYMENT		UNIFORM SERIES				
n	Compound Amount Factor caf'	Present Worth Factor pwf'	Sinking Fund Factor sff	Capital Recovery Factor crf	Compound Amount Factor caf	Present Worth Factor pwf	*n*
	Given P To find S $(1+i)^n$	Given S To find P $\dfrac{1}{(1+i)^n}$	Given S To find R $\dfrac{i}{(1+i)^n-1}$	Given P To find R $\dfrac{i(1+i)^n}{(1+i)^n-1}$	Given R To find S $\dfrac{(1+i)^n-1}{i}$	Given R To find P $\dfrac{(1+i)^n-1}{i(1+i)^n}$	
1	1.050	0.9524	1.00000	1.05000	1.000	0.952	1
2	1.103	0.9070	0.48780	0.53780	2.050	1.859	2
3	1.158	0.8638	0.31721	0.36721	3.153	2.723	3
4	1.216	0.8227	0.23201	0.28201	4.310	3.546	4
5	1.276	0.7835	0.18097	0.23097	5.526	4.329	5
6	1.340	0.7462	0.14702	0.19702	6.802	5.076	6
7	1.407	0.7107	0.12282	0.17282	8.142	5.786	7
8	1.477	0.6768	0.10472	0.15472	9.549	6.463	8
9	1.551	0.6446	0.09069	0.14069	11.027	7.108	9
10	1.629	0.6139	0.07950	0.12950	12.578	7.722	10
11	1.710	0.5847	0.07039	0.12039	14.207	8.306	11
12	1.796	0.5568	0.06283	0.11283	15.917	8.863	12
13	1.886	0.5303	0.05646	0.10646	17.713	9.394	13
14	1.980	0.5051	0.05102	0.10102	19.599	9.899	14
15	2.079	0.4810	0.04634	0.09634	21.579	10.380	15
16	2.183	0.4581	0.04227	0.09227	23.657	10.838	16
17	2.292	0.4363	0.03870	0.08870	25.840	11.274	17
18	2.407	0.4155	0.03555	0.08555	28.132	11.690	18
19	2.527	0.3957	0.03275	0.08275	30.539	12.085	19
20	2.653	0.3769	0.03024	0.08024	33.066	12.462	20
21	2.786	0.3589	0.02800	0.07800	35.719	12.821	21
22	2.925	0.3418	0.02597	0.07597	38.505	13.163	22
23	3.072	0.3256	0.02414	0.07414	41.430	13.489	23
24	3.225	0.3101	0.02247	0.07247	44.502	13.799	24
25	3.386	0.2953	0.02095	0.07095	47.727	14.094	25
26	3.556	0.2812	0.01956	0.06956	51.113	14.375	26
27	3.733	0.2678	0.01829	0.06829	54.669	14.643	27
28	3.920	0.2551	0.01712	0.06712	58.403	14.898	28
29	4.116	0.2429	0.01605	0.06605	62.323	15.141	29
30	4.322	0.2314	0.01505	0.06505	66.439	15.372	30
31	4.538	0.2204	0.01413	0.06413	70.761	15.593	31
32	4.765	0.2099	0.01328	0.06328	75.299	15.803	32
33	5.003	0.1999	0.01249	0.06249	80.064	16.003	33
34	5.253	0.1904	0.01176	0.06176	85.067	16.193	34
35	5.516	0.1813	0.01107	0.06107	90.320	16.374	35
40	7.040	0.1420	0.00828	0.05828	120.800	17.159	40
45	8.985	0.1113	0.00626	0.05626	159.700	17.774	45
50	11.467	0.0872	0.00478	0.05478	209.348	18.256	50
55	14.636	0.0683	0.00367	0.05367	272.713	18.633	55
60	18.679	0.0535	0.00283	0.05283	353.584	18.929	60
65	23.840	0.0419	0.00219	0.05219	456.798	19.161	65
70	30.426	0.0329	0.00170	0.05170	588.529	19.343	70
75	38.833	0.0258	0.00132	0.05132	756.654	19.485	75
80	49.561	0.0202	0.00103	0.05103	971.229	19.596	80
85	63.254	0.0158	0.00080	0.05080	1245.087	19.684	85
90	80.730	0.0124	0.00063	0.05063	1594.607	19.752	90
95	103.035	0.0097	0.00049	0.05049	2040.694	19.806	95
100	131.501	0.0076	0.00038	0.05038	2610.025	19.848	100

TABLE E–12

5½% Compound Interest Factors

| n | SINGLE PAYMENT | | UNIFORM SERIES | | | | n |
| | Compound Amount Factor caf' | Present Worth Factor pwf' | Sinking Fund Factor sff | Capital Recovery Factor crf | Compound Amount Factor caf | Present Worth Factor pwf | |
	Given P To find S $(1+i)^n$	Given S To find P $\dfrac{1}{(1+i)^n}$	Given S To find R $\dfrac{i}{(1+i)^n-1}$	Given P To find R $\dfrac{i(1+i)^n}{(1+i)^n-1}$	Given R To find S $\dfrac{(1+i)^n-1}{i}$	Given R To find P $\dfrac{(1+i)^n-1}{i(1+i)^n}$	
1	1.055	0.9479	1.00000	1.05500	1.000	0.948	1
2	1.113	0.8985	0.48662	0.54162	2.055	1.846	2
3	1.174	0.8516	0.31565	0.37065	3.168	2.698	3
4	1.239	0.8072	0.23029	0.28529	4.342	3.505	4
5	1.307	0.7651	0.17918	0.23418	5.581	4.270	5
6	1.379	0.7252	0.14518	0.20018	6.888	4.996	6
7	1.455	0.6874	0.12096	0.17596	8.267	5.683	7
8	1.535	0.6516	0.10286	0.15786	9.722	6.335	8
9	1.619	0.6176	0.08884	0.14384	11.256	6.952	9
10	1.708	0.5854	0.07767	0.13267	12.875	7.538	10
11	1.802	0.5549	0.06857	0.12357	14.583	8.093	11
12	1.901	0.5260	0.06103	0.11603	16.386	8.619	12
13	2.006	0.4986	0.05468	0.10968	18.287	9.117	13
14	2.116	0.4726	0.04928	0.10428	20.293	9.590	14
15	2.232	0.4479	0.04463	0.09963	22.409	10.038	15
16	2.355	0.4246	0.04058	0.09558	24.641	10.462	16
17	2.485	0.4024	0.03704	0.09204	26.996	10.865	17
18	2.621	0.3815	0.03392	0.08892	29.481	11.246	18
19	2.766	0.3616	0.03115	0.08615	32.103	11.608	19
20	2.918	0.3427	0.02868	0.08368	34.868	11.950	20
21	3.078	0.3249	0.02646	0.08146	37.786	12.275	21
22	3.248	0.3079	0.02447	0.07947	40.864	12.583	22
23	3.426	0.2919	0.02267	0.07767	44.112	12.875	23
24	3.615	0.2767	0.02104	0.07604	47.538	13.152	24
25	3.813	0.2622	0.01955	0.07455	51.153	13.414	25
26	4.023	0.2486	0.01819	0.07319	54.966	13.662	26
27	4.244	0.2356	0.01695	0.07195	58.989	13.898	27
28	4.478	0.2233	0.01581	0.07081	63.234	14.121	28
29	4.724	0.2117	0.01477	0.06977	67.711	14.333	29
30	4.984	0.2006	0.01381	0.06881	72.435	14.534	30
31	5.258	0.1902	0.01292	0.06792	77.419	14.724	31
32	5.547	0.1803	0.01210	0.06710	82.677	14.904	32
33	5.852	0.1709	0.01133	0.06633	88.225	15.075	33
34	6.174	0.1620	0.01063	0.06563	94.077	15.237	34
35	6.514	0.1535	0.00997	0.06497	100.251	15.391	35
40	8.513	0.1175	0.00732	0.06232	136.606	16.046	40
45	11.127	0.0899	0.00543	0.06043	184.119	16.548	45
50	14.542	0.0688	0.00406	0.05906	246.217	16.932	50
55	19.006	0.0526	0.00305	0.05805	327.377	17.225	55
60	24.840	0.0403	0.00231	0.05731	433.450	17.450	60
65	32.465	0.0308	0.00175	0.05675	572.083	17.622	65
70	42.430	0.0236	0.00133	0.05633	753.271	17.753	70
75	55.454	0.0180	0.00101	0.05601	990.076	17.854	75
80	72.476	0.0138	0.00077	0.05577	1299.571	17.931	80
85	94.724	0.0106	0.00059	0.05559	1704.069	17.990	85
90	123.800	0.0081	0.00045	0.05545	2232.731	18.035	90
95	161.802	0.0062	0.00034	0.05534	2923.671	18.069	95
100	211.469	0.0047	0.00026	0.05526	3826.702	18.096	100

TABLE E–13

6% Compound Interest Factors

	Single Payment		Uniform Series				
	Compound Amount Factor caf'	Present Worth Factor pwf'	Sinking Fund Factor sff	Capital Recovery Factor crf	Compound Amount Factor caf	Present Worth Factor pwf	
n	Given P To find S $(1+i)^n$	Given S To find P $\dfrac{1}{(1+i)^n}$	Given S To find R $\dfrac{i}{(1+i)^n-1}$	Given P To find R $\dfrac{i(1+i)^n}{(1+i)^n-1}$	Given R To find S $\dfrac{(1+i)^n-1}{i}$	Given R To find P $\dfrac{(1+i)^n-1}{i(1+i)^n}$	n
1	1.060	0.9434	1.00000	1.06000	1.000	0.943	1
2	1.124	0.8900	0.48544	0.54544	2.060	1.833	2
3	1.191	0.8396	0.31411	0.37411	3.184	2.673	3
4	1.262	0.7921	0.22859	0.28859	4.375	3.465	4
5	1.338	0.7473	0.17740	0.23740	5.637	4.212	5
6	1.419	0.7050	0.14336	0.20336	6.975	4.917	6
7	1.504	0.6651	0.11914	0.17914	8.394	5.582	7
8	1.594	0.6274	0.10104	0.16104	9.897	6.210	8
9	1.689	0.5919	0.08702	0.14702	11.491	6.802	9
10	1.791	0.5584	0.07587	0.13587	13.181	7.360	10
11	1.898	0.5268	0.06679	0.12679	14.972	7.887	11
12	2.012	0.4970	0.05928	0.11928	16.870	8.384	12
13	2.133	0.4688	0.05296	0.11296	18.882	8.853	13
14	2.261	0.4423	0.04758	0.10758	21.015	9.295	14
15	2.397	0.4173	0.04296	0.10296	23.276	9.712	15
16	2.540	0.3936	0.03895	0.09895	25.673	10.106	16
17	2.693	0.3714	0.03544	0.09544	28.213	10.477	17
18	2.854	0.3503	0.03236	0.09236	30.906	10.828	18
19	3.026	0.3305	0.02962	0.08962	33.760	11.158	19
20	3.207	0.3118	0.02718	0.08718	36.786	11.470	20
21	3.400	0.2942	0.02500	0.08500	39.993	11.764	21
22	3.604	0.2775	0.02305	0.08305	43.392	12.042	22
23	3.820	0.2618	0.02128	0.08128	46.996	12.303	23
24	4.049	0.2470	0.01968	0.07968	50.816	12.550	24
25	4.292	0.2330	0.01823	0.07823	54.865	12.783	25
26	4.549	0.2198	0.01690	0.07690	59.156	13.003	26
27	4.822	0.2074	0.01570	0.07570	63.706	13.211	27
28	5.112	0.1956	0.01459	0.07459	68.528	13.406	28
29	5.418	0.1846	0.01358	0.07358	73.640	13.591	29
30	5.743	0.1741	0.01265	0.07265	79.058	13.765	30
31	6.088	0.1643	0.01179	0.07179	84.802	13.929	31
32	6.453	0.1550	0.01100	0.07100	90.890	14.084	32
33	6.841	0.1462	0.01027	0.07027	97.343	14.230	33
34	7.251	0.1379	0.00960	0.06960	104.184	14.368	34
35	7.686	0.1301	0.00897	0.06897	111.435	14.498	35
40	10.286	0.0972	0.00646	0.06646	154.762	15.046	40
45	13.765	0.0727	0.00470	0.06470	212.744	15.456	45
50	18.420	0.0543	0.00344	0.06344	290.336	15.762	50
55	24.650	0.0406	0.00254	0.06254	394.172	15.991	55
60	32.988	0.0303	0.00188	0.06188	533.128	16.161	60
65	44.145	0.0227	0.00139	0.06139	719.083	16.289	65
70	59.076	0.0169	0.00103	0.06103	967.932	16.385	70
75	79.057	0.0126	0.00077	0.06077	1300.949	16.456	75
80	105.796	0.0095	0.00057	0.06057	1746.600	16.509	80
85	141.579	0.0071	0.00043	0.06043	2342.982	16.549	85
90	189.465	0.0053	0.00032	0.06032	3141.075	16.579	90
95	253.546	0.0039	0.00024	0.06024	4209.104	16.601	95
100	339.302	0.0029	0.00018	0.06018	5638.368	16.618	100

TABLE E–14

7% Compound Interest Factors

n	SINGLE PAYMENT		UNIFORM SERIES				n
	Compound Amount Factor caf'	Present Worth Factor pwf'	Sinking Fund Factor sff	Capital Recovery Factor crf	Compound Amount Factor caf	Present Worth Factor pwf	
	Given P To find S $(1+i)^n$	Given S To find P $\dfrac{1}{(1+i)^n}$	Given S To find R $\dfrac{i}{(1+i)^n-1}$	Given P To find R $\dfrac{i(1+i)^n}{(1+i)^n-1}$	Given R To find S $\dfrac{(1+i)^n-1}{i}$	Given R To find P $\dfrac{(1+i)^n-1}{i(1+i)^n}$	
1	1.070	0.9346	1.00000	1.07000	1.000	0.935	1
2	1.145	0.8734	0.48309	0.55309	2.070	1.808	2
3	1.225	0.8163	0.31105	0.38105	3.215	2.624	3
4	1.311	0.7629	0.22523	0.29523	4.440	3.387	4
5	1.403	0.7130	0.17389	0.24389	5.751	4.100	5
6	1.501	0.6663	0.13980	0.20980	7.153	4.767	6
7	1.606	0.6227	0.11555	0.18555	8.654	5.389	7
8	1.718	0.5820	0.09747	0.16747	10.260	5.971	8
9	1.838	0.5439	0.08349	0.15349	11.978	6.515	9
10	1.967	0.5083	0.07238	0.14238	13.816	7.024	10
11	2.105	0.4751	0.06336	0.13336	15.784	7.499	11
12	2.252	0.4440	0.05590	0.12590	17.888	7.943	12
13	2.410	0.4150	0.04965	0.11965	20.141	8.358	13
14	2.579	0.3878	0.04434	0.11434	22.550	8.745	14
15	2.759	0.3624	0.03979	0.10979	25.129	9.108	15
16	2.952	0.3387	0.03586	0.10586	27.888	9.447	16
17	3.159	0.3166	0.03243	0.10243	30.840	9.763	17
18	3.380	0.2959	0.02941	0.09941	33.999	10.059	18
19	3.617	0.2765	0.02675	0.09675	37.379	10.336	19
20	3.870	0.2584	0.02439	0.09439	40.995	10.594	20
21	4.141	0.2415	0.02229	0.09229	44.865	10.836	21
22	4.430	0.2257	0.02041	0.09041	49.006	11.061	22
23	4.741	0.2109	0.01871	0.08871	53.436	11.272	23
24	5.072	0.1971	0.01719	0.08719	58.177	11.469	24
25	5.427	0.1842	0.01581	0.08581	63.249	11.654	25
26	5.807	0.1722	0.01456	0.08456	68.676	11.826	26
27	6.214	0.1609	0.01343	0.08343	74.484	11.987	27
28	6.649	0.1504	0.01239	0.08239	80.698	12.137	28
29	7.114	0.1406	0.01145	0.08145	87.347	12.278	29
30	7.612	0.1314	0.01059	0.08059	94.461	12.409	30
31	8.145	0.1228	0.00980	0.07980	102.073	12.532	31
32	8.715	0.1147	0.00907	0.07907	110.218	12.647	32
33	9.325	0.1072	0.00841	0.07841	118.933	12.754	33
34	9.978	0.1002	0.00780	0.07780	128.259	12.854	34
35	10.677	0.0937	0.00723	0.07723	138.237	12.948	35
40	14.974	0.0668	0.00501	0.07501	199.635	13.332	40
45	21.002	0.0476	0.00350	0.07350	285.749	13.606	45
50	29.457	0.0339	0.00246	0.07246	406.529	13.801	50
55	41.315	0.0242	0.00174	0.07174	575.929	13.940	55
60	57.946	0.0173	0.00123	0.07123	813.520	14.039	60
65	81.273	0.0123	0.00087	0.07087	1146.755	14.110	65
70	113.989	0.0088	0.00062	0.07062	1614.134	14.160	70
75	159.876	0.0063	0.00044	0.07044	2269.657	14.196	75
80	224.234	0.0045	0.00031	0.07031	3189.063	14.222	80
85	314.500	0.0032	0.00022	0.07022	4478.576	14.240	85
90	441.103	0.0023	0.00016	0.07016	6287.185	14.253	90
95	618.670	0.0016	0.00011	0.07011	8823.854	14.263	95
100	867.716	0.0012	0.00008	0.07008	12381.662	14.269	100

TABLE E-15

8% Compound Interest Factors

	Single Payment		Uniform Series				
	Compound Amount Factor caf'	Present Worth Factor pwf'	Sinking Fund Factor sff	Capital Recovery Factor crf	Compound Amount Factor caf	Present Worth Factor pwf	
n	Given P To find S $(1+i)^n$	Given S To find P $\dfrac{1}{(1+i)^n}$	Given S To find R $\dfrac{i}{(1+i)^n - 1}$	Given P To find R $\dfrac{i(1+i)^n}{(1+i)^n - 1}$	Given R To find S $\dfrac{(1+i)^n - 1}{i}$	Given R To find P $\dfrac{(1+i)^n - 1}{i(1+i)^n}$	n
1	1.080	0.9259	1.00000	1.08000	1.000	0.926	1
2	1.166	0.8573	0.48077	0.56077	2.080	1.783	2
3	1.260	0.7938	0.30803	0.38803	3.246	2.577	3
4	1.360	0.7350	0.22192	0.30192	4.506	3.312	4
5	1.469	0.6806	0.17046	0.25046	5.867	3.993	5
6	1.587	0.6302	0.13632	0.21632	7.336	4.623	6
7	1.714	0.5835	0.11207	0.19207	8.923	5.206	7
8	1.851	0.5403	0.09401	0.17401	10.637	5.747	8
9	1.999	0.5002	0.08008	0.16008	12.488	6.247	9
10	2.159	0.4632	0.06903	0.14903	14.487	6.710	10
11	2.332	0.4289	0.06008	0.14008	16.645	7.139	11
12	2.518	0.3971	0.05270	0.13270	18.977	7.536	12
13	2.720	0.3677	0.04652	0.12652	21.495	7.904	13
14	2.937	0.3405	0.04130	0.12130	24.215	8.244	14
15	3.172	0.3152	0.03683	0.11683	27.152	8.559	15
16	3.426	0.2919	0.03298	0.11298	30.324	8.851	16
17	3.700	0.2703	0.02963	0.10963	33.750	9.122	17
18	3.996	0.2502	0.02670	0.10670	37.450	9.372	18
19	4.316	0.2317	0.02413	0.10413	41.446	9.604	19
20	4.661	0.2145	0.02185	0.10185	45.762	9.818	20
21	5.034	0.1987	0.01983	0.09983	50.423	10.017	21
22	5.437	0.1839	0.01803	0.09803	55.457	10.201	22
23	5.871	0.1703	0.01642	0.09642	60.893	10.371	23
24	6.341	0.1577	0.01498	0.09498	66.765	10.529	24
25	6.848	0.1460	0.01368	0.09368	73.106	10.675	25
26	7.396	0.1352	0.01251	0.09251	79.954	10.810	26
27	7.988	0.1252	0.01145	0.09145	87.351	10.935	27
28	8.627	0.1159	0.01049	0.09049	95.339	11.051	28
29	9.317	0.1073	0.00962	0.08962	103.966	11.158	29
30	10.063	0.0994	0.00883	0.08883	113.283	11.258	30
31	10.868	0.0920	0.00811	0.08811	123.346	11.350	31
32	11.737	0.0852	0.00745	0.08745	134.214	11.435	32
33	12.676	0.0789	0.00685	0.08685	145.951	11.514	33
34	13.690	0.0730	0.00630	0.08630	158.627	11.587	34
35	14.785	0.0676	0.00580	0.08580	172.317	11.655	35
40	21.725	0.0460	0.00386	0.08386	259.057	11.925	40
45	31.920	0.0313	0.00259	0.08259	386.506	12.108	45
50	46.902	0.0213	0.00174	0.08174	573.770	12.233	50
55	68.914	0.0145	0.00118	0.08118	848.923	12.319	55
60	101.257	0.0099	0.00080	0.08080	1253.213	12.377	60
65	148.780	0.0067	0.00054	0.08054	1847.248	12.416	65
70	218.606	0.0046	0.00037	0.08037	2720.080	12.443	70
75	321.205	0.0031	0.00025	0.08025	4002.557	12.461	75
80	471.955	0.0021	0.00017	0.08017	5886.935	12.474	80
85	693.456	0.0014	0.00012	0.08012	8655.706	12.482	85
90	1018.915	0.0010	0.00008	0.08008	12723.939	12.488	90
95	1497.121	0.0007	0.00005	0.08005	18701.507	12.492	95
100	2199.761	0.0005	0.00004	0.08004	27484.516	12.494	100

TABLE E–16

10% COMPOUND INTEREST FACTORS

	SINGLE PAYMENT		UNIFORM SERIES				
n	Compound Amount Factor caf'	Present Worth Factor pwf'	Sinking Fund Factor sff	Capital Recovery Factor crf	Compound Amount Factor caf	Present Worth Factor pwf	n
	Given P To find S $(1+i)^n$	Given S To find P $\dfrac{1}{(1+i)^n}$	Given S To find R $\dfrac{i}{(1+i)^n-1}$	Given P To find R $\dfrac{i(1+i)^n}{(1+i)^n-1}$	Given R To find S $\dfrac{(1+i)^n-1}{i}$	Given R To find P $\dfrac{(1+i)^n-1}{i(1+i)^n}$	
1	1.100	0.9091	1.00000	1.10000	1.000	0.909	1
2	1.210	0.8264	0.47619	0.57619	2.100	1.736	2
3	1.331	0.7513	0.30211	0.40211	3.310	2.487	3
4	1.464	0.6830	0.21547	0.31547	4.641	3.170	4
5	1.611	0.6209	0.16380	0.26380	6.105	3.791	5
6	1.772	0.5645	0.12961	0.22961	7.716	4.355	6
7	1.949	0.5132	0.10541	0.20541	9.487	4.868	7
8	2.144	0.4665	0.08744	0.18744	11.436	5.335	8
9	2.358	0.4241	0.07364	0.17364	13.579	5.759	9
10	2.594	0.3855	0.06275	0.16275	15.937	6.144	10
11	2.853	0.3505	0.05396	0.15396	18.531	6.495	11
12	3.138	0.3186	0.04676	0.14676	21.384	6.814	12
13	3.452	0.2897	0.04078	0.14078	24.523	7.103	13
14	3.797	0.2633	0.03575	0.13575	27.975	7.367	14
15	4.177	0.2394	0.03147	0.13147	31.772	7.606	15
16	4.595	0.2176	0.02782	0.12782	35.950	7.824	16
17	5.054	0.1978	0.02466	0.12466	40.545	8.022	17
18	5.560	0.1799	0.02193	0.12193	45.599	8.201	18
19	6.116	0.1635	0.01955	0.11955	51.159	8.365	19
20	6.727	0.1486	0.01746	0.11746	57.275	8.514	20
21	7.400	0.1351	0.01562	0.11562	64.002	8.649	21
22	8.140	0.1228	0.01401	0.11401	71.403	8.772	22
23	8.954	0.1117	0.01257	0.11257	79.543	8.883	23
24	9.850	0.1015	0.01130	0.11130	88.497	8.985	24
25	10.835	0.0923	0.01017	0.11017	98.347	9.077	25
26	11.918	0.0839	0.00916	0.10916	109.182	9.161	26
27	13.110	0.0763	0.00826	0.10826	121.100	9.237	27
28	14.421	0.0693	0.00745	0.10745	134.210	9.307	28
29	15.863	0.0630	0.00673	0.10673	148.631	9.370	29
30	17.449	0.0573	0.00608	0.10608	164.494	9.427	30
31	19.194	0.0521	0.00550	0.10550	181.943	9.479	31
32	21.114	0.0474	0.00497	0.10497	201.138	9.526	32
33	23.225	0.0431	0.00450	0.10450	222.252	9.569	33
34	25.548	0.0391	0.00407	0.10407	245.477	9.609	34
35	28.102	0.0356	0.00369	0.10369	271.024	9.644	35
40	45.259	0.0221	0.00226	0.10226	442.593	9.779	40
45	72.890	0.0137	0.00139	0.10139	718.905	9.863	45
50	117.391	0.0085	0.00086	0.10086	1163.909	9.915	50
55	189.059	0.0053	0.00053	0.10053	1880.591	9.947	55
60	304.482	0.0033	0.00033	0.10033	3034.816	9.967	60
65	490.371	0.0020	0.00020	0.10020	4893.707	9.980	65
70	789.747	0.0013	0.00013	0.10013	7887.470	9.987	70
75	1271.895	0.0008	0.00008	0.10008	12708.954	9.992	75
80	2048.400	0.0005	0.00005	0.10005	20474.002	9.995	80
85	3298.969	0.0003	0.00003	0.10003	32979.690	9.997	85
90	5313.023	0.0002	0.00002	0.10002	53120.226	9.998	90
95	8556.676	0.0001	0.00001	0.10001	85556.760	9.999	95
100	13780.612	0.0001	0.00001	0.10001	137796.123	9.999	100

TABLE E–17

12% COMPOUND INTEREST FACTORS

n	SINGLE PAYMENT		UNIFORM SERIES				n
	Compound Amount Factor caf'	Present Worth Factor pwf'	Sinking Fund Factor sff	Capital Recovery Factor crf	Compound Amount Factor caf	Present Worth Factor pwf	
	Given P To find S $(1+i)^n$	Given S To find P $\dfrac{1}{(1+i)^n}$	Given S To find R $\dfrac{i}{(1+i)^n-1}$	Given P To find R $\dfrac{i(1+i)^n}{(1+i)^n-1}$	Given R To find S $\dfrac{(1+i)^n-1}{i}$	Given R To find P $\dfrac{(1+i)^n-1}{i(1+i)^n}$	
1	1.120	0.8929	1.00000	1.12000	1.000	0.893	1
2	1.254	0.7972	0.47170	0.59170	2.120	1.690	2
3	1.405	0.7118	0.29635	0.41635	3.374	2.402	3
4	1.574	0.6355	0.20923	0.32923	4.779	3.037	4
5	1.762	0.5674	0.15741	0.27741	6.353	3.605	5
6	1.974	0.5066	0.12323	0.24323	8.115	4.111	6
7	2.211	0.4523	0.09912	0.21912	10.089	4.564	7
8	2.476	0.4039	0.08130	0.20130	12.300	4.968	8
9	2.773	0.3606	0.06768	0.18768	14.776	5.328	9
10	3.106	0.3220	0.05698	0.17698	17.549	5.650	10
11	3.479	0.2875	0.04842	0.16842	20.655	5.938	11
12	3.896	0.2567	0.04144	0.16144	24.133	6.194	12
13	4.363	0.2292	0.03568	0.15568	28.029	6.424	13
14	4.887	0.2046	0.03087	0.15087	32.393	6.628	14
15	5.474	0.1827	0.02682	0.14682	37.280	6.811	15
16	6.130	0.1631	0.02339	0.14339	42.753	6.974	16
17	6.866	0.1456	0.02046	0.14046	48.884	7.120	17
18	7.690	0.1300	0.01794	0.13794	55.750	7.250	18
19	8.613	0.1161	0.01576	0.13576	63.440	7.366	19
20	9.646	0.1037	0.01388	0.13388	72.052	7.469	20
21	10.804	0.0926	0.01224	0.13224	81.699	7.562	21
22	12.100	0.0826	0.01081	0.13081	92.502	7.645	22
23	13.552	0.0738	0.00956	0.12956	104.603	7.718	23
24	15.179	0.0659	0.00846	0.12846	118.155	7.784	24
25	17.000	0.0588	0.00750	0.12750	133.334	7.843	25
26	19.040	0.0525	0.00665	0.12665	150.334	7.896	26
27	21.325	0.0469	0.00590	0.12590	169.374	7.943	27
28	23.884	0.0419	0.00524	0.12524	190.699	7.984	28
29	26.750	0.0374	0.00466	0.12466	214.582	8.022	29
30	29.960	0.0334	0.00414	0.12414	241.332	8.055	30
31	33.555	0.0298	0.00369	0.12369	271.292	8.085	31
32	37.582	0.0266	0.00328	0.12328	304.847	8.112	32
33	42.091	0.0238	0.00292	0.12292	342.429	8.135	33
34	47.142	0.0212	0.00260	0.12260	384.520	8.157	34
35	52.799	0.0189	0.00232	0.12232	431.663	8.176	35
40	93.051	0.0107	0.00130	0.12130	767.088	8.244	40
45	163.987	0.0061	0.00074	0.12074	1358.224	8.283	45
50	289.001	0.0035	0.00042	0.12042	2400.008	8.305	50
∞				0.12000		8.333	∞

TABLE E-18

15% Compound Interest Factors

	Single Payment		Uniform Series				
n	Compound Amount Factor caf'	Present Worth Factor pwf'	Sinking Fund Factor sff	Capital Recovery Factor crf	Compound Amount Factor caf	Present Worth Factor pwf	*n*
	Given P To find S $(1+i)^n$	Given S To find P $\dfrac{1}{(1+i)^n}$	Given S To find R $\dfrac{i}{(1+i)^n-1}$	Given P To find R $\dfrac{i(1+i)^n}{(1+i)^n-1}$	Given R To find S $\dfrac{(1+i)^n-1}{i}$	Given R To find P $\dfrac{(1+i)^n-1}{i(1+i)^n}$	
1	1.150	0.8696	1.00000	1.15000	1.000	0.870	1
2	1.322	0.7561	0.46512	0.61512	2.150	1.626	2
3	1.521	0.6575	0.28798	0.43798	3.472	2.283	3
4	1.749	0.5718	0.20026	0.35027	4.993	2.855	4
5	2.011	0.4972	0.14832	0.29832	6.742	3.352	5
6	2.313	0.4323	0.11424	0.26424	8.754	3.784	6
7	2.660	0.3759	0.09036	0.24036	11.067	4.160	7
8	3.059	0.3269	0.07285	0.22285	13.727	4.487	8
9	3.518	0.2843	0.05957	0.20957	16.786	4.772	9
10	4.046	0.2472	0.04925	0.19925	20.304	5.019	10
11	4.652	0.2149	0.04107	0.19107	24.349	5.234	11
12	5.350	0.1869	0.03448	0.18448	29.002	5.421	12
13	6.153	0.1625	0.02911	0.17911	34.352	5.583	13
14	7.076	0.1413	0.02469	0.17469	40.505	5.724	14
15	8.137	0.1229	0.02102	0.17102	47.580	5.847	15
16	9.358	0.1069	0.01795	0.16795	55.717	5.954	16
17	10.761	0.0929	0.01537	0.16537	65.075	6.047	17
18	12.375	0.0808	0.01319	0.16319	75.836	6.128	18
19	14.232	0.0703	0.01134	0.16134	88.212	6.198	19
20	16.367	0.0611	0.00976	0.15976	102.443	6.259	20
21	18.821	0.0531	0.00842	0.15842	118.810	6.312	21
22	21.645	0.0462	0.00727	0.15727	137.631	6.359	22
23	24.891	0.0402	0.00628	0.15628	159.276	6.399	23
24	28.625	0.0349	0.00543	0.15543	184.167	6.434	24
25	32.919	0.0304	0.00470	0.15470	212.793	6.464	25
26	37.857	0.0264	0.00407	0.15407	245.711	6.491	26
27	43.535	0.0230	0.00353	0.15353	283.568	6.514	27
28	50.065	0.0200	0.00306	0.15306	327.103	6.534	28
29	57.575	0.0174	0.00265	0.15265	377.169	6.551	29
30	66.212	0.0151	0.00230	0.15230	434.744	6.566	30
31	76.143	0.0131	0.00200	0.15200	500.956	6.579	31
32	87.565	0.0114	0.00173	0.15173	577.099	6.591	32
33	100.700	0.0099	0.00150	0.15150	664.664	6.600	33
34	115.805	0.0086	0.00131	0.15131	765.364	6.609	34
35	133.175	0.0075	0.00113	0.15113	881.168	6.617	35
40	267.862	0.0037	0.00056	0.15056	1779.1	6.642	40
45	538.767	0.0019	0.00028	0.15028	3585.1	6.654	45
50	1083.652	0.0009	0.00014	0.15014	7217.7	6.661	50
∞				0.15000		6.667	∞

TABLE E–19

20% COMPOUND INTEREST FACTORS

	SINGLE PAYMENT		UNIFORM SERIES				
	Compound Amount Factor caf'	Present Worth Factor pwf'	Sinking Fund Factor sff	Capital Recovery Factor crf	Compound Amount Factor caf	Present Worth Factor pwf	
n	Given P To find S $(1+i)^n$	Given S To find P $\dfrac{1}{(1+i)^n}$	Given S To find R $\dfrac{i}{(1+i)^n-1}$	Given P To find R $\dfrac{i(1+i)^n}{(1+i)^n-1}$	Given R To find S $\dfrac{(1+i)^n-1}{i}$	Given R To find P $\dfrac{(1+i)^n-1}{i(1+i)^n}$	n
1	1.200	0.8333	1.00000	1.20000	1.000	0.833	1
2	1.440	0.6944	0.45455	0.65455	2.200	1.528	2
3	1.728	0.5787	0.27473	0.47473	3.640	2.106	3
4	2.074	0.4823	0.18629	0.38629	5.368	2.589	4
5	2.488	0.4019	0.13438	0.33438	7.442	2.991	5
6	2.986	0.3349	0.10071	0.30071	9.930	3.326	6
7	3.583	0.2791	0.07742	0.27742	12.916	3.605	7
8	4.300	0.2326	0.06061	0.26061	16.499	3.837	8
9	5.160	0.1938	0.04808	0.24808	20.799	4.031	9
10	6.192	0.1615	0.03852	0.23852	25.959	4.192	10
11	7.430	0.1346	0.03110	0.23110	32.150	4.327	11
12	8.916	0.1122	0.02526	0.22526	39.580	4.439	12
13	10.699	0.0935	0.02062	0.22062	48.497	4.533	13
14	12.839	0.0779	0.01689	0.21689	59.196	4.611	14
15	15.407	0.0649	0.01388	0.21388	72.035	4.675	15
16	18.488	0.0541	0.01144	0.21144	87.442	4.730	16
17	22.186	0.0451	0.00944	0.20944	105.931	4.775	17
18	26.623	0.0376	0.00781	0.20781	128.117	4.812	18
19	31.948	0.0313	0.00646	0.20646	154.740	4.844	19
20	38.338	0.0261	0.00536	0.20536	186.688	4.870	20
21	46.005	0.0217	0.00444	0.20444	225.025	4.891	21
22	55.206	0.0181	0.00369	0.20369	271.031	4.909	22
23	66.247	0.0151	0.00307	0.20307	326.237	4.925	23
24	79.497	0.0126	0.00255	0.20255	392.484	4.937	24
25	95.396	0.0105	0.00212	0.20212	471.981	4.948	25
26	114.475	0.0087	0.00176	0.20176	567.377	4.956	26
27	137.370	0.0073	0.00147	0.20147	681.852	4.964	27
28	164.845	0.0061	0.00122	0.20122	819.223	4.970	28
29	197.813	0.0051	0.00102	0.20102	984.067	4.975	29
30	237.376	0.0042	0.00085	0.20085	1181.881	4.979	30
31	284.851	0.0035	0.00070	0.20070	1419.257	4.982	31
32	341.822	0.0029	0.00059	0.20059	1704.108	4.985	32
33	410.186	0.0024	0.00049	0.20049	2045.930	4.988	33
34	492.223	0.0020	0.00041	0.20041	2456.116	4.990	34
35	590.668	0.0017	0.00034	0.20034	2948.339	4.992	35
40	1469.771	0.0007	0.00014	0.20014	7343.9	4.997	40
45	3657.258	0.0003	0.00005	0.20005	18281.3	4.999	45
50	9100.427	0.0001	0.00002	0.20002	45497.1	4.999	50
∞				0.20000		5.000	∞

TABLE E–20

CAPITAL RECOVERY FACTORS FOR INTEREST RATES FROM 25% TO 50%

n	25%	30%	35%	40%	45%	50%	n
1	1.25000	1.30000	1.35000	1.40000	1.45000	1.50000	1
2	0.69444	0.73478	0.77553	0.81667	0.85816	0.90000	2
3	0.51230	0.55063	0.58966	0.62936	0.66966	0.71053	3
4	0.42344	0.46163	0.50076	0.54077	0.58156	0.62308	4
5	0.37185	0.41058	0.45046	0.49136	0.53318	0.57583	5
6	0.33882	0.37839	0.41926	0.46126	0.50426	0.54812	6
7	0.31634	0.35687	0.39880	0.44192	0.48607	0.53108	7
8	0.30040	0.34192	0.38489	0.42907	0.47427	0.52030	8
9	0.28876	0.33124	0.37519	0.42034	0.46646	0.51335	9
10	0.28007	0.32346	0.36832	0.41432	0.46123	0.50882	10
11	0.27349	0.31773	0.36339	0.41013	0.45768	0.50585	11
12	0.26845	0.31345	0.35982	0.40718	0.45527	0.50388	12
13	0.26454	0.31024	0.35722	0.40510	0.45362	0.50258	13
14	0.26150	0.30782	0.35532	0.40363	0.45249	0.50172	14
15	0.25912	0.30598	0.35393	0.40259	0.45172	0.50114	15
16	0.25724	0.30458	0.35290	0.40185	0.45118	0.50076	16
17	0.25576	0.30351	0.35214	0.40132	0.45081	0.50051	17
18	0.25459	0.30269	0.35158	0.40094	0.45056	0.50034	18
19	0.25366	0.30207	0.35117	0.40067	0.45039	0.50023	19
20	0.25292	0.30159	0.35087	0.40048	0.45027	0.50015	20
21	0.25233	0.30122	0.35064	0.40034	0.45018	0.50010	21
22	0.25186	0.30094	0.35048	0.40024	0.45013	0.50007	22
23	0.25148	0.30072	0.35035	0.40017	0.45009	0.50004	23
24	0.25119	0.30055	0.35026	0.40012	0.45006	0.50003	24
25	0.25095	0.30043	0.35019	0.40009	0.45004	0.50002	25
26	0.25076	0.30033	0.35014	0.40006	0.45003	0.50001	26
27	0.25061	0.30025	0.35011	0.40005	0.45002	0.50001	27
28	0.25048	0.30019	0.35008	0.40003	0.45001	0.50001	28
29	0.25039	0.30015	0.35006	0.40002	0.45001	0.50000	29
30	0.25031	0.30011	0.35004	0.40002	0.45001	0.50000	30
31	0.25025	0.30009	0.35003	0.40001	0.45000	0.50000	31
32	0.25020	0.30007	0.35002	0.40001	0.45000	0.50000	32
33	0.25016	0.30005	0.35002	0.40001	0.45000	0.50000	33
34	0.25013	0.30004	0.35001	0.40000	0.45000	0.50000	34
35	0.25010	0.30003	0.35001	0.40000	0.45000	0.50000	35
∞	0.25000	0.30000	0.35000	0.40000	0.45000	0.50000	∞

TABLE E–21

SINGLE PAYMENT PRESENT WORTH FACTORS FOR INTEREST RATES FROM
25% TO 50%

n	25%	30%	35%	40%	45%	50%	n
1	0.8000	0.7692	0.7407	0.7143	0.6897	0.6667	1
2	0.6400	0.5917	0.5487	0.5102	0.4756	0.4444	2
3	0.5120	0.4552	0.4064	0.3644	0.3280	0.2963	3
4	0.4096	0.3501	0.3011	0.2603	0.2262	0.1975	4
5	0.3277	0.2693	0.2230	0.1859	0.1560	0.1317	5
6	0.2621	0.2072	0.1652	0.1328	0.1076	0.0878	6
7	0.2097	0.1594	0.1224	0.0949	0.0742	0.0585	7
8	0.1678	0.1226	0.0906	0.0678	0.0512	0.0390	8
9	0.1342	0.0943	0.0671	0.0484	0.0353	0.0260	9
10	0.1074	0.0725	0.0497	0.0346	0.0243	0.0173	10
11	0.0859	0.0558	0.0368	0.0247	0.0168	0.0116	11
12	0.0687	0.0429	0.0273	0.0176	0.0116	0.0077	12
13	0.0550	0.0330	0.0202	0.0126	0.0080	0.0051	13
14	0.0440	0.0254	0.0150	0.0090	0.0055	0.0034	14
15	0.0352	0.0195	0.0111	0.0064	0.0038	0.0023	15
16	0.0281	0.0150	0.0082	0.0046	0.0026	0.0015	16
17	0.0225	0.0116	0.0061	0.0033	0.0018	0.0010	17
18	0.0180	0.0089	0.0045	0.0023	0.0012	0.0007	18
19	0.0144	0.0068	0.0033	0.0017	0.0009	0.0005	19
20	0.0115	0.0053	0.0025	0.0012	0.0006	0.0003	20
21	0.0092	0.0040	0.0018	0.0009	0.0004	0.0002	21
22	0.0074	0.0031	0.0014	0.0006	0.0003	0.0001	22
23	0.0059	0.0024	0.0010	0.0004	0.0002	0.0001	23
24	0.0047	0.0018	0.0007	0.0003	0.0001	0.0001	24
25	0.0038	0.0014	0.0006	0.0002	0.0001	. . . . .	25
26	0.0030	0.0011	0.0004	0.0002	0.0001	. . . . .	26
27	0.0024	0.0008	0.0003	0.0001	. . . . .	. . . . .	27
28	0.0019	0.0006	0.0002	0.0001	. . . . .	. . . . .	28
29	0.0015	0.0005	0.0002	0.0001	. . . . .	. . . . .	29
30	0.0012	0.0004	0.0001	. . . . .	. . . . .	. . . . .	30
31	0.0010	0.0003	0.0001	. . . . .	. . . . .	. . . . .	31
32	0.0008	0.0002	0.0001	. . . . .	. . . . .	. . . . .	32
33	0.0006	0.0002	0.0001	. . . . .	. . . . .	. . . . .	33
34	0.0005	0.0001	. . . . .	. . . . .	. . . . .	. . . . .	34
35	0.0004	0.0001	. . . . .	. . . . .	. . . . .	. . . . .	35

TABLE E–22

SERIES PRESENT WORTH FACTORS FOR INTEREST RATES FROM 25% TO 50%

n	25%	30%	35%	40%	45%	50%	n
1	0.800	0.769	0.741	0.714	0.690	0.667	1
2	1.440	1.361	1.289	1.224	1.165	1.111	2
3	1.952	1.816	1.696	1.589	1.493	1.407	3
4	2.362	2.166	1.997	1.849	1.720	1.605	4
5	2.689	2.436	2.220	2.035	1.876	1.737	5
6	2.951	2.643	2.385	2.168	1.983	1.824	6
7	3.161	2.802	2.507	2.263	2.057	1.883	7
8	3.329	2.925	2.598	2.331	2.109	1.922	8
9	3.463	3.019	2.665	2.379	2.144	1.948	9
10	3.571	3.092	2.715	2.414	2.168	1.965	10
11	3.656	3.147	2.752	2.438	2.185	1.977	11
12	3.725	3.190	2.779	2.456	2.196	1.985	12
13	3.780	3.223	2.799	2.469	2.204	1.990	13
14	3.824	3.249	2.814	2.478	2.210	1.993	14
15	3.859	3.268	2.825	2.484	2.214	1.995	15
16	3.887	3.283	2.834	2.489	2.216	1.997	16
17	3.910	3.295	2.840	2.492	2.218	1.998	17
18	3.928	3.304	2.844	2.494	2.219	1.999	18
19	3.942	3.311	2.848	2.496	2.220	1.999	19
20	3.954	3.316	2.850	2.497	2.221	1.999	20
21	3.963	3.320	2.852	2.498	2.221	2.000	21
22	3.970	3.323	2.853	2.498	2.222	2.000	22
23	3.976	3.325	2.854	2.499	2.222	2.000	23
24	3.981	3.327	2.855	2.499	2.222	2.000	24
25	3.985	3.329	2.856	2.499	2.222	2.000	25
26	3.988	3.330	2.856	2.500	2.222	2.000	26
27	3.990	3.331	2.856	2.500	2.222	2.000	27
28	3.992	3.331	2.857	2.500	2.222	2.000	28
29	3.994	3.332	2.857	2.500	2.222	2.000	29
30	3.995	3.332	2.857	2.500	2.222	2.000	30
31	3.996	3.332	2.857	2.500	2.222	2.000	31
32	3.997	3.333	2.857	2.500	2.222	2.000	32
33	3.997	3.333	2.857	2.500	2.222	2.000	33
34	3.998	3.333	2.857	2.500	2.222	2.000	34
35	3.998	3.333	2.857	2.500	2.222	2.000	35
∞	4.000	3.333	2.857	2.500	2.222	2.000	∞

TABLE E–23

Factors To Convert a Gradient Series to an Equivalent Uniform Annual Series

This table contains multipliers for a gradient g to convert the n-year end-of-year series $0, g, 2g, \ldots (n-1)g$ to an equivalent uniform annual series for n years.

n	1%	2%	3%	4%	5%	6%	7%	8%	10%	n
2	0.50	0.50	0.49	0.49	0.49	0.49	0.48	0.48	0.48	2
3	0.99	0.99	0.98	0.97	0.97	0.96	0.95	0.95	0.94	3
4	1.49	1.48	1.46	1.45	1.44	1.43	1.42	1.40	1.38	4
5	1.98	1.96	1.94	1.92	1.90	1.88	1.86	1.85	1.81	5
6	2.47	2.44	2.41	2.39	2.36	2.33	2.30	2.28	2.22	6
7	2.96	2.92	2.88	2.84	2.81	2.77	2.73	2.69	2.62	7
8	3.45	3.40	3.34	3.29	3.24	3.20	3.15	3.10	3.00	8
9	3.93	3.87	3.80	3.74	3.68	3.61	3.55	3.49	3.37	9
10	4.42	4.34	4.26	4.18	4.10	4.02	3.95	3.87	3.73	10
11	4.90	4.80	4.70	4.61	4.51	4.42	4.33	4.24	4.06	11
12	5.38	5.26	5.15	5.03	4.92	4.81	4.70	4.60	4.39	12
13	5.86	5.72	5.59	5.45	5.32	5.19	5.06	4.94	4.70	13
14	6.34	6.18	6.02	5.87	5.71	5.56	5.42	5.27	5.00	14
15	6.81	6.63	6.45	6.27	6.10	5.93	5.76	5.59	5.28	15
16	7.29	7.08	6.87	6.67	6.47	6.28	6.09	5.90	5.55	16
17	7.76	7.52	7.29	7.07	6.84	6.62	6.41	6.20	5.81	17
18	8.23	7.97	7.71	7.45	7.20	6.96	6.72	6.49	6.05	18
19	8.70	8.41	8.12	7.83	7.56	7.29	7.02	6.77	6.29	19
20	9.17	8.84	8.52	8.21	7.90	7.61	7.32	7.04	6.51	20
21	9.63	9.28	8.92	8.58	8.24	7.92	7.60	7.29	6.72	21
22	10.10	9.70	9.32	8.94	8.57	8.22	7.87	7.54	6.92	22
23	10.56	10.13	9.71	9.30	8.90	8.51	8.14	7.78	7.11	23
24	11.02	10.55	10.10	9.65	9.21	8.80	8.39	8.01	7.29	24
25	11.48	10.97	10.48	9.99	9.52	9.07	8.64	8.23	7.46	25
26	11.94	11.39	10.85	10.33	9.83	9.34	8.88	8.44	7.62	26
27	12.39	11.80	11.23	10.66	10.12	9.60	9.11	8.64	7.77	27
28	12.85	12.21	11.59	10.99	10.41	9.86	9.33	8.83	7.91	28
29	13.30	12.62	11.96	11.31	10.69	10.10	9.54	9.01	8.05	29
30	13.75	13.02	12.31	11.63	10.97	10.34	9.75	9.19	8.18	30
31	14.20	13.42	12.67	11.94	11.24	10.57	9.95	9.36	8.30	31
32	14.65	13.82	13.02	12.24	11.50	10.80	10.14	9.52	8.41	32
33	15.10	14.22	13.36	12.54	11.76	11.02	10.32	9.67	8.52	33
34	15.54	14.61	13.70	12.83	12.01	11.23	10.50	9.82	8.61	34
35	15.98	15.00	14.04	13.12	12.25	11.43	10.67	9.96	8.71	35
40	18.18	16.89	15.65	14.48	13.38	12.36	11.42	10.57	9.10	40
45	20.33	18.70	17.16	15.70	14.36	13.14	12.04	11.04	9.37	45
50	22.44	20.44	18.56	16.81	15.22	13.80	12.53	11.41	9.57	50
60	26.53	23.70	21.07	18.70	16.61	14.79	13.23	11.90	9.80	60
70	30.47	26.66	23.21	20.20	17.62	15.46	13.67	12.18	9.91	70
80	34.25	29.36	25.04	21.37	18.35	15.90	13.93	12.33	9.96	80
90	37.87	31.79	26.57	22.28	18.87	16.19	14.08	12.41	9.98	90
100	41.34	33.99	27.84	22.98	19.23	16.37	14.17	12.45	9.99	100

TABLE E–23—*Continued*

FACTORS TO CONVERT A GRADIENT SERIES TO AN EQUIVALENT UNIFORM ANNUAL SERIES

This table contains multipliers for a gradient g to convert the n-year end-of-year series $0, g, 2g, \ldots (n-1)g$ to an equivalent uniform annual series for n years.

n	12%	15%	20%	25%	30%	35%	40%	45%	50%	n
2	0.47	0.47	0.45	0.44	0.43	0.43	0.42	0.41	0.40	2
3	0.92	0.91	0.88	0.85	0.83	0.80	0.78	0.76	0.74	3
4	1.36	1.33	1.27	1.22	1.18	1.13	1.09	1.05	1.02	4
5	1.77	1.72	1.64	1.56	1.49	1.42	1.36	1.30	1.24	5
6	2.17	2.10	1.98	1.87	1.77	1.67	1.58	1.50	1.42	6
7	2.55	2.45	2.29	2.14	2.01	1.88	1.77	1.66	1.56	7
8	2.91	2.78	2.58	2.39	2.22	2.06	1.92	1.79	1.68	8
9	3.26	3.09	2.84	2.60	2.40	2.21	2.04	1.89	1.76	9
10	3.58	3.38	3.07	2.80	2.55	2.33	2.14	1.97	1.82	10
11	3.90	3.65	3.29	2.97	2.68	2.44	2.22	2.03	1.87	11
12	4.19	3.91	3.48	3.11	2.80	2.52	2.28	2.08	1.91	12
13	4.47	4.14	3.66	3.24	2.89	2.59	2.33	2.12	1.93	13
14	4.73	4.36	3.82	3.36	2.97	2.64	2.37	2.14	1.95	14
15	4.98	4.56	3.96	3.45	3.03	2.69	2.40	2.17	1.97	15
16	5.21	4.75	4.09	3.54	3.09	2.72	2.43	2.18	1.98	16
17	5.44	4.93	4.20	3.61	3.13	2.75	2.44	2.19	1.98	17
18	5.64	5.08	4.30	3.67	3.17	2.78	2.46	2.20	1.99	18
19	5.84	5.23	4.39	3.72	3.20	2.79	2.47	2.21	1.99	19
20	6.02	5.37	4.46	3.77	3.23	2.81	2.48	2.21	1.99	20
21	6.19	5.49	4.53	3.80	3.25	2.82	2.48	2.21	2.00	21
22	6.35	5.60	4.59	3.84	3.26	2.83	2.49	2.22	2.00	22
23	6.50	5.70	4.65	3.86	3.28	2.83	2.49	2.22	2.00	23
24	6.64	5.80	4.69	3.89	3.29	2.84	2.49	2.22	2.00	24
25	6.77	5.88	4.74	3.91	3.30	2.84	2.49	2.22	2.00	25
26	6.89	5.96	4.77	3.92	3.30	2.85	2.50	2.22	2.00	26
27	7.00	6.03	4.80	3.94	3.31	2.85	2.50	2.22	2.00	27
28	7.11	6.10	4.83	3.95	3.32	2.85	2.50	2.22	2.00	28
29	7.21	6.15	4.85	3.96	3.32	2.85	2.50	2.22	2.00	29
30	7.30	6.21	4.87	3.96	3.32	2.85	2.50	2.22	2.00	30
31	7.38	6.25	4.89	3.97	3.32	2.85	2.50	2.22	2.00	31
32	7.46	6.30	4.91	3.97	3.33	2.85	2.50	2.22	2.00	32
33	7.53	6.34	4.92	3.98	3.33	2.86	2.50	2.22	2.00	33
34	7.60	6.37	4.93	3.98	3.33	2.86	2.50	2.22	2.00	34
35	7.66	6.40	4.94	3.99	3.33	2.86	2.50	2.22	2.00	35
40	7.90	6.52	4.97	4.00	3.33	2.86	2.50	2.22	2.00	40
45	8.06	6.58	4.99	4.00	3.33	2.86	2.50	2.22	2.00	45
50	8.16	6.62	4.99	4.00	3.33	2.86	2.50	2.22	2.00	50
60	8.27	6.65	5.00	4.00	3.33	2.86	2.50	2.22	2.00	60
70	8.31	6.66	5.00	4.00	3.33	2.86	2.50	2.22	2.00	70
80	8.32	6.67	5.00	4.00	3.33	2.86	2.50	2.22	2.00	80
90	8.33	6.67	5.00	4.00	3.33	2.86	2.50	2.22	2.00	90
100	8.33	6.67	5.00	4.00	3.33	2.86	2.50	2.22	2.00	100

TABLE E–24

FACTORS TO COMPUTE THE PRESENT WORTH OF A GRADIENT SERIES
—INTEREST RATES FROM 3% TO 20%

This table contains multipliers for a gradient g to find the present worth of the n-year end-of-year series $0, g, 2g, \ldots (n-1)g$.

n	3%	4%	5%	6%	7%	8%	10%	12%	15%	20%	n
2	0.94	0.92	0.91	0.89	0.87	0.86	0.83	0.80	0.76	0.69	2
3	2.77	2.70	2.63	2.57	2.51	2.45	2.33	2.22	2.07	1.85	3
4	5.44	5.27	5.10	4.95	4.79	4.65	4.38	4.13	3.79	3.30	4
5	8.89	8.55	8.24	7.93	7.65	7.37	6.86	6.40	5.78	4.91	5
6	13.08	12.51	11.97	11.46	10.98	10.52	9.68	8.93	7.94	6.58	6
7	17.95	17.06	16.23	15.45	14.71	14.02	12.76	11.64	10.19	8.26	7
8	23.48	22.18	20.97	19.84	18.79	17.81	16.03	14.47	12.48	9.88	8
9	29.61	27.80	26.13	24.58	23.14	21.81	19.42	17.36	14.75	11.43	9
10	36.31	33.88	31.65	29.60	27.72	25.98	22.89	20.25	16.98	12.89	10
11	43.53	40.38	37.50	34.87	32.47	30.27	26.40	23.13	19.13	14.23	11
12	51.25	47.25	43.62	40.34	37.35	34.63	29.90	25.95	21.18	15.47	12
13	59.42	54.45	49.99	45.96	42.33	39.05	33.38	28.70	23.14	16.59	13
14	68.01	61.96	56.55	51.71	47.37	43.47	36.80	31.36	24.97	17.60	14
15	77.00	69.73	63.29	57.55	52.45	47.89	40.15	33.92	26.69	18.51	15
16	86.34	77.74	70.16	63.46	57.53	52.26	43.42	36.37	28.30	19.32	16
17	96.02	85.96	77.14	69.40	62.59	56.59	46.58	38.70	29.78	20.04	17
18	106.01	94.35	84.20	75.36	67.62	60.84	49.64	40.91	31.16	20.68	18
19	116.27	102.89	91.33	81.31	72.60	65.01	52.58	43.00	32.42	21.24	19
20	126.79	111.56	98.49	87.23	77.51	69.09	55.41	44.97	33.58	21.74	20
21	137.54	120.34	105.67	93.11	82.34	73.06	58.11	46.82	34.64	22.17	21
22	148.51	129.20	112.85	98.94	87.08	76.93	60.69	48.55	35.62	22.55	22
23	159.65	138.13	120.01	104.70	91.72	80.67	63.15	50.18	36.50	22.89	23
24	170.97	147.10	127.14	110.38	96.25	84.30	65.48	51.69	37.30	23.18	24
25	182.43	156.10	134.23	115.97	100.68	87.80	67.70	53.11	38.03	23.43	25
26	194.02	165.12	141.26	121.47	104.98	91.18	69.79	54.42	38.69	23.65	26
27	205.73	174.14	148.22	126.86	109.17	94.44	71.78	55.64	39.29	23.84	27
28	217.53	183.14	155.11	132.14	113.23	97.57	73.65	56.77	39.83	24.00	28
29	229.41	192.12	161.91	137.31	117.16	100.57	75.41	57.81	40.31	24.14	29
30	241.36	201.06	168.62	142.36	120.97	103.46	77.08	58.78	40.75	24.26	30
31	253.35	209.95	175.23	147.29	124.66	106.22	78.64	59.68	41.15	24.37	31
32	265.40	218.79	181.74	152.09	128.21	108.86	80.11	60.50	41.50	24.46	32
33	277.46	227.56	188.13	156.77	131.64	111.38	81.49	61.26	41.82	24.54	33
34	289.54	236.26	194.42	161.32	134.95	113.79	82.78	61.96	42.10	24.60	34
35	301.62	244.88	200.58	165.74	138.13	116.09	83.99	62.61	42.36	24.66	35

TABLE E–25

PRESENT WORTH AT ZERO DATE OF $1 FLOWING UNIFORMLY THROUGHOUT STATED
ONE-YEAR PERIODS, ASSUMING CONTINUOUS COMPOUNDING OF INTEREST AT VARIOUS
STATED EFFECTIVE RATES PER ANNUM

Period	1%	2%	3%	4%	5%	6%	7%	8%	10%
0 to 1	0.9950	0.9902	0.9854	0.9806	0.9760	0.9714	0.9669	0.9625	0.9538
1 to 2	0.9852	0.9707	0.9567	0.9429	0.9295	0.9164	0.9037	0.8912	0.8671
2 to 3	0.9754	0.9517	0.9288	0.9067	0.8853	0.8646	0.8445	0.8252	0.7883
3 to 4	0.9658	0.9331	0.9017	0.8718	0.8431	0.8156	0.7893	0.7641	0.7166
4 to 5	0.9562	0.9148	0.8755	0.8383	0.8030	0.7695	0.7377	0.7075	0.6515
5 to 6	0.9467	0.8968	0.8500	0.8060	0.7647	0.7259	0.6894	0.6551	0.5922
6 to 7	0.9374	0.8792	0.8252	0.7750	0.7283	0.6848	0.6443	0.6065	0.5384
7 to 8	0.9281	0.8620	0.8012	0.7452	0.6936	0.6461	0.6021	0.5616	0.4895
8 to 9	0.9189	0.8451	0.7779	0.7165	0.6606	0.6095	0.5628	0.5200	0.4450
9 to 10	0.9098	0.8285	0.7552	0.6890	0.6291	0.5750	0.5259	0.4815	0.4045
10 to 11	0.9008	0.8123	0.7332	0.6625	0.5992	0.5424	0.4915	0.4458	0.3677
11 to 12	0.8919	0.7964	0.7118	0.6370	0.5706	0.5117	0.4594	0.4128	0.3343
12 to 13	0.8830	0.7807	0.6911	0.6125	0.5435	0.4828	0.4293	0.3822	0.3039
13 to 14	0.8743	0.7654	0.6710	0.5889	0.5176	0.4554	0.4012	0.3539	0.2763
14 to 15	0.8656	0.7504	0.6514	0.5663	0.4929	0.4297	0.3750	0.3277	0.2512
15 to 16	0.8571	0.7357	0.6325	0.5445	0.4695	0.4053	0.3505	0.3034	0.2283
16 to 17	0.8486	0.7213	0.6140	0.5236	0.4471	0.3824	0.3275	0.2809	0.2076
17 to 18	0.8402	0.7071	0.5962	0.5034	0.4258	0.3608	0.3061	0.2601	0.1887
18 to 19	0.8319	0.6933	0.5788	0.4841	0.4055	0.3403	0.2861	0.2409	0.1716
19 to 20	0.8236	0.6797	0.5619	0.4655	0.3862	0.3211	0.2674	0.2230	0.1560
20 to 21	0.8155	0.6664	0.5456	0.4476	0.3678	0.3029	0.2499	0.2065	0.1418
21 to 22	0.8074	0.6533	0.5297	0.4303	0.3503	0.2857	0.2335	0.1912	0.1289
22 to 23	0.7994	0.6405	0.5143	0.4138	0.3336	0.2696	0.2182	0.1770	0.1172
23 to 24	0.7915	0.6279	0.4993	0.3979	0.3178	0.2543	0.2040	0.1639	0.1065
24 to 25	0.7837	0.6156	0.4847	0.3826	0.3026	0.2399	0.1906	0.1518	0.0968
25 to 26	0.7759	0.6035	0.4706	0.3679	0.2882	0.2263	0.1782	0.1405	0.0880
26 to 27	0.7682	0.5917	0.4569	0.3537	0.2745	0.2135	0.1665	0.1301	0.0800
27 to 28	0.7606	0.5801	0.4436	0.3401	0.2614	0.2014	0.1556	0.1205	0.0728
28 to 29	0.7531	0.5687	0.4307	0.3270	0.2490	0.1900	0.1454	0.1116	0.0661
29 to 30	0.7456	0.5576	0.4181	0.3144	0.2371	0.1793	0.1359	0.1033	0.0601
30 to 31	0.7382	0.5466	0.4060	0.3024	0.2258	0.1691	0.1270	0.0956	0.0547
31 to 32	0.7309	0.5359	0.3941	0.2907	0.2151	0.1596	0.1187	0.0886	0.0497
32 to 33	0.7237	0.5254	0.3827	0.2795	0.2048	0.1505	0.1109	0.0820	0.0452
33 to 34	0.7165	0.5151	0.3715	0.2688	0.1951	0.1420	0.1037	0.0759	0.0411
34 to 35	0.7094	0.5050	0.3607	0.2585	0.1858	0.1340	0.0969	0.0703	0.0373
35 to 36	0.7024	0.4951	0.3502	0.2485	0.1769	0.1264	0.0906	0.0651	0.0339
36 to 37	0.6955	0.4854	0.3400	0.2390	0.1685	0.1192	0.0846	0.0603	0.0309
37 to 38	0.6886	0.4759	0.3301	0.2298	0.1605	0.1125	0.0791	0.0558	0.0281
38 to 39	0.6818	0.4666	0.3205	0.2209	0.1528	0.1061	0.0739	0.0517	0.0255
39 to 40	0.6750	0.4574	0.3111	0.2124	0.1456	0.1001	0.0691	0.0478	0.0232
40 to 41	0.6683	0.4484	0.3021	0.2043	0.1386	0.0944	0.0646	0.0443	0.0211
41 to 42	0.6617	0.4396	0.2933	0.1964	0.1320	0.0891	0.0603	0.0410	0.0192
42 to 43	0.6552	0.4310	0.2847	0.1888	0.1257	0.0841	0.0564	0.0380	0.0174
43 to 44	0.6487	0.4226	0.2764	0.1816	0.1198	0.0793	0.0527	0.0352	0.0158
44 to 45	0.6422	0.4143	0.2684	0.1746	0.1141	0.0748	0.0493	0.0326	0.0144
45 to 46	0.6359	0.4062	0.2606	0.1679	0.1086	0.0706	0.0460	0.0302	0.0131
46 to 47	0.6296	0.3982	0.2530	0.1614	0.1035	0.0666	0.0430	0.0279	0.0119
47 to 48	0.6234	0.3904	0.2456	0.1552	0.0985	0.0628	0.0402	0.0259	0.0108
48 to 49	0.6172	0.3827	0.2385	0.1492	0.0938	0.0593	0.0376	0.0239	0.0098
49 to 50	0.6111	0.3752	0.2315	0.1435	0.0894	0.0559	0.0351	0.0222	0.0089

TABLE E-25—*Continued*

PRESENT WORTH AT ZERO DATE OF $1 FLOWING UNIFORMLY THROUGHOUT STATED
ONE-YEAR PERIODS, ASSUMING CONTINUOUS COMPOUNDING OF INTEREST AT VARIOUS
STATED EFFECTIVE RATES PER ANNUM

Period	12%	15%	20%	25%	30%	35%	40%	45%	50%
0 to 1	0.9454	0.9333	0.9141	0.8963	0.8796	0.8639	0.8491	0.8352	0.8221
1 to 2	0.8441	0.8115	0.7618	0.7170	0.6766	0.6399	0.6065	0.5760	0.5481
2 to 3	0.7537	0.7057	0.6348	0.5736	0.5205	0.4740	0.4332	0.3973	0.3654
3 to 4	0.6729	0.6136	0.5290	0.4589	0.4004	0.3511	0.3095	0.2740	0.2436
4 to 5	0.6008	0.5336	0.4408	0.3671	0.3080	0.2601	0.2210	0.1889	0.1624
5 to 6	0.5365	0.4640	0.3674	0.2937	0.2369	0.1927	0.1579	0.1303	0.1083
6 to 7	0.4790	0.4035	0.3061	0.2350	0.1822	0.1427	0.1128	0.0899	0.0722
7 to 8	0.4277	0.3508	0.2551	0.1880	0.1402	0.1057	0.0806	0.0620	0.0481
8 to 9	0.3818	0.3051	0.2126	0.1504	0.1078	0.0783	0.0575	0.0427	0.0321
9 to 10	0.3409	0.2653	0.1772	0.1203	0.0829	0.0580	0.0411	0.0295	0.0214
10 to 11	0.3044	0.2307	0.1476	0.0962	0.0638	0.0430	0.0294	0.0203	0.0143
11 to 12	0.2718	0.2006	0.1230	0.0770	0.0491	0.0318	0.0210	0.0140	0.0095
12 to 13	0.2427	0.1744	0.1025	0.0616	0.0378	0.0236	0.0150	0.0097	0.0063
13 to 14	0.2167	0.1517	0.0854	0.0493	0.0290	0.0175	0.0107	0.0067	0.0042
14 to 15	0.1935	0.1319	0.0712	0.0394	0.0223	0.0129	0.0076	0.0046	0.0028
15 to 16	0.1727	0.1147	0.0593	0.0315	0.0172	0.0096	0.0055	0.0032	0.0019
16 to 17	0.1542	0.0997	0.0494	0.0252	0.0132	0.0071	0.0039	0.0022	0.0013
17 to 18	0.1377	0.0867	0.0412	0.0202	0.0102	0.0053	0.0028	0.0015	0.0008
18 to 19	0.1229	0.0754	0.0343	0.0161	0.0078	0.0039	0.0020	0.0010	0.0006
19 to 20	0.1098	0.0656	0.0286	0.0129	0.0060	0.0029	0.0014	0.0007	0.0004
20 to 21	0.0980	0.0570	0.0238	0.0103	0.0046	0.0021	0.0010	0.0005	0.0002
21 to 22	0.0875	0.0496	0.0199	0.0083	0.0036	0.0016	0.0007	0.0003	0.0002
22 to 23	0.0781	0.0431	0.0166	0.0066	0.0027	0.0012	0.0005	0.0002	0.0001
23 to 24	0.0698	0.0375	0.0138	0.0053	0.0021	0.0009	0.0004	0.0002	0.0001
24 to 25	0.0623	0.0326	0.0115	0.0042	0.0016	0.0006	0.0003	0.0001	
25 to 26	0.0556	0.0284	0.0096	0.0034	0.0012	0.0005	0.0002	0.0001	
26 to 27	0.0497	0.0247	0.0080	0.0027	0.0010	0.0004	0.0001	0.0001	
27 to 28	0.0443	0.0214	0.0067	0.0022	0.0007	0.0003	0.0001		
28 to 29	0.0396	0.0186	0.0055	0.0017	0.0006	0.0002	0.0001		
29 to 30	0.0353	0.0162	0.0046	0.0014	0.0004	0.0001			
30 to 31	0.0316	0.0141	0.0039	0.0011	0.0003	0.0001			
31 to 32	0.0282	0.0123	0.0032	0.0009	0.0003	0.0001			
32 to 33	0.0252	0.0107	0.0027	0.0007	0.0002	0.0001			
33 to 34	0.0225	0.0093	0.0022	0.0006	0.0002				
34 to 35	0.0201	0.0081	0.0019	0.0005	0.0001				
35 to 36	0.0179	0.0070	0.0015	0.0004	0.0001				
36 to 37	0.0160	0.0061	0.0013	0.0003	0.0001				
37 to 38	0.0143	0.0053	0.0011	0.0002	0.0001				
38 to 39	0.0127	0.0046	0.0009	0.0002					
39 to 40	0.0114	0.0040	0.0007	0.0001					
40 to 41	0.0102	0.0035	0.0006	0.0001					
41 to 42	0.0091	0.0030	0.0005	0.0001					
42 to 43	0.0081	0.0026	0.0004	0.0001					
43 to 44	0.0072	0.0023	0.0004	0.0001					
44 to 45	0.0065	0.0020	0.0003						
45 to 46	0.0058	0.0017	0.0002						
46 to 47	0.0051	0.0015	0.0002						
47 to 48	0.0046	0.0013	0.0002						
48 to 49	0.0041	0.0011	0.0001						
49 to 50	0.0037	0.0010	0.0001						

TABLE E–26

Present Worth at Zero Date of $1 Per Year Flowing Uniformly Throughout Stated Periods Starting at Zero Date, Assuming Continuous Compounding of Interest at Various Stated Effective Rates Per Annum

Period	1%	2%	3%	4%	5%	6%	7%	8%	10%
0 to 1	0.995	0.990	0.985	0.981	0.976	0.971	0.967	0.962	0.954
0 to 2	1.980	1.961	1.942	1.924	1.906	1.888	1.871	1.854	1.821
0 to 3	2.956	2.913	2.871	2.830	2.791	2.752	2.715	2.679	2.609
0 to 4	3.921	3.846	3.773	3.702	3.634	3.568	3.504	3.443	3.326
0 to 5	4.878	4.760	4.648	4.540	4.437	4.338	4.242	4.150	3.977
0 to 6	5.824	5.657	5.498	5.346	5.202	5.063	4.931	4.805	4.570
0 to 7	6.762	6.536	6.323	6.121	5.930	5.748	5.576	5.412	5.108
0 to 8	7.690	7.398	7.124	6.867	6.623	6.394	6.178	5.974	5.597
0 to 9	8.609	8.244	7.902	7.583	7.284	7.004	6.741	6.494	6.042
0 to 10	9.519	9.072	8.658	8.272	7.913	7.579	7.267	6.975	6.447
0 to 11	10.419	9.884	9.391	8.935	8.512	8.121	7.758	7.421	6.815
0 to 12	11.311	10.681	10.103	9.572	9.083	8.633	8.218	7.834	7.149
0 to 13	12.194	11.461	10.794	10.184	9.627	9.116	8.647	8.216	7.453
0 to 14	13.069	12.227	11.465	10.773	10.144	9.571	9.048	8.570	7.729
0 to 15	13.934	12.977	12.116	11.339	10.637	10.001	9.423	8.897	7.980
0 to 16	14.791	13.713	12.749	11.884	11.107	10.406	9.774	9.201	8.209
0 to 17	15.640	14.434	13.363	12.407	11.554	10.789	10.101	9.482	8.416
0 to 18	16.480	15.141	13.959	12.911	11.979	11.149	10.407	9.742	8.605
0 to 19	17.312	15.835	14.538	13.395	12.385	11.490	10.693	9.983	8.777
0 to 20	18.136	16.514	15.100	13.860	12.771	11.811	10.961	10.206	8.932
0 to 21	18.951	17.181	15.645	14.308	13.139	12.114	11.210	10.412	9.074
0 to 22	19.759	17.834	16.175	14.738	13.489	12.399	11.444	10.604	9.203
0 to 23	20.558	18.475	16.689	15.152	13.823	12.669	11.662	10.781	9.320
0 to 24	21.349	19.102	17.188	15.550	14.141	12.923	11.866	10.945	9.427
0 to 25	22.133	19.718	17.673	15.932	14.443	13.163	12.057	11.096	9.524
0 to 26	22.909	20.322	18.144	16.300	14.732	13.389	12.235	11.237	9.612
0 to 27	23.677	20.913	18.601	16.654	15.006	13.603	12.402	11.367	9.692
0 to 28	24.438	21.493	19.044	16.994	15.268	13.804	12.557	11.487	9.765
0 to 29	25.191	22.062	19.475	17.321	15.517	13.994	12.703	11.599	9.831
0 to 30	25.937	22.620	19.893	17.636	15.754	14.174	12.838	11.702	9.891
0 to 31	26.675	23.166	20.299	17.938	15.979	14.343	12.965	11.798	9.945
0 to 32	27.406	23.702	20.693	18.229	16.195	14.502	13.084	11.887	9.995
0 to 33	28.129	24.228	21.076	18.508	16.399	14.653	13.195	11.969	10.040
0 to 34	28.846	24.743	21.447	18.777	16.594	14.795	13.299	12.044	10.081
0 to 35	29.555	25.248	21.808	19.035	16.780	14.929	13.396	12.115	10.119
0 to 40	32.999	27.628	23.460	20.186	17.585	15.493	13.793	12.395	10.260
0 to 45	36.275	29.784	24.885	21.132	18.215	15.915	14.076	12.587	10.348
0 to 50	39.392	31.737	26.114	21.909	18.709	16.230	14.278	12.717	10.403
0 to 55	42.358	33.505	27.174	22.548	19.096	16.466	14.422	12.805	10.437
0 to 60	45.179	35.107	28.089	23.073	19.399	16.642	14.525	12.865	10.458
0 to 65	47.864	36.558	28.878	23.505	19.636	16.773	14.598	12.906	10.471
0 to 70	50.419	37.872	29.558	23.859	19.822	16.871	14.650	12.934	10.479
0 to 75	52.850	39.063	30.145	24.151	19.968	16.945	14.688	12.953	10.484
0 to 80	55.162	40.141	30.652	24.391	20.082	17.000	14.714	12.966	10.487
0 to 85	57.363	41.117	31.088	24.588	20.172	17.041	14.733	12.975	10.489
0 to 90	59.456	42.001	31.465	24.749	20.242	17.071	14.747	12.981	10.490
0 to 95	61.448	42.802	31.790	24.883	20.297	17.094	14.756	12.985	10.491
0 to 100	63.344	43.528	32.071	24.992	20.340	17.111	14.763	12.988	10.491

TABLE E–26—*Continued*

PRESENT WORTH AT ZERO DATE OF $1 PER YEAR FLOWING UNIFORMLY THROUGHOUT
STATED PERIODS STARTING AT ZERO DATE, ASSUMING CONTINUOUS COMPOUNDING OF
INTEREST AT VARIOUS STATED EFFECTIVE RATES PER ANNUM

Period	12%	15%	20%	25%	30%	35%	40%	45%	50%
0 to 1	0.945	0.933	0.914	0.896	0.880	0.864	0.849	0.835	0.822
0 to 2	1.790	1.745	1.676	1.613	1.556	1.504	1.456	1.411	1.370
0 to 3	2.543	2.450	2.311	2.187	2.077	1.978	1.889	1.809	1.736
0 to 4	3.216	3.064	2.840	2.646	2.477	2.329	2.198	2.083	1.979
0 to 5	3.817	3.598	3.281	3.013	2.785	2.589	2.419	2.271	2.142
0 to 6	4.353	4.062	3.648	3.307	3.022	2.782	2.577	2.402	2.250
0 to 7	4.832	4.465	3.954	3.542	3.204	2.924	2.690	2.492	2.322
0 to 8	5.260	4.816	4.209	3.730	3.344	3.030	2.771	2.554	2.370
0 to 9	5.642	5.121	4.422	3.880	3.452	3.108	2.828	2.596	2.402
0 to 10	5.983	5.386	4.599	4.000	3.535	3.166	2.869	2.626	2.424
0 to 11	6.287	5.617	4.747	4.096	3.599	3.209	2.899	2.646	2.438
0 to 12	6.559	5.818	4.870	4.173	3.648	3.241	2.920	2.660	2.447
0 to 13	6.802	5.992	4.972	4.235	3.686	3.265	2.935	2.670	2.454
0 to 14	7.018	6.144	5.058	4.284	3.715	3.282	2.945	2.677	2.458
0 to 15	7.212	6.276	5.129	4.324	3.737	3.295	2.953	2.681	2.461
0 to 16	7.385	6.390	5.188	4.355	3.754	3.305	2.958	2.684	2.463
0 to 17	7.539	6.490	5.238	4.381	3.767	3.312	2.962	2.686	2.464
0 to 18	7.676	6.577	5.279	4.401	3.778	3.317	2.965	2.688	2.465
0 to 19	7.799	6.652	5.313	4.417	3.785	3.321	2.967	2.689	2.465
0 to 20	7.909	6.718	5.342	4.430	3.791	3.324	2.968	2.690	2.466
0 to 21	8.007	6.775	5.366	4.440	3.796	3.326	2.969	2.690	2.466
0 to 22	8.095	6.824	5.385	4.448	3.800	3.328	2.970	2.691	2.466
0 to 23	8.173	6.868	5.402	4.455	3.802	3.329	2.971	2.691	2.466
0 to 24	8.243	6.905	5.416	4.460	3.804	3.330	2.971	2.691	2.466
0 to 25	8.305	6.938	5.427	4.465	3.806	3.330	2.971	2.691	2.466
0 to 26	8.360	6.966	5.437	4.468	3.807	3.331	2.972	2.691	2.466
0 to 27	8.410	6.991	5.445	4.471	3.808	3.331	2.972	2.691	2.466
0 to 28	8.454	7.012	5.452	4.473	3.809	3.331	2.972	2.691	2.466
0 to 29	8.494	7.031	5.457	4.474	3.810	3.332	2.972	2.691	2.466
0 to 30	8.529	7.047	5.462	4.476	3.810	3.332	2.972	2.691	2.466
0 to 31	8.561	7.061	5.466	4.477	3.810	3.332	2.972	2.691	2.466
0 to 32	8.589	7.073	5.469	4.478	3.811	3.332	2.972	2.691	2.466
0 to 33	8.614	7.084	5.471	4.479	3.811	3.332	2.972	2.691	2.466
0 to 34	8.637	7.093	5.474	4.479	3.811	3.332	2.972	2.691	2.466
0 to 35	8.657	7.101	5.476	4.480	3.811	3.332	2.972	2.691	2.466
0 to 40	8.729	7.128	5.481	4.481	3.811	3.332	2.972	2.691	2.466
0 to 45	8.770	7.142	5.483	4.481	3.811	3.332	2.972	2.691	2.466
0 to 50	8.793	7.148	5.484	4.481	3.811	3.332	2.972	2.691	2.466
0 to 55	8.807	7.152	5.485	4.481	3.811	3.332	2.972	2.691	2.466
0 to 60	8.814	7.153	5.485	4.481	3.811	3.332	2.972	2.691	2.466
0 to 65	8.818	7.154	5.485	4.481	3.811	3.332	2.972	2.691	2.466
0 to 70	8.821	7.155	5.485	4.481	3.811	3.332	2.972	2.691	2.466
0 to 75	8.822	7.155	5.485	4.481	3.811	3.332	2.972	2.691	2.466
0 to 80	8.823	7.155	5.485	4.481	3.811	3.332	2.972	2.691	2.466
0 to 85	8.823	7.155	5.485	4.481	3.811	3.332	2.972	2.691	2.466
0 to 90	8.824	7.155	5.485	4.481	3.811	3.332	2.972	2.691	2.466
0 to 95	8.824	7.155	5.485	4.481	3.811	3.332	2.972	2.691	2.466
0 to 100	8.824	7.155	5.485	4.481	3.811	3.332	2.972	2.691	2.466

F
Selected References

ANTHONY, R. N. *Management Accounting*. Homewood, Ill.: Richard D. Irwin, Inc., 1956.

ARIES, R. S., and NEWTON, R. D. *Chemical Engineering Cost Estimation*. New York: McGraw-Hill Book Co., Inc., 1950.

BARDES, P., MAHON, J. J., JR., McCULLOUGH, J., and RICHARDSON, M. E., eds. *Montgomery's Federal Taxes, 37th ed.* New York: The Ronald Press Co., 1958. This reference work edited by partners of Lybrand, Ross Bros. & Montgomery, is frequently revised; secure the most recent edition.

BONBRIGHT, J. C. *Valuation of Property*. New York: McGraw-Hill Book Co., Inc., 1937.

BOWMAN, E. H., and FETTER, R. B. *Analysis for Production Management*. Homewood, Ill.: Richard D. Irwin, Inc., 1957.

BULLINGER, C. E. *Engineering Economy*. New York: McGraw-Hill Book Co., Inc., 1958.

CANFIELD, D. T., and BOWMAN, J. H. *Business, Legal, and Ethical Phases of Engineering*. New York: McGraw-Hill Book Co., Inc., 1954.

CARSON, G. B., ed. *Production Handbook*. 2d ed. New York: The Ronald Press Co., 1958.

CHARNES, A., COOPER, W. W., and HENDERSON, A. *An Introduction to Linear Programming*. New York: John Wiley & Sons, Inc., 1953.

CHURCHMAN, C. W., ACKOFF, R. L., and ARNOFF, E. L. *Introduction to Operations Research*. New York: John Wiley & Sons, Inc., 1957.

CLARK, J. M. *Studies in the Economics of Overhead Costs*. Chicago: University of Chicago Press, 1923.

DEAN, JOEL. *Capital Budgeting*. New York: Columbia University Press, 1951.

———. *Managerial Economics*. Englewood Cliffs, N.J.: Prentice-Hall, Inc., 1951.

Engineering Economist, The. A quarterly journal published by the Engineering Economy Division of the American Society for Engineering Education. Published at Stevens Institute of Technology, Hoboken, N.J.; first issue was in 1955.

ENGINEERING NEWS-RECORD. *Construction Costs*. Published annually; secure the most recent issue.

FINCH, J. K. *An Introduction to the Economics of Civil Engineering*. New York: Columbia University Press, 1942.

FISH, J. C. L. *Engineering Economics*. New York: McGraw-Hill Book Co., Inc., 1923.

GOETZ, B. E. *Management Planning and Control*. New York: McGraw-Hill Book Co., Inc., 1949.

GRANT, E. L. *Basic Accounting and Cost Accounting*. New York: McGraw-Hill Book Co., Inc., 1956.

———. *Statistical Quality Control*. New York: McGraw-Hill Book Co., Inc., 1952.

GRANT, E. L., and NORTON, P. T., JR. *Depreciation*, rev. printing. New York: The Ronald Press Co., 1955.

HAPPEL, JOHN. *Chemical Process Economics*. New York, N.Y.: John Wiley & Sons, Inc., 1958.

HEWES, L. I., and OGLESBY, C. H. *Highway Engineering*. New York: John Wiley & Sons, Inc., 1954.

HUR, J. J., ed. *Chemical Process Economics in Practice*. New York: Reinhold Publishing Corp., 1956.

IRESON, W. G. *Factory Planning and Plant Layout*. Englewood Cliffs, N.J.: Prentice-Hall, Inc., 1952.

IRESON, W. G., and GRANT, E. L., eds. *Handbook of Industrial Engineering and Management*. Englewood Cliffs, N.J.: Prentice-Hall, Inc., 1955.

KELLEY, W. *Company Procedural Manual on Equipment Analysis*. Chicago: William Kelley & Co., 1951.

KRUTILLA, J. V., and ECKSTEIN, O. *Multiple Purpose Development Studies in Applied Economic Analysis*. Baltimore: Johns Hopkins Press, 1958.

MACHINERY AND ALLIED PRODUCTS INSTITUTE. *MAPI Replacement Manual*. Washington, D.C.: Machinery and Allied Products Institute, 1950.

MARSTON, A., WINFREY, R., and HEMPSTEAD, J. C. *Engineering Valuation and Depreciation*. New York: McGraw-Hill Book Co., Inc., 1953.

MAYNARD, H. B., ed. *Industrial Engineering Handbook*. New York: McGraw-Hill Book Co., Inc., 1956.

McCLOSKEY, J. F., and TREFETHEN, F. N. *Operations Research for Management*. Baltimore: Johns Hopkins Press, Vol. I, 1955; Vol. II, 1956.

McKEAN, R. W. *Efficiency in Government Through Systems Analysis*. New York: John Wiley & Sons, Inc., 1958.

NORTON, P. T., JR. *Economic Lot Sizes in Manufacturing*. Virginia Polytechnic Institute, Bulletin No. 31. Blacksburg, Va., 1934.

―――. *The Selection and Replacement of Manufacturing Equipment*. Virginia Polytechnic Institute, Bulletin No. 32. Blacksburg, Va., 1934.

OSBURN, J. O., and KAMMERMEYER, KARL. *Money and the Chemical Engineer*. Englewood Cliffs, N.J.: Prentice-Hall, Inc., 1958.

PETERS, M. S. *Plant Design and Economics for Chemical Engineers*. New York: McGraw-Hill Book Co., Inc., 1958.

PEURIFOY, R. L. *Estimating Construction Costs*. New York: McGraw-Hill Book Co., Inc., 1958.

PULVER, H. E. *Construction Estimates and Costs*. New York: McGraw-Hill Book Co., Inc., 1947.

SCHNEIDER, ERICH. *Wirtschaftlichkeits-rechnung*. Tübingen, Germany: J. C. B. Mohr (Paul Siebeck), 1957.

SCHWEYER, H. E. *Process Engineering Economics*. New York: McGraw-Hill Book Co., Inc., 1955.

STEINBERG, M. J., and GLENDINNING, W. *Engineering Economics and Practice*. Bayside, N.Y.: W. Glendinning, 1949.

SUBCOMMITTEE ON EVALUATION STANDARDS OF INTER-AGENCY COMMITTEE ON WATER RESOURCES. *Proposed Practices for Economic Analysis of River Basin Projects*. Washington, D.C.: Government Printing Office, 1958. In many writings on the economics of public works, this useful pamphlet is referred to as the "Green Book."

TERBORGH, GEORGE. *Business Investment Policy*. Washington, D.C.: Machinery and Allied Products Institute, 1958.

―――. *Dynamic Equipment Policy*. New York: McGraw-Hill Book Co., Inc., 1949.

―――. *Realistic Depreciation Policy*. Washington, D.C.: Machinery and Allied Products Institute, 1954.

THUESEN, H. G. *Engineering Economy*. Englewood Cliffs, N.J.: Prentice-Hall, Inc., 1957.

TYLER, C. *Chemical Engineering Economics*. New York: McGraw-Hill Book Co., Inc., 1948.

WELLINGTON, A. M. *The Economic Theory of Railway Location*. New York: John Wiley & Sons, Inc., 1887.

WINFREY, ROBLEY. *Statistical Analysis of Industrial Property Retirements*. Ames, Iowa: Bulletin 125, Iowa Engineering Experiment Station, 1935.

WOODS, B. M., and DeGARMO, E. P. *Introduction to Engineering Economy*. New York: The Macmillan Co., 1953.

Index